GLENCOE

Pre-Algebra
An Integrated Transition to Algebra & Geometry

Solutions Manual

GLENCOE
McGraw-Hill

New York, New York   Columbus, Ohio   Woodland Hills, California   Peoria, Illinois

Contents

Glencoe/McGraw-Hill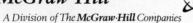

A Division of The McGraw·Hill Companies

Send all inquiries to:
Glencoe/McGraw-Hill
8787 Orion Place
Columbus, OH 43240

Pre-Algebra
Solutions Manual

ISBN: 0-02-825053-2

7 8 9 10 045 05 04 03 02 01 00 99

Chapter 1 Tools for Algebra and Geometry

1-1 Problem-Solving Strategy: Make a Plan

Page 9 Checking Your Understanding

1. Explore—Read and decide what is given and what is to be found.
   Plan—Plan a method for solution.
   Solve—Execute the plan.
   Examine—Reflect on whether the solution answers the question and makes sense.

2. Sample answer: To make sure that it answers the question and makes sense.

3. See students' work.

4. See students' work.

5. **a.** We know the bonus for 2, 4, 6, and 8 over plan. We need to know the bonus for 16 over plan.

   b. Extend the pattern. By looking at the table, the bonus should be about $250.

   c.

2	4	6	8	10	12	14	16
$100	$125	$150	$175	$200	$225	$250	$275

   Mr. Diaz will get a bonus of $275 if he sells 16 software packages more than the plan.

   d. The answer is reasonable and answers the question.

6. **a.** Sample answer: estimation. The question asks for "about how many times," so an exact answer is not necessary.

   b. Explore—We know the average number of times per day that people wash their hands or faces. We need to know the number of times that a person washes his or her hands or face in one year.
   Plan—Multiply the average number of times per day by the number of days in one year. Since an exact answer is not necessary, solve by using estimation.
   Solve—$6.8 \times 365 \rightarrow 7 \times 350 = 2450$
   A person washes his or her hands or face about 2450 times in one year.
   Examine—The actual answer is 6.8×365 or 2482. So, the estimate of 2450 times per year is reasonable.

   c. Sample answer: No, it is an average. A person can only wash his or her hands a whole number of times.

Page 10 Exercises

7. Explore—We know how much money Ana needs and the amounts that she has saved and earned. We need to determine if Ana has enough money for the trip.
   Plan—Add the amount saved to the amounts earned to determine if she has $300.
   Estimate: $265 + 20 + 25 \rightarrow 250 + 20 + 30 = 300$.
   Solve—$265 + 20 + 25 = 310$.
   Ana has $310. So, she has enough money for the trip.
   Examine—The total amount of $310 is very close to the estimate, so the answer is correct.

8. Explore—We know the costs of the individual building supplies. We need to find the total cost.
   Plan—Add the costs of the individual building supplies to find the total.
   Estimate: $\begin{array}{rcl} \$ \ 2.34 & \rightarrow & \$ \ \ \ 0 \\ 9.28 & \rightarrow & 10 \\ 92.34 & \rightarrow & 90 \\ 501.38 & \rightarrow & 500 \\ 0.34 & \rightarrow & \underline{\ \ \ \ 0} \\ & & \$600 \end{array}$
   The total cost should be about $600.
   Solve—Use a calculator to find the total cost.
   $2.34 + 9.28 + 92.34 + 501.38 + 0.34 = 605.68$.
   The total cost of the building supplies is $605.68.
   Examine—The total cost of $605.68 is very close to the estimate, so the answer is reasonable.

9. Explore—We know the cost of mailing a 1, 2, 3, 4, or 5 ounce first-class letter. We need to know the cost of mailing a letter that weighs 8 ounces.
   Plan—Extend the pattern to 8 ounces. By looking at the chart, the cost should be about $2.00.
   Solve—

1	2	3	4	5	6	7	8
$0.32	$0.57	$0.82	$1.07	$1.32	$1.57	$1.82	$2.07

   It will cost $2.07 to send an 8 ounce letter.
   Examine—The answer is close to the estimate and answers the question.

10. Explore—We know how many pounds a space shuttle can carry and the weight of a compact car. We need to find the number of compact cars that could be carried on the space shuttle.
    Plan—Divide the number of pounds that a space shuttle can carry by the weight of a compact car to find the number of cars that could be carried on the shuttle. Since an exact answer is not necessary, solve by using estimation.
    Solve—$65,000 \div 2450 \rightarrow 65,000 \div 2500 = 26$
    The space shuttle can carry about 26 compact cars.

Examine—The actual answer is $65,000 \div 24,500$ or approximately 26.53. Therefore, the estimate of 26 compact cars is reasonable.

11. a.

b. 2, 4, 6, 8, 10, 12

c. 1, 2, 3, 4, 5, 6

d. The number of cuts is half the number of pieces.

12. No, it should be about 30.

1-2	**Order of Operations**

Page 14 Checking Your Understanding

1. Add 13 and 11.

2. No; to evaluate $9(4 + 3)$, you would add 4 and 3 and then multiply the sum by 9; to evaluate $9 \cdot 4 + 3$, you would multiply 9 and 4 and then add 3 to the product.

3. See students' work.

4. Sample answer: $7 \times (9 - 5)$.

5. See students' work.

6. multiplication
$$9 + 2 \cdot 5 = 9 + 10$$
$$= 19$$

7. division
$$65 - 32 \div 8 = 65 - 4$$
$$= 61$$

8. division
$$33 \div 3 + 6 = 11 + 6$$
$$= 17$$

9. multiplication
$$17 - 6(2) = 17 - 12$$
$$= 5$$

10. addition
$$8(2 + 4) = 8 \cdot 6$$
$$= 48$$

11. subtraction
$$\frac{20 - 8}{9 - 5} = (20 - 8) \div (9 - 5)$$
$$= 12 \div 4$$
$$= 3$$

12. a. $4(\$11.99) + \$18.99$

b. $4(\$11.99) + \$18.99 = \$47.96 + \$18.99$
$$= \$66.95$$

Pages 14–15 Exercises

13. $15 \div 3 + 12 \div 4 = 5 + 12 \div 4$
$$= 5 + 3$$
$$= 8$$

14. $3 \cdot (4 + 5) - 7 = 3 \cdot 9 - 7$
$$= 27 - 7$$
$$= 20$$

15. $15 \div 5 \times 3 = 3 \times 3$
$$= 9$$

16. $40 \cdot (6 - 2) = 40 \cdot 4$
$$= 160$$

17. $12(7 - 2 \times 3) = 12(7 - 6)$
$$= 12 \cdot 1$$
$$= 12$$

18. $36 - 6 \cdot 5 = 36 - 30$
$$= 6$$

19. $\frac{18 + 66}{35 - 14} = (18 + 66) \div (35 - 14)$
$$= 84 \div 21$$
$$= 4$$

20. $\frac{16 + 8}{15 - 7} = (16 + 8) \div (15 - 7)$
$$= 24 \div 8$$
$$= 3$$

21. $\frac{2(14 - 6)}{4} = \frac{2 \cdot 8}{4}$
$$= (2 \cdot 8) \div 4$$
$$= 16 \div 4$$
$$= 4$$

22. $96 \div (12 \cdot 4) \div 2 = 96 \div 48 \div 2$
$$= 2 \div 2$$
$$= 1$$

23. $72 \div (9 \times 4) \div 2 = 72 \div 36 \div 2$
$$= 2 \div 2$$
$$= 1$$

24. $(30 \times 2) - (6 \cdot 9) = 60 - (6 \cdot 9)$
$$= 60 - 54$$
$$= 6$$

25. $3[6(12 - 3)] - 17 = 3[6 \cdot 9] - 17$
$$= 3 \cdot 54 - 17$$
$$= 162 - 17$$
$$= 145$$

26. $7[5 + (13 - 4) \div 3 = 7[5 + 9 \div 3]$
$$= 7[5 + 3]$$
$$= 7 \cdot 8$$
$$= 56$$

27. $4[3(21 - 17) + 3] = 4[3 \cdot 4 + 3]$
$$= 4[12 + 3]$$
$$= 415$$
$$= 60$$

28. $5[(12 + 5) - 3(19 - 14)] = 5[17 - 3(19 - 14)]$
$$= 5[17 - 3 \cdot 5]$$
$$= 5[17 - 15]$$
$$= 5 \cdot 2$$
$$= 10$$

29. $8[(26 + 10) - 4(3 + 2)] = 8[36 - 4(3 + 2)]$
$$= 8[36 - 4 \cdot 5]$$
$$= 8[36 - 20]$$
$$= 8 \cdot 16$$
$$= 128$$

30. $10[8(15 - 7) - 4 \cdot 3] = 10[8 \cdot 8 - 4 \cdot 3]$
$$= 10[64 - 4 \cdot 3]$$
$$= 10[64 - 12]$$
$$= 10 \cdot 52$$
$$= 520$$

31. $71 - (17 + 4) = 50$

32. $(8 - 5) \times (4 + 2) = 18$

33. $18 \div (3 + 6) + 12 = 14$

34. Answers may vary. Sample answer:
$$111 - (1 + 1 + 1) \times (11 + 1)$$

35. a. 3($330) + 2($247) + 4($229)

b. 3($330) + 2($247) + 4($229) = $990 + $494 + $916
$$= \$2400$$

c. See students' work.

36. a. 2(360) + 1(1221) + 4(205) = 720 + 1221 + 820
$$= 2761$$

b. $(2 \cdot 0 + 270) \div 2 = (0 + 270) \div 2$
$$= 270 \div 2$$
$$= 135$$

37. 7($35) + $7 = $245 + $7
$$= \$252$$

38. a. Sample answer: estimate.

b. Explore—We know the number of strokes it takes to swim a pool's length and the number of laps it takes to swim across the channel. We need to find the number of strokes a swimmer would use to swim across the channel.

Plan—Multiply the number of strokes by the number of laps to determine the number of strokes a swimmer would use to swim across the channel. Since an exact answer is not necessary, solve by using estimation.

Solve—$24 \times 1470 \rightarrow 25 \times 1500 = 37,500$
A good swimmer would use about 37,500 strokes to swim across the English Channel.

Examine—$24 \times 1470 = 35,280$. So, the estimate of 37,500 strokes is reasonable.

39. Sample answer: The first number in each multiplication problem ends with a 4 and the second number ends with a 6. Also, every product ends with 24.

$$\begin{aligned} 4 \times 6 &= 24 \\ 14 \times 16 &= 224 \\ 24 \times 26 &= 624 \\ 34 \times 36 &= 1224 \\ 44 \times 46 &= 2024 \\ 54 \times 56 &= 3024 \\ 64 \times 66 &= 4224 \\ 74 \times 76 &= 5624 \\ 84 \times 86 &= 7224 \end{aligned}$$

1-3 Variables and Expressions

Pages 18–19 Checking Your Understanding

1. Sample answer: a letter that serves as a placeholder for an unknown value in an equation.

2. $7 \times a$, $7 \cdot a$

3. 5 less than the number of games the Jets won

4. a.

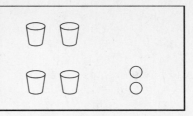

b.

$$4 + 3x$$

5. $8 + n = 8 + 11$
$$= 19$$

6. $10 - q = 10 - 5$
$$= 5$$

7. $3m = 3(4)$
$$= 12$$

8. $24 - 4q = 24 - 4(5)$
$$= 24 - 20$$
$$= 4$$

9. $\frac{5m}{2} = \frac{5(4)}{2}$
$$= 5(4) \div 2$$
$$= 20 \div 2$$
$$= 10$$

10. $n + 110 - 2p = 11 + 110 - 2(2)$
$$= 11 + 110 - 4$$
$$= 121 - 4$$
$$= 117$$

11. $3 + v$

12. $h - 7$

13. $6n$

14. $2w$

15. a. $6x$

b. $6x = 6(34)$
$$= 204$$

Pages 19–20 Exercises

16. $a + 22 = 6 + 22$
$$= 28$$

17. $2b - 4 = 2(3) - 4$
$$= 6 - 4$$
$$= 2$$

18. $ca - ab = (7)(6) - (6)(3)$
$$= 42 - 18$$
$$= 24$$

19. $4a - (b + c) = 4(6) - (3 + 7)$
$$= 4(6) - 10$$
$$= 24 - 10$$
$$= 14$$

20. $5c + 5b = 5(7) + 5(3)$
$$= 35 + 15$$
$$= 50$$

21. $\frac{8h}{a} = \frac{8(3)}{6}$
$$= 8(3) \div 6$$
$$= 24 \div 6$$
$$= 4$$

22. $2c + 3a + 6b = 2(7) + 3(6) + 6(3)$
$$= 14 + 18 + 18$$
$$= 50$$

23. $\frac{6a}{b} = \frac{6(6)}{3}$
$= 6(6) \div 3$
$= 36 \div 3$
$= 12$

24. $9a - (4b + 2c) = 9(6) - (4 \cdot 3 + 2 \cdot 7)$
$= 9(6) - (12 + 14)$
$= 54 - 26$
$= 28$

25. $\frac{3(4a - 3c)}{c - 4} = \frac{3(4 \cdot 6 - 3 \cdot 7)}{7 - 4}$
$= [3(4 \cdot 6 - 3 \cdot 7)] \div [7 - 4]$
$= [3(24 - 21)] \div [7 - 4]$
$= [3 \cdot 3] \div [7 - 4]$
$= 9 \div 3$
$= 3$

26. $12b - \frac{2c - 4}{a + 4} = 12(3) - \frac{2(7) - 4}{6 + 4}$
$= 12(3) - [2(7) - 4] \div [6 + 4]$
$= 12(3) - [14 - 4] \div [6 + 4]$
$= 12(3) - 10 \div 10$
$= 36 - 1$
$= 35$

27. $\frac{15ab}{3c + 6} = \frac{15(6)(3)}{3(7) + 6}$
$= [15(6)(3)] \div [3(7) + 6]$
$= [270] \div [21 + 6]$
$= 270 \div 27$
$= 10$

28. $x \div 8$ **29.** $92 \div c$

30. $g + 8$ **31.** $p - 5$

32. $11 + f$ **33.** $u - 10$

34. $2n$ **35.** $88 \div b$

36. $g + \$500$ **37.** $3k$

38. $3n - 18$ **39.** $2s + 2$

40. Some number plus 4

41. 16 less some number

42. seven times some number

43. the quotient of some number and 5

44. twice the sum of some number and one

45. twice some number plus one

46. $100x + 10y + z$

47. a. $c \div 4 + 37$
b. $c \div 4 + 37 = 124 \div 4 + 37$
$= 31 + 37$
$= 68$
The approximate temperature when a cricket chirps 124 times in a minute is 68°.

48. a. $\frac{a + 6 + c}{3}$
b. $\frac{a + b + c}{3} = \frac{51 + 66 + 63}{3}$
$= (51 + 66 + 63) \div (3)$
$= 180 \div 3$
$= 60$

49. $6 \times 8 - (9 + 12) = 6 \times 8 - 21$
$= 48 - 21$
$= 27$

50. a. $4(\$6.25) + 2(\$3.75)$
b. $4(\$6.25) + 2(\$3.75) = \$25.00 + \$7.50$
$= \$32.50$
c. See students' work.

51. Explore—We know the first seven numbers in the sequence. We need to find the next number.
Plan—Extend the pattern to determine the next number. By looking at the numbers in the sequence, the next number should be about 30.
Solve—
$$\overset{+1}{1,} \overset{+2}{2,} \overset{+3}{4,} \overset{+4}{7,} \overset{+5}{11,} \overset{+6}{16,} \overset{+7}{22,} 29$$
The next number in the sequence is 29.
Examine—The solution is close to the estimate and answers the question.

52. a. An estimate is appropriate because an exact answer is not needed.
b. $250,000 \div 46,000 \to 250,000 \div 50,000 = 5$
About 5 flowers and plants were planted per square foot.

Page 20   From the Funny Papers

1. See students' work.

2. She would multiply 3 and $(2 + 8)$ instead of multiplying 3 times x by $(2 + 8)$.

3. See students' work.

1-3B   Math Lab: Evaluating Expressions

Page 21

1. 14   **2.** 0   **3.** 7

4. 12   **5.** 55   **6.** 56

7. Use REPLAY then change the expression.

8. Display shows / for $\boxed{\div}$ and * for $\boxed{\times}$.

1-4   Properties

Page 24   Checking Your Understanding

1. Sample answer: Both properties involve multiplication and addition. The associate property involves grouping numbers that are being added or multiplied. The commutative property involves the order in which numbers are added or multiplied.

2. Sample answer:
Commutative addition: $8 + 9 = 9 + 8$
Commutative multiplication: $6 \times 3 = 3 \times 6$
Associative addition: $3 + (5 + 4) = (3 + 5) + 4$
Associative multiplication: $7 \times (3 \times 1) = (7 \times 3) \times 1$
Identity addition: $8 + 0 = 8$
Identity multiplication: $17 \times 1 = 17$
Multiplicative zero: $12 \times 0 = 0$

3. See students' works.

4.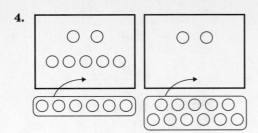

    a. They are the same.

    b. See students' work. The values are all the same.

5. associative, addition

6. commutative, addition

7. commutative, addition

8. identity, addition

9. $12 + 9 + 8 = (12 + 8) + 9$
$$= 20 + 9$$
$$= 29$$

10. $5 \cdot 3 \cdot 8 = (5 \cdot 8) \cdot 3$
$$= 40 \cdot 3$$
$$= 120$$

11. $4 + 13 + 26 + 5 = (4 + 26) + (13 + 5)$
$$= 30 + 18$$
$$= 48$$

12. $(y + 9) + 8 = y + (9 + 8)$
$$= y + 17$$

13. $7(6z) = (7 \cdot 6)z$
$$= 42z$$

14. $(k \cdot 8)3 = k(8 \cdot 3)$
$$= 24k$$

15. $\$1.25 + \$3.35 + \$3.75 = (\$1.25 + \$3.35) + \$3.75$
$$= \$4.60 + \$3.75$$
$$= \$8.35$$

Page 25   Exercises

16. identity, multiplication

17. commutative, multiplication

18. commutative, multiplication

19. multiplicative, zero

20. commutative, multiplication

21. commutative, addition

22. commutative, addition

23. commutative, addition

24. associative, multiplication

25. commutative, addition

26. identity, multiplication

27. associative, addition

28. $16 + 7 + 14 = (16 + 14) + 7$
$$= 30 + 7$$
$$= 37$$

29. $2 \cdot 9 \cdot 20 = (2 \cdot 20) \cdot 9$
$$= 40 \cdot 9$$
$$= 360$$

30. $82 + 58 + 23 + 37 = (82 + 58) + (23 + 37)$
$$= 140 + 60$$
$$= 200$$

31. $18 \cdot 6 \cdot 0 = 18 \cdot (6 \cdot 0)$
$$= 18 \cdot 0$$
$$= 0$$

32. $7 + 99 + 123 = (7 + 123) + 99$
$$= 130 + 99$$
$$= 229$$

33. $2 \cdot 13 \cdot 5 = (2 \cdot 5) \cdot 13$
$$= 10 \cdot 13$$
$$= 130$$

34. $7 + 2 + 13 + 18 = (7 + 13) + (2 + 18)$
$$= 20 + 20$$
$$= 40$$

35. $6 \cdot 11 \cdot 10 = 6 \cdot (11 \cdot 10)$
$$= 6 \cdot 110$$
$$= 660$$

36. $129 \cdot 8 \cdot 0 = (29 \cdot 0) \cdot 8$
$$= 0 \cdot 8$$
$$= 0$$

37. $5 + 9 = 9 + 5$

38. $8a + 6 = 6 + 8a$

39. $9 + 18w = 18w + 9$

40. $(y + 7) + 6 = y + (7 + 6)$
$$= y + 13$$

41. $(b \cdot 6) \cdot 5 = b(6 \cdot 5)$
$$= 30b$$

42. $2(8f) = (2 \cdot 8)f$
$$= 16f$$

43. $13 + (11 + m) = (13 + 11) + m$
$$= 24 + m$$

44. $3(2z) = (3 \cdot 2)z$
$$= 6z$$

45. $(p \cdot 7) \cdot 4 = p(7 \cdot 4)$
$$= 28p$$

46. $(u + 8) + 16 = u + (8 + 16)$
$$= u + 24$$

47. $(15 + 4w) + w = 15 + (4w + w)$
$$= 15 + 5w$$

48. $0(3x) = (0 \cdot 3)x$
$$= 0$$

49. a. See students' work.

    b. Sample answer: Division is not commutative.

50. a. (3 feet + 3 inches) + (4 feet + 8 inches)

    b. (3 ft + 3 in.) + (4 ft + 8 in.) = (3 ft + 4 ft) +
$$(3 \text{ in.} + 8 \text{ in.})$$
$$= 7 \text{ ft} + 11 \text{ in.}$$

    The distance from the floor to the top of the net is 7 feet 11 inches; see students' explanations.

51. See students' work.

52. $18n$

53. $8xy + 6 = 8(0)(2) + 6$
$$= 0 + 6$$
$$= 6$$

54. $7 \cdot (9 - 3) + 4 = 7 \cdot 6 + 4$
$$= 42 + 4$$
$$= 46$$

55. a. $w \div 16$

    b. $w \div 16 = 144 \div 16$
$$= 9$$
There are 9 pints of blood in JT's body.

56.

$$\overset{-1}{\frown}\ \overset{-2}{\frown}\ \overset{-3}{\frown}\ \overset{-4}{\frown}\ \overset{-5}{\frown}$$
$$15,\quad 14,\quad 12,\quad 9,\quad 5,\quad 0$$
The next number in the sequence is 0.

Page 28 Checking Your Understanding

1. $7(5) + 7(3); 7 \cdot 5 + 7 \cdot 3; 7 \times 5 + 7 \times 3$

2. Sample answer: $8x$ and $2x$ both contain only the variable x

3. Sample answer:
Simplest form: $7x; 9a + 2; u + uv$
Not in simplest form: $12x + x; 7 + 6; 2(7y)$
Expressions are in simplest form when no terms can be combined.

4. See students' work.

5. $5(7 + 8) = 5(7) + 5(8)$

6. $6(2 + 4) = 6(2) + 6(4)$

7. $4(x + 3) = 4(x) + 4(3)$

8. $6 \cdot 5 + 9 \cdot 6 = 30 + 54$
$= 84$

9. $12a + a + 7 = 12a + 1a + 7$
$= (12 + 1)a + 7$
$= 13a + 7$

10. $x + 9x = 1 + 9x$
$= (1 + 9)x$
$= 10x$

11. $6c + c + 7 = 6c + 1c + 7$
$= (6 + 1)c + 7$
$= 7c + 7$

12. $22c + 4(2 + 4c) = 22c + 4 \cdot 2 + 4 \cdot 4c$
$= 22c + 8 + 16c$
$= 22c + 16c + 8$
$= (22 + 16)c + 8$
$= 38c + 8$

13. $4ab + 6ab + 10ab = (4 + 6 + 10)ab$
$= 20ab$

14. a. $\$5.25(4 + 8)$ or $4 \cdot \$5.25 + 8 \cdot \$5.25$
b. $\$5.25(4 + 8) + \$35.50 = \$5.25 \cdot 12 + \$35.50$
$= \$63.00 + \$35.50$
$= \$98.50$

Pages 28–30 Exercises

15. $3(11 + 12) = 3(11) + 3(12)$

16. $(5 + 7)x = 5(x) + 7(x)$

17. $6t + 11t = t(6 + 11)$

18. $2a + 4b = 2(a + 2b)$

19. $2r + 12s = 2(r + 6s)$

20. $6x + 6y + 1 = 6(x + y) + 1$

21. $(9 + 8)v = 9(v) + 8(v)$

22. $12r + 12s = 12(r + s)$

23. $(4x + 9y)2 = 2(4x) + 2(9y)$

24. $6d + d + 15 = 6d + 1d + 15$
$= (6 + 1)d + 15$
$= 7d + 15$

25. $17a + 21a + 45 = (17 + 21)a + 45$
$= 38a + 45$

26. $m + m = 1m + 1m$
$= (1 + 1)m$
$= 2m$

27. $c + 24c + 16 = 1c + 24c + 16$
$= (1 + 24)c + 16$
$= 25c + 16$

28. $q + 4 + 11 + 4q = q + 4q + 4 + 11$
$= 1q + 4q + 4 + 11$
$= (1 + 4)q + 4 + 11$
$= 5q + 15$

29. $18y + 5(7 + 3y) = 18y + 5 \cdot 7 + 5 \cdot 3y$
$= 18y + 35 + 15y$
$= 18y + 15y + 35$
$= (18 + 15)y + 35$
$= 33y + 35$

30. $14(b + 3) + 8b = 14b + 14 \cdot 3 + 8b$
$= 14b + 42 + 8b$
$= 14b + 8b + 42$
$= (14 + 8)b + 42$
$= 22b + 42$

31. $30(b + 2) + 2b = 30b + 30 \cdot 2 + 2b$
$= 30b + 60 + 2b$
$= 30b + 2b + 60$
$= (30 + 2)b + 60$
$= 32b + 60$

32. $3(8 + a) + 7(6 + 4a) = 3 \cdot 8 + 3a + 7 \cdot 6 + 7 \cdot 4a$
$= 24 + 3a + 42 + 28a$
$= 24 + 42 + 3a + 28a$
$= 24 + 42 + (3 + 28)a$
$= 66 + 31a$

33. $8(9 + 3f) + f = 8 \cdot 9 + 8 \cdot 3f + f$
$= 72 + 24f + f$
$= 72 + 24f + 1f$
$= 72 + (24 + 1)f$
$= 72 + 25f$

34. $x + 5x + 8(x + 2) = x + 5x + 8x + 8 \cdot 2$
$= x + 5x + 8x + 16$
$= 1x + 5x + 8x + 16$
$= (1 + 5 + 8)x + 16$
$= 14x + 16$

35. $3(x + y) + 4(2x + 3y) = 3x + 3y + 4 \cdot 2x + 4 \cdot 3y$
$= 3x + 3y + 8x + 12y$
$= 3x + 8x + 3y + 12y$
$= 11x + 15y$

36. See students' work.

37. $\frac{d(a + b)}{2} \times L = \frac{6(52 + 48)}{2} \times 40$
$= [6(52 + 48) \div 2] \times 40$
$= [6(100) \div 2] \times 40$
$= [600) \div 2] \times 40$
$= 300 \times 40$
$= 12,000$
The volume of earth to remove is 12,000 cubic meters.

38. a. $3(0 + 6 + 0 + 3 + 6 + 5) + (3 + 8 + 0 + 0 + 8)$
b. $3(0 + 6 + 0 + 3 + 6 + 5) + (3 + 8 + 0 + 0 + 8)$
$= 3(20) + 19$
$= 60 + 19$
$= 79$
$80 - 79 = 1$
Yes, the check digit verifies the code.

39. $(8 + 19) + 17 = 8 + (19 + 17)$

40. multiplicative identity

41. $n \div 9$

42. $75 - 10n = 75 - 10(7)$
$= 75 - 70$
$= 5$

43. $15(\$4.25) + 36(\$3.75) + 22(\$7.45)$
$= \$63.75 + \$135.00 + \$163.90$
$= \$362.65$

44. The number of sides increases by 1, so the next figure will have 6 sides.

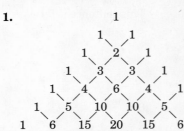

45. $528 \times 7 \rightarrow 500 \times 7 = 3500$
So, the answer of 3696 is reasonable.

Page 30   Self Test

1.

```
               1
             1   1
           1   2   1
         1   3   3   1
       1   4   6   4   1
     1   5   10   10   5   1
   1   6   15   20   15   6   1
```
Each row begins and ends with 1. the numbers in each row are attained by adding the two adjacent numbers in the previous row.

2. a. Estimate. It says *about*, so an exact answer is not needed.

b. Explore—We know how many truckloads of rock were removed and the truck's capacity per load. We need to determine how much rock was removed.

Plan—Multiply the number of truckloads by the truck's capacity per load. Since an exact answer is not necessary, solve by using estimation.

Solve—$29,000 \times 5 \rightarrow 30,000 \times 5 = 150,000$
About 150,000 cubic yards of rock was removed.

Examine—$29,000 \times 5 = 145,000$. So, the estimate is reasonable.

3. $9(2 + 5) - 4 = 9 \cdot 7 - 4$
$= 63 - 4$
$= 59$

4. $\frac{19 - 11}{2(4)} = [19 - 11] \div [2(4)]$
$= [19 - 11] \div [8]$
$= 8 \div 8$
$= 1$

5. $\frac{ab}{c} = \frac{(3)(8)}{12}$
$= (3)(8) \div 12$
$= 24 \div 12$
$= 2$

6. $8c - (b + 3a) = 8(12) - (8 + 3 \cdot 3)$
$= 8(12) - (8 + 9)$
$= 96 - 17$
$= 79$

7. commutative, addition

8. commutative, addition

9. $5(\$12.50) = \$62.50$

10. $2n + 4(n + 8n) = 2n + 4n + 4 \cdot 8n$
$= 2n + 4n + 32n$
$= (2 + 4 + 32)n$
$= 38n$

1-5B   Math Lab: Distributive Property

Page 31

1. False. $2x + 3$ means

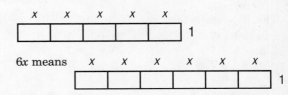

2. True. $2x$ means

$x + x$ means

3. True. $3x + 3$ means

$3(x + 1)$ means

4. False. $3x + 2x$ means

$6x$ means

5. False. $3x + 3$ means

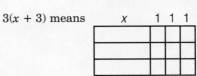

$3(x + 3)$ means

6. True. $3x + 2x$ means

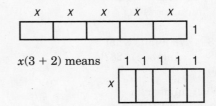

$x(3 + 2)$ means

7. See students' work.

Variables and Equations

1. See students' work.

2. Sample answers: $5 + 2 = 7$; $5 + 2 = 9$

3. Explore—We know the equation. We need to find the solution to the equation.
   Plan—Replace the variable with a number that makes the equation true. Since the numbers are simple, solve the equation mentally.
   Solve—$8 + 4 = 12$
       The sentence is true. The solution is 4.
   Examine—The solution makes sense for the equation.

4. Sample answer: $3 + x = 6$; $3 + 8 = 6$

5. **a.** 9   **b.** 0   **c.** 2

6. $7 - x = 4$ $7 - x = 4$
   $7 - 3 = 4$ $7 - 4 = 4$
   $\quad 4 = 4$ $\quad 3 = 4$
   This sentence is true.   This sentence is false.
   The solution is 3.

   $7 - x = 4$
   $7 - 6 = 4$
   $\quad 1 = 4$
   This sentence is false.

7. $y + 19 = 32$ $y + 19 = 32$
   $9 + 19 = 32$ $13 + 19 = 32$
   $\quad 28 = 32$ $\quad 32 = 32$
   This sentence is false.   This sentence is true.
                              The solution is 13.

   $y + 19 = 32$
   $19 + 19 = 32$
   $\quad 38 = 32$
   This sentence is false.

8. $2x + 1 = 7$ $2x + 1 = 7$
   $2(3) + 1 = 7$ $2(4) + 1 = 7$
   $\quad 6 + 1 = 7$ $\quad 8 + 1 = 7$
   $\quad\quad 7 = 7$ $\quad\quad 9 = 7$
   This sentence is true.   This sentence is false.
   The solution is 3.

   $2x + 1 = 7$
   $2(5) + 1 = 7$
   $\quad 10 + 1 = 7$
   $\quad\quad 11 = 7$
   This sentence is false.

9. $t + 5 = 10$ What number
   $5 + 5 = 10$ plus 5 is 10?
   $\quad t = 5$

10. $19 - q = 11$ 19 minus what
    $19 - 8 = 11$ number is 11?
    $\quad q = 8$

11. $78 - r = 28$ 78 minus what
    $78 - 50 = 28$ number is 28?
    $\quad r = 50$

12. $\frac{12}{x} = 3$ What number
    $\frac{12}{4} = 3$ times 3 is 12?
    $\quad x = 4$

13. **a.** $220 + d = 360$
    b. $\quad 220 + d = 360$ 220 plus what
    $\quad 220 + 140 = 360$ number is 360?
    $\quad\quad\quad d = 140$

14. $12 - c = 8$ $12 - c = 8$
    $12 - 2 = 8$ $12 - 4 = 8$
    $\quad 10 = 8$ $\quad 8 = 8$
    This sentence is false.   This sentence is true.
                              The solution is 4.

    $12 - c = 8$
    $12 - 7 = 8$
    $\quad 5 = 8$
    This sentence is false.

15. $t + 33 = 72$ $t + 33 = 72$
    $29 + 33 = 72$ $34 + 33 = 72$
    $\quad 62 = 72$ $\quad 67 = 72$
    This sentence is false.   This sentence is false.

    $t + 33 = 72$
    $39 + 33 = 72$
    $\quad 72 = 72$
    This sentence is true.
    The solution is 39.

16. $8 = \frac{16}{a}$ $8 = \frac{16}{a}$
    $8 = 16 \div a$ $8 = 16 \div a$
    $8 = 16 \div 1$ $8 = 16 \div 2$
    $8 = 16$ $8 = 8$
    This sentence is false.   This sentence is true.
                              The solution is 2.

    $8 = \frac{16}{a}$
    $8 = 16 \div a$
    $8 = 16 \div 4$
    $8 = 4$
    This sentence is false.

17. $8 = \frac{g}{4}$ $8 = \frac{g}{4}$
    $8 = g \div 4$ $8 = g \div 4$
    $8 = 32 \div 4$ $8 = 24 \div 4$
    $8 = 8$ $8 = 6$
    This sentence is true.   This sentence is false.
    The solution is 32.
    $8 = \frac{g}{4}$
    $8 = g \div 4$
    $8 = 16 \div 4$
    $8 = 4$
    This sentence is false.

18. $3x + 1 = 10$ $3x + 1 = 10$
    $3(2) + 1 = 10$ $3(3) + 1 = 10$
    $\quad 6 + 1 = 10$ $\quad 9 + 1 = 10$
    $\quad\quad 7 = 10$ $\quad\quad 10 = 10$
    This sentence is false.   This sentence is true.
                              The solution is 3.

    $3x + 1 = 10$
    $3(4) + 1 = 10$
    $\quad 12 + 1 = 10$
    $\quad\quad 13 = 10$
    This sentence is false.

19.
$7 = 5b + 2$
$7 = 5(0) + 2$
$7 = 0 + 2$
$7 = 2$
This sentence is false.

$7 = 5b + 2$
$7 = 5(1) + 2$
$7 = 5 + 2$
$7 = 7$
This sentence is true.
The solution is 1.

$7 = 5b + 2$
$7 = 5(2) + 2$
$7 = 10 + 2$
$7 = 12$
This sentence is false.

20.
$110 = 145 - t$
$110 = 145 - 35$
$110 = 110$
This sentence is true.
The solution is 35.

$110 = 145 - t$
$110 = 145 - 40$
$110 = 105$
This sentence is false.

$110 = 145 - t$
$110 = 145 - 45$
$110 = 100$
This sentence is false.

21.
$8 = \frac{48}{m}$
$8 = 48 \div m$
$8 = 48 \div 3$
$8 = 16$
This sentence is false.

$8 = \frac{48}{m}$
$8 = 48 \div m$
$8 = 48 \div 4$
$8 = 12$
This sentence is false.

$8 = \frac{48}{m}$
$8 = 48 \div m$
$8 = 48 \div 6$
$8 = 8$
This sentence is true.
The solution is 6.

22. $m + 8 = 10$ What number plus
$2 + 8 = 10$ 8 is 10?
$ m = 2$

23. $129 - q = 9$ 129 minus what
$129 - 120 = 9$ number is 9?
$ q = 120$

24. $17 = k - 3$ What number
$17 = 20 - 3$ minus 3 is 17?
$ k = 20$

25. $8x = 64$ What number
$8 \cdot 8 = 64$ times 8 is 64?
$ x = 8$

26. $\frac{50}{h} = 5$ What number
$\frac{50}{10} = 5$ times 5 is 50?
$ h = 10$

27. $63 = 7j$ What number
$63 = 7 \cdot 9$ times 7 is 63?
$ j = 9$

28. $56 - s = 10$ 56 minus what
$56 - 56 = 0$ number is 0 ?
$ s = 56$

29. $99 = 9x$ What number
$99 = 9 \cdot 11$ times 9 is 99?
$ x = 11$

30. $\frac{72}{c} = 8$ What number
$\frac{72}{9} = 8$ times 8 is 72?
$ c = 9$

31. $6x = 42$ What number
$6 \cdot 7 = 42$ times 6 is 42?
$ x = 7$

32. $18 = 2w$ What number
$18 = 2 \cdot 9$ times 2 is 18?
$ w = 9$

33. $\frac{21}{y} = 3$ What number
$\frac{21}{7} = 3$ times 3 is 21?
$ y = 7$

34. a. Sample answer: $5 - x = 3$; $2x = 4$
b. Sample answer: $5 + x = 4$; $8 - x = 9$

35. a. $3973.05 + c = 4003.33$
b. $3973.05 + c = 4003.33$
$3973.05 + 29.92 = 4003.33$
$4002.97 = 4003.33$
This sentence is false.
$3973.05 + c = 4003.33$
$3973.05 + 30.28 = 4003.33$
$4003.33 = 4003.33$
This sentence is true.
The solution is 30.28.
$3973.05 + c = 4003.33$
$3973.05 + 33.32 = 4003.33$
$4006.37 = 4003.33$
This sentence is false.

36. a. $60° + x° + 90° = 180°$
b. $60° + x° + 90° = 180°$
$60° + 90° + x° = 180°$
$150° + x° = 180°$ 150° plus what
$150° + 30° = 180°$ number is 180°?
$180° = 180°$
$ x = 30°$

37. $5x + 2x + 1 = (5 + 2)x + 1$
$ = 7x + 1$

38. $8 (3 \cdot 6) = (8 \cdot 3)6$

39. $1943 + n$

40. nine less than a number

41. $8 + 9 - 6 \cdot 2 = 8 + 9 - 12$
$ = 17 - 12$
$ = 5$

42. rectangles with area 1 unit   =   6
rectangles with area 2 units =   5
rectangles with area 3 units =   4
rectangles with area 4 units =   3
rectangles with area 5 units =   2
rectangles with area 6 units =   1
$\overline{\text{21 Total rectangles}}$

Page 38   Checking Your Understanding

1.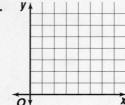

2. See students' work.

3. Sample answer: Seats at a concert hall.

4. Jamal; to graph (4, 7) you move 4 units right and 7 up and to graph (7, 4) you move 7 units right and 4 up.

5. (3, 2)   6. no   7. State Capitol

8. (10, 10)   9. no

Pages 39–40   Excerises

10. *D*   11. *M*   12. *S*
13. *L*   14. *A*   15. *T*
16. *H*   17. *J*   18. (1, 2)
19. (6, 4)   20. (7, 8)   21. (5, 0)
22. (7, 1)   23. (9, 2)   24. (0, 7)
25. (10, 8)   26. (2, 1)
27. **a.** (a, 0)   **b.** (0, b)   **c.** origin

28.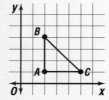

a. The point for (2, 1) is *A*.
The point for (2, 4) is *B*.
The point for (5, 1) is *C*.
The figure is a triangle.

b. 2(2, 1) = (4, 2) = *A*
2(2, 4) = (4, 8) = *B*
2(5, 1) = (10, 2) = *C*
The figure is a triangle.

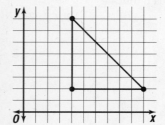

c. Sample answer: The figures are both triangles of the same shape. The figures are different sizes.

29. **a.**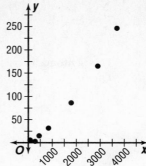

b. 1.5 billion = 1500 million.
When the *x* value is 1500 million miles, the *y* value is about 78. The planet would take about 78 years to orbit the sun.

30. **a.**

x (depth)	35*x* + 20	*y* (temperature)	(*x*, *y*)
0	35(0) + 20	20	(0, 20)
2	35(2) + 20	90	(2, 90)
4	35(4) + 20	160	(4, 160)
6	35(6) + 20	230	(6, 230)
8	35(8) + 20	300	(8, 300)

b.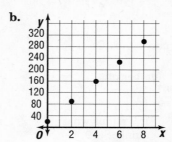

31. **a.** 50 cars are waiting at the light at 7:00 A.M. and 10 cars are waiting at 9:00 A.M.

b. The workday started at most businesses in the area.

c.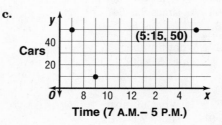

Time (7 A.M.– 5 P.M.)

Sample answer: About the same number of cars will take people away from work that took them there in the morning.

32.   7*a* = 28   What number
    7 · 4 = 28   times 7 is 28?
    a = 4

33. 3*m* + 7*m* + 1 = (3 + 7)*m* + 1
    = 10*m* + 1

34. 3*x*

Pre-Algebra   Chapter 1

35. $4r = 4(3)$
$\quad = 12$

36. $4c + 2a = 4(7) + 2(2)$
$\quad\quad\quad = 28 + 4$
$\quad\quad\quad = 32$

37. $6 \cdot 3 \div 9 - 1 = 18 \div 9 - 1$
$\quad\quad\quad\quad\quad\quad = 2 - 1$
$\quad\quad\quad\quad\quad\quad = 1$

Page 40   The Shape of Things to Come

How does the GPS use the satellite distances to determine position?

Sample answer: The Global Positioning System receives signals from the satellites and then finds the distances to three or four different satellites to tell your location.

What are some of the ways consumers are using the GPS? What are the plans for the GPS?

Sample answer: Consumers are using the GPS to determine the location of restaurants and hotels when traveling. They also use the system to determine their direction, speed, and time of arrival. Companies are inventing a system that enables motorists to avoid traffic jams. Eventually, they hope to invent a system that will drive the car.

Why was the GPS first developed?
It was developed by the U.S. Defense Department to direct smart bombs.

What is the approximate latitude and longitude of your hometown?
See students' work.

1-8   **Solving Equations Using Inverse Operations**

Pages 43–44   Checking Your Understanding

1. Sample answer: $8 + 7 = 15$, $15 - 8 = 7$

2. losing 5 yards

3. Defining a variable is choosing a variable and a quantity for it to represent.

4. a.

fare	times	number of slugs	equals	total cost
$1.25	$\times$	165,000	$=$	t

$\$1.25 \times 165{,}000 = t$
$\quad\quad\quad \$206{,}250 = t$
The New York Subway System lost $206,250 each month.

b. See students' work.

5. $12 - 9 = 3$ or $12 - 3 = 9$

6. $39 \div 3 = t$ or $39 \div t = 3$

7. $4 + 12 = 16$

8. $44x = 4x \cdot 11$

9. $8 + y = 22$
$\quad\quad y = 22 - 8$
$\quad\quad y = 14$

10. $\quad 77 = 7h$
$\quad 77 \div 7 = h$
$\quad\quad 11 = h$

11. $\quad 5.4 = \frac{w}{2.2}$
$\quad 2.2 \times 5.4 = w$
$\quad\quad 11.88 = w$

12. Twice a number is 6
$\quad\quad 2x \quad\quad = 6$
$\quad 2x = 6$
$\quad\quad x = 6 \div 2$
$\quad\quad x = 3$

13. 27 more than a number is 31
$\quad\quad n + 27 \quad\quad = 31$
$\quad\quad n = 31 - 27$
$\quad\quad n = 4$

14. Sample answer: Dana earns $6 per hour. How many hours must she work to earn $135?

15. Sample answer: Evan missed 7 questions on the quiz. If his score was 28, how many points were possible?

16. a. h = Heritage Classic prize
b. $h + 135{,}000 = 360{,}000$
c. $h + 135{,}000 = 360{,}000$
$\quad\quad\quad\quad h = 360{,}000 - 135{,}000$
$\quad\quad\quad\quad h = 225{,}000$
The Heritage Classic prize is $225,000.
d. $225,000 is $135,000 less than $360,000.

Pages 44–45   Exercises

17. $14 = 11 + 3$

18. $23 - 17 = n$ or $23 - n = 17$

19. $14 = 28 \div 2$ or $2 = 28 \div 14$

20. $x = 12 \cdot 11$

21. $h = 48 \div 6$ or $6 = 48 \div h$

22. $k = 13 \cdot 7$

23. $6 + n = 28$
$\quad\quad n = 28 - 6$
$\quad\quad n = 22$

24. $g + 11 = 15$
$\quad\quad g = 15 - 11$
$\quad\quad g = 4$

25. $\quad 86 = c - 2$
$\quad 86 + 2 = c$
$\quad\quad 88 = c$

26. $\quad 144 = 12h$
$\quad 144 \div 12 = h$
$\quad\quad 12 = h$

27. $\quad 8 = \frac{v}{15}$
$\quad 8 \cdot 15 = v$
$\quad\quad 120 = v$

28. $\quad 210 = 15w$
$\quad 210 \div 15 = w$
$\quad\quad 14 = w$

29. $\quad 5.56 - q = 4.73$
$\quad\quad 5.56 = 4.73 + q$
$\quad 5.56 - 4.73 = q$
$\quad\quad 0.83 = q$

30. $\quad 3.7 = \frac{r}{5.4}$
$\quad 5.4 \times 3.7 = r$
$\quad\quad 19.98 = r$

31. $f + 15.98 = 19.75$
$\quad\quad f = 19.75 - 15.98$
$\quad\quad f = 3.77$

32. $6.8b = 34.68$
$\quad b = 34.68 \div 6.8$
$\quad b = 5.1$

33. $1.5 + b = 2.1$
$\quad\quad b = 2.1 - 1.5$
$\quad\quad b = 0.6$

34. $\frac{p}{2} = 9$
$\quad p = 9 \cdot 2$
$\quad p = 18$

35. $3x = 18$
$\quad x = 18 \div 3$
$\quad x = 6$

36. $n - 10 = 19$
$\quad\quad n = 19 + 10$
$\quad\quad n = 29$

37. $n - 7 = 22$
$n = 22 + 7$
$n = 29$

38. $8t = 88$
$t = 88 \div 8$
$t = 11$

39. $n \div 4 = 14$
$n = 14 \cdot 4$
$n = 56$

40. $x \div 3 = 13$
$x = 13 \cdot 3$
$x = 39$

41. Sample answer: Jack scored 16 points in this week's game. That is two more than twice what he scored last week. How much did Jack score last week?

42. Sample answer: Service Plus charges $30 per hour for a service call. The total for the service call on the furnace was $90, how many hours of labor were there?

43. Sample answer: The product of any number and 0 is 0 according to the Multiplicative property of zero. Thus, we could rewrite $5 = a \cdot 0$ as $5 = 0$. $5 \neq 0$, so division by zero does not make sense.

44. a. f = entrance fee

b.

number of players	times	fee	equals	$500,000
20	$\times$	f	$=$	500,000
		$20f$	$=$	500,000

c. $20f = 500,000$
$f = 500,000 \div 20$
$f = 25,000$
The entrance fee was $25,000.

d. See students' work.

45. 49ers appeared 35 times.

Dolphins	equal	11	more than	49ers
x	$=$	11	$+$	35

$x = 11 + 35$
$x = 46$
The Miami Dolphins appeared 46 times.

46 a. C **b.** $(5, 0)$

47. $77 + b = 96$ $77 + b = 96$
$77 + 13 = 96$ $77 + 16 = 96$
$90 = 96$ $93 = 96$
This sentence is false.   This sentence is false.
$77 + b = 96$
$77 + 19 = 96$
$96 = 96$
This sentence is true.
The solution is 19.

48. $13 \cdot 13 = 169$

49. Associative property of addition

50. $b + cd = 2 + 5 \cdot 7$
$= 2 + 35$
$= 37$

51. $5 \cdot t$

52. $(18 + 6) \div (8 - 2) = 24 \div 6$
$= 4$

53. a. Sample answer: calculator

b. Examine—We know the number of miles driven each year. We need to find the number of miles each week.

Plan—Divide the number of miles each year by the number of miles each week.
Estimate: $16,500 \div 52 \to 17,000 \div 50 = 340$.

Solve—Use a calculator.
$16,500 \div 52 = 317.3076923$
The average American man drives about 317 miles each week.

Examine—The answer is close to the estimate. So, the answer is reasonable.

1-9   Inequalities

Pages 47–48   Checking Your Understanding

1. $x > 6$ is all numbers greater than 6; $x \geq 6$ is 6 and all numbers greater than 6.

2. Sample answer: 3

3. Sample answer: Equations and inequalities are both number sentences. Equations contain equal signs and inequalities contain a symbol indicating something other than equality; like $>$ or $\leq$.

4. See students' work. It is sometimes impossible to make a true inequality. For example, if you drew two cards with the same digit and a $<$ or $>$ sign.

5. false   **6.** false   **7.** true

8. $n + 2 > 4, n = 8$ **9.** $15 \leq 2q, q = 9$
$8 + 2 > 4$ $15 \leq 2 \times 9$
$10 > 4$ $15 \leq 18$
This sentence is true.   This sentence is true.

10. The phrase *is less than* implies a less than relationship. Let n represent the number.
$n < 6$

11. Eggs that weigh 27 ounces or more per dozen are labeled "extra large." Let d represent the weight of a dozen eggs.
$d \geq 27$

12. Citizens who are 18 years or older can vote. Let v represent the voting age.
$v \geq 18$

Pages 48–49   Exercises

13. true   **14.** false   **15.** open
16. open   **17.** true   **18.** open
19. true   **20.** open   **21.** open

22. $22 - w > 4, w = 11$ **23.** $24 \geq 3c, c = 6$
$22 - 11 > 4$ $24 \geq 3 \cdot 6$
$11 > 4$ $24 \geq 18$
This sentence is true   This sentence is true.

24. $h - 9 > 6, h = 10$ **25.** $2x - 7 \leq 7$
$10 - 9 > 6$ $27 - 7 \leq 7$
$1 > 6$ $14 - 7 \leq 7$
          $7 \leq 7$
This sentence is false.   This sentence is true.

26. $4x + 8x < 7, x = 1$
$4 \cdot 1 + 8 \cdot 1 < 7$
$4 + 8 < 7$
$12 < 7$
This sentence is false.

27. $5z - 16 \leq 11, z = 4$
$5 \cdot 4 - 16 \leq 11$
$20 - 16 \leq 11$
$4 \leq 11$
This sentence is true.

28. $n > 24$ **29.** $t \geq \$100$ **30.** $a \leq 75$

31. $l \geq 3$ **32.** $k \geq 16$ **33.** $p < 15$

34. a. x is between 6 and 18.
   b. Sample answers: 7, 8, 9, 10, 11, 12, . . ., or 17

35. More than 80,000 fans were in attendance. Let f represent the number of fans.
$f > 80,000$

36. Employees are limited to the maximum amount of $9240. Let a represent the amount that an employee may invest.
$a \leq \$9240$

37. a. $t \leq 10$ years **b.** $t \leq 1$ year

38. a. $m =$ monthly donations
   b. $\underbrace{\text{Each month}}_{12}$ $\underbrace{\text{times}}_{\times}$ $\underbrace{\text{monthly donations}}_{m}$
   is
   $=$ total amount
   $\$14,400$
   $12m = 14,400$
   c. $12m = 14,400$
   $m = 14,400 \div 12$
   $m = 1200$
   TWA collects $1200 in a month.
   d. $12(1200) = 14,400$

39. $7b = 77$ What number
$7 \cdot 11 = 77$ times 7 is 77?
$b = 11$

40. $4 \cdot 8 + 4 \cdot 2 = 4(8 + 2)$
$= 4 \cdot 10$
$= 40$

41. $8(7c) = (8 \cdot 7)c$
$= 56c$

42. $9t - 2s = 9 \cdot 3 - 2 \cdot 8$
$= 27 - 16$
$= 11$

43. $\frac{84 - 12}{14 - 6} = (84 - 12) \div (14 - 6)$
$= 72 \div 8$
$= 9$

44. $8 \xrightarrow{+2} 10 \xrightarrow{+4} 14 \xrightarrow{+8} 22 \xrightarrow{+16} 38 \xrightarrow{+32} 70$

1-10A **Math Lab: Gathering Data**

Page 50

1. 9−11 hours.
2. See students' work.
3. See students' work.
4. See students' work.
5. See students' work.

1-10 **Integration: Statistics Gathering and Recording Data**

Pages 53–54 Checking Your Understanding

1. Sample answer: A frequency table contains categories and the number of times that the answers occur.
2. Only people that visit Epcot Center can be included in the survey. These people have chosen to come there and may not represent people who did not.
3. A frequency table shows each response and a bar graph shows the responses in a visual way. A frequency table is good when you want to know specific numbers. A bar graph is good for giving a general idea quickly.
4. See students' work.
5. **a.** See students' work.
   b. See students' work.
6. San Diego
7. Miami Metrozoo and Toledo
8. 1.3 million
9. $0.9 + 2.0 + 1.3 + 1.3 + 0.8 + 3.0 + 3.5 + 0.8 = 13.6$
   13.6 million
10.

Attendance at Major Zoos

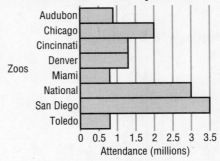

Pages 54–55 Exercises

11. 15
12. 16, restricted
13. yes, the total of the states is 51

14.

Driver's License

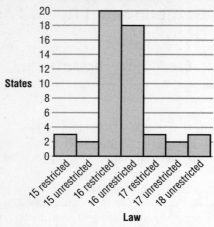

15. Most states will issue a driver's license to a 16-year-old, all to an 18-year-old.

16. Answers will vary.

17.

Height	0–100	101–200	201–300	301–400	401–500
Buildings	0	0	0	4	8

Height	500–600	601–700	701–800	801–900	901–1000
Buildings	4	1	3	0	1

18. 400–500 feet

19. **Seattle, Wa Buildings**

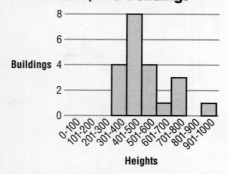

20. a. See students' work.

   b. See students' work.

21. a. 41

   b. 72–74 inches

   c. You cannot tell from the frequency table how many presidents were exactly six feet tall. The table shows how many presidents fell in different height ranges not exact heights.

   d. Leadership is associated with tallness.

   e. See students' work.

22. See students' work.

23. Let s represent the amount that a middle income family will spend. $s \geq \$210,070$.

24. $t - 8 = 42$
$t = 42 + 8$
$t = 50$

25.

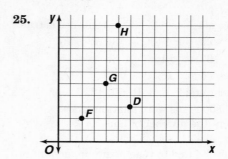

26. $(t + 17) + 6 = t + (17 + 6)$
$= t + 23$

27. $6g - 12h = 6(9) - 12(4)$
$= 54 - 48$
$= 6$

28. $\frac{gh}{3} = \frac{(9)(4)}{3}$
$= (9)(4) \div 3$
$= 36 \div 3$
$= 12$

Chapter 1   Study Guide and Assessment

Page 57   Understanding and Using Vocabulary

1. algebraic expression

2. commutative

3. in simplest form

4. x-coordinate

5. addition

6. sample

7. like terms

Pages 58–60   Skills and Concepts

8. $8(16 + 14) = 8(30)$
$= 240$

9. $3(9 - 3 \cdot 2) = 3(9 - 6)$
$= 3(3)$
$= 9$

10. $14 \div 2 + 4 \cdot 3 = 7 + 4 \cdot 3$
$= 7 + 12$
$= 19$

11. $12 \div 3 \cdot 4 = 4 \cdot 4$
$= 16$

12. $\frac{14 + 4}{11 - 2} = (14 + 4) \div (11 - 2)$
$= 18 \div 9$
$= 2$

13. $\frac{3(2 + 6)}{4} = [3(2 + 6) \div 4]$
$= [3(8) \div 4]$
$= 24 \div 4$
$= 6$

14. $9(12 - 5) - 11(21 - 8 \cdot 2) = 9(7) - 11(21 - 8 \cdot 2)$
$= 9(7) - 11(21 - 16)$
$= 9(7) - 11(5)$
$= 63 - 55$
$= 8$

15. $12[3(17 - 6) - 7 \cdot 4] = 12[3(11) - 7 \cdot 4]$
$$= 12[33 - 28]$$
$$= 12[5]$$
$$= 60$$

16. $14 - a + b = 14 - 10 + 8$
$$= 4 + 8$$
$$= 12$$

17. $2b - d = 2(8) - 12$
$$= 16 - 12$$
$$= 4$$

18. $d - c = 12 - 6$
$$= 6$$

19. $c + (d - b) = 6 + (12 - 8)$
$$= 6 + 4$$
$$= 10$$

20. $5a + 4b = 5(10) + 4(8)$
$$= 50 + 32$$
$$= 82$$

21. $\frac{a}{b + 2} = \frac{10}{8 + 2}$
$$= (10) \div (8 + 2)$$
$$= 10 \div 10$$
$$= 1$$

22. $ab - cd = (10)(8) - (6)(12)$
$$= 80 - 72$$
$$= 8$$

23. $6(d - b) = 6(12 - 8)$
$$= 6(4)$$
$$= 24$$

24. $n + 7$

25. $10n$

26. $2n$

27. $b + 10$

28. $4 + 2w$

29. $r - 12$

30. additive identity

31. commutative addition

32. associative addition

33. associative multiplication

34. multiplicative property of zero

35. identity multiplication

36. $7 \cdot 8 + 7 \cdot 3 = 7(8 + 3)$
$$= 7(11)$$
$$= 77$$

37. $n + 7n = 1n + 7n$
$$= n(1 + 7)$$
$$= n(8)$$
$$= 8n$$

38. $7b + 12b - 10 = b(7 + 12) - 10$
$$= b(19) - 10$$
$$= 19b - 10$$

39. $16x + 2x + 8 = x(16 + 2) + 8$
$$= x(18) + 8$$
$$= 18x + 8$$

40. $8(5ab + 4) - 3(2ab + 2) = 8 \cdot 5ab + 8 \cdot 4 +$
$$3 \cdot 2ab + 3 \cdot 2$$
$$= 40ab + 32 + 6ab + 6$$
$$= 40ab + 6ab + 32 + 6$$
$$= ab(40 + 6) + 38$$
$$= ab(46) + 38$$
$$= 46ab + 38$$

41. $2(x + y) + 8(x + 3y) = 2(x) + 2(y) + 8(x) + 8(3y)$
$$= 2x + 2y + 8x + 24y$$
$$= 2x + 8x + 2y + 24y$$
$$= x(2 + 8) + y(2 + 24)$$
$$= 10x + 26y$$

42. $10(u - 3) + 4(5 - u) = 10 \cdot u + 10 \cdot 3 + 4 \cdot 5 + 4 \cdot u$
$$= 10u + 30 + 20 + 4u$$
$$= 10u + 4u + 30 + 20$$
$$= u(10 + 4) + 50$$
$$= u(14) + 50$$
$$= 14u + 50$$

43. $15 - h = 9$ $15 - h = 9$
$15 - 4 = 9$ $15 - 6 = 9$
$11 = 9$ $9 = 9$
This sentence is false.   This sentence is true.
                    The solution is 6.

$15 - h = 9$
$15 - 7 = 9$
$8 = 9$
This sentence is true.

44. $7 = \frac{m}{4}$ $7 = \frac{m}{4}$
$7 = m \div 4$ $7 = m \div 4$
$7 = 21 \div 4$ $7 = 28 \div 4$
$7 = 5.25$ $7 = 7$
This sentence is false.   This sentence is true.
                    The solution is 28.

$7 = \frac{m}{4}$
$7 = m \div 4$
$7 = 35 \div 4$
$7 = 8.75$
This sentence is false.

45. $5b = 45$ $5b = 45$
$5 \cdot 7 = 45$ $5 \cdot 9 = 45$
$35 = 45$ $45 = 45$
This sentence is false.   This sentence is true.
                    The solution is 9.

$5b = 45$
$5 \cdot 11 = 45$
$55 = 45$
This sentence is false.

46. $18 - n = 18$ $18 - n = 18$
$18 - 18 = 18$ $18 - 1 = 18$
$0 = 18$ $17 = 18$
This sentence is false.   This sentence is false.
$18 - n = 18$
$18 - 0 = 18$
$18 = 18$
This sentence is true.
The solution is 0.

47.

$12 = 9x - 15$	$12 = 9x - 15$
$12 = 9 \cdot 3 - 15$	$12 = 9 \cdot 6 - 15$
$12 = 27 - 15$	$12 = 54 - 15$
$12 = 12$	$12 = 39$
This sentence is true.	This sentence is false.
The solution is 3.	

$12 = 9x - 15$
$12 = 9 \cdot 9 - 15$
$12 = 81 - 15$
$12 = 66$
This sentence is false.

48.

$16 = 144 \div k$	$16 = 144 \div k$
$16 = 144 \div 9$	$16 = 144 \div 12$
$16 = 16$	$16 = 12$
This sentence is true.	This sentence is false.
The solution is 9.	

$16 = 144 \div k$
$16 = 144 \div 16$
$16 = 9$
This sentence is false.

49.

$\frac{35}{r+2} = 5$	$\frac{35}{r+2} = 5$
$35 \div (r + 2) = 5$	$35 \div (r + 2) = 5$
$35 \div (3 + 2) = 5$	$35 \div (5 + 2) = 5$
$35 \div 5 = 5$	$35 \div 7 = 5$
$7 = 5$	$5 = 5$
This sentence is false.	This sentence is true.
	The solution is 5.

$\frac{35}{r+2} = 5$
$35 \div (r + 2) = 5$
$35 \div (7 + 2) = 5$
$35 \div 9 = 5$
$3.89 = 5$

50. T

51. N

52. U

53. $(5, 6)$

54. $(6, 6)$

55. $(0, 4)$

56.
$72 = 8n$
$72 \div 8 = n$
$9 = n$

57. $19 - g = 7$
$19 = 7 + g$
$19 - 7 = g$
$12 = g$

58. $6n = 84$
$n = 84 \div 6$
$n = 14$

59. $\frac{y}{4.5} = 6.3$
$y = 6.3 \times 4.5$
$y = 28.35$

60.
$19.9 - x = 17.6$
$19.9 = 17.6 + x$
$19.9 - 17.6 = x$
$2.3 = x$

61.
$9 = \frac{w}{12}$
$12 \cdot 9 = w$
$108 = w$

62. $7n = 84$
$n = 84 \div 7$
$n = 12$

63. $37 - z \le 9$
$37 - 22 \le 9$
$15 \le 9$
This sentence is false.

64.
$5x + 8 > 0$
$5(0) + 8 > 0$
$0 + 8 > 0$
$8 > 0$
This sentence is true.

65.
$7c + 9c \ge 17c$
$7(8) + 9(8) \ge 17(8)$
$56 + 72 \ge 136$
$128 \ge 136$
This sentence is false.

66. A number exceeds 25. Let n represent the number.
$n > 25$.

67. Fewer than 60 points. Let p represent the number of points scored.
$p < 60$

68. The phrase *no less than* implies a greater than or equal relationship. Let h represent the number of hours.
$h \ge 7$

69.

Representatives	States
1 – 10	38
11 – 20	7
21 – 30	3
31 – 40	1
41 – 50	0
51 – 60	1

70. Congressional Representatives

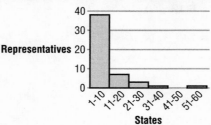

71. a. Sample answer: Estimation because an exact answer is not needed.

b. Explore—We know how many miles the space shuttle traveled and the number of times it circled Earth. We need to determine the number of miles the shuttle traveled on each trip around Earth.

Plan—Divide the total number of miles by the number of times the shuttle circled Earth. Since an exact answer is not needeed, solve by using estimation.

Solve—$6,900,000 \div 262 \rightarrow 7,000,000 \div 250 = 28,000$
The space shuttle traveled about 28,000 miles on each trip around Earth.

Examine—The circumference of Earth is about 25,000 miles. So, an orbit of 28,000 miles is reasonable.

72. a. 5 feet 5 inches = 65 inches

$w = 100 + 5(h - 60)$

$w = 100 + 5(65 - 60)$

$w = 100 + 5(5)$

$w = 100 + 25$

$w = 125$

Cassie's ideal weight is 125 pounds.

b. 6 feet 3 inches = 75 inches

$w = 100 + 6(h - 60)$

$w = 100 + 6(75 - 60)$

$w = 100 + 6(15)$

$w = 100 + 90$

$w = 190$

Rituso's ideal weight is 190 pounds.

c. $w = 100 + 6(h - 60)$

$w = 100 + 6(h) - 6(60)$

$w = 100 + 6h - 360$

$w = 6h + 100 - 360$

$w = 6h - 260$

males: $w = 6h - 260$

$w = 100 + 5(h - 60)$

$w = 100 + 5(h) - 5(60)$

$w = 100 + 5h - 300$

$w = 5h + 100 - 300$

$w = 5h - 200$

females: $w = 5h - 200$

Page 61   Alternative Assessment

1. 300 to 800

2. $2(20) + 1(0) = 2(20) + 0$

$= 40 + 0$

$= 40$

3. a. $192 + C$ or $C + 192$

b. $192 + C = 192 + 588$

$= 780$

4. There is less than 1 Calorie in 16 ounces of Diet Pepsi. No, since $6 > 1$ there could not be 6 Calories.

5. See students' work.

Page 61   Thinking Critically

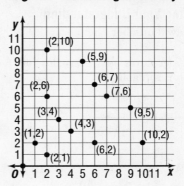

Sample answer: If the grid was folded so that the x- and y-axes coincide, the points (a, b) and (b, a) would match. The graphs of (a, b) and (b, a) are the same point when the x-coordinates and the y-coordinates are the same. $6 = 3$ is an example of an equation that has no solution. The equation has no solution because the sentence is never true.

Page 61   Portfolio

See students' work.

Page 61   Self Evaluation

See students' work.

Chapter 2   Exploring Integers

Pages 68–69   Checking Your Understanding

1. Sample answer: Draw a number line. Locate -7. Draw a dot there.

2. Sample answer: temperatures below zero, loss of money, below par scores in golf

3. -3, -1, 1, 3

4.
   -5-4-3-2-1 0 1 2 3 4 5

5. a.
   -4 ⊖ ⊖ ⊖ ⊖

   b.
   5 ⊕ ⊕ ⊕ ⊕ ⊕

6. A:-4, B:6, C:3, D:-2, E:1

7. -5

   -6-5-4-3-2-1 0 1 2 3 4 5 6

8. -12
   -12 -10   -5   0

9. +13
   0   5   10 13

10. +1200
    0 200 400 600 800 1000 1200 1400

11. $|-5| = 5$ 12. $|8| = 8$

13. $|13| - |-3| = 13 - 3$
    $= 10$

14. $|15| + |-8| = 15 + 8$
    $= 23$

15. $7 + |d| = 7 + |-5|$ 16. $|d| - r = |-5| - 3$
    $= 7 + 5$ $= 5 - 3$
    $= 12$ $= 2$

17. a. 15 meters below: -15
       9 meters lower: -24

    b.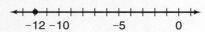
       -25   -20   -15

Pages 69–70   Exercises

18.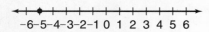
    -4-3-2-1 0 1 2 3 4 5 6

19. -5-4-3-2-1 0 1 2 3 4 5

20. -6-5-4-3-2-1 0 1 2 3 4

21. -9-8-7-6-5-4-3-2-1 0 1

22. A:5, B:-4, C:2, D:-1

23. +400   24. -50

25. -3   26. +9

27. +5   28. -6

29. $|-11| = 11$ 30. $-|24| = -24$

31. $|0| = 0$ 32. $|7| = 7$

33. $|-5| + |3| = 5 + 3$ 34. $|-8| + |-10| = 8 + 10$
    $= 8$ $= 18$

35. $|14| - |-5| = 14 - 5$
    $= 9$

36. $|-15| + |-12| = 15 + 12$
    $= 27$

37. $|0 + 12| = |12|$ 38. $|16 - 2| = |14|$
    $= 12$ $= 14$

39. $-|-36| = -36$

40. $-||-4| + |-21|| = |4 + 21|$
    $= -|25|$
    $= -25$

41. $|c| - 2 = |-4| - 2$ 42. $12 - |b| = 12 - |2|$
    $= 4 - 2$ $= 12 - 2$
    $= 2$ $= 10$

43. $b + a + |c| = 2 + 0 + |-4|$
    $= 2 + 0 + 4$
    $= 6$

44. $ac + |-30| = 0 \cdot -4 + |-30|$
    $= 0 \cdot -4 + 30$
    $= 0 + 30$
    $= 30$

45. $|c| - b = |-4| - 2$
    $= 4 - 2$
    $= 2$

46. $|b| \cdot |c| + |a| = |2| \cdot |-4| + |0|$
    $= 2 \cdot 4 + 0$
    $= 8 + 0$
    $= 8$

47. Each number in the pattern decreases by 8.
    32, 24, 16, 8, 0, -8

48. Each number in the pattern increases by 5.
    -23, -18, -13, -8, -3, 2

49. Sample answer: -1.5

50. Sample answer: The contestant had 500 points and answered two 400-point questions incorrectly.

51.
    ```
              ×   ×       ×
        ×   × ×   ×   × ×
    -5-4-3-2-1 0 1 2 3 4 5
    ```

52. 25   **53.** $17 - 18$ **54.** $11 - 12$

55.

Physical Science Test Scores

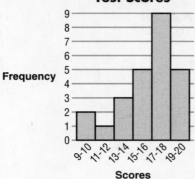

56. $16 = z - 25$
      $16 + 25 = z$
          $41 = z$

57. $A = \ell \cdot w$
   $A = 15 \cdot 12$
   $A = 180$
   The garden is 180 square feet.

58. $5a + 3(7 + 2a) = 5a + 3(7) + 3(2a)$
   $= 5a + 21 + 6a$
   $= 5a + 6a + 21$
   $= a(5 + 6) + 21$
   $= 11a + 21$

59. $3x - 8$

60. a. $15 \times \$3.00 + 8 \times \$2.50$
   b. $15 \times \$3.00 + 8 \times \$2.50 = \$45.00 + \$20.00$
   $= \$65.00$

2-1B   **Math Lab: Statistical Line Plots**

Page 71   Activity

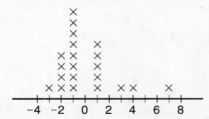

1. −1

2. Sample answer: 7

3. Sample answer: There seems to be a cluster between −2 and 1.

4. total number of House members in 1980: 310
   total number of House members in 1990: 310
   There was no net change in the number of House members.

5. Sample answer: Northern states are losing House members while southern states are gaining House members.

2-2   Integration: Geometry
The Coordinate System

Page 74   Checking Your Understanding

1. See students' work.

2. Sample answer: (4, 8) represents a point 4 units to the right and 8 units up from the origin. (8, 4) represents a point 8 units to the right and 4 units up from the origin.

3. Sample answer: (0, 0), (9, 0)

4. Danny; coordinates of points in Quadrant I are both positive.

5. B
6. H
7. D
8. F
9. Quadrant IV
10. Quadrant II
11. none
12. Quadrant III
13. a. Quadrant I
   b. Quadrant III
   c. Quadrant II

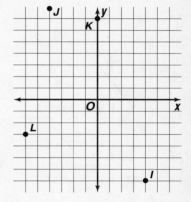

Pages 75–76   Exercises

14. $(-2, 4)$
15. $(4, -2)$
16. $(-3, -5)$
17. $(1, -4)$
18. $(-4, 2)$
19. $(4, 3)$
20. $(0, -2)$
21. $(2, 2)$
22. $(3, 0)$
23. $(-1, 5)$
24. Quadrant I
25. Quadrant II
26. Quadrant IV
27. Quadrant III
28. Quadrant II
29. Quadrant IV
30. Quadrant III
31. Quadrant I
32. Quadrant IV
33. Quadrant III
34. none
35. none

36. a 5-point star

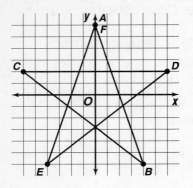

37. a kite

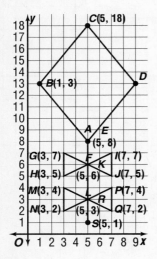

38.

39.

40. origin or x- or y-axes

41. a. $P(2, 2), Q(2, 5), R(7, 5), S(7, 2)$

   b. $P(2, 2) \rightarrow P(2, -2)$
        $Q(2, 5) \rightarrow Q(2, 1)$
        $R(7, 5) \rightarrow R(7, 1)$
        $S(7, 2) \rightarrow S(7, -2)$

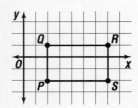

A rectangle is formed. Rectangle $PQRS$ shifted 4 units down.

   c. $P(2, 2) \rightarrow P(-2, -2)$
        $Q(2, 5) \rightarrow Q(-2, -5)$
        $R(7, 5) \rightarrow R(-7, -5)$
        $S(7, 2) \rightarrow S(-7, -2)$

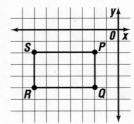

A rectangle shaped like $PQRS$ in quadrant III.

42. a. 30°S, 150°E

   b. 30°S, 50°W

   c. 30°S, 30°E

43. $|15| - |-3| = 15 - 3$
                $= 12$

44.

$$\begin{array}{ccccccccc} \bullet & \bullet & \bullet & & \bullet & & \bullet \\ -4 & -3 & -2 & -1 & 0 & 1 & 2 & 3 \end{array}$$

45. Today there are more than 500,000 skaters. The number of skaters several years ago, when doubled, cannot exceed 500,000. Therefore, the inequality $s < 250,000$ describes how many skaters there were several years ago.

46. associative property of multiplication

47. a. $9a - (4b + 2c) = 9 \cdot 4 - (4 \cdot 2 + 2 \cdot 3)$
                          $= 9 \cdot 4 - (8 + 6)$
                          $= 9 \cdot 4 - 14$
                          $= 36 - 14$
                          $= 22$

   b. $\frac{6(a + b)}{3c} = [6(a + b)] \div [3c]$
               $= [6(4 + 2)] \div [3 \cdot 3]$
               $= [6(6)] \div [3 \cdot 3]$
               $= 36 \div 9$
               $= 4$

48. $7[(12 + 5) - 3(19 - 14)] = 7[(17) - 3(5)]$
                                $= 7[17 - 15]$
                                $= 7(2)$
                                $= 14$

49. Students should use guess and check.
36 points $- 2$(3-points shots) $=$ remaining points.
$36 - 2(3) = 36 - 6$
           $= 30$ points
11 2-point baskets; 8 1-point baskets
$11(2) + 8(1) = 22 + 8$
               $= 30$ points

21

2-2B   Math Lab: Plotting Points

Page 77

1.
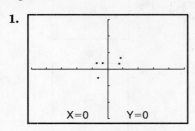

2.
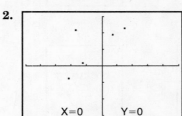

3.
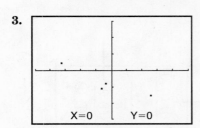

4.
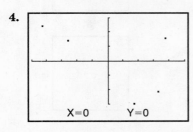

5. **a.** [-10, 10] by [-10, 10]
   b. [-47, 47] by [-31, 31]
6. **a.** Sample answers: For Quadrant II, set Xmin to -10, Xmax to 0, Ymin to 0, and Ymax to 10. For Quadrant IV, set Xmin to 0, Xmax to 10, Ymin to -10, and Ymax to 0.
   b. Sample answer: Set Xmin to -50, and Ymax to 40.

2-3   Comparing and Ordering

Page 79   Checking Your Understanding

1. Sample answer: $-61 < 12$, $12 > -61$
2. $-4, -2, 0, 3, 5$
3. See students' work.
4. Sample answer: The number farthest to the left on a number line is the lesser number. Inequality symbols always point to the lesser number.
5. $2 > -5$ or $-5 < 2$

6. $5 > -3$ or $-3 < 5$
7. $-19 < -9$ 8. $0 > -8$
9. $4 = |-4|$ 10. $|-3| < |8|$
11. $\{-88, -9, -4, 0, 3, 43, 234\}$
12. $-6 < -2, -2 > -6$ 13. $-2 < 3, 3 > -2$
14. **a.** $-5, -2, -2, -1, 0, +1, +1, +2, +3, +4$
    b. -5

Pages 80–81   Exercises

15. $9 > -11$ 16. $-3 > -5$ 17. $|-3| = 3$
18. $-10 < -3$ 19. $-7 > -13$ 20. $-|15| = -15$
21. $-4 < 0$ 22. $0 > -2$ 23. $0 < |-8|$
24. $-33 < 5$ 25. $-439 < -23$ 26. $-10 < -3$
27. $3 > 2$ or $2 < 3$ 28. $20 > 15$ or $15 < 20$
29. $60 < 75$ or $75 > 60$ 30. $41 > -3$ or $-3 < 41$
31. $565 > 344$ or $344 < 565$
32. $212 > 32$ or $32 < 212$
33. $66 < 265$ or $265 > 66$
34. $-3 < 1; 1 > -3$ 35. $-8 < -3; -3 > -8$
36. $-40 > -80; -80 < -40$ 37. $0 > -8; -8 < 0$
38. $\{-5, 0, 7\}$ 39. $\{-11, -3, 8\}$
40. $\{-8, -5, -1, 0\}$ 41. $\{-65, -6, 1, 29, 56\}$
42. $\{-99, -4, 0, 7, 9, 33\}$
43. $\{-65, -53, 48, 87, 199\}$

44.
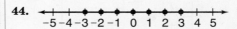

45. **a.** See students' work.
    b. Lead
    c. Helium
46. See students' work.
46. **a.** $-58 < -4$ or $-4 > -58$
    b. $93 > 63$ or $63 < 93$

47–48.
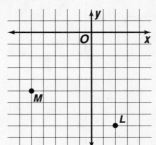

49. Six seconds before lift off: -6
    120 seconds after lift off: 120
50. $15 < 3m + 7$
    $15 < 3(4) + 7$
    $15 < 12 + 7$
    $15 < 19$
    This statement is true.
51. Sample answer: $(6 \times 20) + (6 \times 6)$
52. $4a + b \cdot b = 4 \cdot 4 + 2 \cdot 2$
    $= 16 + 4$
    $= 20$

53. Students should use guess and check.
4 adults
$$26(3) + 4(5) = 78 + 20$$
$$= 98$$

Pages 80–81   Earth Watch

1. from 1865 to 1872:
$7,000,000 - 15,000,000$ or $-8,000,000$
from 1872 to 1900:
$< 1000 - 7,000,000$ or $> 6,999,000$
from 1900 to 1972:
$30,000 - < 1000$ or $> 29,000$
from 1972 to 1993:
$120,000 - 30,000$ or $90,000$

2. 1851 to 1865 showed the greatest loss in the population of buffalo.
1972 to 1993 showed the most growth in the population of buffalo.

3. See students' work.

2-4B   Adding Integers

Page 82

1.

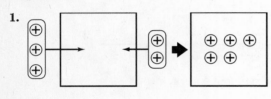

$3 + 2 = 5$

2.

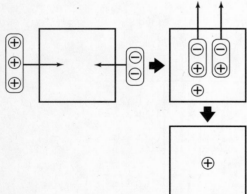

$3 + (-2) = 1$

3.

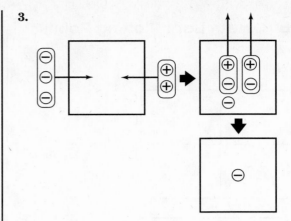

$-3 + 2 = -1$

4.

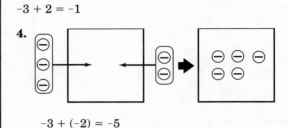

$-3 + (-2) = -5$

5.

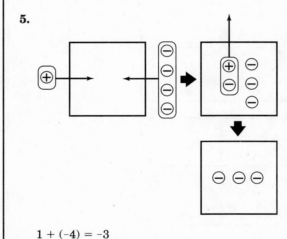

$1 + (-4) = -3$

6.

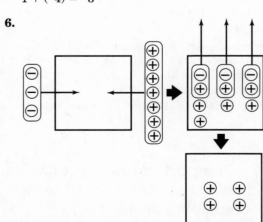

$-3 + 7 = 4$

7.

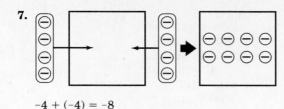

$-4 + (-4) = -8$

8.

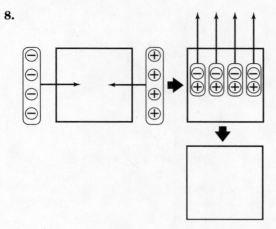

$-4 + 4 = 0$

9. Sample answer: First, place the appropriate number and kind of counters on the mat. Then match all positive counters with all the possible negative counters. These pairs can then be removed because zero does not affect the value of the set on the mat. The remaining counters give you the sum.

2-4   Adding Integers

Pages 85–86   Checking Your Understanding

1. Sample answer: If the signs are the same, add. If the signs differ, subtract.

2. a. $3 + (-2) = 1$ **b.** $-5 + 2 = -3$

3.

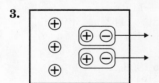

4. Sample answer: Use the distributive property to write the expression as $[-3 + 12 + (-14)]a$. Then use the commutative property to write it as $[-3 + (-14) + 12]a$. Add -3 and -14 to get -17. Then subtract the absolute value of 12 from the absolute value of -17 and give the result a negative sign. The simplified expression is $-5a$.

5. Sample answer: If the signs are alike, just add and keep the sign. For example, $-4 + (-3) = -7$. If the signs differ, subtract the integer with the smaller absolute value from the integer with the larger absolute value and give the result the sign of the integer with the larger absolute value. For example, $-6 + 4 = -2$.

6. $-3 + 7 = 4$ **7.** $8 + (-5) = 3$

---

8. $3 + (-5) = -2$ **9.** $-4 + 9 = 5$

10. negative

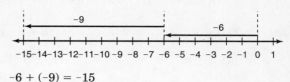

$-6 + (-9) = -15$

11. positive

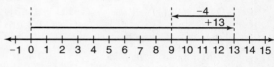

$13 + (-4) = 9$

12. positive

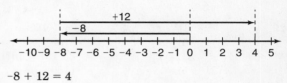

$-8 + 12 = 4$

13. negative

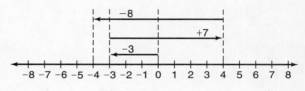

$-3 + 7 + (-8) = -4$

14. $r = -13 + (-5) + 7$
$r = -(|-13| + |-5|) + 7$
$r = -(13 + 5) + 7$
$r = -18 + 7$
$r = -(|-18| - 7)$
$r = -(18 - 7)$
$r = -11$

15. $(-83) + (-21) + (-7) = z$
$-(|-83| + |-21| + |-7|) = z$
$-(83 + 21 + 7) = z$
$-111 = z$

16. $-3z + (-17z) = [-3 + (-17)]z$
$= -20z$

17. $-8a + 14a + (-12a) = [(-8) + 14 + (-12)]a$
$= -6a$

18. $-6 + 2 + 0 + 0 = -6 + 2$
$= -(|6| - |2|)$
$= -(6 - 2)$
$= -4$

-4 or 4 under par

Pages 86–87   Exercises

19. $18 + (-5) = x$ **20.** $b = -8 + (-3)$
$+(|18| - |-5|) = x$ $b = -(|-8| + |-3|)$
$+18 - 5 = x$ $b = -(8 + 3)$
$+13 = x$ $b = -11$

21.
$$16 + (-9) = m$$
$$+(|16| - |-9|) = m$$
$$+(16 - 9) = m$$
$$+7 = m$$

22.
$$v = -12 + (-4)$$
$$v = -(|-12| + |-4|)$$
$$v = -(12 + 4)$$
$$v = -16$$

23.
$$k = 9 + (-13)$$
$$k = (-13) + 9$$
$$k = (|-13| - |9|)$$
$$k = -(13 - 9)$$
$$k = -4$$

24.
$$-15 + 6 = q$$
$$-(|-15| - |6|) = q$$
$$-(15 - 6) = q$$
$$-9 = q$$

25.
$$g = 19 + (-7)$$
$$g = +(|19| - |-7|)$$
$$g = +(19 - 7)$$
$$g = +12$$

26.
$$-11 + (-15) = t$$
$$-(|-11| + |-15|) = t$$
$$-(11 + 15) = t$$
$$-26 = t$$

27.
$$-23 + (-43) = h$$
$$-(|-23| + |-43|) = h$$
$$-(23 + 43) = h$$
$$-66 = h$$

28.
$$-3 + 18 = n$$
$$18 + (-3) = n$$
$$+(|18| - |-3|) = n$$
$$+(18 - 3) = n$$
$$+15 = n$$

29.
$$-5 + 31 = r$$
$$31 + (-5) = r$$
$$+(|31| - |-5|) = r$$
$$+(31 - 5) = r$$
$$+26 = r$$

30.
$$y = 6 + (-16)$$
$$y = (-16) + 6$$
$$y = -(|-16| - |6|)$$
$$y = -(16 - 6)$$
$$y = -10$$

31.
$$m = 8 + (-17)$$
$$m = (-17) + 8$$
$$m = -(|-17| - |8|)$$
$$m = -(17 - 8)$$
$$m = -9$$

32.
$$z = -12 + (-5)$$
$$z = -(|-12| + |-5|)$$
$$z = -(12 + 5)$$
$$z = -17$$

33.
$$-12 + 5 = s$$
$$-(|-12| - |5|) = s$$
$$-(12 - 5) = s$$
$$-7 = s$$

34.
$$500 + (-700) = (-700) + 500$$
$$= -(|-700| - |500|)$$
$$= -(700 - 500)$$
$$= -200$$

35.
$$-7 + 12 = 12 + (-7)$$
$$= +(|12| - |-7|)$$
$$= +(12 - 7)$$
$$= +5$$

36.
$$-1500 + (-1250) = -(|-1500| + |-1250|)$$
$$= -(1500 + 1250)$$
$$= -2750$$

37. See students' work.

38.
$$m = 3 + (-11) + (-5)$$
$$m = (-11) + (-5) + 3$$
$$m = -(|-11| + |-5|) + 3$$
$$m = -(11 + 5) + 3$$
$$m = -16 + 3$$
$$m = (|-16| - |3|)$$
$$m = -(16 - 3)$$
$$m = -13$$

39.
$$k = 14 + 9 + (-2)$$
$$k = 23 + (2)$$
$$k = +(|23| - |-2|)$$
$$k = +(23 - 2)$$
$$k = 21$$

40.
$$-18 + (-23) + 10 = c$$
$$-(|-18| + |-23|) + 10 = c$$
$$-(18 + 23) + 10 = c$$
$$-(18 + 23) + 10 = c$$
$$-41 + 10 = c$$
$$-(|-41| - |10|) = c$$
$$-(41 - 10) = c$$
$$-31 = c$$

41.
$$-16 + (-6) + (-5) = a$$
$$-(|-16| + |-6| + |-5|) = a$$
$$-(16 + 6 + 5) = a$$
$$-27 = a$$

42.
$$-12 + (17) + (-7) = x$$
$$-12 + (-7) + (17) = x$$
$$-(|-12| + |-7|) + (17) = x$$
$$-(12 + 7) + (17) = x$$
$$-19 + 17 = x$$
$$-(|-19| - |17|) = x$$
$$-(19 - 17) = x$$
$$-2 = x$$

43.
$$y = 47 + 32 + (-16)$$
$$y = 79 + (-16)$$
$$y = +(|79| - |-16|)$$
$$y = +(79 - 16)$$
$$y = 63$$

44.
$$6x + (-15)x = [6 + (-15)]x$$
$$= -9x$$

45.
$$-11y + 14y = (-11 + 14)y$$
$$= 3y$$

46.
$$-14k + (-7)k + 15k = [-14 + (-7) + 15]k$$
$$= -6k$$

47.
$$8m + (-23)m = [8 + (-23)]m$$
$$= -15m$$

48.
$$14b + (-21b) + 37b = [14 + (-21) + 37]b$$
$$= 30b$$

49.
$$16d + (-9d) + (-27d) = [16 + (-9) + (-27)]d$$
$$= -20d$$

50. -177 **51.** 7666 **52.** $-12{,}044$

53. false

54.
$$112 + (-252) = (-252) + 112$$
$$= -(|-252| - |112|)$$
$$= -(252 - 112)$$
$$= -140$$

55. a. Akita—from 1992 to 1993:
$$11{,}383 - 11{,}574 = -191$$

beagle—from 1992 to 1993:
$$60{,}661 - 61{,}051 = -390$$

chow chow—from 1992 to 1993:
$$42{,}670 - 33{,}824 = +8846$$

dachshund—from 1992 to 1993:
$$50{,}046 - 48{,}573 = +1473$$

Labrador retriever—from 1992 to 1993:
$$120{,}879 - 124{,}899 = -4020$$

pug—from 1992 to 1993:
$$16{,}008 - 15{,}722 = +286$$

b. (total in 1993) − (total in 1992) = total change
$$301{,}647 - 295{,}643 = +6004$$

56. $\{-8, -4, -3, 0\}$

57. false

58. −282

59. $48 = r \cdot 16$
  $48 \div 16 = r$
  $3 = r$

60. true

61. $r - 9 = 15$
  $r = 15 + 9$
  $r = 24$

62. $\begin{array}{ll} 3x = 87 & 3x = 87 \\ 3 \cdot 19 = 87 & 3 \cdot 29 = 87 \\ 57 = 87 & 87 = 87 \\ \end{array}$

  This sentence is false. This sentence is true.
  The solution is 29.

  $3x = 87$
  $3 \cdot 39 = 87$
  $117 = 87$
  This sentence is false.

63. $(n + 8) + 9 = n + (8 + 9)$
  $= n + 17$

64. Sample answer: two times a number plus three

65. $6 \div 2 + 5 \times 4 = 32$
  $3 + 5 \times 4 = 32$
  $3 + 20 = 32$
  $23 = 32$
  false

2-5A Math Lab: Subtracting Integers

Page 88

1.

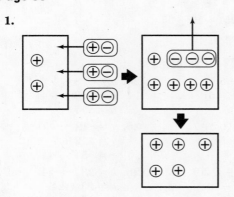

$2 - (-3) = 5$

2.

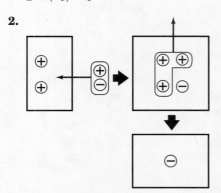

$2 - 3 = -1$

3.

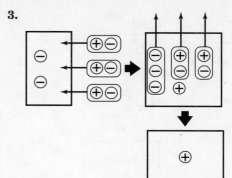

$-2 - (-3) = 1$

4.

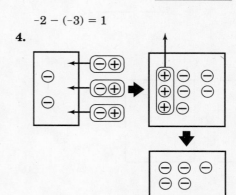

$-2 - 3 = -5$

5.

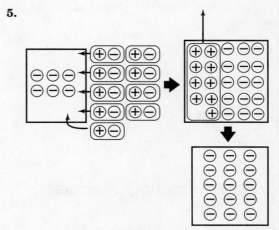

$-6 - 9 = -15$

6.

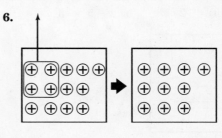

$13 - 4 = 9$

7.

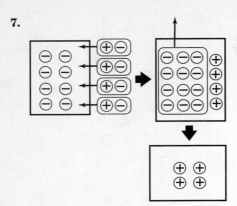

$-8 - (-12) = 4$

8.

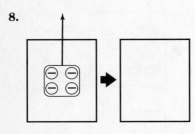

$-4 - (-4) = 0$

9. Sample answer: The answers to each set of exercises are the same. The exercises differ in that the second term of the subtraction exercises is the additive inverse of the second term of the addition exercises.

10. negative
$-6 - (-3) = -3$

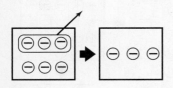

| 2-5 | **Subtracting Integers** |

Page 91 Checking Your Understanding

1. Sample answer: subtraction is adding the opposite.

2. a. $-6 - (-4) = -2$ **b.** $2 - 5 = -3$

3.

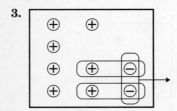

4. Sample answer: First, subtract $14y$ by adding $-14y$. Then use the distributive property to rewrite the expression. Find the sum of 12 and -14.

5. a. $4 - 6 = -2$
b. $2 - (-3) = 5$

---

c. $-3 - 1 = -4$
d. $-5 - (-4) = -1$

6. -7

7. 8

8. a

9. $-9x$

10.
$6 - 15 = m$
$6 + (-15) = m$
$-9 = m$

11.
$-7 - 11 = x$
$-7 + (-11) = x$
$-18 = x$

12.
$-16 - 7 = z$
$-16 + (-7) = z$
$-23 = z$

13. $8 - (-3) = b$
$8 + 3 = b$
$11 = b$

14. $-24 - (-8) = r$
$-24 + 8 = r$
$-16 = r$

15. $-14 - (-19) = y$
$-14 + 19 = y$
$5 = y$

16. $6a - 13a = 6a + (-13)a$
$= [6 + (-13)]a$
$= -7a$

17. $-15x - 12x = -15x + (-12)x$
$= [-15 + (-12)]x$
$= -27x$

18. $-17y - (-3y) = -17y + 3y$
$= (-17 + 3)y$
$= -14y$

19. $x - 3 = -9 - 3$
$= -9 + (-3)$
$= -12$

20. $y - (-8) = 17 - (-8)$
$= 17 + 8$
$= 25$

21. $a - (-7) = -15 - (-7)$
$= -15 + 7$
$= -8$

22. $10 - (-25) = 10 + 25$
$= 35$

Pages 91–93 Exercises

23. $y = -9 - 5$
$y = -9 + (-5)$
$y = -14$

24. $a = -13 - 4$
$a = -13 + (-4)$
$a = -17$

25. $r = -8 - (-5)$
$r = -8 + 5$
$r = -3$

26. $x = -12 - (-7)$
$x = -12 + 7$
$x = -5$

27. $m = 12 - (-20)$
$m = 12 + 20$
$m = 32$

28. $k = 23 - (-24)$
$k = 23 + 24$
$k = 47$

29. $-5 - (-14) = p$
$-5 + 14 = p$
$9 = p$

30. $-12 - (-16) = z$
$-12 + 16 = z$
$4 = z$

31. $31 - (-6) = d$
$31 + 6 = d$
$37 = d$

32. $-17 - 13 = a$
$-17 + (-13) = a$
$-30 = a$

33. $-21 - 8 = b$
$-21 + (-8) = b$
$-29 = b$

34. $38 - (-12) = q$
$38 + 12 = q$
$50 = q$

35. $x = -28 - 35$
$x = -28 + (-35)$
$x = -63$

36. $-7 - 25 = f$
$-7 + (-25) = f$
$-32 = f$

37. $-39 - 7 = s$
$-39 + (-7) = s$
$-46 = s$

---

38. $11 - n = 11 - 5$
$= 11 + (-5)$
$= 6$

39. $-15 - c = -15 - 5$
$= -15 + (-5)$
$= -20$

40. $h - (-17) = -23 - (-17)$
$= -23 + 17$
$= -6$

41. $r - 11 = -16 - 11$
$= -16 + (-11)$
$= -27$

42. $8 - m = 8 - (-12)$
$= 8 + 12$
$= 20$

43. $h - (-13) = -18 - (-13)$
$= -18 + 13$
$= -5$

44. $5 - b = 5 - 8$
$= 5 + (-8)$
$= -3$

45. $7 - (-f) = 7 - (-19)$
$= 7 + 19$
$= 26$

46. $5b - 17b = 5b + (-17)b$
$= [5 + (-17)]b$
$= -12b$

47. $13x - 23x = 13x + (-23)x$
$= [13 + (-23)]x$
$= -10x$

48. $-3a - (-5a) = -3a + 5a$
$= (-3 + 5)a$
$= 2a$

49. $18p - 3p = 18p + (-3)p$
$= [18 + (-3)]p$
$= 15p$

50. $-28d - 17d = -28d + (-17)d$
$= [-28 + (-17)]d$
$= -45d$

51. $12cd - (-12cd) = 12cd + 12cd$
$= 24cd$

52. $-15xy - 18xy = -15xy + (-18)xy$
$= [-15 + (-18)]xy$
$= -33xy$

53. $7a - 14a - a = 7a - 14a - 1a$
$= 7a + (-14)a + (-1)a$
$= [7 + (-14) + (-1)]a$
$= -8a$

54. $-q - (-6q) - (-7q) = -1q - (-6q) - (-7q)$
$= -1q + 6q + 7q$
$= (-1 + 6 + 7)q$
$= 12q$

55. Sample answer: Every integer has an additive inverse because every integer has an opposite. The sum of an integer and its opposite is zero. Zero is its own additive inverse because $0 + 0 = 0$.

56. from 10°F to -4°F is a decrease of 14°F.

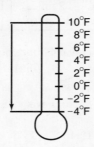
10°F
8°F
6°F
4°F
2°F
0°F
-2°F
-4°F

57. $-12,300 - 2500 = -12,300 + (-2500)$
$= -14,800$
$-14,800 + 18,345 = +3545$
$3545 - 5678 = 3545 + (-5678)$
$= -2133$
The final balance is -$2133.

58. a. $8 - (-1) = 8 + 1$
$= 9$
Rome is 9 hours *ahead* of Los Angeles. So at 2:00 P.M. in Los Angeles, it is 11:00 P.M. in Rome.

b. $5 - 11 = 5 + (-11)$
$= -6$
Honolulu is 6 hours *behind* Miami. So at 11:00 A.M. in Miami, it is 5:00 A.M. in Honolulu.

c. $11 - 0 = 11$
Paris is 11 hours *ahead* of Honolulu. So at 3:00 A.M. in Honolulu, it is 2:00 P.M. in Paris.

59. $9m + 43m + (-16m) = 9m + 43m + (-16)m$
$= [9 + 43 + (-16)]m$
$= 36m$

60. $-1300 + (-1150) = -2450$

61. $4 < 6$

62. $|-15| = 15$

63.

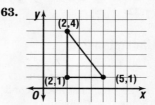

A triangle is formed.

64. $6b = 90$ What number
$6 \cdot 15 = 90$ times 6 is 90?
$b = 15$

65. $y + 9 + 14 + 2y = 1y + 9 + 14 + 2y$
$= 1y + 2y + 9 + 14$
$= (1 + 2)y + 23$
$= 3y + 23$

66. $(a + 3) + 4 = a + (3 + 4)$

67. Sandy Koufax

68. Bob Feller

69. $k + 3$

Page 93   Self Test

1. $|-8| = 8$

2. $|-20| + |-19| = 20 + 19$
$= 39$

3. $-3, 0, 2, 5$

4–6.

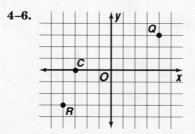

7. $-9 > -15$ **8.** $-11 < 5$ **9.** $|-4| = 4$

10.
$$-7 + 20 = a$$
$$20 + (-7) = a$$
$$+(|20| - |-7|) = a$$
$$+(20 - 7) = a$$
$$13 = a$$

11.
$$-12 + 14 + 8 = d$$
$$14 + 8 + (-12) = d$$
$$22 + (-12) = d$$
$$+(|22| - |-12|) = d$$
$$+(22 - 12) = d$$
$$10 = d$$

12.
$$-42 - 38 = q$$
$$-42 + (-38) = q$$
$$-80 = q$$

13. $b = -34 - (-19)$
$$b = -34 + 19$$
$$b = -15$$

14. $P = I - E$
$$P = 15{,}525 - 17{,}000$$
$$P = -1475$$

2-6	**Problem-Solving Strategy: Look for a Pattern**

Page 95   Checking Your Understanding

1. $1 + 2 + 3 + \ldots + 158 + 159 + 160$

The sum of the least and greatest numbers is $1 + 160$ or 161. The sum of the second least and second greatest number is $2 + 159$ or 161. Continue this pattern. All sums will equal 161. There ae 80 of these sums.

$161 \times 80 = 12{,}880$

2. Sample answer: The formula $\frac{n(n + 1)}{2}$ is another rule for finding the sum of the first n integers.

3. Sample answer: Subtract 2 less each time; first, subtract 9, then subtract 7, and then 5.

4. Julita; the numbers are increasing by 2, 3, 4, . . .

5. $1, \quad 1, \quad 2, \quad 6, \quad 24, \quad 120, \quad 720$
$\ \times 1 \ \times 2 \ \times 3 \ \times 4 \ \times 5 \ \times 6$

6. The first digit of each product is equal to the previous factor that is being multiplied by 8888. The last digit of each product is equal to two less than the previous last digit and all three middle digits of each product are one less than the previous middle digits. So, $8888 \times 5 = 44{,}440$.

7.

Square Size	1×1	2×2	3×3	4×4	5×5	6×6	7×7	8×8
Number of Squares	64	49	36	25	16	9	4	1

The total number of squares is $64 + 49 + 36 + 25 + 16 + 9 + 4 + 1$ or 204 squares.

8.

Number of Cuts	Number of Boards
1	2
2	3
3	4
4	5
5	6
6	7
7	8
8	9
9	10
10	11
11	12

It will take 11 cuts.

Pages 96–97   Exercises

9. $11{,}111 \times 11{,}111 = 123{,}454{,}321$

10. $2, \quad 5, \quad 9, \quad 14, \quad 20, \quad 27, \quad 35$
$\ +3 \ +4 \ +5 \ +6 \ +7 \ +8$

11. Students should use guess and check to find the number of touchdowns that were made in the game. The total number of points must equal 34 and the combined number of touchdowns and field goals is 7.

3 touchdowns	4 field goals	
touchdowns	3×6	$= 18$
field goals	4×3	$= 12$
extra point	$+$	1
		31

This total does not equal 34.

4 touchdowns	3 field goals	
touchdowns	4×6	$= 24$
field goals	3×3	$= 9$
extra point	$+$	1
		34

There were 4 touchdowns.

12.

Brian

time	traveled
1 hour	8 miles
2 hours	16 miles
3 hours	24 miles
4 hours	32 miles
5 hours	40 miles

Maya

time	traveled
1 hour	0 miles
2 hours	10 miles
3 hours	20 miles
4 hours	30 miles
5 hours	40 miles

Maya will travel 4 hours before she catches Brian.

13. 8:45   9:33   10:21   11:09
$\ \ 48 \text{ min} \ \ 48 \text{ min} \ \ 48 \text{ min}$

The ferry departs every 48 minutes. Extend the pattern.

11:57   12:45   1:33
$\ \ 48 \text{ min} \ \ 48 \text{ min}$

Michelle can catch the ferry at 1:33 P.M.

14. Let x = cost of one hot dog and y = cost of one hamburger. Use a calculator and guess and check to solve.

x	y	$2x + y$	$3x + 3y$
40	40	$2(40) + 40 = 120$	$3(40) + 3(40) = 240$
80	80	$2(80) + 80 = 240$	$3(80) + 3(80) = 480$
90	90	$2(90) + 90 = 270$	$3(90) + 3(90) = 540$
100	95	$2(100) + 95 = 295$	$3(100) + 3(95) = 585$
120	99	$2(120) + 99 = 339$	$3(120) + 3(99) = 657$

So one hotdog costs $1.20.

15. a.

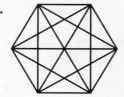

b. 2, 5, 9, 14; 27

16.

Sum of first n odd integers	Sum
1; (1)	1 or 1^2
2; (1 + 3)	4 or 2^2
3; (1 + 3 + 5)	9 or 3^2
4; (1 + 3 + 5 + 7)	16 or 4^2
5; (1 + 3 + 5 + 7 + 9)	25 or 5^2

The sum of the first 50 odd integers is 50^2 or 2500.

17.

$\overline{AB}, \overline{BC}, \overline{CD}, \overline{DE}, \overline{EF}, \overline{FG}, \overline{GH}, \overline{HI},$
$\overline{AC}, \overline{BD}, \overline{CE}, \overline{DF}, \overline{EG}, \overline{FH}, \overline{GI},$
$\overline{AD}, \overline{BE}, \overline{CF}, \overline{DG}, \overline{EH}, \overline{FI},$
$\overline{AE}, \overline{BF}, \overline{CG}, \overline{DH}, \overline{EI},$
$\overline{AF}, \overline{BG}, \overline{CH}, \overline{DI},$
$\overline{AG}, \overline{BH}, \overline{CI},$
$\overline{AH}, \overline{BI},$
$\overline{AI}$

There are 36 line segments.

18. Use the process of elimination. Since the two addends must be less than 10,000, the sum must be less than 20,000. Thus, M = 1.

```
  S E N D
+ 1 O R E
1 O N E Y
```

The greatest sum of any two possible digits is 17, so no more than 1 could be carried over from one place value to the next. Study E and O. If 1 is carried, S + M is at most 11 and at least 10. If 1 is not carried, S + M must be 10. Thus, O = 0 or 1. Since we know that M = 1, O must be 0.

```
  S E N D
+ 1 0 R E
1 0 N E Y
```

Since the hundreds place shows E + 0 and the sum shows N, 1 must have been carried from the tens to the hundreds place. Then, E = N − 1. None of the remaining possible values for E would require carrying over to the thousands. So, we can conclude that S = 9.

```
  9 E N D
+ 1 0 R E
1 0 N E Y
```

The tens digits must carry one hundred and one ten may have carried from the ones digits. So, N + R is at least 9. But 1 and 0 are already assigned. So E cannot be 0 or 1. Thus, N + R must be at least 11. (If N + R was 10, E would be 0 or 1, if N + R was 11 and 1 was carried, E could be 2.) N + R could be at most 8 + 7, since S = 9. So E could be at most 6. Thus, E could be 6, 5, 4, 3, or 2.

Guess and check. Assume E = 6. Then N = 7.

```
  9 6 7 D
+   1 0 R 6
1 0 7 6 Y
```

D could be 8, 4, 3, or 2.

Assume D = 8. Then Y = 4 and R = 8. This is impossible.

Assume D = 4. Then Y = 0. Since O = 0, this is impossible.

Assume D = 3. Then Y = 9. Since S = 9, this is impossible.

Assume D = 2. Then Y = 8 and R = 9. This cannot be.

Thus, our assumption that E = 6 cannot be true.

Assume that E = 5. Then N = 6.

```
  9 5 6 D
+   1 0 R 5
1 0 6 5 Y
```

D could be 8, 7, 4, 3, or 2.

Assume D = 8. Then Y = 3 and R = 8. This is impossible.

Assume that D = 7. Then Y = 2 and R = 8. This leads to no contradictions.

```
  9 5 6 7
+   1 0 8 5
1 0 6 5 2
```

The result checks.

The student requested $10,652.

19. 1, 5, 14, 30, 55

$+(2 \times 2) \quad +(3 \times 3) \quad +(4 \times 4) \quad +(5 \times 5)$

20. See students' work.

21. $42 \times 101 = 4242$
$423 \times 1001 = 423{,}423$

22. $-75 + 30 = -(|-75| - |30|)$
$= -(75 - 30)$
$= -45$

23. $h = 8 + (-15) + 13$
$h = 8 + 13 + (-15)$
$h = 21 + (-15)$
$h = +(|21| - |-15|)$
$h = +(21 - 15)$
$h = 6$

24. $3x + 2x - 9 \geq 17$
$3(6) + 2(6) - 9 \geq 17$
$18 + 12 - 9 \geq 17$
$30 - 9 \geq 17$
$30 + (-9) \geq 17$
$21 \geq 17$
This sentence is true.

25. $5y + 3(7 + 2y) = 5y + 21 + 6y$
$= 5y + 6y + 21$
$= (5 + 6)y + 21$
$= 11y + 21$

26. $2[5(4 + 6) -3] = 2[5(10) - 3]$
$= 2[50 - 3]$
$= 2(47)$
$= 94$

| 2-7A |

Math Lab: Multiplying Integers

Page 98

1.

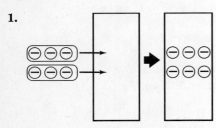

$2 \times (-3) = -6$

2.

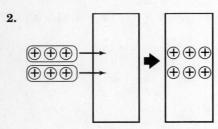

$2 \times 3 = 6$

3.

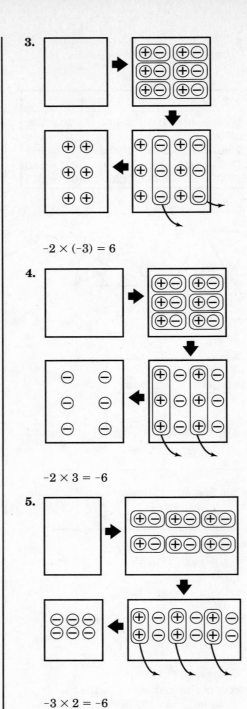

$-2 \times (-3) = 6$

4.

$-2 \times 3 = -6$

5.

$-3 \times 2 = -6$

6.

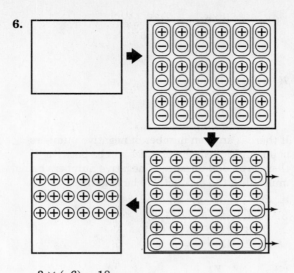

$-3 \times (-6) = 18$

7.

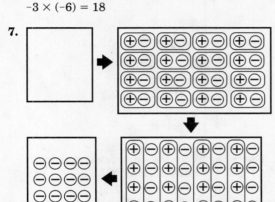

$-4 \times 4 = 16$

8.

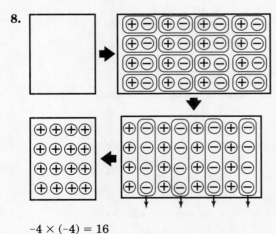

$-4 \times (-4) = 16$

9. Sample answer: -2×4 means to remove 2 sets of 4 positive 1-tiles after putting in 8 zero pairs.

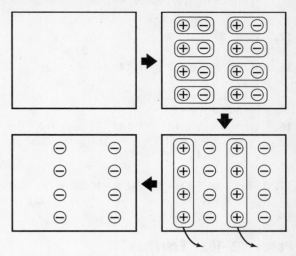

10. They both represent the same product. The commutative property changed their position.

| **2-7** | **Multiplying Integers** |

Page 101–102 Checking Your Understanding

1. Sample answer:
$$-4 \cdot 2 = -8$$
$$-4 \cdot 1 = -4$$
$$-4 \cdot 0 = 0$$
$$-4 \cdot (-1) = 4$$
$$-4 \cdot (-2) = 8$$
$$-4 \cdot (-3) = 12$$

2. Use the associative property of multiplication to rewrite the expression as $[12 \cdot (-4)]y$. Then multiply. Since the integers have different signs, the product is $-48y$.

3. a. $3(-4) = -12$
   b. $-2(-3) = 6$

4.

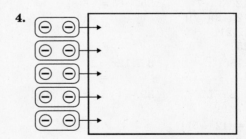

5. negative
   $-8 \cdot 7 = -56$

6. negative
   $5(-9) = -45$

7. positive
   $14 \cdot 37 = 518$

8. positive
   $-35(-57) = 1995$

9. positive
$$(-9)(2)(-3) = [(-9)(2)](-3)$$
$$= -18(-3)$$
$$= 54$$

10. negative

$(-3)(-5)(-7) = [(-3)(-5)](-7)$
$= 15(-7)$
$= -105$

11. $t = -9 \cdot 3$
$t = -27$

12. $-7(-3) = u$
$21 = u$

13. $8(-10)(4) = v$
$8[(-10)(4)] = v$
$8(-40) = v$
$-320 = v$

14. $4m = 4(-12)$
$= -48$

15. $-3gh = -3(-4)(-11)$
$= -3[(-4)(-11)]$
$= -3(44)$
$= -132$

16. $-5 \cdot 3w = (-5 \cdot 3)w$
$= -15w$

17. $8(-5x) = (8 \cdot -5)x$
$= -40x$

18. $-4(-3y) = (-4 \cdot -3)y$
$= -12y$

19. $-2(28) = -56$

Pages 102–103   Exercises

20. $m = -6(-8)$
$m = 48$

21. $x = -7(-4)$
$x = 28$

22. $a = -3(12)$
$a = -36$

23. $r = 13(-2)$
$r = -26$

24. $-5 \cdot 7 = b$
$-35 = b$

25. $-15(-5) = y$
$75 = y$

26. $-4(-5)(6) = z$
$-4[(-5)(6)] = z$
$-4(-30) = z$
$120 = z$

27. $9(-13)(5) = q$
$9[(-13)(5)] = q$
$9(-65) = q$
$-585 = q$

28. $6(-5)(-8) = g$
$6[-5)(-8)] = g$
$6(40) = g$
$240 = g$

29. $h = 2 \cdot 7 \cdot 12$
$h = (2 \cdot 7) \cdot 12$
$h = 14 \cdot 12$
$h = 168$

30. $-7(-7)(3) = p$
$-7[(-7)(3)] = p$
$-7(-21) = p$
$147 = p$

31. $11(-4)(7) = s$
$11[(-4)(7)] = s$
$11(-28) = s$
$-308 = s$

32. $-5n = -5(-7)$
$= 35$

33. $st = (7)(8)$
$= 56$

34. $12ab = 12(-3)(-7)$
$= 12[(-3)(-7)]$
$= 12(21)$
$= 252$

35. $-6b = -6(8)$
$= -48$

36. $-15c = -15(-1)$
$= 15$

37. $12x = 12(-3)$
$= -36$

38. $8(-5x) = (8 \cdot -5)x$
$= -40x$

39. $-4 \cdot 3b = (-4 \cdot 3)b$
$= -12b$

40. $12(-5n) = (12 \cdot -5)n$
$= -60n$

41. $(-12)(-4)b = [(-12)(-4)]b$
$= 48b$

42. $(7y)(5z) = [(7)(5)]yz$
$= 35yz$

43. $(-10r)(5s) = [(-10)(5)]rs$
$= -50rs$

44. $2ab \cdot 6 \cdot (-2) = (2 \cdot 6)ab \cdot (-2)$
$= 12ab \cdot (-2)$
$= [12 \cdot (-2)]ab$
$= -24ab$

45. $-3(-a)(-b) = -3(-1a)(-1b)$
$= -3[(-1)(-1)]ab$
$= -3(1)ab$
$= -3ab$

46. $7(-m)(k) = 7(-1m)(1k)$
$= 7[(-1)(1)]mk$
$= 7(-1)mk$
$= -7mk$

47. If there is an even number of negative numbers being multiplied, the product will be positive. If there is an odd number of negative numbers being multiplied, the product will be negative.

48. a. $P(-1, 0)$, $Q(-3, -2)$, $R(-2, -4)$

b. $P(-1, 0) \times -1 \rightarrow P'(1, 0)$
$Q(-3, -2) \times -1 \rightarrow Q'(3, 2)$
$R(-2, -4) \times -1 \rightarrow R'(2, 4)$

c.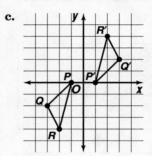

d. The triangles are the same size and shape. $\triangle P'Q'R'$ is rotated from $\triangle PQR$.

49. $(-1500)(24) = -36{,}000$ feet
$-36{,}000$ feet $= 36{,}000 \div 5280$ or about -6.8 miles

50. no; $7 \neq 4 \times 2$

51. $45 - (-4) = 45 + 4$
$= 49$

52. positive
$-10 + 9 + 8 = 9 + 8 + (-10)$
$= 17 + (-10)$
$= +(|17| - |-10|)$
$= +(17 - 10)$
$= 7$

53. Sample answer: $65 > 34$

54.
```
◄──┼──┼──┼──┼──●──┼──●──┼──┼──●──┼──┼──►
  -4 -3 -2 -1  0  1  2  3  4  5  6
```

55. $35{,}892 = a - 3285$
$35{,}892 + 3285 = a$
$39{,}177 = a$

56. $\dfrac{18}{a} = 9$ What number
$a = 2$ times 9 is 18?

57. Commutative property of addition

58. $21 \div 7 + 4 \cdot 11 = 3 + 4 \cdot 11$
$= 3 + 44$
$= 47$

2-8 Dividing Integers

Pages 106–107 Checking Your Understanding

1. Sample answer:
$$4 \div 2 = 2$$
$$2 \div 2 = 1$$
$$0 \div 2 = 0$$
$$-2 \div 2 = -1$$
$$-4 \div 2 = -2$$
$$-6 \div 2 = -3$$
$$-8 \div 2 = -4$$
$$-10 \div 2 = -5$$

2.

3. $-8 \div 4 = -2$

4. See students' work.

5. negative
$-56 \div 8 = -7$

6. positive
$63 \div 9 = 7$

7. negative
$42 \div (-7) = -6$

8. positive
$\frac{91}{7} = 91 \div 7$
$= 13$

9. negative
$\frac{105}{-7} = 105 \div (-7)$
$= -15$

10. negative
$\frac{222}{-37} = 222 \div (-37)$
$= -6$

11. $d = \frac{-240}{-6}$
$d = -240 \div (-6)$
$d = 40$

12. $-96 \div 24 = k$
$-4 = k$

13. $\frac{-105}{-15} = m$
$-105 \div (-15) = m$
$7 = m$

14. $n = \frac{-804}{67}$
$n = -804 \div 67$
$n = 12$

15. $\frac{x}{-5} = x \div (-5)$
$= -65 \div (-5)$
$= 13$

16. $\frac{y}{5} = y \div 5$
$= -50 \div 5$
$= -10$

17. $\frac{42}{z} = 42 \div z$
$= 42 \div (-14)$
$= -3$

18. $\frac{b}{-7} = b \div (-7)$
$= -98 \div (-7)$
$= 14$

19. $-60 \div 4 = y$
$-15 = y$

Pages 107–108 Exercises

20. $56 \div (-7) = -8$

21. $48 \div (-12) = -4$

22. $-72 \div 8 = -9$

23. $-36 \div (-6) = 6$

24. $84 \div (-12) = -7$

25. $-52 \div (-4) = 13$

26. $64 \div 4 = 16$

27. $-555 \div 5 = -111$

28. $\frac{24}{6} = 24 \div 6$
$= 4$

29. $\frac{27}{-3} = 27 \div (-3)$
$= -9$

30. $\frac{-570}{19} = -570 \div 19$
$= -30$

31. $\frac{-804}{67} = -804 \div 67$
$= -12$

32. $-54 \div 9 = -6$

33. $63 \div (-7) = -9$

34. $121 \div 11 = 11$

35. $-28 \div (-7) = 4$

36. $m = \frac{91}{-7}$
$m = 91 \div (-7)$
$m = -13$

37. $r = \frac{76}{-4}$
$r = 76 \div (-4)$
$r = -19$

38. $\frac{-63}{-21} = a$
$-63 \div (-21) = a$
$3 = a$

39. $\frac{-90}{18} = z$
$-90 \div 18 = z$
$-5 = z$

40. $\frac{45}{-15} = k$
$45 \div (-15) = k$
$-3 = k$

41. $\frac{-119}{-17} = x$
$-119 \div (-17) = x$
$7 = x$

42. $p = \frac{-143}{13}$
$p = -143 \div 13$
$p = -11$

43. $b = \frac{-144}{16}$
$b = -144 \div 16$
$b = -9$

44. $t = \frac{-175}{-25}$
$t = -175 \div (-25)$
$t = 7$

45. $\frac{x}{6} = x \div 6$
$= -102 \div 6$
$= -17$

46. $\frac{105}{m} = 105 \div m$
$= 105 \div (-21)$
$= -5$

47. $\frac{y}{-9} = y \div (-9)$
$= -108 \div (-9)$
$= 12$

48. $\frac{112}{z} = 112 \div z$
$= 112 \div (-7)$
$= -16$

49. $\frac{126}{a} = 126 \div a$
$= 126 \div (-18)$
$= -7$

50. $\frac{-144}{p} = -144 \div p$
$= -144 \div 9$
$= -16$

51. $\frac{v}{q} = v \div q$
$= -24 \div 8$
$= -3$

52. $\frac{n \times (-n)}{m} = [n \times (-n)] \div m$
$= [-9 \times (-(-9))] \div 27$
$= [-9 \times 9] \div 27$
$= -81 \div 27$
$= -3$

53. Sample answer: $x = -144$; $y = 12$; $z = -12$
- $12 > -144$, $-12 < 12$, and $-144 < 0$
- $-144 \div (-12) = -12$
- -12 is divisible by 2 and 3.
- $-144 \div 12 = -12$

54. $-430 \div 5 = -86$

55. 4351 billion = 4,351,000,000,000
4065 billion = 4,065,000,000,000
4351 billion − 4065 billion = 286,000,000,000
$286{,}000{,}000{,}000 \div 261{,}000{,}000 \approx 1095.79$
About $1096

56. $y = 7(-11)$
$y = -77$

57. 8:05, 8:51, 8:55, 9:41, 9:45, . . .
46 min. 4 min. 46 min. 4 min.
The next three bells will ring at 10:31, 10:35, and 11:21.

58. Postal Services

59. 41

60.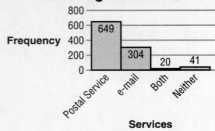

Message Services

(Bar graph)
- y-axis: Frequency 0, 200, 400, 600, 800
- Postal Service: 649
- e-mail: 304
- Both: 20
- Neither: 41
- x-axis label: Services

61. 649 + 304 + 20 + 41 or 1014

62. $35m = 280$
$m = 280 \div 35$
$m = 8$

63. $r + 11 = 17$ What number
$r = 6$ added to 11 is 17?

64. commutative property of addition

65. $12 \div 3 + 12 \div 4 = 4 + 12 \div 4$
$= 4 + 3$
$= 7$

66. $(25 \cdot 3) + (15 \cdot 3) = 75 + 45$
$= 120$

67. $144 \div 16 \cdot 9 \div 3 = 9 \cdot 9 \div 3$
$= 81 \div 3$
$= 27$

Chapter 2   Study Guide and Assessment

Page 109   Understanding and Using Vocabulary

1. F; an integer less than zero–negative integer

2. G; the four regions separated by the axes on a coordinate plane–quadrants

3. C; the number that corresponds to a point on the number line–coordinate

4. B; an integer and its opposite–additive inverses

5. E; positive and negative whole numbers–integers

6. D; a dot placed at the point named by the ordered pair–graph

7. A; the distance a number is from the zero point on the number line–absolute value

Pages 110–112   Skills and Concepts

8. (number line: −8 −6 −4 −2 0 2 4 6 8 10 12)

9. (number line: −20 0 20 40 60 80)

10. (number line: −40 −20 0 20 40 60 80 100)

11. (number line: −16 −14 −12 −10 −8 −6 −4 −2 0 2 4)

12. $|-31| = 31$

13. $|24| = 24$

14. $-|18| = -18$

15. $-|40| = -40$

16. $-|6 - 2| = -|4|$
$= -4$

17. $|-8| + |-21| = 8 + 21$
$= 29$

18. $|17 - 29| = |-12|$
$= 12$

19. $||7| - |-19|| = |7 - 19|$
$= |-12|$
$= 12$

20. Quadrant I

21. Quadrant III

22. Quadrant II

23. Quadrant II

24. Quadrant III

25. Quadrant IV

(coordinate grid with points G, A, W, O, M, R, x, y, L)

26. $9 > -9$

27. $-3 = -3$

28. $6 < 13$

29. $-12 > -21$

30. $-2 < 0$

31. $-43 < 43$

32. $1{,}027{,}974 > 109{,}592$ or $109{,}592 < 1{,}027{,}974$

33. $17 < 35$ or $35 > 17$

34. −3, 0, 5, 6, 8

35. −16, −4, 2, 3

36. −88, −75, −34, 4, 21

37. −300, −33, 9, 124, 210

38. $a = -4 + (-5)$
$a = -(|-4| + |-5|)$
$a = -(4 + 5)$
$a = -9$

39. $8 + (-11) = s$
$(-11) + 8 = s$
$-(|-11| - |8|) = s$
$-(11 - 8) = s$
$-3 = s$

40. $-12 + 4 = t$
$-(|-12| - |4|) = t$
$-(12 - 4) = t$
$-8 = t$

41. $k = -15 + 9$
$k = -(|-15| - |9|)$
$k = -(15 - 9)$
$k = -6$

42. $g = 18 + (-25)$
$g = (-25) + 18$
$g = -(|-25| - |18|)$
$g = -(25 - 18)$
$g = -7$

43. $h = -13 + (-2)$
$h = -(|-13| + |-2|)$
$h = -(13 + 2)$
$h = -15$

44. $-6 + (-18) + 40 = q$
$-(|-6| + |-18|) + 40 = q$
$-(6 + 18) + 40 = q$
$-24 + 40 = q$
$40 + (-24) = q$
$+(|40| - |-24|) = q$
$+(40 - 24) = q$
$+16 = q$

45. $a = 7 + (-3) + (-14)$
$a = (-3) + (-14) + 7$
$a = -(|-3| + |-14|) + 7$
$a = -(3 + 14) + 7$
$a = -17 + 7$
$a = -(|-17| - |7|)$
$a = -(17 - 7)$
$a = -10$

46. $g = -8 - 7$
$g = -8 + (-7)$
$g = -15$

47. $-33 - (-3) = s$
$-33 + 3 = s$
$-30 = s$

48. $-17 - 8 = w$
$-17 + (-8) = w$
$-25 = w$

49. $t = 15 - (-6)$
$t = 15 + 6$
$t = 21$

50. $2a - 5a = 2a + (-5)a$
$= [2 + (-5)]a$
$= -3a$

51. $-12b - (-5b) = -12b + 5b$
$= (-12 + 5)b$
$= -7b$

52. $14m - (-12m) = 14m + 12m$
$= (14 + 12)m$
$= 26m$

53. $-15r - (-21r) = -15r + 21r$
$= (-15 + 21)r$
$= 6r$

54. $z = -9 \cdot 4$
$z = -36$

55. $(-4)(2) = k$
$-8 = k$

56. $(-11)(-15) = y$
$165 = y$

57. $p = -5 \cdot (-13)$
$p = 65$

58. $(-2)(8z)(3) = (-2)(3)(8z)$
$= [(-2)(3)](8z)$
$= -6(8z)$
$= -48z$

59. $6 \cdot (-6c) \cdot (-d) = 6 \cdot (-6c) \cdot (-1d)$
$= 6 \cdot [(-6) \cdot (-1)]cd$
$= 6 \cdot (6)cd$
$= 36cd$

60. $-15x(5y) = -15(5)xy$
$= -75xy$

61. $(-25y) \cdot (-6) \cdot (-2z) = (-6) \cdot (-25y) \cdot (-2z)$
$= -6 \cdot [(-25)(-2)]yz$
$= -6 \cdot (50)yz$
$= -300yz$

62. $k = 88 \div -4$
$k = -22$

63. $-14 \div (-2) = h$
$7 = h$

64. $99 \div -11 = n$
$-9 = n$

65. $q = -45 \div (-3)$
$q = 15$

66. $d \div 8 = 120 \div 8$
$= 15$

67. $64 \div m = 64 \div (-4)$
$= -16$

68. $-700 \div k = -700 \div (-10)$
$= 70$

69. $z \div -12 = -228 \div -12$
$= 19$

Page 112   Applications and Problem Solving

70.

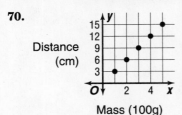

71. $20 - 38 = 20 + (-38)$
$= -18$

72.

1, $\;\;-2,\;\;\;3,\;\;\;-4,\;\;\;5,\;\;\;-6$
$\quad$ $-3\;\;\;+5\;\;\;-7\;\;\;+9\;\;\;-11$

73. The first digit of each product is equal to the factor that is being multiplied by 1089. The last digit of each product is equal to the previous last digit decreased by one. The two middle digits are equal to the previous middle digits increased by 9.
$1089 \cdot 5 = 5445$
$1089 \cdot 6 = 6534$
$1089 \cdot 7 = 7623$

74. a. -1.2m/s^2 for 11 seconds $= (-1.2\text{m/s}^2)(11\text{s})$
$= -13.2 \text{m/s}^2$

b. -3.6 m/s in 12 seconds
$-3.6 \div 12 = -0.3$ m/s^2

Alternative Assessment

Page 113
1–6. See students' work.

Page 113   Thinking Critically
If the point (a, b) is located in Quadrant IV then $a > 0$ and $b < 0$.
Quadrant I : $(+, +)$
Quadrant II: $(-, +)$
Quadrant III: $(-, -)$
Quadrant IV: $(+, -)$

Page 113   Portfolio
See students' work.

Page 113   Self Assessment
See students' work.

Ongoing Assessment

Pages 114–115
1. $D; 3 \times 8 - 6 \div 2 = 24 - 6 \div 2$
$= 24 - 3$
$= 21$

2. $B; b = s + 2$
$b - 2 = s$

3. $A; 2(\ell + w) = 2(10 + 8)$
$= 2(18)$
$= 36$

4. $D; -5(12) = -60$

5. $C; 36 - b = 20$
$36 = 20 + b$
$36 - 20 = b$
$16 = b$

6. $C; 7 \times (10 + 5) = (7 \times 10) + (7 \times 5)$

7. $B; B(4, 3)$

8. $C; G(-4, 3)$

9. $C; 4 + 5 + 6 + 4 + 1$ or 20

10. $D; 2a + b = 2(5) + 20$
$= 10 + 20$
$= 30$

11. $(x + 2) + 12 = x + (2 + 12)$
$ = x + 14$

12. $h > 48$

13. $18 \div 1.875 \rightarrow 20 \div 2 = 10$
about 10

14. $[(-22) + (-20) + (-18)] \div 3 = -60 \div 3$
$ = -20$

15. $x - 16 = 12$
$ x = 12 + 16$
$ x = 28$

16. $12 + (-6) = +(|12| - |-6|)$
$ = +(12 - 6)$
$ = +6$

17. Answers will vary.
Sample answer: seven more than six times a number

18.

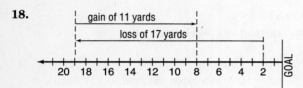

The team is 2 yards from the goal line. After a loss of 17 yards and a gain of 11 yards, the team is 8 yards from the goal line.

19. $-5 + 7 = 7 + (-5)$
$ = +(|7| - |-5|)$
$ = +(7 - 5)$
$ = +2$

20. See students' work.

21. There is a total of 10 people.

guest #1 = 9 handshakes
guest #2 = 8 handshakes
guest #3 = 7 handshakes
guest #4 = 6 handshakes
guest #5 = 5 handshakes
guest #6 = 4 handshakes
guest #7 = 3 handshakes
guest #8 = 2 handshakes
guest #9 = 1 handshakes
guest #10 = <u>0 handshakes</u>
45 handshakes

22. If y is an integer, then y belongs to the set {. . ., -3, -2, -1, 0, 1, 2, 3, . . .}. If y is a positive integer, then $y \cdot y$ is positive. For example, $3 \cdot 3 = 9$. If y is a negative integer, then $y \cdot y$ is positive. For example, $(-3) \cdot (-3) = 9$. 0 is an integer and $0 \cdot 0 = 0$. Therefore, the least value that $y \cdot y$ could have is 0.

23. The gymnasium holds 1400 people in addition to the 268 graduates. The number of tickets offered to friends and family cannot exceed 1400. Since there are 268 graduates, each should be offered 5 tickets. $268 \times 5 = 1340$. If the graduates were each offered more than five tickets, then there would be more than 1400 people in the gymnasium.

Chapter 3   Solving One-Step Equations and Inequalities

3-1	Problem-Solving Strategy: Eliminate Possibilities

Pages 120–121   Checking Your Understanding

1. Sample answer: It can help narrow down the acceptable solutions.

2. Sample answer: "Guess-and-check" method takes a solution and tests it. "Elimination" method narrows down the possible answers to a select few before the answer is tested.

3. **a–c.** See students' work.

4.

	Matt	Stacey	Keisha
Cheese pizza	X	X	O
Hot dog	O	X	X
Hamburger	X	O	X

Keisha—cheese pizza, Stacey—hamburger, Matt—hot dog

5.

	Odd number divisible by 3	Greater than 6000 and less than 7000	Sum of the digits is 21
4235	X	X	X
8765	X	X	X
4223	X	X	X
6087	O	O	O
6444	O	O	X
5163	O	X	X
9635	X	X	X
7123	X	X	X
6668	X	O	X
5228	X	X	X
8224	X	X	X
9296	X	X	X

The number is 6087

6.

Choice	Value for x	$(x + 5) \cdot 8$	Is $(x + 5) \cdot 8$ = 168?
a	42	$(42 + 5) \cdot 8$ = $47 \cdot 8$ or 376	no
b	26	$(26 + 5) \cdot 8$ = $31 \cdot 8$ or 248	no
c	16	$(16 + 5) \cdot 8$ = $21 \cdot 8$ or 168	yes
d	128	$(128 + 5) \cdot 8$ = $133 \cdot 8$ or 1064	no

The original number is 16
Therefore, c is the correct choice.

7. The number is not divisible by 5. So, eliminate 25, 60, 120, 15, and 5.
The number is even. So, eliminate 7, 13, 321, 9, 27, 43 and 561.
The number is divisible by 3. So, eliminate 124, 76, and 8.
The number has 2 digits. So, eliminate 6.
The sum of the digits is 6. So, eliminate 252, 18, and 78.
By eliminating possibilities, the mystery number is 24.

8. mustard = 1 package of hot dogs.
Therefore,
Ketchup = 3 packages of hot dogs.

9.

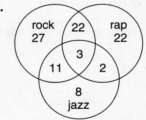

People who like rock, rap, or jazz:
$27 + 22 + 8 + 22 + 11 + 2 + 3$ or 95
People who do not like rock, rap, or jazz: $100 - 95$ or 5
Five people do not like rock, rap or jazz.

10.

Choice	Value for x	$x \cdot (-4) - 9$	Is $x \cdot (-4) - 9 > 7$?
a	5	$5 \cdot (-4) - 9$ $= -20 - 9$ or $^-29$	no
b	4	$4 \cdot (-4) - 9$ $= -16 - 9$ or -25	no
c	-3	$-3 \cdot (-4) - 9$ $= 12 - 9$ or 3	no
d	-5	$-5 \cdot (-4) - 9$ $= 20 - 9$ or 11	yes

The number is $^-5$. So the correct choice is d.

11. Students should use guess-and-check. Try numbers that give a remainder of 6 when divided by 9, the largest number.

Number	÷ by 7	÷ by 8	÷ by 9
87	12R3	10R7	9R6
159	22R5	19R7	17R6
222	31R5	27R6	24R6
330	47R1	41R2	36R6
438	62R4	54R6	48R6
501	71R4	62R5	55R6

The least positive number that gives a remainder of 4 when divided by 7, a remainder of 5 when divided by 8, and a remainder of 6 when divided by 9 is 501.

12. Let x = number of small candy bars. Let $y = 500 - x$ or number of large candy bars.

Choice	x	y	$x(.40) + y(.65)$	= 255?
a	320	180	$320(.40) + 180(.65)$ $= 128 + 117$ or 245	no
b	280	220	$280(.40) + 220(.65)$ $= 112 + 143$ or 255	yes
c	220	280	$220(.40) + 280(.65)$ $= 88 + 182$ or 270	no
d	77	423	$77(.40) + 423(.65)$ $= 30.8 + 274.95$ or 305.75	no

The concession stand sold 280 small candy bars. So, b is the correct choice.

13. You would buy 4 pairs of $70 shoes at a cost of $280 before the $200 pair wore out. It is less expensive to buy the $200 pair of shoes that lasts longer. But, if the shoes are uncomfortable or go out of style, it may make more sense to buy the less expensive shoes.

14.

	Thomas	Amber	Cynthia	Vernita	Carlos
Sommie	X	X	X	O	X
Samantha	X	O	X	X	X
Friar	O	X	X	X	X
Claude	X	X	X	X	O
Blaze	X	X	O	X	X

Thomas—Friar, Cynthia—Blaze, Vernita—Sommie, Carlos—Claude, Amber—Samantha

15. The student in back could not tell what color hat he was wearing, so the students in front of him must be wearing both blue, or one blue and one green hat. If the middle student saw a green hat on the head of the front student, she would have known she was wearing blue. Therefore, the student in front was wearing a blue hat.

16. $x = \frac{-120}{-15}$
$x = -120 \div (-15)$
$x = 8$

17. $0, \underset{+1}{\frown} 1, \underset{+2}{\frown} 3, \underset{+3}{\frown} 6, \underset{+4}{\frown} 10, \underset{+5}{\frown} 15, \underset{+6}{\frown} 21$

18. $-3 + 7 = 7 + (-3)$
$\qquad = + (|7| - |-3|)$
$\qquad = + (7 - 3)$
$\qquad = 4 \qquad$ gain of 4 yards

19. $21k + 3(k + 1) = 21k + 3k + 3$
$\qquad\qquad\qquad = (21 + 3)k + 3$
$\qquad\qquad\qquad = 24k + 3$

20. $35 - c - b = 35 - 7 - 13$
$\qquad\qquad = 35 + (-7) + (-13)$
$\qquad\qquad = 35 + (-20)$
$\qquad\qquad = 15$

3-2A **Math Lab: Solving Equations with Cups and Counters**

Page 123   Your Turn

1.

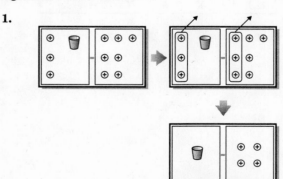

$x = 4$

38

2.

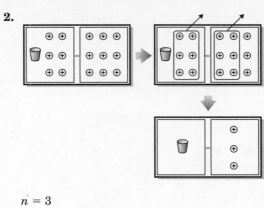

$n = 3$

3.

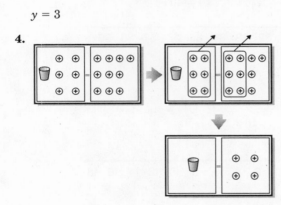

$y = 3$

4.

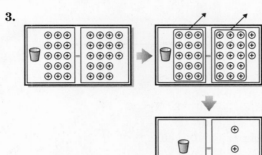

$x = 4$

5.

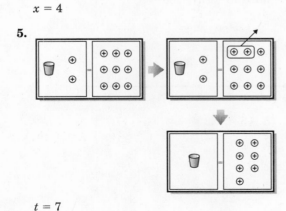

$t = 7$

6.

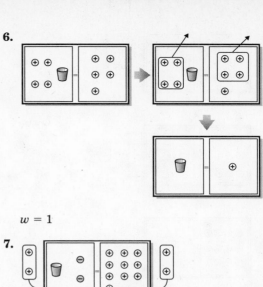

$w = 1$

7.

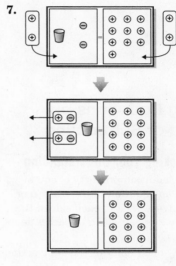

$x = 12$

8.

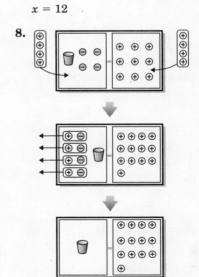

$n = 13$

9.

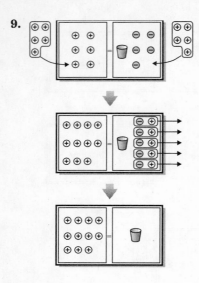

$q = 11$

3-2A   ## Solving Equations by Adding or Subtracting

Pages 126–127   Checking Your Understanding

1. Sample answer: The addition property of equality can be used to solve an equation like $x + a = b$ or $x - a = b$. Add the inverse of a to each side of the equation to solve $x + a = b$ or add a to each side to solve $x - a = b$.

2. the addition property of equality or the subtraction property of equality

3. Sample answer: $2 + x = 6$ and $x = 4$; $x - 7 = 14$ and $x = 14$

4. Sample answer: $x - 5 = -17$

5. Both Ellen and Tertius are correct. Ellen rewrote the equation and used the subtraction property of equality. Tertius used the addition property of equality.

6.

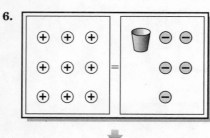

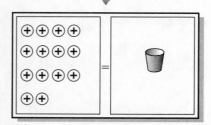

$w = 14$

---

7. $$w + 8 = -17$$
$$w + 8 - 8 = -17 - 8$$
$$w = -25$$
Check: $w + 8 = -17$
$$-25 + 8 \overset{?}{=} -17$$
$$-17 = -17 ✔$$

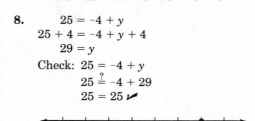

8. $$25 = -4 + y$$
$$25 + 4 = -4 + y + 4$$
$$29 = y$$
Check: $25 = -4 + y$
$$25 \overset{?}{=} -4 + 29$$
$$25 = 25 ✔$$

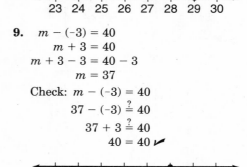

9. $$m - (-3) = 40$$
$$m + 3 = 40$$
$$m + 3 - 3 = 40 - 3$$
$$m = 37$$
Check: $m - (-3) = 40$
$$37 - (-3) \overset{?}{=} 40$$
$$37 + 3 \overset{?}{=} 40$$
$$40 = 40 ✔$$

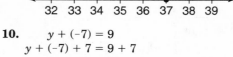

10. $$y + (-7) = 9$$
$$y + (-7) + 7 = 9 + 7$$
$$y = 16$$
Check: $y + (-7) = 9$
$$16 + (-7) \overset{?}{=} 9$$
$$9 = 9 ✔$$

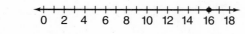

11. $$k - 36 = -37$$
$$k - 36 + 36 = -37 + 36$$
$$k = -1$$
Check: $k - 36 = -37$
$$-1 - 36 \overset{?}{=} -37$$
$$-37 = -37 ✔$$

12. $$h - 8 = -22$$
$$h - 8 + 8 = -22 + 8$$
$$h = -14$$
Check: $h - 8 = -22$
$$-14 - 8 \overset{?}{=} -22$$
$$-22 = -22 ✔$$

13. $$322 = 264 + e$$
$$322 - 264 = 264 + e - 264$$
$$58 = e$$

14.
$$y + 7 = 21$$
$$y + 7 - 7 = 21 - 7$$
$$y = 14$$
Check: $y + 7 = 21$
$$14 + 7 \stackrel{?}{=} 21$$
$$21 = 21 \checkmark$$

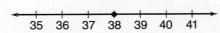

15.
$$k - 6 = 32$$
$$k - 6 + 6 = 32 - 6$$
$$k = 38$$
Check: $k - 6 = 32$
$$38 - 6 \stackrel{?}{=} 32$$
$$32 = 32 \checkmark$$

16.
$$19 = g - 5$$
$$19 + 5 = g - 5 + 5$$
$$24 = g$$
Check: $19 = g - 5$
$$19 \stackrel{?}{=} 24 - 5$$
$$19 = 19 \checkmark$$

17.
$$-24 = h - 22$$
$$-24 + 22 = h - 22 + 22$$
$$-2 = h$$
Check: $-24 = h - 22$
$$-24 \stackrel{?}{=} -2 - 22$$
$$-24 = -24 \checkmark$$

18.
$$x + 49 = 13$$
$$x + 49 - 49 = 13 - 49$$
$$x = -36$$
Check: $x + 49 = 13$
$$-36 + 49 \stackrel{?}{=} 13$$
$$13 = 13 \checkmark$$

19.
$$f + 34 = 2$$
$$f + 34 - 34 = 2 - 34$$
$$f = -32$$
Check: $f + 34 = 2$
$$-32 + 34 \stackrel{?}{=} 2$$
$$2 = 2 \checkmark$$

20.
$$d - (-3) = 2$$
$$d + 3 = 2$$
$$d + 3 - 3 = 2 - 3$$
$$d = -1$$
Check: $d - (-3) = 2$
$$-1 - (-3) \stackrel{?}{=} 2$$
$$-1 + 3 \stackrel{?}{=} 2$$
$$2 = 2 \checkmark$$

21.
$$a - (-26) = 5$$
$$a + 26 = 5$$
$$a + 26 - 26 = 5 - 26$$
$$a = -21$$
Check: $a - (-26) = 5$
$$-21 - (-26) \stackrel{?}{=} 5$$
$$-21 + 26 \stackrel{?}{=} 5$$
$$5 = 5 \checkmark$$

22.
$$12 + p = -14$$
$$12 + p - 12 = -14 - 12$$
$$p = -26$$
Check: $12 + p = -14$
$$12 + (-26) \stackrel{?}{=} -14$$
$$-14 = -14 \checkmark$$

23.
$$x + 18 = 14$$
$$x + 18 - 18 = 14 - 18$$
$$x = -4$$
Check: $x + 18 = 14$
$$-4 + 18 \stackrel{?}{=} 14$$
$$14 = 14 \checkmark$$

24.
$$59 = s + 95$$
$$59 - 95 = s + 95 - 95$$
$$-36 = s$$
Check: $59 = s + 95$
$$59 \stackrel{?}{=} -36 + 95$$
$$59 = 59 \checkmark$$

25.
$$x - 27 = 63$$
$$x - 27 + 27 = 63 + 27$$
$$x = 90$$
Check: $x - 27 = 63$
$$90 - 27 \stackrel{?}{=} 63$$
$$63 = 63 \checkmark$$

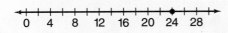

26.
$$-7 = z - (-12)$$
$$-7 = z + 12$$
$$-7 - 12 = z + 12 - 12$$
$$-19 = z$$

Check: $-7 = z - (-12)$
$$-7 \overset{?}{=} -19 - (-12)$$
$$-7 \overset{?}{=} -19 + 12$$
$$-7 = -7 \ \checkmark$$

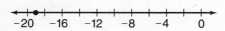

27.
$$34 + r = 84$$
$$34 + r - 34 = 84 - 34$$
$$r = 50$$

Check: $34 + r = 84$
$$34 + 50 \overset{?}{=} 84$$
$$84 = 84 \ \checkmark$$

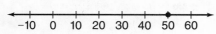

28.
$$-234 = x + 183$$
$$-234 - 183 = x + 183 - 183$$
$$-417 = x$$

Check: $-234 = x + 183$
$$-234 \overset{?}{=} -417 + 183$$
$$-234 = -234 \ \checkmark$$

29.
$$y - 94 = 562$$
$$y - 94 + 94 = 562 + 94$$
$$y = 656$$

Check: $y - 94 = 562$
$$656 - 94 \overset{?}{=} 562$$
$$562 = 562 \ \checkmark$$

30.
$$-591 = m - (-112)$$
$$-591 = m + 112$$
$$-591 - 112 = m + 112 - 112$$
$$-703 = m$$

Check: $-591 = m - (-112)$
$$-591 \overset{?}{=} -703 - (-112)$$
$$-591 \overset{?}{=} -703 + 112$$
$$-591 = -591 \ \checkmark$$

31.
$$846 + t = -538$$
$$846 + t - 846 = -538 - 846$$
$$t = -1384$$

Check: $846 + t = -538$
$$846 + (-1384) \overset{?}{=} -538$$
$$-538 = -538 \ \checkmark$$

32. c;
$$x + 5 = 11$$
$$x + 5 - 5 = 11 - 5$$
$$x = 6$$

33. a;
$$-8 = t - 4$$
$$-8 + 4 = t - 4 + 4$$
$$-4 = t$$

34.
$$(f + 5) + (-2) = 6$$
$$f + 5 - 2 = 6$$
$$f + 3 = 6$$
$$f + 3 - 3 = 6 - 3$$
$$f = 3$$

Check: $(f + 5) + (-2) = 6$
$$(3 + 5) + (-2) \overset{?}{=} 6$$
$$8 + (-2) \overset{?}{=} 6$$
$$6 = 6 \ \checkmark$$

35.
$$[y + (-3)] + 2 = 4$$
$$[y - 3] + 2 = 4$$
$$y - 3 + 2 = 4$$
$$y - 1 = 4$$
$$y - 1 + 1 = 4 + 1$$
$$y = 5$$

Check: $[y + (-3)] + 2 = 4$
$$[5 + (-3) + 2 \overset{?}{=} 4$$
$$2 + 2 \overset{?}{=} 4$$
$$4 = 4 \ \checkmark$$

36.
$$16 = [n - (-2)] + (-3)$$
$$16 = n + 2 + (-3)$$
$$16 = n - 1$$
$$16 + 1 = n - 1 + 1$$
$$17 = n$$

Check: $16 = [n - (-2)] + (-3)$
$$16 \overset{?}{=} [17 - (-2)] + (-3)$$
$$16 \overset{?}{=} [17 + 2] + (-3)$$
$$16 \overset{?}{=} 19 + (-3)$$
$$16 = 16 \ \checkmark$$

37.
$$-10 = [b + (-4)] + 2$$
$$-10 = b - 4 + 2$$
$$-10 = b - 2$$
$$-10 + 2 = b - 2 + 2$$
$$-8 = b$$

Check: $-10 = [b + (-4)] + 2$
$$-10 \overset{?}{=} [-8 + (-4)] + 2$$
$$-10 \overset{?}{=} -12 + 2$$
$$-10 = -10 \ \checkmark$$

38. Sample Answer: $x + 8 = 3$

39.
$$14 + x = 26$$
$$14 + x - 14 = 26 - 14$$
$$x = 12$$

40. a.
$$44 - 100 = x$$
$$-56 = x$$

b.
$$-5 + 43 = x$$
$$38 = x$$

41. $1995 - 70 = 1925$
So, Charles Schultz was born in 1925. Therefore, in 1950, he was 25 years old.

42. $600 \div 10 = 60$
The bus traveled 60 miles in 1 hour. So, the bus could travel $60 \cdot 4$ or 240 miles in 4 hours. The correct choice is c.

43. $y = (-9)(18)$
$y = -162$

44. $\quad 7 - 25 = h$
$\quad 7 + (-25) = h$
$\quad\quad\quad -18 = h$

45. $-3, -1, 3, 15$

46.

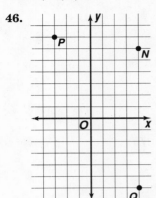

point N—Quadrant I, point P—Quadrant II, point Q—Quadrant IV

47. a. let v = Calories burned in one hour of volleyball
b. $v + 120 = 384$
c. $\quad\quad v + 120 = 384$
$\quad v + 120 - 120 = 384 - 120$
$\quad\quad\quad\quad\quad v = 264$
d. 264 is 120 less than 384.

48. $7 + 8 \div 2 \cdot 6 - 1 = 7 + 4 \cdot 6 - 1$
$\quad\quad\quad\quad\quad\quad\quad = 7 - 24 - 1$
$\quad\quad\quad\quad\quad\quad\quad = 31 - 1$
$\quad\quad\quad\quad\quad\quad\quad = 30$

3-3 Solving Equations by Multiplying or Dividing

Pages 131–132 Checking Your Understanding

1. Multiplying each side by 4.

2. Sample answer: The division property is similar to the multiplication property since multiplying by the reciprocal is the same as dividing. Use the division property when a number is multiplied by x and the multiplication property when x is divided by a number.

3. Sample answer: $8x = -40$

4. Division by zero is undefined.

5. $5x = 45$
$\dfrac{5x}{5} = \dfrac{45}{5}$
$x = 9$
Check: $5x \stackrel{?}{=} 45$
$\quad\quad 5(9) \stackrel{?}{=} 45$
$\quad\quad\quad 45 = 45\ \checkmark$

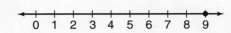

6. $8y = -64$
$\dfrac{8y}{8} = \dfrac{-64}{8}$
$y = -8$
Check: $8y = -64$
$\quad\quad 8(-8) \stackrel{?}{=} -64$
$\quad\quad\quad -64 = -64\ \checkmark$

7. $\quad -\dfrac{p}{3} = 4$
$-\dfrac{p}{3}(-3) = 4\,(-3)$
$\quad\quad p = -12$
Check: $-\dfrac{p}{3} = 4$
$\quad\quad \dfrac{-(-12)}{3} \stackrel{?}{=} 4$
$\quad\quad\quad \dfrac{12}{3} \stackrel{?}{=} 4$
$\quad\quad\quad 4 = 4\ \checkmark$

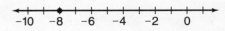

8. $\quad \dfrac{a}{-5} = 8$
$\dfrac{a}{-5}(-5) = 8(-5)$
$\quad\quad a = -40$
Check: $\dfrac{a}{-5} = 8$
$\quad\quad \dfrac{-40}{-5} \stackrel{?}{=} 8$
$\quad\quad\quad 8 = 8\ \checkmark$

9. $-3g = -51$
$\dfrac{-3g}{-3} = \dfrac{-51}{-3}$
$g = 17$
Check: $-3g = -51$
$\quad\quad -3(17) \stackrel{?}{=} -51$
$\quad\quad\quad -51 = -51\ \checkmark$

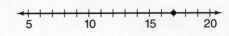

10. $-2 = \frac{p}{6}$

$-2(6) = \frac{p}{6}(6)$

$-12 = p$

Check: $-2 = \frac{p}{6}$

$-2 \stackrel{?}{=} \frac{-12}{6}$

$-2 = -2$ ✔

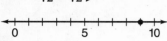

11. $40d = 960$

$\frac{40d}{40} = \frac{960}{40}$

$d = 24$

Pages 132–133   Exercises

12. $8x = 72$

$\frac{8x}{8} = \frac{72}{8}$

$x = 9$

Check: $8x = 72$

$8(9) \stackrel{?}{=} 72$

$72 = 72$ ✔

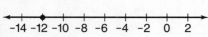

13. $-5y = 95$

$\frac{-5y}{-5} = \frac{95}{-5}$

$y = -19$

Check: $-5y = 95$

$-5(-19) \stackrel{?}{=} 95$

$95 = 95$ ✔

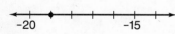

14. $\frac{k}{-2} = 7$

$\frac{k}{-2}(-2) = 7(-2)$

$k = -14$

Check: $\frac{k}{-2} = 7$

$\frac{-14}{-2} \stackrel{?}{=} 7$

$7 = 7$ ✔

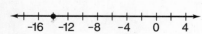

15. $-\frac{h}{7} = 20$

$-\frac{h}{7}(-7) = 20(-7)$

$h = -140$

Check: $-\frac{h}{7} = 20$

$-\frac{(-140)}{7} \stackrel{?}{=} 20$

$\frac{140}{7} \stackrel{?}{=} 20$

$20 = 20$ ✔

16. $86 = 2v$

$\frac{86}{2} = \frac{2v}{2}$

$43 = v$

Check: $86 = 2v$

$86 \stackrel{?}{=} 2(43)$

$86 = 86$ ✔

17. $-21 = -\frac{g}{8}$

$-21(-8) = -\frac{g}{8}(-8)$

$168 = g$

Check: $-21 = -\frac{g}{8}$

$-21 \stackrel{?}{=} -\frac{168}{8}$

$-21 = -21$ ✔

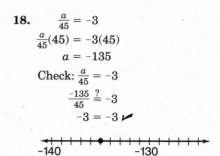

18. $\frac{a}{45} = -3$

$\frac{a}{45}(45) = -3(45)$

$a = -135$

Check: $\frac{a}{45} = -3$

$\frac{-135}{45} \stackrel{?}{=} -3$

$-3 = -3$ ✔

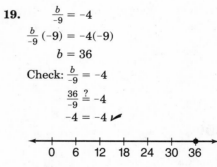

19. $\frac{b}{-9} = -4$

$\frac{b}{-9}(-9) = -4(-9)$

$b = 36$

Check: $\frac{b}{-9} = -4$

$\frac{36}{-9} \stackrel{?}{=} -4$

$-4 = -4$ ✔

20. $672 = -21t$

$\frac{672}{-21} = \frac{-21t}{-21}$

$-32 = t$

Check: $672 = -21t$

$672 \stackrel{?}{=} -21(-32)$

$672 = 672$ ✔

21. $-56 = -7p$

$\dfrac{-56}{-7} = \dfrac{-7p}{-7}$

$8 = p$

Check: $-56 = -7p$

$-56 \overset{?}{=} -7(8)$

$-56 = -56$ ✔

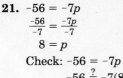

22. $-116 = -4u$

$\dfrac{-116}{-4} = \dfrac{-4u}{-4}$

$29 = u$

Check: $-116 = -4u$

$-116 \overset{?}{=} -4(29)$

$-116 = -116$ ✔

23. $-\dfrac{y}{11} = 132$

$-\dfrac{y}{11}(-11) = 132(-11)$

$y = -1452$

Check: $-\dfrac{y}{11} = 132$

$-\dfrac{(-1452)}{11} \overset{?}{=} 132$

$132 = 132$ ✔

24. $\dfrac{f}{-34} = -14$

$\dfrac{f}{-34}(-34) = -14\,(-34)$

$f = 476$

Check: $\dfrac{f}{-34} = -14$

$\dfrac{476}{-34} \overset{?}{=} -14$

$-14 = -14$ ✔

25. $\dfrac{y}{8} = 117$

$\dfrac{y}{8}(8) = 117(8)$

$y = 936$

Check: $\dfrac{y}{8} = 117$

$\dfrac{936}{8} \overset{?}{=} 117$

$117 = 117$ ✔

26. $17r = -357$

$\dfrac{17r}{17} = \dfrac{-357}{17}$

$r = -21$

Check: $17r = -357$

$17(-21) \overset{?}{=} -357$

$-357 = -357$ ✔

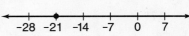

27. $-18p = 306$

$\dfrac{-18p}{-18} = \dfrac{306}{-18}$

$p = -17$

Check: $-18p = 306$

$-18(-17) \overset{?}{=} 306$

$306 = 306$ ✔

28. $-144 = 8x$

$\dfrac{-144}{8} = \dfrac{8x}{8}$

$-18 = x$

Check: $-144 = 8x$

$-144 \overset{?}{=} 8(-18)$

$-144 = -144$ ✔

29. $-384 = -3m$

$\dfrac{-384}{-3} = \dfrac{-3m}{-3}$

$128 = m$

Check: $-384 = -3m$

$-384 \overset{?}{=} -3(128)$

$-384 = -384$ ✔

30. $\dfrac{b}{46} = 216$

$\dfrac{b}{46}(46) = 216(46)$

$b = 9936$

Check: $\dfrac{b}{46} = 216$

$\dfrac{9936}{46} \overset{?}{=} 216$

$216 = 216$ ✔

31. $-71 = \dfrac{x}{31}$

$-71(31) = \dfrac{x}{31}(31)$

$-2201 = x$

Check: $-71 = \dfrac{x}{31}$

$-71 \overset{?}{=} \dfrac{-2201}{31}$

$-71 = -71$ ✔

32. $-171 = \frac{x}{-12}$

$-171(-12) = \frac{x}{-12}(-12)$

$2052 = x$

Check: $-171 = \frac{x}{-12}$

$-171 \stackrel{?}{=} \frac{2052}{-12}$

$-171 = -171$ ✔

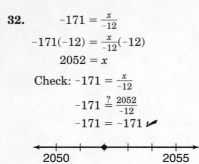

33. $584 = -\frac{s}{23}$

$584(-23) = -\frac{s}{23}(-23)$

$-13,432 = s$

Check: $584 = -\frac{s}{23}$

$584 \stackrel{?}{=} -\frac{(-13,432)}{23}$

$584 = 584$ ✔

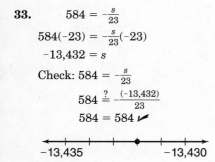

34. $\frac{p}{47} = 123$

$\frac{p}{47}(47) = 123(47)$

$p = 5781$

Check: $\frac{p}{47} = 123$

$\frac{5781}{47} \stackrel{?}{=} 123$

$123 = 123$ ✔

```
  +---+---+--•--+---+---+
    5780           5785
```

35. $-67w = -5561$

$\frac{-67w}{-67} = \frac{-5561}{-67}$

$w = 83$

Check: $-67w = -5561$

$-67(83) \stackrel{?}{=} -5561$

$-5561 = -5561$ ✔

```
  ←+---+---+---+--•--+---+---+→
    80  81  82  83  84  85
```

36. a. $3x = 126$

$\frac{3x}{3} = \frac{126}{3}$

$x = 42$

b. $\frac{x}{6} = -24$

$\frac{x}{6}(6) = -24(6)$

$x = -144$

c. $-4x = 88$

$\frac{-4x}{-4} = \frac{88}{-4}$

$x = -22$

37. Answers will vary.

38. $80x = 4000$

$\frac{80x}{80} = \frac{4000}{80}$

$x = 50$

39. a. $6x = 300,000,000$

b. $15x = 300,000,000$

c. Most species lay between 20 and 5 million eggs.

40. a–c. Answers will vary.

41. $4x = 72$

$\frac{4x}{4} = \frac{72}{4}$

$x = 18$ cm

42. $121 = k - 34$

$121 + 34 = k - 34 + 34$

$155 = k$

Check: $121 = k - 34$

$121 \stackrel{?}{=} 155 - 34$

$121 = 121$ ✔

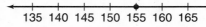

```
  ←+---+---+---+---+--•--+---+---+→
   135 140 145 150 155 160 165
```

43.

Choice	Value	$52 - (4x)$	Is $52 - (4x)$ $= 12$?
a	-3	$52 - (4 \cdot -3)$ $= 52 + 12$ or 64	no
b	0	$52 - (4 \cdot 0)$ $= 52 - 0$ or 52	no
c	12	$52 - (4 \cdot 12)$ $= 52 - 48$ or 4	no
d	16	$52 - (4 \cdot 16)$ $= 52 - 64$ or 12	yes

The number is 16. So, the correct choice is d.

44. $(-7)(-15) = 105$

45. $|-5| + |12| = 5 + 12$

$= 17$

46. true

47. $7n = 70$ What number

$7 \cdot 10 = 70$ times 7 is 70?

$n = 10$

48. $2s - 150$

49. a. Estimation; an exact answer is not needed.

b. Explore—We know the cost of each item. We need to determine if the total cost is less than or equal to $7.00.

Plan—Add the cost of each item to determine if the total is less than or equal to 7. Since an exact answer is not needed, solve by using estimation.

Solve—$0.98 + 2.29 + 3.29 \rightarrow 1 + 2 + 3$ or 6. The total cost is about $6.00. So, $7 will be enough money.

Examine—The actual total is $0.98 + $2.29 + $3.29 or $6.56. Therefore, the assumption that $7 is enough money is correct.

3-4 Using Formulas

Page 135 Checking Your Understanding

1. Substitute numbers given for appropriate variables and evaluate.

2. Sample answers: $d = rt$ for finding the time needed for a car trip, $A = \ell w$ for finding the area of the yard to buy fertilizer.

3.

Number of sides	3	4	6	8	10
Number of triangles	1	2	4	6	8

formula: $x - 2$; 98; 1248

4. $d = rt$
$315 = 45t$
$\frac{315}{45} = \frac{45t}{45}$
$7 = t$

5. $s = \ell - d$
$35 = \ell - 10$
$35 + 10 = \ell - 10 + 10$
$45 = \ell$

6. $m \div g = mpg$
$271.7 \div 9.6 = mpg$
$28.3 = mpg$

7. $d = rt$
$d = (55)(3)$
$d = 165$ miles

8. Monique   Dennis
$s = g + h$ $s = g + h$
$s = 145 + 35$ $s = 153 + 30$
$s = 180$ $s = 183$
Dennis has the higher handicap score.

Pages 135–137 Exercises

9. $d = rt$
$d = (120)(3)$
$d = 360$

10. $F = \frac{9}{5}C + 32$
$F = \frac{9}{5}(30) + 32$
$F = 54 + 32$
$F = 86$

11. $P = 5s$
$65 = 5s$
$\frac{65}{5} = \frac{5s}{5}$
$13 = s$

12. $h = 69 + 2.2F$
$h = 69 + 2.2(14)$
$h = 69 + 30.8$
$h = 99.8$

13. $d = 2r$
$d = 2(1.7)$
$d = 3.4$

14. $A = \frac{b + d}{2}$
$A = \frac{11 + 13}{2}$
$A = \frac{24}{2}$
$A = 12$

15. $d = rt$
$56 = r(4)$
$\frac{56}{4} = \frac{r(4)}{4}$
14 mph $= r$

16. $m \div g = mpg$
$464 \div 16 = mpg$
$29 = mpg$

17. $d = rt$
$600 = 55t$
$\frac{600}{55} = \frac{55t}{55}$
10.9 hrs $= t$

18. $d = rt$
$5200 = 650t$
$\frac{5200}{650} = \frac{650t}{650}$
8 hrs $= t$

19. $s = \ell - d$

20. $d = 2r$

21. a. $A = \frac{b \cdot h}{2}$
$A = \frac{12 \cdot 5}{2}$
$A = \frac{60}{2}$
$A = 30$ sq in.

b. $A = \frac{b \cdot h}{2}$
$24 = \frac{b \cdot 8}{2}$
$24 = b \cdot 4$
$\frac{24}{4} = \frac{b \cdot 4}{4}$
6 cm $= b$

22. Answers will vary.

23. a. $d = rt$
$8 = 10t$
$\frac{8}{10} = \frac{10}{10}t$
$0.8 = t$
0.8 hours or 48 minutes

b. $d = rt$
$8 = r(0.9)$
$\frac{8}{0.9} = \frac{r(0.9)}{0.9}$
8.9 mph $= r$

24. $S = \frac{D + P}{\frac{W}{10} + H - 60}$
$S = \frac{4 + 8}{\frac{120}{10} + 60 - 60}$
$S = \frac{4 + 8}{12 + 60 - 60}$
$S = \frac{12}{12}$
$S = 1$

25. a. $a = \frac{f - s}{t}$

b. $a = \frac{f - s}{t}$
$a = \frac{14 - 2}{6}$
$a = \frac{12}{6}$
$a = 2$ m/s^2

c. $a = \frac{f - s}{t}$
$a = \frac{0 - 6}{3}$
$a = \frac{-6}{3}$
$a = -2$ m/s^2

d. negative

26. $17p = 119$
$$\frac{17p}{17} = \frac{119}{17}$$
$$p = 7$$
Check: $17p = 119$
$$17(7) \overset{?}{=} 119$$
$$119 = 119 \checkmark$$

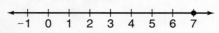

27. $-81 \div 3 = -27$

28. $n = 8 + (-21)$
$$n = -13$$

29. $x + 11 = 25$
$$x + 11 - 11 = 25 - 11$$
$$x = 14$$

30. associative property of addition

Page 137 Self Test

1.

	Stiers	Gibson	Means	Hunt	Bedard
Ratcliffe	O	X	X	X	X
Smith	X	O	X	X	X
Pocahontas	X	X	X	X	O
Willow	X	X	X	O	X
Powhatan	X	X	O	X	X

Stiers—Ratcliffe, Gibson—Smith, Means—Powhatan, Hunt—Willow, Bedard—Pocahontas

2. $18 + m = -57$
$$18 + m - 18 = -57 - 18$$
$$m = -75$$
Check: $18 + m = -57$
$$18 + (-75) \overset{?}{=} -57$$
$$-57 = -57 \checkmark$$

3. $v - 11 = -5$
$$v - 11 + 11 = -5 + 11$$
$$v = 6$$
Check: $v - 11 = -5$
$$6 - 11 \overset{?}{=} -5$$
$$-5 = -5 \checkmark$$

4. $67 = h + 38$
$$67 - 38 = h + 38 - 38$$
$$29 = h$$
Check: $67 = h + 38$
$$67 \overset{?}{=} 29 + 38$$
$$67 = 67 \checkmark$$

5. $d - (-16) = 9$
$$d + 16 = 9$$
$$d + 16 - 16 = 9 - 16$$
$$d = -7$$
Check: $d - (-16) = 9$
$$-7 - (-16) \overset{?}{=} 9$$
$$-7 + 16 \overset{?}{=} 9$$
$$9 = 9 \checkmark$$

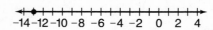

6. $4h = -52$
$$\frac{4h}{4} = \frac{-52}{4}$$
$$h = -13$$
Check: $4h = -52$
$$4(-13) \overset{?}{=} -52$$
$$-52 = -52 \checkmark$$

7. $\frac{x}{5} = 20$
$$\frac{x}{5}(5) = 20(5)$$
$$x = 100$$
Check: $\frac{x}{5} = 20$
$$\frac{100}{5} \overset{?}{=} 20$$
$$20 = 20 \checkmark$$

8. $\frac{m}{11} = -10$
$$\frac{m}{11}(11) = -10(11)$$
$$m = -110$$
Check: $\frac{m}{11} = -10$
$$\frac{-110}{11} \overset{?}{=} -10$$
$$-10 = -10 \checkmark$$

9. $-2b = -13$
$$\frac{-2b}{-2} = \frac{-13}{-2}$$
$$b = \frac{13}{2}$$
Check: $-2b = -13$
$$-2\left(\frac{13}{2}\right) \overset{?}{=} -13$$
$$-13 = -13 \checkmark$$

10. $I = \frac{V}{R}$
$$I = \frac{12}{3}$$
$$I = 4 \text{ amps}$$

Math Lab: Area and Perimeter

Page 138   Your Turn

Area (square units)	Greatest Perimeter (units)
1	4
2	6
3	8
5	12
6	14

1. 18 units

2. 22 units

3. 32 units

4. 102 units

5. The two figures have the same perimeter because the squares still share the same number of sides.

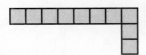

6. $2x + 2$ units

3-5

Integration: Geometry Area and Perimeter

Pages 141–142   Checking Your Understanding

1. Answers will vary

2. Sample answer: Perimeter and area are the same in the respect that they both deal with the dimensions and the shape of an object. They are different in the respect that perimeter deals with the outer boundary of an object whereas area deals with the space an object occupies.

3. Sample answer:

2 in.
7 in.

4. To find the perimeter, multiply each dimension by 2 and then find the sum. To find the area, multiply the two dimensions.

5. $P = 2(\ell + w)$ $A = \ell \cdot w$
$P = 2(4 + 3)$ $A = 4 \cdot 3$
$P = 2(7)$ $A = 23$ sq cm
$P = 14$ cm

6. $P = 2(\ell + w)$ $A = \ell \cdot w$
$P = 2(30 + 30)$ $A = 30 \cdot 30$
$P = 2(60)$ $A = 900$ sq cm
$P = 120$ m

7. $P = 2(\ell + w)$ $A = \ell \cdot w$
$P = 2(15 + 6)$ $A = 15 \cdot 6$
$P = 2(21)$ $A = 90$ sq ft
$P = 42$ ft

8. $P = 2(\ell + w)$
   $P = 2\ell + 2w$
$32 = 2(12) + 2w$
$32 = 24 + 2w$
$32 - 24 = 24 + 2w - 24$
$8 = 2w$
$\frac{8}{2} = \frac{2w}{2}$
4 in. $= w$

9. $A = \ell \cdot w$
$96 = \ell \cdot 8$
$\frac{96}{8} = \frac{\ell \cdot 8}{8}$
12 m $= \ell$

10. $P = 2(\ell + w)$ $A = \ell \cdot w$
$P = 2(90 + 18)$ $A = 90 \cdot 18$
$P = 2(108)$ $A = 1620$ sq ft
$P = 216$ ft

Pages 142–144   Exercises

11. $P = 2(\ell + w)$ $A = \ell \cdot w$
$P = 2(24 + 11)$ $A = 24 \cdot 11$
$P = 2(35)$ $A = 264$ sq ft
$P = 70$ ft

12. $P = 2(\ell + w)$ $A = \ell \cdot w$
$P = 2(9.1 + 9.1)$ $A = (9.1)(9.1)$
$P = 2(18.2)$ $A = 82.81$ sq in.
$P = 36.4$ in.

13. $P = 2(\ell + w)$ $A = \ell \cdot w$
$P = 2(15 + 2)$ $A = 15 \cdot 2$
$P = 2(17)$ $A = 30$ sq km
$P = 34$ km

14. $P = 2(\ell + w)$ $A = \ell \cdot w$
$P = 2(8 + 8)$ $A = 8 \cdot 8$
$P = 2(16)$ $A = 64$ sq cm
$P = 32$ cm

15. $P = 2(\ell + w)$ $A = \ell \cdot w$
$P = 2(5.8 + 1.7)$ $A = (5.8)(1.7)$
$P = 2(7.5)$ $A = 9.86$ sq m
$P = 15$ m

16. $P = 2(\ell + w)$ $A = \ell \cdot w$
$P = 2(500 + 180)$ $A = 500 \cdot 180$
$P = 2(680)$ $A = 90,000$ sq in.
$P = 1360$ in.

17. $P = 2(\ell + w)$ $A = \ell \cdot w$
$P = 2(0.9 + 0.9)$ $A = (0.9)(0.9)$
$P = 2(1.8)$ $A = 0.81$ sq m
$P = 3.6$ m

18. $P = 2(\ell + w)$ $A = \ell \cdot w$
$P = 2(21 + 1)$ $A = 21 \cdot 1$
$P = 2(22)$ $A = 21$ sq ft
$P = 44$ ft

19. $P = 2(\ell + w)$ $A = \ell \cdot w$
$P = 2(3.1 + 3.1)$ $A = (3.1)(3.1)$
$P = 2(6.2)$ $A = 9.61$ sq cm
$P = 12.4$ cm

20. $P = 2(\ell + w)$ $A = \ell \cdot w$
 $P = 2(3.8 + 1.1)$ $A = (3.8)(1.1)$
 $P = 2(4.9)$ $A = 4.18$ sq m
 $P = 9.8$ m

21. $P = 2(\ell + w)$ $A = \ell \cdot w$
 $P = 2(4.8 + 4.8)$ $A = (4.8)(4.8)$
 $P = 2(9.6)$ $A = 23.04$ sq mm
 $P = 19.2$ mm

22. $P = 2(\ell + w)$ $A = \ell \cdot w$
 $P = 2\left(11 + 8\frac{1}{2}\right)$ $A = 11 \cdot 8\frac{1}{2}$
 $P = 2\left(19\frac{1}{2}\right)$ $A = 93.5$ sq in.
 $P = 39$ in.

23. $A = \ell \cdot w$ **24.** $A = \ell \cdot w$
 $35 = 7w$ $270 = \ell \cdot 15$
 $\frac{35}{7} = \frac{7w}{7}$ $\frac{270}{15} = \frac{\ell \cdot 15}{15}$
 5 m $= w$ 18 cm $= \ell$

25. $A = \ell \cdot w$ **26.** $A = \ell \cdot w$
 $176 = 16 \cdot w$ $264 = 11 \cdot w$
 $\frac{176}{16} = \frac{16 \cdot w}{16}$ $\frac{264}{11} = \frac{11 \cdot w}{11}$
 11 yd $= w$ 24 km $= w$

27. $A = \ell \cdot w$ **28.** $A = \ell \cdot w$
 $468 = \ell \cdot 12$ $1547 = \ell \cdot 91$
 $\frac{468}{12} = \frac{\ell \cdot 12}{12}$ $\frac{1547}{91} = \frac{\ell \cdot 91}{91}$
 39 ft $= \ell$ 17 yd $= \ell$

29. $\ell = 32.2 - 8.6 - 8.6$ or 15
 $w = 20 - 5$ or 15
 $A = \ell \cdot w$
 $A = 15 \cdot 15$ or 225 sq in.

30. Area of blue part = Area of larger square − Area of smaller square

Area of larger square:
$A = \ell \cdot w$
$A = (17.7)(17.7)$ or 313.29 sq cm

Area of smaller square:
$A = \ell \cdot w$
$A = (12.5)(12.5)$ or 156.25 sq cm

Area of the blue part = Area of larger square − Area of smaller square
$A = 313.29 - 156.25$ or 157.04 sq cm

31.

2 by 2	—	8	—	4	—
4 by 4	× by 2	16	× by 2	16	× by 4
6 by 6	× by 3	24	× by 3	36	× by 9
8 by 8	× by 4	32	× by 4	64	× by 16

31. a.

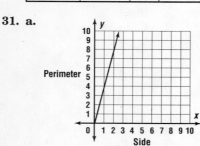

The perimeter is four times the length of a side.

b.

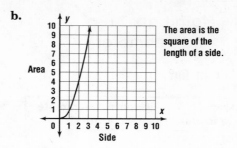

The area is the square of the length of a side.

c. perimeter: $8x$ units; area: $4x^2$ square units

32. a. Determine this area by subtracting the area of the house and the area of the driveway from the area of the yard.
 $A = A(\text{yard}) - A(\text{house}) - A(\text{driveway})$
 $A = 23{,}100 - 1350 - 900$
 $A = 20{,}850$ sq ft

b. $20{,}850 \div 5000 = 4.17$
So, he should buy 5 bags of fertilizer.

33. a. $P = 2(\ell + w)$ **b.** $A = \ell \cdot w$
 $P = 2(60 + 15)$ $A = 60 \cdot 15$
 $P = 2(75)$ or 150 ft $A = 900$ sq ft

34. Area (decking materials) = Area (deck) − A (2 wells)
Area (deck) $= 15 \cdot 40$
         $= 600$
Area (2 wells) $= 2(5)(5)$ or 50
Area (decking materials) $= 600 - 50$ or 550 sq ft

35. See students' work.

36. $d = r \cdot t$
 $371 = r \cdot 7$
 $\frac{371}{7} = \frac{r \cdot 7}{7}$
 53 mph $= r$

37. $b + (-14) = 6$
    $b - 14 = 6$
 $b - 14 + 14 = 6 + 14$
    $b = 20$
 Check: $b + (-14) = 6$
    $20 + (-14) \stackrel{?}{=} 6$
    $6 = 6$ ✔

$$\begin{array}{ccccccccc} & -30 & -20 & -10 & 0 & 10 & 20 & 30 & 40 \end{array}$$

38. $-6ab = -6(-3)(-5)$
    $= -6(15)$
    $= -90$

39. $375 > 210$

40. $121 = 11x$ What number
 $121 = 11(11)$ times 11 is 121?
 $11 = x$

41. $6d + 14(d + 2) = 6d + 14d + 28$
    $= (6 + 14)d + 28$
    $= 20d + 28$

42. $8 + 9 \cdot (7 - 4) = 8 + 9 \cdot 3$
    $= 8 + 27$ or 35

Page 144 From the Funny Papers

1. half off the price
2. the sizes of the sheets
3. See students' diagrams. The areas of the sheets that are not on sale.

Page 145

1. 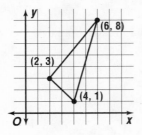 9 sq units

2. 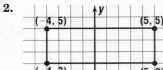 27 sq units

3. 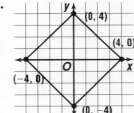 32 sq units

4. 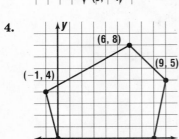 57 sq units

5. Both give the same result.

3-6   Solving Inequalities by Adding or Subtracting

Pages 148–149   Checking Your Understanding

1. Answers will vary. Sample answer: Add 6 to each side of the inequality to get m alone. The answer is $m < 9$.

2. Sample answer: You can add the same number to each side of an inequality and the inequality is still true.

3. The solution of $n + 5 = -3$ is $n = -8$. The solution of $n + 5 > -3$ is $n > -8$. This is all numbers greater than -8.

4. Derrick; *no less* means that many or more.

5. See students' work.

6. $x > -2$

7. $y \le -1$

8. $d > 7$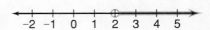

9. $d < 75$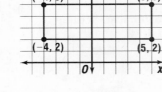

10. $z + (-5) > -3$
    $z - 5 > -3$
    $z - 5 + 5 > -3 + 5$
    $z > 2$

    Check: Try 4, a number greater than 2.
    $z + (-5) > -3$
    $4 + (-5) \overset{?}{>} -3$
    $-1 > -3$ ✔

    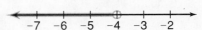

11. $m + 4 < -9$
    $m + 4 - 4 < -9 - 4$
    $m < -13$

    Check: Try -15, a number less than -13.
    $m + 4 < -9$
    $-15 + 4 \overset{?}{<} -9$
    $-11 < -9$ ✔

12. $9 < x - 7$
    $9 + 7 < x - 7 + 7$
    $16 < x$

    Check: Try 18, a number greater than 16.
    $9 < x - 7$
    $9 \overset{?}{<} 18 - 7$
    $9 < 11$ ✔

13. $-6 > y - 2$
    $-6 + 2 > y - 2 + 2$
    $-4 > y$

    Check: Try -6, a number less than -4.
    $-6 > y - 2$
    $-6 \overset{?}{>} -6 - 2$
    $-6 > -8$ ✔

14. $k + (-1) \geq -6$
$k - 1 \geq -6$
$k - 1 + 1 \geq -6 + 1$
$k \geq -5$

Check: Try -5 and -2, numbers greater
than or equal to -5.

$k + (-1) \geq -6 \qquad k + (-1) \geq -6$
$-5 + (-1) \overset{?}{\geq} -6 \qquad -2 + (-1) \overset{?}{\geq} -6$
$-6 \geq -6 \ ✔ \qquad -3 \geq -6 \ ✔$

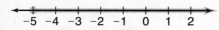

15. $18 + a \leq -13$
$18 + a - 18 \leq -13 - 18$
$a \leq -31$

Check: Try -31 and -34, numbers less
than or equal to -31.

$18 + a \leq -13 \qquad 18 + a \leq -13$
$18 + (-31) \overset{?}{\leq} -13 \qquad 18 + (-34) \overset{?}{\leq} -13$
$-13 \leq -13 \ ✔ \qquad -16 \leq -13 \ ✔$

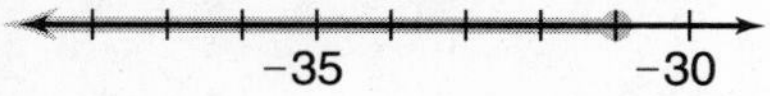

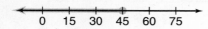

16. $25 - 6 > x$
$19 > x$

Pages 149–150   Exercises

17. $x < 6$ **18.** $y \leq 0$
19. $y > 1$ **20.** $x \geq 21$
21. $t \leq 14$

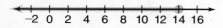

22. $r \leq 45$

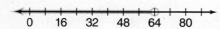

23. $m < 64$

24. $c > 200$

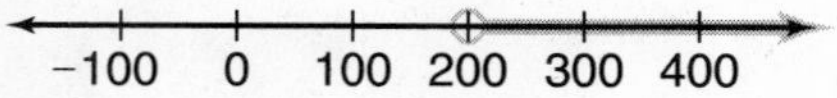

25. $m - 6 < 13$
$m - 6 + 6 < 13 + 6$
$m < 19$

Check: Try 14, a number less than 19.

$m - 6 < 13$
$14 - 6 \overset{?}{<} 13$
$8 < 13 \ ✔$

26. $r \leq -12 - 8$
$r \leq -20$

Check: Try -20 and -24, numbers less
than or equal to -20.

$r \leq -12 - 8 \qquad r \leq -12 - 8$
$-20 \overset{?}{\leq} -12 - 8 \qquad -24 \overset{?}{\leq} -12 - 8$
$-20 \leq -20 \ ✔ \qquad -24 \leq -20 \ ✔$

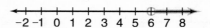

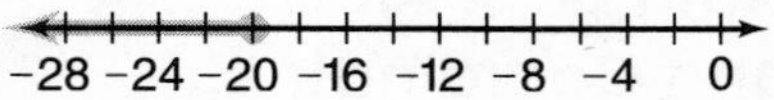

27. $y + 7 > 13$
$y + 7 - 7 > 13 - 7$
$y > 6$

Check: Try 8, a number greater than 6.

$y + 7 > 13$
$8 + 7 \overset{?}{>} 13$
$15 > 13 \ ✔$

28. $k + 9 \geq 21$
$k + 9 - 9 \geq 21 - 9$
$k \geq 12$

Check: Try 12 and 15, numbers greater
than or equal to 12.

$k + 9 \geq 21 \qquad k + 9 \geq 21$
$12 + 9 \overset{?}{\geq} 21 \qquad 15 + 9 \overset{?}{\geq} 21$
$21 \geq 21 \ ✔ \qquad 24 \geq 21 \ ✔$

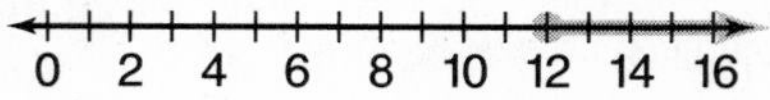

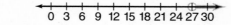

29. $-4 + x > 23$
$-4 + x + 4 > 23 + 4$
$x > 27$

Check: Try 30, a number greater than 27.

$-4 + x > 23$
$-4 + 30 \overset{?}{>} 23$
$26 > 23 \ ✔$

30. $14 \geq a + (-2)$
$14 + 2 \geq a - 2 + 2$
$16 \geq a$

Check: Try 16 and 10, numbers less
than or equal to 16.

$14 \geq a + (-2) \qquad 14 \geq a + (-2)$
$14 \overset{?}{\geq} 16 + (-2) \qquad 14 \overset{?}{\geq} 10 + (-2)$
$14 \geq 14 \ ✔ \qquad 14 \geq 8 \ ✔$

31.
$$-7 + x < -3$$
$$-7 + x + 7 < -3 + 7$$
$$x < 4$$

Check: Try 0, a number less than 4.
$$-7 + x < -3$$
$$-7 + 0 \overset{?}{<} -3$$
$$-7 < -3 \checkmark$$

32.
$$-13 + y \geq 8$$
$$-13 + y + 13 \geq 8 + 13$$
$$y \geq 21$$

Check: Try 21 and 24, numbers greater than or equal to 21.
$$-13 + y \geq 8 \qquad\qquad -13 + y \geq 8$$
$$-13 + 21 \overset{?}{\geq} 8 \qquad -13 + 24 \overset{?}{\geq} 8$$
$$8 \geq 8 \checkmark \qquad\qquad 11 \geq 8 \checkmark$$

33.
$$m + (-2) > -11$$
$$m - 2 > -11$$
$$m - 2 + 2 > -11 + 2$$
$$m > -9$$

Check: Try -5, a number greater than -9.
$$m + (-2) > 11$$
$$-5 + (-2) \overset{?}{>} -11$$
$$-7 > -11 \checkmark$$

34.
$$f + (-5) \geq 14$$
$$f - 5 \geq 14$$
$$f - 5 + 5 \geq 14 + 5$$
$$f \geq 19$$

Check: Try 19 and 20, numbers greater than or equal to 19.
$$f + (-5) \geq 14 \qquad\qquad f + (-5) \geq 14$$
$$19 + (-5) \overset{?}{\geq} 14 \qquad 20 + (-5) \overset{?}{\geq} 14$$
$$14 \geq 14 \checkmark \qquad\qquad 15 \geq 14 \checkmark$$

35.
$$19 \geq z + (-9)$$
$$19 \geq z - 9$$
$$19 + 9 \geq z - 9 + 9$$
$$28 \geq z$$

Check: Try 28 and 16, numbers less than or equal to 28.
$$19 \geq z + (-9) \qquad\qquad 19 \geq z + (-9)$$
$$19 \overset{?}{\geq} 28 + (-9) \qquad 19 \overset{?}{\geq} 16 + (-9)$$
$$19 \geq 19 \checkmark \qquad\qquad 19 \geq 7 \checkmark$$

36.
$$-41 < m - 12$$
$$-41 + 12 < m - 12 + 12$$
$$-29 < m$$

Check: Try -20, a number greater than -29.
$$-41 < m - 12$$
$$-41 \overset{?}{<} -20 - 12$$
$$-41 < -32 \checkmark$$

37.
$$73 + k < 47$$
$$73 + k - 73 < 47 - 73$$
$$k < -26$$

Check: Try -28, a number less than -26.
$$73 + k < 47$$
$$73 + (-28) \overset{?}{<} 47$$
$$45 < 47 \checkmark$$

38.
$$33 < m - (-6)$$
$$33 < m + 6$$
$$33 - 6 < m + 6 - 6$$
$$27 < m$$

Check: Try 29, a number greater than 27.
$$33 < m - (-6)$$
$$33 \overset{?}{<} 29 - (-6)$$
$$33 \overset{?}{<} 29 + 6$$
$$33 < 35 \checkmark$$

39.
$$-31 \geq x + (-5)$$
$$-31 \geq x - 5$$
$$-31 + 5 \geq x - 5 + 5$$
$$-26 \geq x$$

Check: Try -26 and -27, numbers less than or equal to -26.
$$-31 \geq x + (-5) \qquad\qquad -31 \geq x + (-5)$$
$$-31 \overset{?}{\geq} -26 + (-5) \qquad -31 \overset{?}{\geq} -27 + (-5)$$
$$-31 \geq -31 \checkmark \qquad\qquad -31 \geq -32 \checkmark$$

40.
$$22 < n - (-16)$$
$$22 < n + 16$$
$$22 - 16 < n + 16 - 16$$
$$6 < n$$

Check: Try 8, a number greater than 6.
$$22 < n - (-16)$$
$$22 \overset{?}{<} 8 - (-16)$$
$$22 \overset{?}{<} 8 + 16$$
$$22 < 24 \checkmark$$

41.
$$-30 \leq c + (-5)$$
$$-30 \leq c - 5$$
$$-30 + 5 \leq c - 5 + 5$$
$$-25 \leq c$$

Check: Try -25 and -10, numbers greater than or equal to -25.

$$-30 \leq c + (-5) \qquad\qquad -30 \leq c + (-5)$$
$$-30 \overset{?}{\leq} -25 + (-5) \qquad -30 \overset{?}{\leq} -10 + (-5)$$
$$-30 \leq -30 ✔ \qquad\qquad -30 \leq -15 ✔$$

Number line: −40 −30 −20 −10 0

42.
$$56 > w + 72$$
$$56 - 72 > w + 72 - 72$$
$$-16 > w$$

Check: Try −20, a number less than −16.
$$56 > w + 72$$
$$56 \overset{?}{>} -20 + 72$$
$$56 > 52 ✔$$

Number line: −20 −18 −16 −14 −12 −10 −8 −6

43. Number line: −2 −1 0 1 2 3 4

44. Number line: −6 −5 −4 −3 −2 −1 0 1 2 3 4

45.
$$x + 285 \geq 375$$
$$x + 285 - 285 \geq 375 - 285$$
$$x \geq 90$$

46.
$$x + 3(4) \geq 100$$
$$x + 12 \geq 100$$
$$x + 12 - 12 \geq 100 - 12$$
$$x \geq 88$$

47.
$$x + 52 \leq 189$$
$$x + 52 - 52 \leq 189 - 52$$
$$x \leq 137$$
$$x \leq 137 \text{ minutes or 2 hours 17 minutes}$$

48.
$$A = \ell \cdot w$$
$$96 = 8 \cdot w$$
$$\frac{96}{8} = \frac{8 \cdot w}{8}$$
$$12 \text{ ft} = w$$

49. $f = t - h$
$$f = 125 - 25$$
$$f = 100$$

50. $300 + $150 = $450

51.
$$10a - 12a = 10a + (-12)a$$
$$= [10 + (-12)]a$$
$$= -2a$$

52.
$$-12 + 7 = -(|-12| - |7|)$$
$$= -(12 - 7)$$
$$= -5$$

53. a. $150 - 101 = 49$
49 million

b.
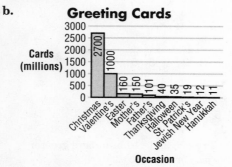

54. $\frac{36}{b} = -4$
$$\frac{36}{-9} = -9$$
$$b = -9$$

What number times −4 is 36?

55. Identity property of multiplication

<hr/>

3-7 ## Solving Inequalities by Multiplying or Dividing

Pages 153–154 Checking Your Understanding

1. Sample answer: $5 > 2$

2. Sample answer: $5x < 20$

3. When you solve inequalities involving multiplication or division, you must do the same operation to each side of the equation. When you solve an inequality involving multiplication, you divide each side by the coefficient. When you solve an inequality involving division, you multiply each side by the divisor.

4. See students' work. **5.** 5, no

6. 4, no   **7.** −3, yes

8.
$$-3y \geq -18$$
$$\frac{-3y}{-3} \leq \frac{-18}{-3}$$
$$y \leq 6$$

Check: Try 6 and 4, numbers less than or equal to 6.
$$-3y \geq -18 \qquad\qquad -3y \geq -18$$
$$-3(6) \overset{?}{\geq} -18 \qquad -3(4) \overset{?}{\geq} -18$$
$$-18 \geq -18 ✔ \qquad -12 \geq -18 ✔$$

Number line: 0 1 2 3 4 5 6 7

9.
$$-8 \leq -4x$$
$$\frac{-8}{-4} \geq \frac{-4x}{-4}$$
$$2 \geq x$$

Check: Try 2 and 0, numbers less than or equal to 2.
$$-8 \leq -4x \qquad\qquad -8 \leq -4x$$
$$-8 \overset{?}{\leq} -4(2) \qquad -8 \overset{?}{\leq} -4(0)$$
$$-8 \leq -8 ✔ \qquad -8 \leq 0 ✔$$

Number line: −3 −2 −1 0 1 2 3

10.
$$\frac{z}{-2} > -2$$
$$\frac{z}{-2} \cdot (-2) < -2 \cdot (-2)$$
$$z < 4$$

Check: Try 2, a number less than 4.
$$\frac{z}{-2} > -2$$
$$\frac{2}{-2} \overset{?}{>} -2$$
$$-1 > -2 ✔$$

Number line: −1 0 1 2 3 4 5

11. $\frac{p}{-3} > -35$

$\frac{p}{-3} \cdot (-3) < -35 \cdot (-3)$

$p < 105$

Check. Try 90, a number less than 105.

$\frac{p}{-3} > -35$

$\frac{90}{-3} \stackrel{?}{>} -35$

$-30 > -35$ ✔

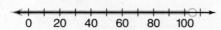

12. $13y \geq -26$

$\frac{13y}{13} \geq \frac{-26}{13}$

$y \geq -2$

Check: Try -2 and 0, numbers greater than or equal to -2.

$13y \geq -26$	$13y \geq -26$
$13(-2) \stackrel{?}{\geq} -26$	$13(0) \stackrel{?}{\geq} -26$
$-26 \geq -26$ ✔	$0 \geq -26$ ✔

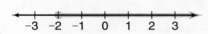

13. $6 > \frac{a}{-7}$

$6 \cdot (-7) > \frac{a}{-7} \cdot (-7)$

$-42 < a$

Check: Try -35, a number greater than -42.

$6 > \frac{a}{-7}$

$6 \stackrel{?}{>} \frac{-35}{-7}$

$6 > 5$ ✔

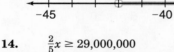

14. $\frac{2}{5}x \geq 29,000,000$

$\left(\frac{5}{2}\right) \cdot \frac{2}{5}x \geq 29,000,000 \cdot \left(\frac{5}{2}\right)$

$x \geq 72,500,000$

at least 72.5 million

Pages 154–155 Exercises

15. $-4y < -36$

$\frac{-4y}{-4} > \frac{-36}{-4}$

$y > 9$

Check: Try 10, a number greater than 9.

$-4y < -36$

$-4(10) \stackrel{?}{<} -36$

$-40 < -36$ ✔

16. $-3m \geq -24$

$\frac{-3m}{-3} \leq \frac{-24}{-3}$

$m \leq 8$

Check: Try 8 and 3, numbers less than or equal to 8.

$-3m \geq -24$	$-3m \geq -24$
$-3(8) \stackrel{?}{\geq} -24$	$-3(3) \stackrel{?}{\geq} -24$
$-24 \geq -24$ ✔	$-9 \geq -24$ ✔

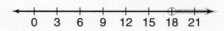

17. $-72 > -4x$

$\frac{-72}{-4} < \frac{-4x}{-4}$

$18 < x$

Check: Try 20, a number greater than 18.

$-72 > -4x$

$-72 \stackrel{?}{>} -4(20)$

$-72 > -80$ ✔

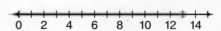

18. $-6s \geq -78$

$\frac{-6s}{-6} \leq \frac{-78}{-6}$

$s \leq 13$

Check: Try 13 and 10, numbers less than or equal to 13.

$-6s \geq -78$	$-6s \geq -78$
$-6(13) \stackrel{?}{\geq} -78$	$-6(10) \stackrel{?}{\geq} -78$
$-78 \geq -78$ ✔	$-60 \geq -78$ ✔

19. $-70 \leq 5p$

$\frac{-70}{5} \leq \frac{5p}{5}$

$-14 \leq p$

Check: Try -14 and -8, numbers greater than or equal to -14.

$-70 \leq 5p$	$-70 \leq 5p$
$-70 \stackrel{?}{\leq} 5(-14)$	$-70 \stackrel{?}{\leq} 5(-8)$
$-70 \leq -70$ ✔	$-70 \leq -40$ ✔

20. $9x \geq -72$

$\frac{9x}{9} \geq \frac{-72}{9}$

$x \geq -8$

Check: Try -8 and -5, numbers greater than or equal to -8.

$9x \geq -72$	$9x \geq -72$
$9(-8) \stackrel{?}{\geq} -72$	$9(-5) \stackrel{?}{\geq} -72$
$-72 \geq -72$ ✔	$-45 \geq -72$ ✔

21. $\frac{x}{3} < -7$

$\frac{x}{3} \cdot (3) < -7 \cdot (3)$

$x < -21$

Check: Try -24, a number less than -21.

$\frac{x}{3} < -7$

$\frac{-24}{3} \overset{?}{<} -7$

$-8 < -7$ ✔

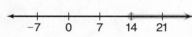

22. $-8 > \frac{y}{4}$

$-8 \cdot (4) > \frac{y}{4} \cdot (4)$

$-32 > y$

Check: Try -36, a number less than -32.

$-8 > \frac{y}{4}$

$-8 \overset{?}{>} \frac{-36}{-4}$

$-8 > -9$ ✔

(number line: -40 -32 -24 -16 -8 0)

23. $\frac{m}{-2} \le -7$

$\frac{m}{-2} \cdot (-2) \ge -7 \cdot (-2)$

$m \ge 14$

Check: Try 14 and 16, numbers greater than or equal to 14.

$\frac{m}{-2} \le -7$ $\frac{m}{-2} \le -7$

$\frac{14}{-2} \overset{?}{\le} -7$ $\frac{16}{-2} \overset{?}{\le} -7$ ✔

$-7 \le -7$ ✔ $-8 \le -7$ ✔

(number line: -7 0 7 14 21)

24. $\frac{p}{-4} < 20$

$\frac{p}{-4} \cdot (-4) > 20 \cdot (-4)$

$p > -80$

Check: Try -76, a number greater than -80.

$\frac{p}{-4} < 20$

$\frac{-76}{-4} \overset{?}{<} 20$

$19 < 20$ ✔

(number line: -100 0)

25. $-7 \le \frac{z}{14}$

$-7 \cdot (14) \le \frac{z}{14} \cdot (14)$

$-98 \le z$

Check: Try -98 and -84, numbers greater than or equal to -98.

$-7 \le \frac{z}{14}$ $-7 \le \frac{z}{14}$

$-7 \overset{?}{\le} \frac{-98}{14}$ $-7 \overset{?}{\le} \frac{-84}{14}$

$-7 \le -7$ ✔ $-7 \le -6$ ✔

(number line: -100 -95)

26. $-13a \ge -273$

$\frac{-13a}{-13} \le \frac{-273}{-13}$

$a \le 21$

Check: Try 21 and 12, numbers less than or equal to 21.

$-13a \ge -273$ $-13a \ge -273$

$-13(21) \overset{?}{\ge} -273$ $-13(12) \overset{?}{\ge} -273$

$-273 \ge -273$ ✔ $-156 \ge -273$ ✔

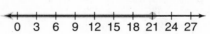

27. $-378 < 18r$

$\frac{-378}{18} < \frac{18r}{18}$

$-21 < r$

Check: Try -20, a number greater than -21.

$-378 < 18r$

$-378 \overset{?}{<} 18(-20)$

$-378 < -360$ ✔

(number line: -24 -18 -12 -6 0)

28. $\frac{a}{14} \le -17$

$\frac{a}{14} \cdot (14) \le -17 \cdot (14)$

$a \le -238$

Check: Try -238 and -252, numbers less than or equal to -238.

$\frac{a}{14} \le -17$ $\frac{a}{14} \le -17$

$\frac{-238}{14} \overset{?}{\le} -17$ $\frac{-252}{14} \overset{?}{\le} -17$

$-17 \le -17$ ✔ $-18 \le 17$ ✔

(number line: -240 -235)

29.
$$-14 \le \frac{s}{-23}$$
$$-14 \cdot (-23) \ge \frac{s}{-23} \cdot (-23)$$
$$322 \ge s$$

Check: Try 322 and 299, numbers less than or equal to 322.

$$-14 \le \frac{s}{-23} \qquad\qquad -14 \le \frac{s}{-23}$$
$$-14 \overset{?}{\le} \frac{322}{-23} \qquad\qquad -14 \overset{?}{\le} \frac{299}{-23}$$
$$-14 \le -14 ✔ \qquad\qquad -14 \le -13 ✔$$

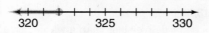

30.
$$\frac{g}{-21} > 33$$
$$\frac{g}{-21} \cdot (-21) < 33 \cdot (-21)$$
$$g < -693$$

Check: Try -714, a number less than -693.

$$\frac{g}{-21} > 33$$
$$\frac{-714}{-21} \overset{?}{>} 33$$
$$34 > 33 ✔$$

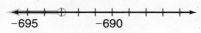

31.
$$-4 > \frac{x}{3}$$
$$-4 \cdot (3) > \frac{x}{3} \cdot (3)$$
$$-12 > x$$

Check: Try -15, a number less than -12.

$$-4 > \frac{x}{3}$$
$$-4 \overset{?}{>} \frac{-15}{3}$$
$$-4 > -5 ✔$$

$$\begin{array}{ccccccc} & & & & & & \\ -12 & -10 & -8 & -6 & -4 & -2 & 0 \end{array}$$

32.
$$-25a \le 400$$
$$\frac{-25a}{-25} \ge \frac{400}{-25}$$
$$a \ge -16$$

Check: Try -16 and -10, numbers greater than or equal to -16.

$$-25a \le 400 \qquad\qquad -25a \le 400$$
$$-25(-16) \overset{?}{\le} 400 \qquad -25(-10) \overset{?}{\le} 400$$
$$400 \le 400 ✔ \qquad\qquad 250 \le 400 ✔$$

$$\begin{array}{ccccc} & & & & \\ -24 & -16 & -8 & 0 & 8 \end{array}$$

33.
$$-4n > -24$$
$$\frac{-4n}{-4} < \frac{-24}{-4}$$
$$n < 6$$

The greatest integer that meets this condition is 5.

34.
$$26x > 2,600,000$$
$$\frac{26x}{26} > \frac{2,600,000}{26}$$
$$x > 100,000$$

35.
$$100x = 80,000$$
$$\frac{100x}{100} = \frac{80,000}{100}$$
$$x = 800$$

36. a. $15 \cdot 10 = 150$ **b.** $15 \cdot 20 = 300$
So, $x \ge \$150$ So, $x \le \$300$

37. $t > 12 \cdot 6$ months
$t > 6$ years

38. a. $f < (5280)(59,000)$
$f < 311,520,000$

   b. $248,710,000p < 311,520,000$
$$\frac{248,710,000p}{248,710,000} < \frac{311,520,000}{248,710,000}$$
$$p < 1.25 \text{ feet}$$

   c. No. The average American buys less than 1.25 feet of floss each year. That amount would allow you to floss once or twice, but not each day.

39.
$$m + (-5) < 23$$
$$m - 5 < 23$$
$$m - 5 + 5 < 23 + 5$$
$$m < 28$$

40.
$$\begin{array}{ll} P = 2(\ell + w) & A = \ell \cdot w \\ P = 2(6.5 + 6.5) & A = (6.5)(6.5) \\ P = 2(13.0) & A = 42.25 \text{ sq ft} \\ P = 26 \text{ feet} & \end{array}$$

41.

Choice	Value	Is $x + 5 = \frac{1}{3}(3x - 5)$?
a	5	$5 + 5 = \frac{1}{3}(3 \cdot 5 - 5)$ $10 = \frac{1}{3}(10)$ $10 = \frac{10}{3}$ No
b	3	$3 + 5 = \frac{1}{3}(3 \cdot 3 - 5)$ $8 = \frac{1}{3}(4)$ $8 = \frac{4}{3}$ No

5 and 3 are real numbers. So, eliminate the possibility that any real number will be the value of x. Thus, the correct choice is d.

42. $-126 \div 3 = -42$

43. $8 \cdot (-7y) = [8 \cdot (-7)]y$
$= -56y$

44. $-|-4| = -4$

45. a. $[(3 \times 4) + (2 \times 3) + (1 \times 2) + (1 \times 1)] \div 7$

   b. $[(3 \times 4) + (2 \times 3) + (1 \times 2) + (1 \times 1)] \div 7$
$= [12 + 6 + 2 + 1] \div 7$
$= 21 \div 7$
$= 3.0$

3-8   Applying Equations and Inequalities

Pages 157–158   Checking Your Understanding

1. Sample answer: You can solve the problem effectively and you can check the answer to make sure it is accurate.

2. less than or equal to, no more than, at most.

3. Rosa, more than 2100 pounds of mix was used.

4. x = integer
$$x + 12 = 28$$
$$x + 12 - 12 = 28 - 12$$
$$x = 16$$

5. n = number
$$4n < 96$$
$$\frac{4n}{4} < \frac{96}{4}$$
$$n < 24$$

6. a. What is greatest possible cost of the labor?

   b. What is the greatest possible cost?

   c. $39 + x \leq 63$

   d. $$39 + x \leq 63$$
   $$39 + x - 39 \leq 63 - 39$$
   $$x \leq 24 \text{ dollars}$$

7. Sample answer: The total cost of a car repair was $187. If the labor cost $169, how much did the parts cost?

Pages 158–159 Exercises

8. h = hours worked
$$13h \geq 52$$
$$\frac{13h}{13} \geq \frac{52}{13}$$
$$h \geq 4$$

9. n = number
$$\frac{n}{-3} > 5$$
$$\frac{n}{-3} \cdot (-3) < 5 \cdot (-3)$$
$$n < -15$$

10. t = winner's time
$$88 = 2t$$
$$\frac{88}{2} = \frac{2t}{2}$$
$$44 = t$$

11. a = account balance
$$a + 50 > 400$$
$$a + 50 - 50 > 400 - 50$$
$$a > 350$$

12. n = number
$$7n < 84$$
$$\frac{7n}{7} < \frac{84}{7}$$
$$n < 12$$

13. p = original purchase price
$$4p \leq 85,000$$
$$\frac{4p}{4} \leq \frac{85,000}{4}$$
$$p \leq 21,250$$

14. Sample answer: The warriors scored 24 points in this game. That is 9 more than three times what their opponent scored. What did the opponent score.

15. Sample answer: The low temperature was 16°F on Tuesday. This is at least 9° more than the Wednesday low. What was the low temperature on Wednesday?

16. Sample answer: Fashion Barn charges $30 for a pair of jeans. How many pairs of jeans must they sell to generate more than $300?

17. $|x| < 4$
   -3, -2, -1, 0, 1, 2, 3

18. a. How many pizzas have to be delivered to make $20?

   b. $20 or more in tips.

   c. $1.5 > 20$
   $$\frac{1.5x}{1.5} > \frac{20}{1.5}$$
   $$x > 13.33 \text{ or } 14 \text{ pizzas}$$

   d. No. You can't deliver less than a whole pizza.

19. a = average
$$35a < 600$$
$$\frac{35a}{35} < \frac{600}{35}$$
$$a < 17.14$$
Her average was less than 17 points per game.

20. a. w = weight
$$w + 100 \leq 900$$
$$w + 100 - 100 \leq 900 - 100$$
$$w \leq 800 \text{ lb}$$

   b. $5w \leq 800$
   $$\frac{5w}{5} \leq \frac{800}{5}$$
   $$w \leq 160 \text{ lb}$$

21. c = changes in price
$$8c = 32$$
$$\frac{8c}{8} = \frac{32}{8}$$
$$c = 4$$
4 times the 1971 price/oz

22. t = changes in speed
$$30t = 600$$
$$\frac{30t}{30} = \frac{600}{30}$$
$$t = 20$$
20 times faster

23. h = height
$$5(8)h = 440$$
$$40h = 440$$
$$\frac{40h}{40} = \frac{440}{40}$$
$$h = 11 \text{ centimeters}$$

24. f = female farmers in 1987
$$145,156 = f + 14,386$$
$$145,156 - 14,386 = f + 14,386 - 14,386$$
$$130,770 = f$$
130,770 female farmers

25. x = sample scores
$$80 - 6 \leq x \leq 80 + 6$$
$$74 \leq x \leq 86$$
The scores could be less than or equal to 86 or greater than or equal to 74.

26. a. g = minimum number of games
First Round:

$g > \frac{1}{2}(5)$

$g > \frac{5}{2}$ or $2\frac{1}{2}$

A team can only win a whole number of games. So, the minimum number of games in the first round is 3.

Conference semifinals:

$g > \frac{1}{2}(7)$

$g > \frac{7}{2}$ or $3\frac{1}{2}$

The minimum number of games in the conference semifinals is 4.

Conference finals:

$g > \frac{1}{2}(7)$

$g > \frac{7}{2}$ or $3\frac{1}{2}$

The minimum number of games in the conference finals is 4.

NBA finals:

$g > \frac{1}{2}(7)$

$g > \frac{7}{2}$ or $3\frac{1}{2}$

The minimum number of games in the NBA finals is 4.

Therefore, the minimum number of games an NBA Champion would have to win is $3 + 4 + 4 + 4$ or 15.

b. A team plays a total of 26 games. If the minimum number of games an NBA Champion would have to win is 15, then the maximum number of games that the team can lose is $26 - 15$ or 11.

$g \le 11$.

27. $-3h < -39$

$\frac{-3h}{-3} > \frac{-39}{-3}$

$h > 13$

Check: Try 15, a number greater than 13.

$-3h < -39$

$-3(15) \overset{?}{<} -39$

$-45 < -39$ ✔

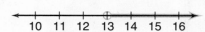

28. $E \times O = M$

$10 \times 43 = M$

$430 = M$

29. $-12y + 5y = (-12 + 5)y$

$= -7y$

30. 9

31. $\frac{t}{3} = 8$ What number divided by 3 is 8?

$\frac{24}{3} = 8$

$t = 24$

Chapter 3 Study Guide and Assessment

Page 161   Understanding and Using Vocabulary

1. true   **2.** false   **3.** false

4. true   **5.** true   **6.** true

7. false

Pages 162–164   Skills and Concepts

8. $f + 31 = -5$

$f + 31 - 31 = -5 - 31$

$f = -36$

Check: $f + 31 = -5$

$-36 + 31 \overset{?}{=} -5$

$-5 = -5$ ✔

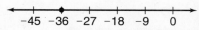

9. $r + (-11) = 40$

$r - 11 = 40$

$r - 11 + 11 = 40 + 11$

$r = 51$

Check: $r + (-11) = 40$

$r - 11 \overset{?}{=} 40$

$r - 11 + 11 \overset{?}{=} 40 + 11$

$r = 51$ ✔

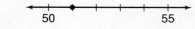

10. $12 = k - 7$

$12 + 7 = k - 7 + 7$

$19 = k$

Check: $12 = k - 7$

$12 \overset{?}{=} 19 - 7$

$12 = 12$ ✔

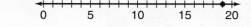

11. $-9 = r + (-15)$

$-9 = r - 15$

$-9 + 15 = r - 15 + 15$

$6 = r$

Check: $-9 = r + (-15)$

$-9 \overset{?}{=} 6 + (-15)$

$-9 = -9$ ✔

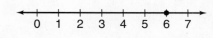

12.
$$16 = h - (-4)$$
$$16 = h + 4$$
$$16 - 4 = h + 4 - 4$$
$$12 = h$$

Check: $16 = h - (-4)$

$16 \stackrel{?}{=} 12 - (-4)$

$16 \stackrel{?}{=} 12 + 4$

$16 = 16$ ✔

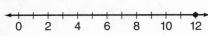

13.
$$7 = q - 12$$
$$7 + 12 = q - 12 + 12$$
$$19 = q$$

Check: $7 = q - 12$

$7 \stackrel{?}{=} 19 - 12$

$7 = 7$ ✔

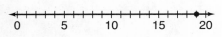

14.
$$m - 3 = -10$$
$$m - 3 + 3 = -10 + 3$$
$$m = -7$$

Check: $m - 3 = -10$

$-7 - 3 \stackrel{?}{=} -10$

$-10 = -10$ ✔

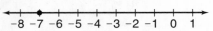

15.
$$z - (-51) = 36$$
$$z + 51 = 36$$
$$z + 51 - 51 = 36 - 51$$
$$z = -15$$

Check: $z - (-51) = 36$

$-15 - (-51) \stackrel{?}{=} 36$

$-15 + 51 \stackrel{?}{=} 36$

$36 = 36$ ✔

(number line: −20 −15 −10 −5 −0 5)

16.
$$\frac{c}{6} = -29$$
$$\frac{c}{6} \cdot 6 = -29 \cdot 6$$
$$c = -174$$

Check: $\frac{c}{6} = -29$

$\frac{-174}{6} \stackrel{?}{=} -29$

$-29 = -29$ ✔

(number line: −175 −170)

17.
$$\frac{p}{-3} = -42$$
$$\frac{p}{-3} \cdot (-3) = -42 \cdot (-3)$$
$$p = 126$$

Check: $\frac{p}{-3} = -42$

$\frac{126}{-3} \stackrel{?}{=} -42$

$-42 = -42$ ✔

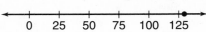

18.
$$840 = -28r$$
$$\frac{840}{-28} = \frac{-28r}{-28}$$
$$-30 = r$$

Check: $840 = -28r$

$840 \stackrel{?}{=} -28(-30)$

$840 = 840$ ✔

(number line: −40 −30 −20 −10 0)

19.
$$13b = -299$$
$$\frac{13b}{13} = \frac{-299}{13}$$
$$b = -23$$

Check: $13b = -299$

$13(-23) \stackrel{?}{=} -299$

$-299 = -299$ ✔

(number line: −25 −20)

20.
$$14x = 224$$
$$\frac{14x}{14} = \frac{224}{14}$$
$$x = 16$$

Check: $14x = 224$

$14(16) \stackrel{?}{=} 224$

$224 = 224$ ✔

(number line: 0 4 8 12 16)

21.
$$\frac{-y}{10} = -33$$
$$\frac{-y}{10} \cdot (-10) = -33 \cdot (-10)$$
$$y = 330$$

Check: $\frac{-y}{10} = -33$

$\frac{-330}{10} \stackrel{?}{=} -33$

$-33 = -33$ ✔

(number line: 300 350)

22. $\frac{g}{-9} = 21$

$\frac{g}{-9} \cdot (-9) = 21 \cdot (-9)$

$g = -189$

Check: $\frac{g}{-9} = 21$

$\frac{-189}{-9} \overset{?}{=} 21$

$21 = 21$ ✔

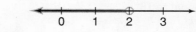

23. $25d = -1775$

$\frac{25d}{25} = \frac{-1775}{25}$

$d = -71$

Check: $25d = -1775$

$25(-71) \overset{?}{=} -1775$

$-1775 = -1775$ ✔

24. $A = \ell \cdot w$

$105 = 7 \cdot w$

$\frac{105}{7} = \frac{7 \cdot w}{7}$

$15 = w$

25. $I = p \cdot r \cdot t$

$I = (200)(0.06)(2)$

$I = 24$

26. $A = \frac{b \cdot h}{2}$

$72 = \frac{6 \cdot h}{2}$

$72 = 3 \cdot h$

$\frac{72}{3} = \frac{3h}{3}$

$24 = h$

27. $C = 2\pi r$

$C = (2)(3.14)(9)$

$C = 56.52$

28. $P = 2(\ell + w)$ $A = \ell \cdot w$

$P = 2(6 + 4)$ $A = 6 \cdot 4$

$P = 2(10)$ $A = 24$ sq cm

$P = 20$ cm

29. $P = 2(\ell + w)$ $A = \ell \cdot w$

$P = 2(12 + 6)$ $A = 12 \cdot 6$

$P = 2(18)$ $A = 72$ sq in.

$P = 36$ in.

30. $P = 2(\ell + w)$ $A = \ell \cdot w$

$P = 2(12 + 4)$ $A = 12 \cdot 4$

$P = 2(16)$ $A = 48$ sq m

$P = 32$ m

31. $P = 2(\ell + w)$ $A = \ell \cdot w$

$P = 2(15 + 5)$ $A = 15 \cdot 5$

$P = 2(20)$ $A = 75$ sq ft

$P = 40$ ft

32. $P = 2(\ell + w)$ $A = \ell \cdot w$

$P = 2(22 + 22)$ $A = 22 \cdot 22$

$P = 2(44)$ $A = 484$ sq yd

$P = 88$ yd

33. $x - 2 < -14$

$x - 2 + 2 < -14 + 2$

$x < -12$

Check: Try -15, a number less than -12.

$x - 2 < -12$

$-15 - 2 \overset{?}{<} -12$

$-17 < -12$ ✔

34. $12 + a > -9$

$12 + a - 12 > -9 - 12$

$a > -21$

Check: Try -20, number greater than -21.

$12 + a > -9$

$12 + (-20) \overset{?}{>} -9$

$-8 > -9$ ✔

35. $-7 + b < -5$

$-7 + b + 7 < -5 + 7$

$b < 2$

Check: Try 0, a number less than 2.

$-7 + b < -5$

$-7 + 0 \overset{?}{<} -5$

$-7 < -5$ ✔

36. $4 < y - 23$

$4 + 23 < y - 23 + 23$

$27 < y$

Check: Try 30, a number greater than 27.

$4 < y - 23$

$4 \overset{?}{<} 30 - 23$

$4 < 7$ ✔

37. $f + (-8) > -12$

$f - 8 > -12$

$f - 8 + 8 > -12 + 8$

$f > -4$

Check: Try -1, a number greater than -4.

$f + (-8) > -12$

$-1 + (-8) \overset{?}{>} -12$

$-9 > -12$ ✔

38. $w + 9 \leq -5$

$w + 9 \leq -5 - 9$

$w \leq -14$

Check: Try -14, and -16, numbers less than or equal to -14.

$\begin{aligned} w + 9 &\leq -5 \\ -14 + 9 &\overset{?}{\leq} -5 \\ -5 &\leq -5 \checkmark \end{aligned}$ $\qquad$ $\begin{aligned} w + 9 &\leq -5 \\ -16 + 9 &\overset{?}{\leq} -5 \\ -7 &\leq -5 \checkmark \end{aligned}$

39. $\frac{m}{-15} < 9$

$\frac{m}{-15} \cdot (-15) > 9 \cdot (-15)$

$m > -135$

Check: Try -120, a number greater than -135.

$\frac{m}{-15} < 9$

$\frac{-120}{-15} \overset{?}{<} 9$

$8 < 9 \checkmark$

40. $-72 \geq -4k$

$\frac{-72}{-4} \leq \frac{-4k}{-4}$

$18 \leq k$

Check: Try 18 and 20, numbers greater than or equal to 18.

$\begin{aligned} -72 &\geq -4k \\ -72 &\overset{?}{\geq} -4(18) \\ -72 &\geq -72 \checkmark \end{aligned}$ $\qquad$ $\begin{aligned} -72 &\geq -4k \\ -72 &\overset{?}{\geq} -4(20) \\ -72 &\geq -80 \checkmark \end{aligned}$

(number line: 0, 9, 18, 27, 36, 45)

41. $\frac{t}{12} < 11$

$\frac{t}{12} \cdot 12 < 11 \cdot 12$

$t < 132$

Check: Try 120, a number less than 132.

$\frac{t}{12} < 11$

$\frac{120}{12} \overset{?}{<} 11$

$10 < 11 \checkmark$

(number line: 130, 135)

42. $144 < 9k$

$\frac{144}{9} < \frac{9k}{9}$

$16 < k$

Check: Try 18, a number greater than 16.

$\begin{aligned} 144 &< 9k \\ 144 &\overset{?}{<} 9(18) \\ 144 &< 162 \checkmark \end{aligned}$

(number line: 0, 4, 8, 12, 16, 20)

43. $88 > -8p$

$\frac{88}{-8} < \frac{-8p}{-8}$

$-11 < p$

Check: Try -10, a number greater than -11.

$\begin{aligned} 88 &> -8p \\ 88 &\overset{?}{>} -8(-10) \\ 88 &> 80 \checkmark \end{aligned}$

(number line: -12, -10, -8, -6, -4, -2, 0)

44. $\frac{s}{-22} < -7$

$\frac{s}{-22} \cdot (-22) > -7 \cdot (-22)$

$s > 154$

Check: Try 176, a number greater than 154.

$\frac{s}{-22} < -7$

$\frac{176}{-22} \overset{?}{<} -7$

$-8 < -7 \checkmark$

(number line: 150, 155)

45. $285 \leq 19f$

$\frac{285}{19} \leq \frac{19f}{19}$

$15 \leq f$

Check: Try 15 and 17, numbers greater than or equal to 15.

$\begin{aligned} 285 &\leq 19f \\ 285 &\overset{?}{\leq} 19 \cdot 15 \\ 285 &\leq 285 \checkmark \end{aligned}$ $\qquad$ $\begin{aligned} 285 &\leq 19f \\ 285 &\overset{?}{\leq} 19 \cdot 17 \\ 285 &\leq 323 \checkmark \end{aligned}$

(number line: 0, 5, 10, 15, 20, 25)

46. $18 \leq \frac{r}{6}$

$18 \cdot 6 \leq \frac{r}{6} \cdot 6$

$108 \leq r$

Check: Try 108 and 114, numbers greater than or equal to 108.

$\begin{aligned} 18 &\leq \frac{r}{6} \\ 18 &\overset{?}{\leq} \frac{108}{6} \\ 18 &\leq 18 \checkmark \end{aligned}$ $\qquad$ $\begin{aligned} 18 &\leq \frac{r}{6} \\ 18 &\overset{?}{\leq} \frac{114}{6} \\ 18 &\leq 19 \checkmark \end{aligned}$

(number line: 100, 110)

47. x = amount of money each person paid for dinner

$3x < 36$

$\frac{3x}{3} < \frac{36}{3}$

$x < \$12$

48. n = number

$4n > 76$

$\frac{4n}{4} > \frac{76}{4}$

$n > 19$

49. x = amount of boxes of cookies
$$576 + x > 800$$
$$576 + x - 576 > 800 - 576$$
$$x > 224$$
more than 224 boxes

Page 164   Applications and Problem Solving

50.

	South	Kennedy	Lincoln	Anthony
Last	X	X	X	O

The runner who came in last represented Anthony High School. So, d is the correct choice.

51. $365x = 37,807$
$$\frac{365x}{365} = \frac{37,807}{365}$$
$$x = 103.5 \qquad \text{daily average of 103 people}$$

52. $a = \frac{f - s}{t}$
$$a = \frac{6.8 - 1.2}{4}$$
$$a = \frac{5.6}{4}$$
$$a = 1.4 \text{ miles per hour per minute}$$

Page 165   Alternative Assessment

1. c = Calories in peanut butter cookies
$$c - 100 = 90$$
$$c - 100 + 100 = 90 + 100$$
$$c = 190$$
Peanut butter cookies have 190 Calories per serving.

2. f = fat in peanut butter cookies
$$\frac{f}{2} = 8$$
$$\frac{f}{2} \cdot 2 = 8 \cdot 2$$
$$f = 16$$
Peanut butter cookies have 16 grams of fat.

3. s = sodium in chocolate-chip cookies
$$20s = 80$$
$$\frac{20s}{20} = \frac{80}{20}$$
$$s = 4$$
Chocolate-chip cookies have 4 grams of fat.

4. See students' work.

5. The label states that there is less than 1 gram of sugar in one serving of the product. If x represents the number of grams of sugar in the product, then $x < 1$. Thus, six servings of the product will contain less than 6 grams of sugar. Since $5 < 6$, it is possible that there will be less than 5 grams of sugar in 6 servings of the product.

Page 165   Thinking Critically

a.

The perimeter increases by 2 inches.

$A = \ell \cdot w$	$A = \ell \cdot w$
$A = 7 \cdot w$	$A = 7(w + 1)$
$A = 7w$ sq in.	$A = 7w + 7$ sq in.

The area increases by 7 sq in.

b.

$P = 2(\ell + w)$	$P = 2(\ell + w)$
$P = 2(10 + w)$	$P = 2(10 + w + 1)$
$P = 20 + 2w$	$P = 2(11 + w)$
	$P = 22 + 2w$

No; the change in the perimeter does not differ. There is still an increase of 2 inches.

c.

$A = \ell \cdot w$	$A = \ell \cdot w$
$A = 10 \cdot w$	$A = 10(w + 1)$
$A = 10w$ sq in.	$A = 10w + 10$ sq in.

Yes; the area increases by 10 sq in.

Page 165   Portfolio

See students' work.

Page 165   Self Evaluation

See students' work.

Chapter 4   Exploring Factors and Fractions

4-1   Factors and Monomials

Pages 172–173   Checking Your Understanding

1. Because a solid rectangular shape can be made.
2. Yes; with 78 squares, a 6×13 rectangle can be made.
3. Yes; it is a product of an integer and a variable.
4. 1
5. Possible answers: $2 \cdot 3 \cdot 6 = 36$; $1 \cdot 1 \cdot 36$; $3 \cdot 3 \cdot 4$; $2 \cdot 2 \cdot 9$; $1 \cdot 3 \cdot 12$; $1 \cdot 2 \cdot 18$
6. 3   7. 2
8. 2, 3, 6   9. 2, 3, 5, 6, 10
10. yes; an integer
11. yes; product of an integer and a variable
12. no; involves addition
13. yes; product of an integer and variables
14. $78 \div 6 = 13$
    Therefore, the band can be arranged in rows of 6.

Pages 173–174   Exercises

15. 3   16. 2   17. 2, 5, 10
18. 2   19. 5   20. 2, 5, 10
21. 3   22. 2, 3, 5, 6, 10   23. none
24. none   25. 2   26. 2, 3, 6
27. yes; an integer
28. no; involves subtraction
29. yes; product of an integer and a variable
30. yes; product of an integer and variables
31. no; involves subtraction
32. yes; a variable
33. no; involves addition
34. yes; product of an integer and a variable
35. 0, 4, or 8
36. Sample answer: 30   37. Sample answer: 1035
38. Sample answer: 343   39. Sample answer: 5555
40. a. 997   b. 101
41. a. Answers will vary.
    b. 1996
       1996 + 12 or 2008
       2008 + 12 or 2020
       2020 + 12 or 2032
       2032 + 12 or 2044
42. a. in a 6-by-8 arrangement
    b. See students' work. It could be a 1-by-51 or a 3-by-17 rectangle, but neither of these is well suited to the space available.
43. a. $1 + 2 + 3 = 6$
    b. $1 + 2 + 4 + 7 + 14 = 28$

44. $103,730 < 2x$
    $\frac{103,730}{2} < \frac{2x}{2}$
    $51,865 < x$
    Arkansas is more than 51,865 square miles.

45. $\quad 89 = \frac{x}{-3}$ 46. $f = -64 \div -4$
    $89 \cdot (-3) = \frac{x}{-3} \cdot (-3)$ $f = 16$
    $\quad -267 = x$

47. $t = -6 + (-14) + 12$
    $t = -20 + 12$
    $t = -(|-20| - |12|)$
    $t = -(20 - 12)$
    $t = -8$

48. $\quad 5b = 95$ What number
    $5 \cdot 19 = 95$ times 5 is 95?
    $\quad b = 19$

49. $ac - 3b = (7)(6) - 3(3)$
    $\qquad\quad = 42 - 9$
    $\qquad\quad = 33$

50. $3 \cdot (3 + 5) \div 2 = 3 \cdot 8 \div 2$
    $\qquad\qquad\qquad = 24 \div 2$
    $\qquad\qquad\qquad = 12$

4-2   Powers and Exponents

Page 177   Checking Your Understanding

1. Multiply 3 and 3, or use 3 as a factor twice to obtain 9.
2. $10^5 = 10 \times 10 \times 10 \times 10 \times 10 = 100,000$
3. Since 1 multiplied by itself is always 1, no matter how many times 1 appears as a factor, the value of this expression is always 1.
4. Cardida is correct. If n is between 0 and 1, then $n^2 < n$.
5. See students' work.   6. 10^3
7. m^3 8. 3^3
9. $2 \cdot 2 \cdot 2$ 10. $(-8)(-8)(-8)(-8)$
11. $10 \cdot 10 \cdot 10 \cdot 10 \cdot 10 \cdot 10$
12. $x^4 = 5^4$ 13. $y^2 + z^3 = 9^2 + (-3)^3$
    $\quad = 625$ $= 81 + (-27)$
    $\qquad\qquad\qquad\qquad\qquad\quad = 54$
14. $(5 \times 10^2) + (9 \times 10^1) + (8 \times 10^0)$
15. a. $S.A. = 6(5^2)$ or 150 in^2
    b. $V = 5^3$ or 125 in^3
    c. The surface area is multiplied by 4 and the volume is multiplied by 8.

Pages 178–179   Exercises

16. 5^3 17. n^4 18. 1^5
19. 14^1 20. p^4 21. 3^{15}
22. 6^5 23. b^4 24. $(-5)^2$
25. $12 \cdot 12$ 26. $y \cdot y \cdot y \cdot y \cdot y \cdot y$

27. $(-7)(-7)(-7)$

28. $(-f)(-f)$

29. $\underbrace{6 \cdot 6 \cdot \ldots \cdot 6 \cdot 6}_{20 \text{ factors}}$

30. $(x + 1)(x + 1)$

31. $\underbrace{1 \cdot 1 \cdot \ldots \cdot 1 \cdot 1}_{55 \text{ factors}}$

32. $q \cdot q \cdot q$

33. $(-1)(-1)(-1)(-1)$

34. $a^4 + b = 3^4 + 9$
$= 81 + 9$
$= 90$

35. $c^2 + ab = (-2)^2 + (3)(9)$
$= 4 + (3)(9)$
$= 4 + 27$
$= 31$

36. $b^0 - 10 = 1 - 10$
$= -9$

37. $2b^2 = 2(9)^2$
$= 2(81)$
$= 162$

38. $10a^5 + c^2 = 10(3)^5 + (-2)^2$
$= 10(243) + 4$
$= 2430 + 4$
$= 2434$

39. $a - b^2 = 3 - 9^2$
$= 3 - 81$
$= -78$

40. $(5 \times 10^1) + (6 \times 10^0)$

41. $(1 \times 10^2) + (4 \times 10^1) + (9 \times 10^0)$

42. $(2 \times 10^3) + (5 \times 10^1) + (3 \times 10^0)$

43. 23,405

44. The exponent of the first term in each product increases by one and the second term is the same. For each value, the base remains the same and the exponent is the sum of the exponents of the terms in the product.

44. a. 10^7 **b.** 10^{12} **c.** 10^{x+2}

45. a. $0 - 1$ or -1 **b.** $1 \div 2$ or $\frac{1}{2}$

     c. See students' work.   **d.** $\frac{1}{3}$

46. a. $P = I^2R$ **b.** $P = 3362$ watts
     $P = (41)^2(2)$

47. The volume of a cube with sides s units long is s^3.

48. $10^{12} + 1 = 1{,}000{,}000{,}000{,}001$

49. a. $2^0, 2^1, 2^2$ **b.** 2^3 **c.** 2^{29} cents

     d. 536,870,912

     e. $2^0 + 2^1 + 2^2 + \ldots + 2^{29}$

     f. No; the reward will cost \$10,737,418.23 over the 30-day period.

50. 3, 5

51. $-7x < 84$
$\frac{-7x}{-7} > \frac{84}{-7}$
$x > -12$

$\xleftarrow{\quad}$ -14 -12 -10 -8 -6 -4 -2 0 2 4 $\xrightarrow{\quad}$

52. $P = 2(\ell + w)$ $A = \ell \cdot w$
$P = 2(12 + 4)$ $A = 12 \cdot 4$
$P = 2(16)$ $A = 48 \text{ m}^2$
$P = 32 \text{ m}$

53. $67 - x = 49$
$67 - x + x = 49 + x$
$67 = 49 + x$
$67 - 49 = 49 + x - 49$
$18 = x$

54. $m = \frac{126}{-21}$
$m = -6$

55. $18p - 26p = (18 - 26)p$
$= -8p$

56. $x = 536 - 497$
$x = 39$ students

57. $b + 4$

Page 179   From the Funny Papers

1. Sample answer: The man has been working on the problem for a long time and the cleaning person gives him the answer by saying "squared."

2. The exponent on c is different in each one.

3. $c = 300{,}000$
$c^2 = 90{,}000{,}000{,}000 \text{ km}^2/\text{s}^2$

4-2B   Math Lab: Evaluating Expressions with Exponents

Page 180

1. 62   **2.** 4   **3.** 2

4. 4   **5.** 1024   **6.** −475

7. No. Sample answer: The order of operations will be different. The value of the first expression is −24 and the value of the second expression is 0.

4-3   Problem-Solving Strategy: Draw a Diagram

Page 182   Checking Your Understanding

1. Sample answer: Diagrams allow you to gain an overview of the problem at a glance. They may also give you a perspective and a way to solve the problem that had not been thought of before.

2. Sample answer: No, there are times when another strategy is more useful.

3.

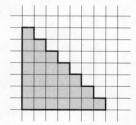

28 blocks

Pre-Algebra Chapter 4

4. $5 + 4 + 3 + 2 + 1$ or 15 flights

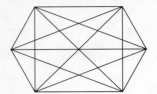

5.

| First Round | Second Round | Third Round |

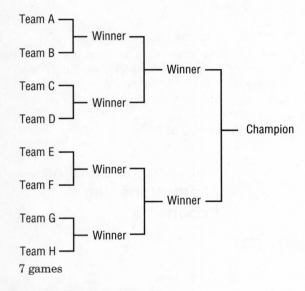

7 games

Pages 182–183 Exercises

6. *West*

Team #1 → must play all 8 teams
Team #2 → must play all 8 teams
Team #3 → must play all 8 teams
Team #4 → must play all 8 teams
Team #5 → must play all 8 teams
Team #6 → must play all 8 teams
Team #7 → must play all 8 teams
$8 + 8 + 8 + 8 + 8 + 8 + 8$ or 56 games

7. $(4 + 3) \times 6 + 3 = 45$

8.

Time		Red	Blue
1	Red gain	+2	−2
2	Blue gain	+1	−1
3	Red gain	+3	−3
4	Blue gain	+2	−2
5	Red gain	+4	−4
6	Blue gain	+3	−3
7	Red gain	+5	−5
8	Blue gain	+4	−4
9	Red gain	+6	−6
10	Blue gain	+5	−5
11	Red gain	+7	−7
12	Blue gain	+6	−6
13	Red gain	+8	−8
14	Blue gain	+7	−7
15	Red gain	+9	−9
16	Blue gain	+8	−8
17	Red gain	+10	−10

17 minutes

9. Stretch: 7 minutes
Run: 18 minutes
Walk : 8 minutes
Leg lifts: 7 minutes
Stretch: 4 minutes
Total workout time is $7 + 18 + 8 + 7 + 4$ or 44 minutes. So, 2:07 P.M. − 44 minutes is 1:23 P.M.

10. M = Mother
D = Father

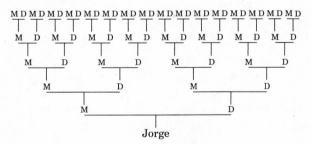

62 people

11.

4	15	1	14
9	6	12	7
16	3	13	2
5	10	8	11

The sum of the numbers on each row, column, and diagonal is 34.

12. a.

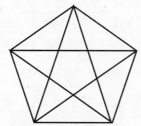

5 diagonals

b.

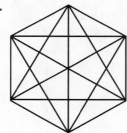

9 diagonals

c.

Sides	Diagonals
4	2 ⎫ +3
5	5 ⎫ +4
6	9 ⎫ +5
7	14

A heptagon should have 14 diagonals.

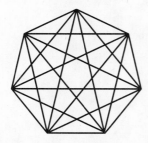

d. A polygon with n sides has
$(2 + 3 + \ldots + (n - 2))$ diagonals.

13. Old Car
$12{,}000 \div 22 \times \$1.10 = \$600$
New Car
$12{,}000 \div 37 \times \$1.10 = \$356.77$
Charlie will save $\$600 - \$356.77$ or about $\$243$.

14. 1, 2, 3, 5, 7, 9, 11, 15

15. 1 person = 9 square feet
100 people = 900 square feet
The hotel must provide 900 square feet for the dance floor. This is a 30-ft by 30-ft square. So, each side should be 30 feet.

16. x^5

17.
$$x - 8 \le -17$$
$$x - 8 + 8 \le -17 + 8$$
$$x \le -9$$

18. 3, 3, 6, 18, 72
$\underset{\times 1}{} \underset{\times 2}{} \underset{\times 3}{} \underset{\times 4}{}$

19.
$$5 + (-8) + 7 = 5 + 7 + (-8)$$
$$= 12 + (-8)$$
$$= (|12| - |-8|)$$
$$= (12 - 8)$$
$$= 4$$

20. Associative property of multiplication

4-4 **Prime Factorization**

Page 187   Checking Your Understanding

1. Sample answer: A prime number only has 1 and itself as factors, a composite number has more.

2.
$$84 = 2 \cdot 42$$
$$= 2 \cdot 2 \cdot 21$$
$$= 2 \cdot 2 \cdot 3 \cdot 7$$

$$\begin{array}{r} 7 \\ 3\overline{)21} \\ 2\overline{)42} \\ 2\overline{)84} \end{array}$$

$84 = 2^2 \cdot 3 \cdot 7$; the results are the same since each number has only one prime factorization.

3. Mansi; 4 is not prime

4. prime   **5.** composite   **6.** composite

7. $38 = 2 \cdot 19$

8. $66 = 2 \cdot 33$
$= 2 \cdot 3 \cdot 11$

9. $56 = 2 \cdot 28$
$= 2 \cdot 2 \cdot 14$
$= 2 \cdot 2 \cdot 2 \cdot 7$

10. $8x^2y^3 = 2 \cdot 4 \cdot x^2 \cdot y^3$
$= 2 \cdot 2 \cdot 2 \cdot x \cdot x \cdot y \cdot y \cdot y$

11. $-42abc = -1 \cdot 42 \cdot a \cdot b \cdot c$
$= -1 \cdot 2 \cdot 21 \cdot a \cdot b \cdot c$
$= -1 \cdot 2 \cdot 3 \cdot 7 \cdot a \cdot b \cdot c$

12. $25(xy)^2 = 25 \cdot x^2 \cdot y^2$
$= 5 \cdot 5 \cdot x \cdot x \cdot y \cdot y$

13. Damon is correct that 3067 is prime, but it has two factors—1 and 3067.

Pages 187–188   Exercises

14. composite   **15.** prime

16. composite   **17.** prime

18. prime

19. $51 = 3 \cdot 17$

20. $-63 = -1 \cdot 63$
$= -1 \cdot 3 \cdot 21$
$= -1 \cdot 3 \cdot 3 \cdot 7$

21. $41 = 1 \cdot 41$

22. $-95 = -1 \cdot 95$
$= -1 \cdot 5 \cdot 19$

23.
$\begin{array}{r} 11 \\ 5\overline{)55} \\ 2\overline{)110} \end{array}$
$110 = 2 \cdot 5 \cdot 11$

24.
$\begin{array}{r} 37 \\ 3\overline{)111} \\ 3\overline{)333} \\ -1\overline{)-333} \end{array}$
$-333 = -1 \cdot 3 \cdot 3 \cdot 37$

25.
$\begin{array}{r} 3 \\ 3\overline{)9} \\ 3\overline{)27} \\ 3\overline{)81} \end{array}$
$81 = 3 \cdot 3 \cdot 3 \cdot 3$

26.
$\begin{array}{r} 59 \\ 1\overline{)59} \end{array}$
$59 = 1 \cdot 59$

27. $13 = 1 \cdot 13$

28.
$\begin{array}{r} 2 \\ 2\overline{)4} \\ 2\overline{)8} \\ 2\overline{)16} \\ 2\overline{)32} \\ 2\overline{)64} \\ 2\overline{)128} \\ 2\overline{)256} \\ 2\overline{)512} \\ 2\overline{)1024} \end{array}$
$1024 = 2 \cdot 2 \cdot 2 \cdot 2 \cdot 2 \cdot 2 \cdot 2 \cdot 2 \cdot 2 \cdot 2$

29. $42xy^2 = 42 \cdot x \cdot y^2$
$= 2 \cdot 21 \cdot x \cdot y \cdot y$
$= 2 \cdot 3 \cdot 7 \cdot x \cdot y \cdot y$

30. $38mnp = 38 \cdot m \cdot n \cdot p$
$= 2 \cdot 19 \cdot m \cdot n \cdot p$

31. $21xy^3 = 21 \cdot x \cdot y^3$
$= 3 \cdot 7 \cdot x \cdot y \cdot y \cdot y$

32. $560x^4y^2 = 2 \cdot 280 \cdot x^4 \cdot y^2$
$= 2 \cdot 2 \cdot 140 \cdot x \cdot x \cdot x \cdot x \cdot y \cdot y$
$= 2 \cdot 2 \cdot 2 \cdot 70 \cdot x \cdot x \cdot x \cdot x \cdot y \cdot y$
$= 2 \cdot 2 \cdot 2 \cdot 2 \cdot 35 \cdot x \cdot x \cdot x \cdot x \cdot y \cdot y$
$= 2 \cdot 2 \cdot 2 \cdot 2 \cdot 5 \cdot 7 \cdot x \cdot x \cdot x \cdot x \cdot y \cdot y$

33. $28f^2g = 2 \cdot 14 \cdot f^2 \cdot g$
$= 2 \cdot 2 \cdot 7 \cdot f \cdot f \cdot g$

34. $275st^3 = 5 \cdot 55 \cdot s \cdot t^3$
$= 5 \cdot 5 \cdot 11 \cdot s \cdot t \cdot t \cdot t$

35. $210mn^3 = 2 \cdot 105 \cdot m \cdot n^3$
$= 2 \cdot 3 \cdot 35 \cdot m \cdot n \cdot n \cdot n$
$= 2 \cdot 3 \cdot 5 \cdot 7 \cdot m \cdot n \cdot n \cdot n$

36. $-8a^3b^2 = -1 \cdot 8 \cdot a^3 \cdot b^2$
$= -1 \cdot 2 \cdot 4 \cdot a \cdot a \cdot a \cdot b \cdot b$
$= -1 \cdot 2 \cdot 2 \cdot 2 \cdot a \cdot a \cdot a \cdot b \cdot b$

37. $75m^2k = 3 \cdot 25 \cdot m^2 \cdot k$
$= 3 \cdot 5 \cdot 5 \cdot m \cdot m \cdot k$

38. $-400a^2b^3 = -1 \cdot 400 \cdot a^2 \cdot b^3$
$= -1 \cdot 2 \cdot 200 \cdot a \cdot a \cdot b \cdot b \cdot b$
$= -1 \cdot 2 \cdot 2 \cdot 100 \cdot a \cdot a \cdot b \cdot b \cdot b$
$= -1 \cdot 2 \cdot 2 \cdot 2 \cdot 50 \cdot a \cdot a \cdot b \cdot b \cdot b$
$= -1 \cdot 2 \cdot 2 \cdot 2 \cdot 2 \cdot 25 \cdot a \cdot a \cdot b \cdot b \cdot b$
$= -1 \cdot 2 \cdot 2 \cdot 2 \cdot 2 \cdot 5 \cdot 5 \cdot a \cdot a \cdot b \cdot b \cdot b$

39. Students should use guess-and-check. Try numbers that give a remainder of 1 when divided by 7, the largest number.

Number	÷ by 2	÷ by 3	÷ by 5	÷ by 7
29	14R1	9R2	5R4	4R1
64	32	21R1	12R4	9R1
92	46	30R2	18R2	13R1
120	60	40	24	17R1
155	77R1	51R2	31	22R1
211	105R1	70R1	42R1	30R1

The least number that gives a remainder of 1 when divided by 2, 3, 5, or 7 is 211.

40.

Month	Day
February	2, 3, 5, 7, 11, 13, 17, 19, 23, 29
March	2, 3, 5, 7, 11, 13, 17, 19, 23, 29, 31
May	2, 3, 5, 7, 11, 13, 17, 19, 23, 29, 31
July	2, 3, 5, 7, 11, 13, 17, 19, 23, 29, 31
November	2, 3, 5, 7, 11, 13, 17, 19, 23, 29

There are 53 prime days in a leap year.

41.

x	$1643 \div x$	factor of 1643?
7	234.714	no
11	149.364	no
13	126.385	no
17	96.647	no
19	86.474	no
23	71.435	no
29	56.655	no
31	53	yes

If $n = 1643$, then p and q are 31 and 53.

42. 3 and 5, 5 and 7, 11 and 13,
17 and 19, 29 and 31, 41 and 43,
59 and 61, 71 and 73

43. a. 23 **b.** yes

44. It factors large numbers.

45.

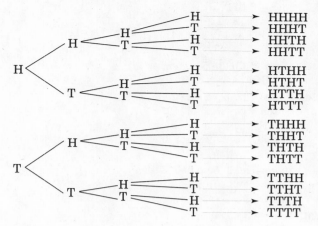

Toss #1	Toss #2	Toss #3	Toss #4	

16 outcomes

46. $(-8)(-8)(-8)(-8)(-8)(-8)(-8)$

47. $P = 2(\ell + w)$ $A = \ell \cdot w$
$P = 2(17 + 9)$ $A = 17 \cdot 9$
$P = 2(26)$ $A = 153$ sq in.
$P = 52$ in.

48. $\dfrac{x}{-7} = -28$ **49.** $6 > -6$

    $\dfrac{x}{-7} \cdot (-7) = -28 \cdot (-7)$

          $x = 196$

50. $3 \cdot (12 - 4) = 3 \cdot 12 - 3 \cdot 4$

51. $x + 15$

52. a. Sample answer: calculator because of large numbers

b. Explore—We know how much money the average American earns and pays in taxes in a lifetime. We need to find the average American's lifetime take-home pay.

c. Plan—Subtract the amount that the average American pays in taxes from the amount that the average American earns to find the lifetime take-home pay. Estimate: $1,235,720 - 178,364 \rightarrow 1,200,000 - 200,000$ or $1,000,000$. So the lifetime take-home pay should be about 1,000,000.

Solve—Use a calculator to find the amount. $1,235,720 - 178,364 = 1,057,356$ The average American's lifetime take-home pay is $1,057,356.

Examine—The amount is very close to the estimate, so the answer is reasonable.

4-4b Math Lab: Factor Patterns

Page 189 Your Turn

Exactly 2 Factors	Exactly 3 Factors	Exactly 4 Factors	Exactly 5 Factors	Exactly 6 Factors
19: 1, 19	25: 1, 5, 25	21: 1, 3, 7, 21		20: 1, 2, 4, 5, 10, 20
23: 1, 23		22: 1, 2, 11, 22		28: 1, 2, 4, 7, 14, 28
29: 1, 29		26: 1, 2, 13, 26		
		27: 1, 3, 9, 27		32: 1, 2, 4, 8, 16, 32
31: 1, 31	49: 1, 7, 49	33: 1, 3, 11, 33		44: 1, 2, 4, 11, 22, 44
37: 1, 37		34: 1, 2, 17, 34		45: 1, 3, 5, 9, 15, 45
41: 1, 41		35: 1, 5, 7, 35		50: 1, 2, 5, 10, 25, 50
43: 1, 43		38: 1, 2, 19, 38		
47: 1, 47		39: 1, 3, 13, 39		
		46: 1, 2, 23, 46		

More than 6 factors
24: 1, 2, 3, 4, 6, 8, 12, 24
30: 1, 2, 3, 5, 6, 10, 15, 30
36: 1, 2, 3, 4, 6, 9, 12, 18, 36
40: 1, 2, 4, 5, 8, 10, 20, 40
42: 1, 2, 3, 6, 7, 14, 21, 42
48: 1, 2, 3, 4, 6, 8, 12, 16, 24, 48

1. Sample answer: 67, 121, 55, 81, 63, 66

2. Sample answer:
Column one contains prime numbers.
Column two contains squares of prime numbers.
Column three contains composite numbers whose prime factorization contains two different prime numbers that are each used as factors exactly once, and prime numbers raised to the third power.
Column four contains prime numbers raised to the fourth power.
Column five contains composite numbers whose prime factorization includes two different prime numbers—one that is used as a factor once and one that is used as a factor twice; and prime numbers to the fifth power.
Numbers with more than six factors include: prime numbers raised to any power greater than or equal to six; composite numbers with four or more prime numbers as factors, if there are at least two primes that are different.

4-5 Greatest Common Factor (GCF)

Pages 192 Checking Your Understanding

1. Find the prime factorizations for each number. Multiply all the common prime factors.

2.   21 $45 = 5 \cdot 9$
     $3 \cdot 7$ $= 5 \cdot 3 \cdot 9$
Common factor is 3.

3. Sample answer: 15 and 30.

4.

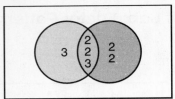

5. $6 = \boxed{2} \cdot 3$
$8 = \boxed{2} \cdot 2 \cdot 2$
The GCF is 2.

6. $12 = \boxed{2} \cdot \boxed{2} \cdot 3$
$8 = \boxed{2} \cdot \boxed{2} \cdot 2$
The GCF is $2 \cdot 2$ or 4.

7. The GCF of 1 and 20 is 1.

8. $12x = \boxed{2} \cdot \boxed{2} \cdot 3 \cdot \boxed{x}$
$40x^2 = \boxed{2} \cdot \boxed{2} \cdot 2 \cdot 5 \cdot \boxed{x} \cdot x$
The GCF is $2 \cdot 2 \cdot x$ or $4x$.

9. $-5ab = -1 \cdot 5 \cdot a \cdot \boxed{b}$
$6b^2 = 2 \cdot 3 \cdot b \cdot \boxed{b}$
The GCF is b.

10. $15a^2b^2 = \boxed{3} \cdot 5 \cdot \boxed{a} \cdot \boxed{a} \cdot \boxed{b} \cdot \boxed{b}$
$27a^3b^3 = \boxed{3} \cdot 3 \cdot 3 \cdot \boxed{a} \cdot \boxed{a} \cdot a \cdot \boxed{b} \cdot \boxed{b} \cdot b$
The GCF is $3 \cdot a \cdot a \cdot b \cdot b$ or $3a^2b^2$.

11. $48 = \boxed{2} \cdot \boxed{2} \cdot 2 \cdot 2 \cdot \boxed{3}$
$60 = \boxed{2} \cdot \boxed{2} \cdot \boxed{3} \cdot 5$
Each side should be $2 \cdot 2 \cdot 3$ or 12 inches.

Pages 192–194 Exercises

12. $16 = \boxed{2} \cdot \boxed{2} \cdot \boxed{2} \cdot 2$
$56 = \boxed{2} \cdot \boxed{2} \cdot \boxed{2} \cdot 7$
The GCF is $2 \cdot 2 \cdot 2$ or 8.

13. $24 = \boxed{2} \cdot \boxed{2} \cdot \boxed{2} \cdot 3$
$40 = \boxed{2} \cdot \boxed{2} \cdot \boxed{2} \cdot 5$
The GCF is $2 \cdot 2 \cdot 2$ or 8.

14. $6 = \boxed{2} \cdot 3$
$8 = \boxed{2} \cdot 2 \cdot 2$
$12 = \boxed{2} \cdot 2 \cdot 3$
The GCF is 2.

15. $12 = \boxed{2} \cdot \boxed{2} \cdot \boxed{3}$
$24 = \boxed{2} \cdot \boxed{2} \cdot 2 \cdot \boxed{3}$
$36 = \boxed{2} \cdot \boxed{2} \cdot 3 \cdot \boxed{3}$
The GCF is $2 \cdot 2 \cdot 3$ or 12.

16. $20 = 2 \cdot 2 \cdot 5$
$21 = 3 \cdot 7$
$25 = 5 \cdot 5$
The GCF is 1.

17. $108 = \boxed{2} \cdot \boxed{2} \cdot 3 \cdot \boxed{3} \cdot \boxed{3}$
$144 = \boxed{2} \cdot \boxed{2} \cdot 2 \cdot 2 \cdot \boxed{3} \cdot \boxed{3}$
The GCF is $2 \cdot 2 \cdot 3 \cdot 3$ or 36.

18. $14n = \boxed{2} \cdot \boxed{7} \cdot \boxed{n}$
$42n^2 = \boxed{2} \cdot 3 \cdot \boxed{7} \cdot \boxed{n} \cdot n$
The GCF is $2 \cdot 7 \cdot n$ or $14n$.

19. $40x^2 = \boxed{2} \cdot \boxed{2} \cdot \boxed{2} \cdot 5 \cdot \boxed{x} \cdot x$
$16x = \boxed{2} \cdot \boxed{2} \cdot \boxed{2} \cdot 2 \cdot \boxed{x}$
The GCF is $2 \cdot 2 \cdot 2 \cdot x$ or $8x$.

20. $24a^2 = 2 \cdot \boxed{2} \cdot \boxed{2} \cdot \boxed{3} \cdot a \cdot \boxed{a}$
$-60a = -1 \cdot \boxed{2} \cdot \boxed{2} \cdot \boxed{3} \cdot 5 \cdot \boxed{a}$
The GCF is $2 \cdot 2 \cdot 3 \cdot a$ or $12a$.

21. $14b = \boxed{2} \cdot \boxed{7} \cdot \boxed{b}$
$-56b^2 = -1 \cdot \boxed{2} \cdot 2 \cdot 2 \cdot \boxed{7} \cdot \boxed{b} \cdot b$
The GCF is $2 \cdot 7 \cdot b$ or $14b$.

22. $33y^2 = 3 \cdot \boxed{11} \cdot y \cdot \boxed{y}$
$44y = 2 \cdot 2 \cdot \boxed{11} \cdot \boxed{y}$
The GCF is $11 \cdot y$ or $11y$.

23. $-18 = -1 \cdot 2 \cdot \boxed{3} \cdot \boxed{3}$
$45mn = \boxed{3} \cdot \boxed{3} \cdot 5 \cdot m \cdot n$
The GCF is $3 \cdot 3$ or 9.

24. $32mn^2 = \boxed{2} \cdot \boxed{2} \cdot 2 \cdot 2 \cdot 2 \cdot m \cdot \boxed{n} \cdot n$
$16n = \boxed{2} \cdot \boxed{2} \cdot 2 \cdot 2 \cdot \boxed{n}$
$12n^3 = \boxed{2} \cdot \boxed{2} \cdot 3 \cdot \boxed{n} \cdot n \cdot n$
The GCF is $2 \cdot 2 \cdot n$ or $4n$.

25. $18a = \boxed{2} \cdot \boxed{3} \cdot 3 \cdot a$
$30ab = \boxed{2} \cdot \boxed{3} \cdot 5 \cdot a \cdot b$
$42b = \boxed{2} \cdot \boxed{3} \cdot 7 \cdot b$
The GCF is $2 \cdot 3$ or 6.

26. $15v^2 = 3 \cdot 5 \cdot v \cdot v$
$36w^2 = 2 \cdot 2 \cdot 3 \cdot 3 \cdot w \cdot w$
$70vw = 2 \cdot 5 \cdot 7 \cdot v \cdot w$
The GCF is 1.

27. $24x^3 = \boxed{2} \cdot 2 \cdot 2 \cdot \boxed{3} \cdot x \cdot x \cdot x$
$36y^3 = \boxed{2} \cdot 2 \cdot \boxed{3} \cdot 3 \cdot y \cdot y \cdot y$
$18xy = \boxed{2} \cdot \boxed{3} \cdot 3 \cdot x \cdot y$
The GCF is $2 \cdot 3$ or 6.

28. $15r^2 = 3 \cdot \boxed{5} \cdot r \cdot r$
$35s^2 = \boxed{5} \cdot 7 \cdot s \cdot s$
$70rs = 2 \cdot \boxed{5} \cdot 7 \cdot r \cdot s$
The GCF is 5.

29. $18ab = \boxed{2} \cdot \boxed{3} \cdot 3 \cdot \boxed{a} \cdot b$
$6a^2 = \boxed{2} \cdot \boxed{3} \cdot a \cdot \boxed{a}$
$42a^2b = \boxed{2} \cdot \boxed{3} \cdot 7 \cdot \boxed{a} \cdot a \cdot b$
The GCF is $2 \cdot 3 \cdot a$ or $6a$.

30. $8 = \boxed{1} \cdot 2 \cdot 4 \cdot 8$
$9 = \boxed{1} \cdot 3 \cdot 9$
yes

31. $11 = \boxed{1} \cdot 11$
$13 = \boxed{1} \cdot 13$
yes

32. $21 = \boxed{1} \cdot 3 \cdot \boxed{7} \cdot 21$
$14 = \boxed{1} \cdot 2 \cdot \boxed{7} \cdot 14$
no

33. $25 = \boxed{1} \cdot \boxed{5} \cdot 25$
$30 = \boxed{1} \cdot 2 \cdot 3 \cdot \boxed{5} \cdot 6 \cdot 10 \cdot 15 \cdot 30$
no

34. $21 = \boxed{1} \cdot 3 \cdot 7 \cdot 21$
$23 = \boxed{1} \cdot 23$
yes

35. $9 = \boxed{1} \cdot \boxed{3} \cdot 9$
$12 = \boxed{1} \cdot 2 \cdot \boxed{3} \cdot 4 \cdot 6 \cdot 12$
no

36. No; because a number cannot be a factor of a smaller number.

37. 15, 30, 45, 60, 75, ...
 +15 +15 +15 +15
The GCF is 15.

38.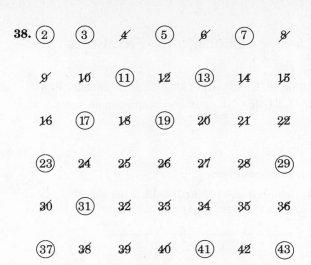

The GCF of 30 and 42 is 6. In the process of crossing out every second number after 2, 30 and 42 are crossed out. Also, 30 and 42 are included in the process of crossing out every third number after 3. So, 30 and 42 have 2 and 3 as common factors and the product of these prime factors, $2 \cdot 3$ or 6 is the greatest common factor.

39. $48 = 2 \cdot 2 \cdot 2 \cdot 2 \cdot 3$
$16 = 2 \cdot 2 \cdot 2 \cdot 2$
The GCF is 16. Since the GCF is one of the numbers, there will be no waste. Since $48 \div 16 = 3$, the 48-inch side should be cut into three 16-inch sections.
$72 = 2 \cdot 2 \cdot 2 \cdot 3 \cdot 3$
$12 = 2 \cdot 2 \cdot 3$
The GCF is 12. Since the GCF is one of the numbers, there will be no waste. Since $72 \div 12 = 6$, the 72-inch side should be cut into six 72-inch sections.

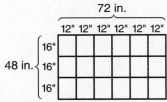

72 in.

12" 12" 12" 12" 12" 12"

48 in. 16" 16" 16"

18 shelves

40. $b - a = 86 - 42$
$= 44$
The result is not a factor of both numbers.
$44 - 42 = 2$
The result is a factor of both numbers.

41. $308 = 2 \cdot 1540$
$= 2 \cdot 2 \cdot 770$
$= 2 \cdot 2 \cdot 2 \cdot 385$
$= 2 \cdot 2 \cdot 2 \cdot 5 \cdot 77$
$= 2 \cdot 2 \cdot 2 \cdot 5 \cdot 7 \cdot 11$

42. $\dfrac{r}{4} \geq -14$
$\dfrac{r}{4} \cdot 4 = -14 \cdot 4$
$r \geq -56$

43. $|a| - |b| \cdot |c| = |-16| - |2| \cdot |3|$
$= 16 - 2 \cdot 3$
$= 16 - 6$
$= 10$

44.

Sports Costs

Cost (dollars) — Bowling, Golf, Racquetball, Skiing, Tennis

Sport

45. $c - 15 = 120$
$c = 120 + 15$
$c = 135$

46. $c + \$1.50$

47. $12 \cdot 12 \cdot 12 = 1728$
There are 1728 items in a great gross.

48. a. Sample answer: mental math because of simple numbers

b. Explore—We know that the odometer reads 56,893 miles and that a car's oil should be changed every 3000 miles. We need to determine the next oil change.

Plan—Add 3000 to the current odometer reading to determine the mileage of the next oil change. Estimate: $56,893 + 3000 \rightarrow 57,000 + 3000$ or 60,000. The next oil change should be about 60,000 miles.

Solve—$56,893 + 3000 + 59,893$
The next oil change should be when the odometer reads 59,893.

Examine—The mileage is very close to the estimate, so the answer is reasonable.

Page 194 Self Test

1. 3   **2.** 2, 3, 6   **3.** 3

4. 9^5 **5.** 2^3 **6.** k^{28}

7. 1, 6, 11, 16, 21, 26, 31, 36, 41, 46, 51, 56, 61, 66, 71,
+5 +5

76, 81, 86, 91, 96, 101, 106, 111, 116, 121
The twenty-fifth building has 121 cubes.

8. $80 = 2 \cdot 40$
$= 2 \cdot 2 \cdot 20$
$= 2 \cdot 2 \cdot 2 \cdot 10$
$= 2 \cdot 2 \cdot 2 \cdot 2 \cdot 5$

9. $-26 = -1 \cdot 26$
$= -1 \cdot 2 \cdot 13$

10. $42xy^2 = 2 \cdot 21 \cdot x \cdot y^2$
$= 2 \cdot 3 \cdot 7 \cdot x \cdot y \cdot y$

11. $42 = 2 \cdot 3 \cdot 7$
$56 = 2 \cdot 2 \cdot 2 \cdot 7$
The GCF is $2 \cdot 7$ or 14.

12. $9 = 3 \cdot 3$
$15 = 3 \cdot 5$
$24 = 2 \cdot 2 \cdot 2 \cdot 3$
The GCF is 3.

13. $-18 = -1 \cdot 2 \cdot 3 \cdot 3$
$45xy = 3 \cdot 3 \cdot 5 \cdot x \cdot y$
The GCF is $3 \cdot 3$ or 9.

4-6A   Math Lab: Equivalent Fractions

Page 195

1. Shade 2 of 6 sections.   **2.** $\frac{5}{8}$

3. They are equal in size.

4. Yes; the shaded regions are equal in size.

5. Yes; sample answer: $\frac{1}{4}$

6.

$\frac{1}{2}$ $\frac{5}{10}$

yes, $\frac{1}{2} = \frac{5}{10}$

7.
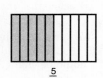

$\frac{1}{3}$ $\frac{3}{9}$

yes, $\frac{1}{3} = \frac{3}{9}$

8.

$\frac{1}{7}$

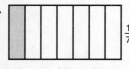

$\frac{2}{12}$

no, $\frac{1}{7} \neq \frac{2}{12}$

4-6   Simplifying Fractions

Pages 197–198   Checking Your Understanding

1. The GCF of the numerator and denominator is 1.

2. $\frac{12}{14} = \frac{\cancel{2} \cdot 2 \cdot 3}{\cancel{2} \cdot 7}$
$= \frac{6}{7}$

3. Sample answers: $\frac{1}{3}, \frac{3}{4}; \frac{2}{4}, \frac{8}{12}$

4. Sample answer: Simplified fractions are the most easily understood in everyday usage.

5.
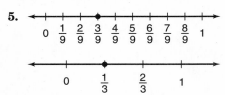

Yes, they are equivalent.

6. $\frac{6}{10}; \frac{3}{5}$ **7.** $\frac{1}{7}$

8. $\frac{20}{100}; \frac{1}{5}$ **9.** $\frac{11}{15}$

10. simplified

11. $\frac{15}{21} = \frac{\cancel{3} \cdot 5}{\cancel{3} \cdot 7}$
$= \frac{5}{7}$

12. $\frac{51}{60} = \frac{\cancel{3} \cdot 17}{2 \cdot 2 \cdot \cancel{3} \cdot 5}$
$= \frac{17}{20}$

13. $\frac{18}{44} = \frac{\cancel{2} \cdot 3 \cdot 3}{2 \cdot \cancel{2} \cdot 11}$
$= \frac{9}{22}$

14. $\frac{x}{x^3} = \frac{\cancel{x}}{\cancel{x} \cdot x \cdot x}$
$= \frac{1}{x^2}$

15. $\frac{11t}{121t^2} = \frac{\cancel{11} \cdot \cancel{t}}{\cancel{11} \cdot 11 \cdot \cancel{t} \cdot t}$
$= \frac{1}{11t}$

16. $\frac{8z^2}{16z} = \frac{\cancel{2} \cdot \cancel{2} \cdot \cancel{2} \cdot \cancel{z} \cdot z}{\cancel{2} \cdot \cancel{2} \cdot \cancel{2} \cdot 2 \cdot \cancel{z}}$
$= \frac{z}{2}$

17. simplified

18. a. $\frac{6}{100} = \frac{\cancel{2} \cdot 3}{\cancel{2} \cdot 2 \cdot 5 \cdot 5}$
$= \frac{3}{50}$

b. $\frac{14}{100} = \frac{\cancel{2} \cdot 7}{\cancel{2} \cdot 2 \cdot 5 \cdot 5}$
$= \frac{7}{50}$

Pages 198–199   Exercises

19. $\frac{2}{14} = \frac{1 \cdot \cancel{2}}{\cancel{2} \cdot 7}$
$= \frac{1}{7}$

20. simplified

21. $\frac{34}{38} = \frac{\cancel{2} \cdot 17}{\cancel{2} \cdot 19}$
$= \frac{17}{19}$

22. simplified

23. $\frac{17}{51} = \frac{1 \cdot \cancel{17}}{3 \cdot \cancel{17}}$
$= \frac{1}{3}$

24. $\frac{9}{15} = \frac{\cancel{3} \cdot 3}{\cancel{3} \cdot 5}$
$= \frac{3}{5}$

25. $\frac{25}{40} = \frac{\cancel{5} \cdot 5}{2 \cdot 2 \cdot 2 \cdot \cancel{5}}$
$= \frac{5}{8}$

26. $\frac{30}{51} = \frac{2 \cdot \cancel{3} \cdot 5}{\cancel{3} \cdot 17}$
$= \frac{10}{17}$

27. simplified

28. $\frac{16}{64} = \frac{\overset{1}{\cancel{2}} \cdot \overset{1}{\cancel{2}} \cdot \overset{1}{\cancel{2}} \cdot \overset{1}{\cancel{2}}}{\underset{1}{\cancel{2}} \cdot \underset{1}{\cancel{2}} \cdot \underset{1}{\cancel{2}} \cdot \underset{1}{\cancel{2}} \cdot 2 \cdot 2}$

$= \frac{1}{4}$

29. simplified

30. simplified

31. $\frac{124}{222} = \frac{\overset{1}{\cancel{2}} \cdot 2 \cdot 31}{\underset{1}{\cancel{2}} \cdot 111}$

$= \frac{62}{111}$

32. $\frac{12m}{15m} = \frac{2 \cdot 2 \cdot \overset{1}{\cancel{3}} \cdot m}{\underset{1}{\cancel{3}} \cdot 5 \cdot m}$

$= \frac{4}{5}$

33. $\frac{12x}{15y} = \frac{2 \cdot 2 \cdot \overset{1}{\cancel{3}} \cdot x}{\underset{1}{\cancel{3}} \cdot 5 \cdot y}$

$= \frac{4x}{5y}$

34. $\frac{40a}{42a} = \frac{\overset{1}{\cancel{2}} \cdot 2 \cdot 2 \cdot 5 \cdot \overset{1}{\cancel{a}}}{\underset{1}{\cancel{2}} \cdot 3 \cdot 7 \cdot \underset{1}{\cancel{a}}}$

$= \frac{20}{21}$

35. $\frac{82t}{14t} = \frac{\overset{1}{\cancel{2}} \cdot 41 \cdot t}{\underset{1}{\cancel{2}} \cdot 7 \cdot t}$

$= \frac{41}{7}$

36. simplified

36. simplified

37. $\frac{xyz^3}{x^2y} = \frac{\overset{1}{\cancel{x}} \cdot y \cdot z \cdot z \cdot \overset{1}{\cancel{z}}}{\underset{1}{\cancel{x}} \cdot x \cdot \underset{1}{\cancel{y}}}$

$= \frac{z^3}{x}$

38. $\frac{30x^2}{51xy} = \frac{2 \cdot \overset{1}{\cancel{3}} \cdot 5 \cdot \overset{1}{\cancel{x}} \cdot x}{\underset{1}{\cancel{3}} \cdot 17 \cdot \underset{1}{\cancel{x}} \cdot y}$

$= \frac{10x}{17y}$

39. $\frac{40p^2q}{52pq} = \frac{\overset{1}{\cancel{2}} \cdot \overset{1}{\cancel{2}} \cdot 2 \cdot 5 \cdot \overset{1}{\cancel{p}} \cdot p \cdot \overset{1}{\cancel{q}}}{\underset{1}{\cancel{2}} \cdot \underset{1}{\cancel{2}} \cdot 13 \cdot \underset{1}{\cancel{p}} \cdot \underset{1}{\cancel{q}} \cdot q}$

$= \frac{10p}{13q}$

40. $\frac{17k^2z}{51z} = \frac{1 \cdot \overset{1}{\cancel{17}} \cdot k \cdot k \cdot \overset{1}{\cancel{z}}}{3 \cdot \underset{1}{\cancel{17}} \cdot \underset{1}{\cancel{z}}}$

$= \frac{k^2}{3}$

41. simplified

42. $\frac{52rst}{26rst} = \frac{2 \cdot \overset{1}{\cancel{2}} \cdot \overset{1}{\cancel{13}} \cdot \overset{1}{\cancel{r}} \cdot \overset{1}{\cancel{s}} \cdot \overset{1}{\cancel{t}}}{\underset{1}{\cancel{2}} \cdot \underset{1}{\cancel{13}} \cdot \underset{1}{\cancel{r}} \cdot \underset{1}{\cancel{s}} \cdot \underset{1}{\cancel{t}}}$

$= 2$

43. simplified

44. $(1 \times 10^2) + (2 \times 10^4) + (3 \times 10^1) + (4 \times 10^3) =$
24,130

So, $\frac{a+b+c+d}{16} = \frac{2+4+1+3}{16}$

$= \frac{10}{16}$

$= \frac{\overset{1}{\cancel{2}} \cdot 5}{\underset{1}{\cancel{2}} \cdot 2 \cdot 2 \cdot 2}$

$= \frac{5}{8}$

45. $\frac{22}{60 \cdot 24} = \frac{22}{1440}$

$= \frac{\overset{1}{\cancel{2}} \cdot 11}{\underset{1}{\cancel{2}} \cdot 2 \cdot 2 \cdot 2 \cdot 2 \cdot 3 \cdot 3 \cdot 5}$

$= \frac{11}{720}$

46. a. 30,000:2,500,000

b. $\frac{30,000}{2,500,000} = \frac{\overset{1}{\cancel{2}} \cdot \overset{1}{\cancel{2}} \cdot \overset{1}{\cancel{2}} \cdot \overset{1}{\cancel{2}} \cdot 2 \cdot 3 \cdot \overset{1}{\cancel{5}} \cdot \overset{1}{\cancel{5}} \cdot \overset{1}{\cancel{5}} \cdot \overset{1}{\cancel{5}}}{\underset{1}{\cancel{2}} \cdot \underset{1}{\cancel{2}} \cdot \underset{1}{\cancel{2}} \cdot \underset{1}{\cancel{2}} \cdot 2 \cdot \underset{1}{\cancel{5}} \cdot \underset{1}{\cancel{5}} \cdot \underset{1}{\cancel{5}} \cdot \underset{1}{\cancel{5}} \cdot 5 \cdot 5 \cdot 5}$

$= \frac{3}{250}$

c. For every 250 Americans over age 85, 3 are over the age of 100.

47. a. 2:6

b. $\frac{2}{6} = \frac{1 \cdot 2}{2 \cdot 3}$

$= \frac{1}{3}$

c. Sample answer: 1 oz. alcohol, 3 oz. water

48. $42x^2y = \boxed{2} \cdot 3 \cdot 7 \cdot \cancel{x} \cdot x \cdot \cancel{y}$
$38xy^2 = \boxed{2} \cdot 19 \cdot \cancel{x} \cdot y \cdot \cancel{y}$
The GCF is $2 \cdot x \cdot y$ or $2xy$.

49. $V = \ell \cdot w \cdot h$
$V = 6 \cdot 3 \cdot 6$
$V = 108$

50. $180 = 15r$
$\frac{180}{15} = \frac{15r}{15}$
$12 = r$

51. $(-4)(-17d) = (-4)(-17)d$
$= 68d$

52. Ohio is $1996 - 1803$ or 193 years old.
Hawaii is $1996 - 1959$ or 37 years old.
$193 > 37$

53. $\frac{144}{x} = 12$ What number
$\frac{144}{12} = 12$ times 12 is 144?
$x = 12$

54. $324 \div (2 \times 3 + 6) = 324 \div (6 + 6)$
$= 324 \div 12$
$= 27$

4-7

Using the Least Common Multiple (LCM)

Pages 202–203 Checking Your Understanding

1. If the definition did not say nonzero, zero would always be the LCM of any set of numbers.

2. See students' work.

3. The LCM involves the common multiples of a set of numbers, the LCD is the LCM of the denominators of two fractions.

4.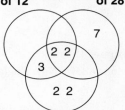

Prime Factors of 12   Prime Factors of 28

Prime Factors of 48

The LCM of 12, 28 and 48 is $2 \cdot 2 \cdot 2 \cdot 2 \cdot 3 \cdot 7$ or 336.

5. $10 = \boxed{2} \cdot 5$
$14 = \boxed{2} \cdot 7$
The LCM is $2 \cdot 5 \cdot 7$ or 70.

6. $7 = \boxed{1} \cdot 7$
$9 = \boxed{1} \cdot 9$
The LCM is $1 \cdot 7 \cdot 9$ or 63.

7. $20a = \boxed{2} \cdot \boxed{2} \cdot 5 \cdot \boxed{a}$
$12a = \boxed{2} \cdot \boxed{2} \cdot 3 \cdot \boxed{a}$
The LCM is $2 \cdot 2 \cdot 3 \cdot 5 \cdot a$ or $60a$.

8. $12 = \boxed{2} \cdot \boxed{2} \cdot \boxed{3}$
$16 = \boxed{2} \cdot \boxed{2} \cdot \boxed{2} \cdot 2$
$24 = \boxed{2} \cdot \boxed{2} \cdot \boxed{2} \cdot \boxed{3}$
The LCM is $2 \cdot 2 \cdot 2 \cdot 2 \cdot 3$ or 48.

9. $45 = 3 \cdot 3 \cdot 5$
$30 = 2 \cdot 3 \cdot 5$
$35 = 5 \cdot 7$
The LCM is $2 \cdot 3 \cdot 3 \cdot 5 \cdot 7$ or 630.

10. $a = 1 \cdot a$
$b = 1 \cdot b$
The LCM is $1 \cdot a \cdot b$ or ab.

11. $5 = 1 \cdot 5$
$2 = 1 \cdot 2$
The LCD is $1 \cdot 2 \cdot 5$ or 10.

12. $4 = 2 \cdot 2$
$8 = 2 \cdot 2 \cdot 2$
The LCD is $2 \cdot 2 \cdot 2$ or 8.

13. $25 = 5 \cdot 5$
$20 = 2 \cdot 2 \cdot 5$
The LCD is $2 \cdot 2 \cdot 5 \cdot 5$ or 100.

14. $\frac{5}{12} < \frac{1}{2}$ **15.** $\frac{5}{7} < \frac{7}{9}$ **16.** $\frac{14}{15} > \frac{9}{10}$

17. a. Pacific $= \frac{3}{20} = \frac{3 \cdot 5}{20 \cdot 5}$ or $\frac{15}{100}$

East Central $= \frac{17}{100}$

$\frac{17}{100} > \frac{15}{100}$

East Central consumed more.

b. Pacific $= \frac{3}{20} = \frac{3 \cdot 5}{20 \cdot 5}$ or $\frac{15}{100}$

Southwest $= \frac{11}{100}$

Southeast $= \frac{9}{50} = \frac{9 \cdot 2}{50 \cdot 2}$ or $\frac{18}{100}$

Mid Atlantic $= \frac{7}{50} = \frac{7 \cdot 2}{50 \cdot 2}$ or $\frac{14}{100}$

New England $= \frac{3}{50} = \frac{3 \cdot 2}{50 \cdot 2}$ or $\frac{6}{100}$

East Central $= \frac{17}{100}$

West Central $= \frac{19}{100}$

West Central consumed the most.

c. Refer to the fractions above. New England ate the fewest.

Pages 203–204 Exercises

18. $20 = 2 \cdot 2 \cdot 5$
$12 = 2 \cdot 2 \cdot 3$
The LCM is $2 \cdot 2 \cdot 3 \cdot 5$ or 60.

19. $2 = 1 \cdot 2$
$9 = 3 \cdot 3$
The LCM $1 \cdot 2 \cdot 3 \cdot 3$ or 18.

20. $15 = 3 \cdot 5$
$75 = 3 \cdot 5 \cdot 5$
The LCM is $3 \cdot 5 \cdot 5$ or 75.

21. $18 = 2 \cdot 3 \cdot 3$
$32 = 2 \cdot 2 \cdot 2 \cdot 2 \cdot 2$
The LCM is $2 \cdot 2 \cdot 2 \cdot 2 \cdot 2 \cdot 3 \cdot 3$ or 288.

22. $24 = 2 \cdot 2 \cdot 2 \cdot 3$
$32 = 2 \cdot 2 \cdot 2 \cdot 2 \cdot 2$
The LCM is $2 \cdot 2 \cdot 2 \cdot 2 \cdot 2 \cdot 3$ or 96.

23. $21 = 3 \cdot 7$
$28 = 2 \cdot 2 \cdot 7$
The LCM is $2 \cdot 2 \cdot 3 \cdot 7$ or 84.

24. $6c = 2 \cdot 3 \cdot c$
$8cd = 2 \cdot 2 \cdot 2 \cdot c \cdot d$
The LCM is $2 \cdot 2 \cdot 2 \cdot 3 \cdot c \cdot d$ or $24cd$.

25. $7y = 1 \cdot 7 \cdot y$
$12y = 2 \cdot 2 \cdot 3 \cdot y$
The LCM is $1 \cdot 2 \cdot 2 \cdot 3 \cdot 7 \cdot y$ or $84y$.

26. $20cd = 2 \cdot 2 \cdot 5 \cdot c \cdot d$
$50d = 2 \cdot 5 \cdot 5 \cdot d$
The LCM is $2 \cdot 2 \cdot 5 \cdot 5 \cdot c \cdot d$ or $100cd$.

27. $10 = 2 \cdot 5$
$20 = 2 \cdot 2 \cdot 5$
$40 = 2 \cdot 2 \cdot 2 \cdot 5$
The LCM is $2 \cdot 2 \cdot 2 \cdot 5$ or 40.

28. $7 = 1 \cdot 7$
$21 = 3 \cdot 7$
$84 = 2 \cdot 2 \cdot 3 \cdot 7$
The LCM is $1 \cdot 2 \cdot 2 \cdot 3 \cdot 7$ or 84.

29. $9 = 3 \cdot 3$
$12 = 2 \cdot 2 \cdot 3$
$15 = 3 \cdot 5$
The LCM is $2 \cdot 2 \cdot 3 \cdot 3 \cdot 5$ or 180.

30. $3b = 1 \cdot 3 \cdot b$
$5c = 1 \cdot 5 \cdot c$
$2 = 1 \cdot 2$
The LCM is $1 \cdot 2 \cdot 3 \cdot 5 \cdot b \cdot c$ or $30bc$.

31. $3t = 1 \cdot 3 \cdot t$
$5t^2 = 1 \cdot 5 \cdot t \cdot t$
$7 = 1 \cdot 7$
The LCM is $1 \cdot 3 \cdot 5 \cdot 7 \cdot t \cdot t$ or $105t^2$.

32. $3a^2 = 1 \cdot 3 \cdot a \cdot a$
$6a^3 = 2 \cdot 3 \cdot a \cdot a \cdot a$
$9a^4 = 3 \cdot 3 \cdot a \cdot a \cdot a \cdot a$
The LCM is $1 \cdot 2 \cdot 3 \cdot 3 \cdot a \cdot a \cdot a \cdot a$ or $18a^4$.

33. $4 = 2 \cdot 2$
$16 = 2 \cdot 2 \cdot 2 \cdot 2$
The LCD is $2 \cdot 2 \cdot 2 \cdot 2$ or 16.

34. $6 = 2 \cdot 3$
$8 = 2 \cdot 2 \cdot 2$
The LCD is $2 \cdot 2 \cdot 2 \cdot 3$ or 24.

35. $5 = 1 \cdot 5$
$7 = 1 \cdot 7$
The LCD is $1 \cdot 5 \cdot 7$ or 35.

36. $9 = 3 \cdot 3$
$12 = 2 \cdot 2 \cdot 3$
The LCD is $2 \cdot 2 \cdot 3 \cdot 3$ or 36.

37. $11 = 1 \cdot 11$
$20 = 2 \cdot 2 \cdot 5$
The LCD is $1 \cdot 2 \cdot 2 \cdot 5 \cdot 11$ or 220.

38. $2 = 1 \cdot 2$
$3 = 1 \cdot 3$
$5 = 1 \cdot 5$
The LCD is $1 \cdot 2 \cdot 3 \cdot 5$ or 30.

39. $5b = 1 \cdot 5 \cdot b$
$25b = 5 \cdot 5 \cdot b$
The LCD is $1 \cdot 5 \cdot 5 \cdot b$ or $25b$.

40. $8a = 2 \cdot 2 \cdot 2 \cdot a$
$15a = 3 \cdot 5 \cdot a$
The LCD is $2 \cdot 2 \cdot 2 \cdot 3 \cdot 5 \cdot a$ or $120a$.

41. $\frac{5}{6} > \frac{9}{11}$ **42.** $\frac{3}{5} > \frac{4}{7}$ **43.** $\frac{35}{51} < \frac{12}{17}$

44. $\frac{10}{12} > \frac{9}{11}$ **45.** $\frac{15}{32} < \frac{1}{2}$ **46.** $\frac{21}{100} > \frac{1}{5}$

47. $\frac{8}{9} < \frac{19}{21}$ **48.** $\frac{7}{9} < \frac{8}{10}$ **49.** $\frac{3}{8} < \frac{5}{12}$

50. $30 = 2 \cdot 3 \cdot 5$
$100 = 2 \cdot 2 \cdot 5 \cdot 5$
The LCM is $2 \cdot 2 \cdot 3 \cdot 5 \cdot 5$.
$30 = 2 \cdot 3 \cdot 5$
$100 = 2 \cdot 2 \cdot 5 \cdot 5$
The GCF is $2 \cdot 5$.
So, the other number is $2^2 \cdot 5^2$ or 100.

51. dog; $\frac{7815}{12} > \frac{4723}{15}$

52. $4 = \boxed{2} \cdot 2$
$6 = \boxed{2} \cdot 3$
The LCM is $2 \cdot 2 \cdot 3$ or 12.
The next presidential year in which she will run is $1992 + 12$ or 2004.

53. a. Cable TV $= \frac{2}{3} = \frac{2 \cdot 100}{3 \cdot 100}$ or $\frac{200}{300}$
Video game player $= \frac{77}{100} = \frac{77 \cdot 3}{100 \cdot 3}$ or $\frac{231}{300}$
More teens said they had a video game player.

b. Cable TV $= \frac{2}{3} = \frac{2 \cdot 100}{3 \cdot 100}$ or $\frac{200}{300}$
Cellular phone $= \frac{7}{20} = \frac{7 \cdot 15}{20 \cdot 15}$ or $\frac{105}{300}$
Computer $= \frac{23}{50} = \frac{23 \cdot 6}{50 \cdot 6}$ or $\frac{138}{300}$
On-line services $= \frac{17}{100} = \frac{17 \cdot 3}{100 \cdot 3}$ or $\frac{51}{300}$.
Video game player $= \frac{77}{100} = \frac{77 \cdot 3}{100 \cdot 3}$ or $\frac{231}{300}$
VCR $= \frac{24}{25} = \frac{24 \cdot 12}{25 \cdot 12}$ or $\frac{288}{300}$
The technology used by most teens is a VCR.

c. Refer to the fractions above.
The technology used least is on-line services.

54. $\frac{30}{36} = \frac{\overset{1}{\cancel{2}} \cdot \overset{1}{\cancel{3}} \cdot 5}{2 \cdot 2 \cdot \underset{1}{\cancel{3}} \cdot 3}$
$= \frac{5}{6}$

55. $\frac{x}{8} > 72$
$\frac{x}{8} \cdot 8 > 72 \cdot 8$
$x > 576$

56. $-13 < x - (-5)$
$-13 < x + 5$
$-13 - 5 < x + 5 - 5$
$-18 < x$

57. $14 = \frac{a}{-7}$
$14 \cdot (-7) = \frac{a}{-7} \cdot (-7)$
$-98 = a$

58. $a \cdot b = (-3)(14)$
$= -42$

59. Utah

60. $801,163 - 41,951 = 759,212$ acres

61.

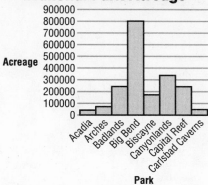

National Park Acreage

62. $5g = 65$
$5 \cdot 13 = 65$
$g = 13$
What number times 5 is 65?

4-8 **Multiplying and Dividing Monomials**

Page 207 Checking Your Understanding

1. Since the numbers have the same base, add the exponents: $6^{6+3} = 6^9$.

2. $2^2 = 4$ and $2^5 = 32$.
$4 \cdot 32 = 128$, which is 2^7.

3. Sample answer: $4^7 \div 4^3$

4. See students' work.

5. $10^4 \cdot 10^3 = 10^{4+3}$
$= 10^7$

6. $\frac{2^5}{2^2} = 2^{5-2}$
$= 2^3$

7. $3^6 \cdot 3^4 = 3^{6+4}$
$= 3^{10}$

8. $\frac{8^4}{8^3} = 8^{4-3}$
$= 8^1$
$= 8$

9. $8^2 \cdot 8^3 \cdot 8 = 8^2 \cdot 8^3 \cdot 8^1$
$= 8^{2+3+1}$
$= 8^6$

10. $m \cdot m^6 = m^1 \cdot m^6$
$= m^{1+6}$
$= m^7$

11. $\frac{y^{11}}{y^9} = y^{11-9}$
$= y^2$

12. $\frac{ab^4}{b^2} = a \cdot (b^{4-2})$
$= ab^2$

13. On the Richter scale, each increase of one means a ten-times increase in intensity. Since $8.2 - 6.8 \rightarrow 8.0 - 7.0$ or 1.0, the earthquake in Bolivia was about 10 times more intense.

Pages 208–209 Exercises

14. $10^5 \cdot 10^5 = 10^{5+5}$
$= 10^{10}$

15. $w \cdot w^5 = w^1 \cdot w^5$
$= w^{1+5}$
$= w^6$

16. $3^3 \cdot 3^2 = 3^{3+2}$
$= 3^5$

17. $b^5 \cdot b^2 = b^{5+2}$
$= b^7$

17. $b^5 \cdot b^2 = b^{5+2}$
$= b^7$

18. $\frac{5^5}{5^2} = 5^{5-2}$
$= 5^3$

19. $\frac{10^{10}}{10^3} = 10^{10-3}$
$= 10^7$

20. $\frac{z^3}{z} = \frac{z^3}{z^1}$
$= z^{3-1}$
$= z^2$

21. $\frac{a^{10}}{a^6} = a^{10-6}$
$= a^4$

22. $\frac{(-2)^6}{(-2)^5} = (-2)^{6-5}$
$= (-2)^1$
$= -2$

23. $(5x^3)(4x^4) = (5 \cdot 4)(x^3 \cdot x^4)$
$= (20)(x^{3+4})$
$= 20x^7$

24. $\frac{(-x)^4}{(-x)^3} = (-x)^{4-3}$
$= (-x)^1$
$= -x$

25. $\frac{f^{20}}{f^8} = f^{20-8}$
$= f^{12}$

26. $(3x^4)(-5x^2) = (3)(-5)(x^4 \cdot x^2)$
$= -15(x^{4+2})$
$= -15x^6$

27. $3a^2 \cdot 4a^3 = (3 \cdot 4)(a^2 \cdot a^3)$
$= 12(a^{2+3})$
$= 12a^5$

28. $(-10x^3)(2x^2) = (-10 \cdot 2)(x^3 \cdot x^2)$
$= -20(x^{3+2})$
$= -20x^5$

29. $a^2b \cdot ab^3 = a^2b^1 \cdot a^1b^3$
$= (a^2 \cdot a^1)(b^1 \cdot b^3)$
$= (a^{2+1}) + (b^{1+3})$
$= a^3b^4$

30. $x^4(x^3y^2) = (x^4 \cdot x^3)y^2$
$= (x^{4+3})y^2$
$= x^7y^2$

31. $t^3t^2 \div t^4 = \frac{t^5}{t^4}$
$= t^{5-4}$
$= t^1$
$= t$

32. $\frac{y^{100}}{y^{100}} = y^{100-100}$
$= y^0$
$= 1$

33. $k^3m^2 \div km = \frac{k^3m^2}{k^1m^1}$
$= (k^{3-1})(m^{2-1})$
$= k^2m^1$
$= k^2m$

34. $(-3y^3z)(7y^4) = (-3 \cdot 7)(y^3 \cdot y^4)z^1$
$= -21(y^{3+4})z^1$
$= -21y^7z^1$
$= -21y^7z$

35. $w^5xy^2 \div wx = \frac{w^5x^1y^2}{w^1x^1}$
$= (w^{5-1})(x^{1-1})y^2$
$= w^4x^0y^2$
$= w^4y^2$

36. $7ab(a^{16}c) = 7a^1b^1(a^{16}c^1)$
$= 7(a^1 \cdot a^{16})b^1c^1$
$= 7(a^{1+16})b^1c^1$
$= 7a^{17}b^1c^1$
$= 7a^{17}bc$

37. $15n^9q^2 \div 5nq^2 = \frac{15n^9q^2}{5n^1q^2}$
$= 3(n^{9-1})(q^{2-2})$
$= 3n^8q^0$
$= 3n^8$

38. $(5^8)(5^3) = 5^{11}$

39. $x(x^2)(x^6) = x^9$

40. $\frac{t^{15}}{t} = t^{14}$

41. $3^5 \cdot 3^3 = 3^8$

42. $\frac{12^5}{12^5} = 1$

43. $\frac{2^5}{4^2} = 2^1$

44. If $10^n \div 10^m = 1$, then $10^n = 10^m$. Thus, $n = m$.

45. a. $10 \cdot 10$ or 100 times   **b.** base

46. a. now: 100
15 minutes: 200
30 minutes: 400

b. Extend this pattern. After 1 hour, there were 1600. After 3 hours, there were 409,600. So, there are 256 times as many after 3 hours than there were after 1 hour.

47. $\frac{5}{8} < \frac{8}{11}$

48. $16ab^3 = 2 \quad \cdot \quad 8 \quad \cdot \quad a \quad \cdot \quad b^3$
$= 2 \cdot 2 \quad \cdot \quad 4 \quad \cdot \quad a \cdot b \cdot b \cdot b$
$= 2 \cdot 2 \cdot 2 \cdot 2 \cdot a \cdot b \cdot b \cdot b$

49. 2

50. Area (matting)
Area (frame) $-$ Area (picture)
Area (picture) $= 9 \cdot 11$
$= 99$ sq in.
Area (frame) $= 10 \cdot 12$
$= 120$ sq in.
Area (matting) $= 120 - 99$
$= 21$ sq in.

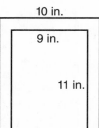

51. $\quad 5 + n = -2$
$5 + n - 5 = -2 - 5$
$\quad\quad\quad n = -7$
Check:
$\quad 5 + n = -2$
$5 + (-7) = -2$
$\quad\quad -7 = -2$ ✔

52. $s = 40 - (-17)$
$s = 40 + 17$
$s = 57$

53. Quadrant II

54. open

55. $2x - 4$

4-9   **Negative Exponents**

Page 210   Your Turn

a. The exponents decrease by 1.

b. Each value is half of the previous.

c. 2^{-1}

d. $\frac{1}{2}$

e. See students' work.

Page 212   Checking Your Understanding

1. $\frac{1}{x^3}$

2. Sample answer: Look for a pattern.
$2^4 = 16$
$2^3 = 8$ $\div 2$
$2^2 = 4$ $\div 2$
$2^1 = 2$ $\div 2$
$2^0 = 1$ $\div 2$

Each successive power is half of the previous power. Therefore, $2^0 = 2^1 \div 2$ or 1.

3. See students' work.

4. $\frac{1}{3^3}$

5. $\frac{1}{15^5}$

6. $\frac{1}{a^{12}}$

7. 10^{-7}

8. 4^{-3}

9. $\frac{1}{9} = \frac{1}{3^2}$
$= 3^{-2}$

10. $2^x = 2^{-2}$
$= \frac{1}{2^2}$
$= \frac{1}{4}$

11. $3n^{-2} = 3(4)^{-2}$
$= 3\left(\frac{1}{4^2}\right)$
$= 3\left(\frac{1}{16}\right)$
$= \frac{3}{16}$

12. a. $\frac{1}{10^7}$ meters

b. $\frac{1}{10^7} = \frac{1}{10,000,000}$
$= 0.0000001$ meters

Pages 212–214   Exercises

13. $\frac{1}{4}$

14. $\frac{1}{5^2}$

15. $\frac{1}{(-2)^5}$

16. $\frac{1}{x}$

17. $\frac{1}{s^2t}$

18. $\frac{m}{n^2}$

19. $\frac{2}{(xy)^2}$

20. 2^2

21. 5^{-3}

22. a^{-1}

23. $\frac{1}{16} = 16^{-1}$
    or
$\frac{1}{16} = \frac{1}{2^4}$
$= 2^{-4}$

24. x^{-6}

25. $2 \cdot 3^{-2}$

26. ab^{-6}

27. fg^{-3}

28. $3mn^{-2}$

29. $3^n = 3^{-3}$
$= \frac{1}{3^3}$
$= \frac{1}{27}$

30. $4x^{-3}y^{-2} = 4(2)^{-3}(6)^2$
$= \frac{4(6)^2}{2^3}$
$= \frac{4(36)}{8}$
$= \frac{144}{8}$
$= 18$

31. $6t^{-2} = 6(3)^{-2}$
$= \frac{6}{(3)^2}$
$= \frac{6}{9}$
$= \frac{2}{3}$

32. $(2b)^{-3} = (2 \cdot -2)^{-3}$
$= (-4)^{-3}$
$= \frac{1}{(-4)^3}$
$= \frac{-1}{64}$

33. $(a^6)(a^{-3}) = a^{6+(-3)}$
$= a^3$

34. $(b^{-10})(b^5) = b^{-10+5}$
$= b^{-5}$
$= \frac{1}{b^5}$

35. $\frac{c^5}{c^{-2}} = c^{5-(-2)}$
$= c^{5+2}$
$= c^7$

36. $\frac{d^2}{d^3} = d^{2-3}$
$= d^{-1}$
$= \frac{1}{d}$

37. $\frac{a^b}{a^{a-b}} = a^{b-(a-b)}$
$= a^{b-a+b}$
$= a^{2b-a}$

38. a. $10^{-6} = \frac{1}{10^6}$

b. $10^{-6} = \frac{1}{10^6} = 0.000001$
$10^{-3} = \frac{1}{10^3} = 0.001$
0.000001 to 0.001 m

39. a. $\frac{6.67}{10^{11}}$ Nm²/kg²

b. $\frac{6.67}{10^{11}} = 0.0000000000667$ Nm²/kg²

40. $\frac{1 \text{ kg} \cdot \text{m}^2}{\text{s}^2}$

41. $(10x)(-5x^3) = (10 \cdot -5)(x^1 \cdot x^3)$
$= -50(x^{1+3})$
$= -50x^4$

42. $\frac{8}{14} = \frac{2-2-2}{2-7}$
$= \frac{4}{7}$

43. 7^5

44. $V = \frac{4}{3}\pi r^3$
$V = \frac{4}{3}(3.14)(5)^3$
$V = \frac{4}{3}(3.14)(125)$
$V = \frac{4}{3}(392.5)$
$V = 523.3$

45. $2230 + x = 4750$
$2230 + x - 2230 = 4750 - 2230$
$x = \$2520$

46. $3c - ac = 3(2) - (-4)(2)$
$= 6 - (-8)$
$= 6 + 8$
$= 14$

47. $n - 8 = 3$
$n - 8 + 8 = 3 + 8$
$n = 11$

48. a. Sample answer: calculator because of several calculations

b. Explore—We know that a person adds 21 minutes to his or her life by walking one mile. We need to find how much time a person would add to his or her life if he or she walked 2 miles each day for a year.

Plan—Multiply 21 minutes, 2 miles, and the number of days in a year to find how many minutes would be added to a person's life. Estimate: $21 \times 2 \times 365 \rightarrow 20 \times 2 \times 400$ or 16,000. About 16,000 minutes would be added.

Solve—Use a calculator.
$21 \times 2 \times 365 = 15,330$
15,330 minutes or 10 days, 15.5 hours would be added to a person's life.

Examine—The answer is very close to the estimate, so the answer is reasonable.

Page 214   Earth Watch

- $\frac{174}{10^7} = 0.0000174$
- See students' work.
- See students' work.
- See students' work.

Chapter 4   Study Guide and Assessment

Page 215   Understanding and Using Vocabulary

1. greatest common factor

2. powers   **3.** factors

4. prime number   **5.** multiple

6. Expanded form

7. least common denominator

8. monomial   **9.** ratio

Pages 216–218   Skills and Concepts

10. none   **11.** 5   **12.** 2, 3, 5, 6, 10

13. 3   **14.** 2, 5, 10   **15.** 2, 3, 6

16. 3   **17.** 2, 3, 6   **18.** 6^5

19. $(c + 2)^3$ **20.** $(-4)^4$ **21.** 1^3

22. $(-16)(-16)(-16)$

23. $k \cdot k \cdot k \cdot k \cdot k \cdot k \cdot k \cdot k \cdot k$

24. $(-w)(-w)(-w)(-w)$

25. $32 \cdot 32 \cdot 32 \cdot 32 \cdot 32 \cdot 32 \cdot 32 \cdot 32 \cdot 32 \cdot 32 \cdot 32$

26. $120 = 2 \cdot 60$
$= 2 \cdot 2 \cdot 30$
$= 2 \cdot 2 \cdot 2 \cdot 15$
$= 2 \cdot 2 \cdot 2 \cdot 3 \cdot 5$

27. $-114 = -1 \cdot 114$
$= -1 \cdot 2 \cdot 57$
$= -1 \cdot 2 \cdot 3 \cdot 19$

28. $630x^3 = 2 \cdot 315 \cdot x^3$
$= 2 \cdot 3 \cdot 105 \cdot x \cdot x \cdot x$
$= 2 \cdot 3 \cdot 3 \cdot 35 \cdot x \cdot x \cdot x$
$= 2 \cdot 3 \cdot 3 \cdot 5 \cdot 7 \cdot x \cdot x \cdot x$

29. $825x^2y = -1 \cdot 825 \cdot x^2 \cdot y$
$= -1 \cdot 3 \cdot 275 \cdot x \cdot x \cdot y$
$= -1 \cdot 3 \cdot 5 \cdot 55 \cdot x \cdot x \cdot y$
$= -1 \cdot 3 \cdot 5 \cdot 5 \cdot 11 \cdot x \cdot x \cdot y$

30. $2805 = 3 \cdot 935$
$= 3 \cdot 5 \cdot 187$
$= 3 \cdot 5 \cdot 11 \cdot 17$

31. $-1827jk^3 = -1 \cdot 1827 \cdot j \cdot k^3$
$= -1 \cdot 3 \cdot 609 \cdot j \cdot k \cdot k \cdot k$
$= -1 \cdot 3 \cdot 3 \cdot 203 \cdot j \cdot k \cdot k \cdot k$
$= -1 \cdot 3 \cdot 3 \cdot 7 \cdot 29 \cdot j \cdot k \cdot k \cdot k$

32. $66g^5h^2 = 2 \cdot 33 \cdot g^5 \cdot h^2$
$= 2 \cdot 3 \cdot 11 \cdot g \cdot g \cdot g \cdot g \cdot g \cdot h \cdot h$

33. $550mnq^2 = 2 \cdot 275 \cdot m \cdot n \cdot q^2$
$= 2 \cdot 5 \cdot 55 \cdot m \cdot n \cdot q \cdot q$
$= 2 \cdot 5 \cdot 5 \cdot 11 \cdot m \cdot n \cdot q \cdot q$

34. $70 = 2 \cdot 5 \cdot 7$
$66 = 2 \cdot 3 \cdot 11$
The GCF is 2.

35. $1092 = 2 \cdot 2 \cdot 3 \cdot 7 \cdot 13$
$325 = 5 \cdot 5 \cdot 13$
The GCF is 13.

36. $100x = 2 \cdot 2 \cdot 5 \cdot 5 \cdot x$
$84xy = 2 \cdot 2 \cdot 3 \cdot 7 \cdot x \cdot y$
$-76x^2 = -1 \cdot 2 \cdot 2 \cdot 19 \cdot x \cdot x$
The GCF is $2 \cdot 2 \cdot x$ or $4x$.

37. $210a^3b^2 = 2 \cdot 3 \cdot 5 \cdot 7 \cdot a \cdot a \cdot a \cdot b \cdot b$
$875a^2b^3 = 5 \cdot 5 \cdot 5 \cdot 7 \cdot a \cdot a \cdot b \cdot b \cdot b$
The GCF is $5 \cdot 7 \cdot a \cdot a \cdot b \cdot b$ or $35a^2b^2$.

38. $112j^5k = 2 \cdot 2 \cdot 2 \cdot 2 \cdot 7 \cdot j \cdot j \cdot j \cdot j \cdot j \cdot k$
$-144j^2 = -1 \cdot 2 \cdot 2 \cdot 2 \cdot 2 \cdot 9 \cdot j \cdot j$
The GCF is $2 \cdot 2 \cdot 2 \cdot 2 \cdot j \cdot j$ or $16j^2$.

39. $40x = 2 \cdot 2 \cdot 2 \cdot 5 \cdot x$
$25y = 5 \cdot 5 \cdot y$
The GCF is 5.

40. $115wx = 5 \cdot 23 \cdot w \cdot x$
$224wz = 2 \cdot 2 \cdot 2 \cdot 2 \cdot 2 \cdot 7 \cdot w \cdot z$
The GCF is w.

41. $441ac = 3 \cdot 3 \cdot 7 \cdot 7 \cdot a \cdot c$
$223bd = 223 \cdot b \cdot d$
The GCF is 1

42. $\frac{72}{88} = \frac{\overset{1}{\cancel{2}} \cdot \overset{1}{\cancel{2}} \cdot \overset{1}{\cancel{2}} \cdot 3 \cdot 3}{\underset{1}{\cancel{2}} \cdot \underset{1}{\cancel{2}} \cdot \underset{1}{\cancel{2}} \cdot 11}$
$= \frac{9}{11}$

43. $\frac{133}{140} = \frac{\overset{1}{\cancel{7}} \cdot 19}{2 \cdot 2 \cdot 5 \cdot \underset{1}{\cancel{7}}}$
$= \frac{19}{20}$

44. $\frac{225}{315} = \frac{\overset{1}{\cancel{3}} \cdot \overset{1}{\cancel{3}} \cdot \overset{1}{\cancel{5}} \cdot 5}{\underset{1}{\cancel{3}} \cdot \underset{1}{\cancel{3}} \cdot \underset{1}{\cancel{5}} \cdot 7}$
$= \frac{5}{7}$

45. $\frac{48}{66} = \frac{\overset{1}{\cancel{2}} \cdot \overset{1}{\cancel{2}} \cdot \overset{1}{\cancel{2}} \cdot 2 \cdot 3}{\underset{1}{\cancel{2}} \cdot \underset{1}{\cancel{3}} \cdot 11}$
$= \frac{8}{11}$

46. simplified

47. $\frac{500x}{1000x} = \frac{\overset{1}{\cancel{2}} \cdot \overset{1}{\cancel{2}} \cdot \overset{1}{\cancel{5}} \cdot \overset{1}{\cancel{5}} \cdot \overset{1}{\cancel{5}} \cdot \overset{1}{\cancel{x}}}{\underset{1}{\cancel{2}} \cdot \underset{1}{\cancel{2}} \cdot 2 \cdot \underset{1}{\cancel{5}} \cdot \underset{1}{\cancel{5}} \cdot \underset{1}{\cancel{5}} \cdot \underset{1}{\cancel{x}}}$
$= \frac{1}{2}$

48. $\frac{-125mn}{625m} = \frac{-1 \cdot \overset{1}{\cancel{5}} \cdot \overset{1}{\cancel{5}} \cdot \overset{1}{\cancel{5}} \cdot \overset{1}{\cancel{m}} \cdot n}{\underset{1}{\cancel{5}} \cdot \underset{1}{\cancel{5}} \cdot 5 \cdot \underset{1}{\cancel{5}} \cdot \underset{1}{\cancel{m}}}$
$= \frac{-n}{5}$

49. simplified

50. $11ab = 1 \cdot 11 \cdot a \cdot b$
$6b = 2 \cdot 3 \cdot b$
The LCM is $1 \cdot 2 \cdot 3 \cdot 11 \cdot a \cdot b$ or $66ab$.

51. $12 = 2 \cdot 2 \cdot 3$
$4 = 2 \cdot 2$
$5 = 1 \cdot 5$
The LCM is $1 \cdot 2 \cdot 2 \cdot 3 \cdot 5$ or 60.

52. $7x^3 = 1 \cdot 7 \cdot x \cdot x \cdot x$
$49xy = 7 \cdot 7 \cdot x \cdot y$
The LCM is $1 \cdot 7 \cdot 7 \cdot x \cdot x \cdot x \cdot y$ or $49x^3y$.

53. $10j = 2 \cdot 5 \cdot j$
$6jk = 2 \cdot 3 \cdot j \cdot k$
$3 = 1 \cdot 3$
The LCM is $1 \cdot 2 \cdot 3 \cdot 5 \cdot j \cdot k$ or $30jk$.

54. $5f^4g = 1 \cdot 5 \cdot f \cdot f \cdot f \cdot f \cdot g$
$13fg^2 = 1 \cdot 13 \cdot f \cdot g \cdot g$
The LCM is $1 \cdot 5 \cdot 13 \cdot f \cdot f \cdot f \cdot f \cdot g \cdot g$ or $65f^4g^2$.

55. $12 = 2 \cdot 2 \cdot 3$
$15 = 3 \cdot 5$
$18 = 2 \cdot 3 \cdot 3$
The LCM is $2 \cdot 2 \cdot 3 \cdot 3 \cdot 5$ or 180.

56. $72x^3 = 2 \cdot 2 \cdot 2 \cdot 3 \cdot 3 \cdot x \cdot x \cdot x$
$64x^5 = 2 \cdot 2 \cdot 2 \cdot 2 \cdot 2 \cdot 2 \cdot x \cdot x \cdot x \cdot x \cdot x$
The LCM is $2 \cdot 2 \cdot 2 \cdot 2 \cdot 2 \cdot 2 \cdot 3 \cdot 3 \cdot x \cdot x \cdot x \cdot x \cdot x$
or $576x^5$.

57. $6ab = 2 \cdot 3 \cdot a \cdot b$
$18c = 2 \cdot 3 \cdot 3 \cdot c$
$36d = 2 \cdot 2 \cdot 3 \cdot 3 \cdot d$
The LCM is $2 \cdot 2 \cdot 3 \cdot 3 \cdot a \cdot b \cdot c \cdot d$ or $36abcd$.

58. $\frac{6}{7} > \frac{5}{14}$ **59.** $\frac{9}{16} > \frac{8}{15}$

60. $\frac{9}{100} < \frac{1}{9}$ **61.** $\frac{1}{11} > \frac{2}{23}$

62. $12^4 \cdot 12^7 = 12^{4+7}$
$= 12^{11}$
63. $\frac{d^9}{d^4} = d^{9-4}$
$= d^5$

64. $n^5 + n^{14} = n^{5+14}$
$= n^{19}$
65. $\frac{(-4)^5}{(-4)} = (-4)^{5-1}$
$= (^-4)^4$

66. $(6w^3)(10w^4) = (6 - 10)(w^3 \cdot w^4)$
$= 60(w^{3+4})$
$= 60w^7$

67. $\frac{6x^{40}}{3x^{18}} = 2x^{40-18}$
$= 2x^{22}$
68. $\frac{30c^2d}{15c} = 2c^{2-1}d$
$= 2cd$

69. $22ab^3 \cdot 5a^9 = (22 \cdot 5)(a^1 \cdot a^9)b^3$
$= 110(a^{1+9})b^3$
$= 110a^{10}b^3$

70. $\frac{1}{(-5)^3}$ **71.** $\frac{4d}{c^2}$

72. 6^{18} **73.** $\frac{4x}{(yz)^2}$

74. $\left(\frac{x}{2}\right)^4$ **75.** $3f^9$

Page 218 Applications and Problem Solving

76.

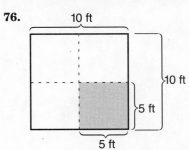

The cleaning team can clean a 5 ft by 5 ft area in 5 minutes.

77.

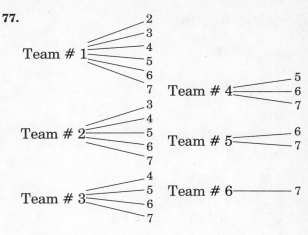

21 games

78. 4, 9

79. $\frac{3}{100} = \frac{1}{50}$
Home improvement is more popular.

Page 219 Alternative Assessment

1. See students' work.

2. $30 = 2 \cdot 15$
$= 2 \cdot 3 \cdot 5$

$24 = 2 \cdot 12$
$= 2 \cdot 2 \cdot 6$
$= 2 \cdot 2 \cdot 2 \cdot 3$

3. 30 = 2, 3, 5, 6, 10, 15
24 = 2, 3, 4, 6, 8, 12
Common factors: 2, 3, 6

4. Yes; 3 is a factor of 30 and 24

5. 6 feet; the greatest common factor of 24 and 30.

6. Each lot is either 15 feet or 25 feet wide.
15: 0, 15, 30, 45, 60, 75, . . .
25: 0, 25, 50, 75, . . .

7. The gardening area contains individual garden plots and each plot is either 15 feet or 25 feet wide. The illustration contains a break in the gardening area, so the exact number of individual plots is unknown. Two possible widths are 75 feet and 150 feet, common multiples of 15 and 25.

8. 75 feet; because 75 is the least common multiple of 15 and 25.

9. 5 feet; 5 is the GCF of 15 and 25.

Page 219 Thinking Critically

- $45 = 3 \cdot 3 \cdot 5$
$72 = 2 \cdot 2 \cdot 2 \cdot 3 \cdot 3$
The GCF is $3 \cdot 3$ or 9.
The LCM is $2 \cdot 2 \cdot 2 \cdot 3 \cdot 3 \cdot 5$ or 360.
- See students' work.
- See students' work.

Page 219 Portfolio

See students' work.

Page 219 Self Evaluation

See students' work.

Ongoing Assessment

1. B; $3 + 4 + 1 = 8$
2. D; $3(-25) = -75$
3. C; $|-12| - |-3| = 12 - 3$
   $$= 9$$
4. A; $250 \div 5 = 50$ ft/min
5. D; $4^{-3} = \frac{1}{4^3}$
   $$= \frac{1}{4 \cdot 4 \cdot 4}$$
6. C; $\frac{12d^2}{25ab}$ is simplified.
7. A; $\{-5, -3, 1, 14\}$
8. B; $d = rt$
   $$9 = 6 \cdot t$$
   $$\frac{9}{6} = \frac{6 \cdot t}{6}$$
   $$1.5 = t$$
   1.5 hours
9. $10 - (-24) = 10 + 24$
   $$= 34$$
10. $$131 - x = 109$$
    $$131 - x + x = 109 + x$$
    $$131 = 109 + x$$
    $$131 - 109 = 109 + x - 109$$
    $$22 = x$$
11. Sample answers: $20' \times 5'$; $25' \times 4'$; $10' \times 10'$; $40' \times 2\frac{1}{2}'$
12. $12a + 8b - 6a = 12a - 6a + 8b$
    $$= 6a + 8b$$
13. $A = \ell \cdot w$
    $A = 94 \cdot 50$
    $A = 4700$ sq ft

14. $176 + p = 250$
15.

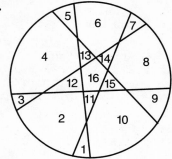

16 pieces can be cut.
16. Yes; for example, three seven-point touchdowns and one safety is 23 points.
17.

	Drina	Susan	Latisha	Joshua
Drums	✗	○	✗	✗
Violin	✗	✗	○	✗
Trumpet	○	✗	✗	✗
Trombone	✗	✗	✗	○

Drina—trumpet; Latisha—violin; Susan—drums; Joshua—trombone
18. 3.5; See students' work.

Chapter 5   Rationals: Patterns in Addition and Subtraction

5-1   Rational Numbers

Page 227   Checking Your Understanding

1. Sample answer: a rational number is a number that can be written in the form of a common fraction. Some sample rationals: 4.8, 7.1, $1\frac{3}{4}$.

2. Sample answer: Yes; integers are always written with a denominator of 1.

3. $\frac{2}{3} < \frac{4}{5}$

4. 0.13 is a rational number, because it can be written in the form $\frac{13}{100}$. $0.\overline{13}$ is rational because it can be written as $\frac{13}{99}$.

5. a.

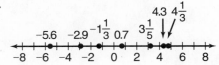

   b. $4\frac{1}{3}$
   c. -5.6

6. $0.8 = \frac{8}{10} = \frac{4}{5}$ 7. $0.05 = \frac{5}{100} = \frac{1}{20}$

8. $-9.64 = -9\frac{64}{100} = -9\frac{16}{25}$

9. Let $N = 0.222\ldots$ Then $10N = 2.222\ldots$
$$10N = 2.222\ldots$$
$$\underline{-\ 1N = 0.222\ldots}$$
$$9N = 2$$
$$N = \frac{2}{9}$$
   Therefore, $0.\overline{2} = \frac{2}{9}$.

10. Integer, Rational   11. Rational

12. Whole, Integer, Rational

13. none

14. $\frac{3}{7} > -\frac{3}{7}$ 15. $\frac{3}{4} = 0.75$ 16. $-3.78 > -3.88$

17. a. $\frac{27}{432} = \frac{1}{16}$

   b. Rational; it is a fraction

Pages 227–228   Exercises

18. $0.4 = \frac{4}{10} = \frac{2}{5}$ 19. $-0.7 = -\frac{7}{10}$

20. $0.23 = \frac{23}{100}$ 21. $0.57 = \frac{57}{100}$

22. $0.48 = \frac{48}{100} = \frac{12}{25}$ 23. $0.03 = \frac{3}{100}$

24. Let $N = 0.888\ldots$ Then $10N = 8.888\ldots$
$$10N = 8.888\ldots$$
$$\underline{-\ 1N = 0.888\ldots}$$
$$9N = 8$$
$$N = \frac{8}{9}$$
   Therefore, $0.\overline{8} = \frac{8}{9}$.

25. Let $N = -0.333\ldots$ Then $10N = -3.333\ldots$
$$10N = -3.333\ldots$$
$$\underline{-\ 1N = -0.333\ldots}$$
$$9N = -3$$
$$N = -\frac{3}{9} \text{ or } -\frac{1}{3}$$
   Therefore, $-0.\overline{333} = -\frac{1}{3}$.

26. $-0.51 = -\frac{51}{100}$

27. Let $N = 0.252525\ldots$ Then $100N = 25.252525\ldots$
$$100N = 25.252525\ldots$$
$$\underline{-\ 1N = \ \ 0.252525\ldots}$$
$$99N = 25$$
$$N = \frac{25}{99}$$
   Therefore, $0.\overline{25} = \frac{25}{99}$.

28. $0.375 = \frac{375}{1000} = \frac{3}{8}$

29. Let $N = 2.343434\ldots$ Then $100N = 234.343434\ldots$
$$100N = 234.343434\ldots$$
$$\underline{-\ 1N = \ \ \ 2.343434\ldots}$$
$$99N = 232$$
$$N = \frac{232}{99} \text{ or } 2\frac{34}{99}.$$
   Therefore, $2.\overline{34} = 2\frac{34}{99}$.

30. Integer, Rational   31. Rational

32. Rational

33. Whole, Integer, Rational

34. Rational   35. none

36. Rational   37. Rational

38. Integer, Rational   39. Rational

40. Integer, Rational   41. none

42. $\frac{3}{4} > -\frac{3}{8}$ 43. $-6\frac{1}{2} > -6.\overline{5}$ 44. $9.9 > 9.\overline{8}$

45. $\frac{3}{5} = 0.6$ 46. $\frac{1}{7} < 0.222\ldots$ 47. $\frac{13}{26} > -\frac{1}{2}$

48. $0.3\overline{4} > 0.\overline{34}$ 49. $\frac{1}{11} < 0.1$ 50. $-1\frac{1}{3} = -1.\overline{3}$

51. $\frac{2}{7}$ 52. $-\frac{3}{5}$

53. Yes; $\frac{6}{2.4} = \frac{5}{2}$ or $\frac{60}{24}$.   54. Yes; $2\frac{3}{8} > 2.37$

55. $0.025 = \frac{25}{1000} = \frac{1}{40}$ 56. $0.0008 = \frac{8}{10,000} = \frac{1}{1250}$

57. a. $\frac{26.9}{807} = \frac{1}{30}$

   b. Yes; it can be written as a fraction.

58. a. $\frac{7.50}{10^7}$ m

   b. 0.00000075 m

59. $4x^2 = 2 \cdot 2 \cdot x \cdot x$
$$3x = 1 \cdot 3 \cdot x$$
$$5 = 1 \cdot 5$$
   The LCM is $2 \cdot 2 \cdot 3 \cdot 5 \cdot x \cdot x$ or $60x^2$

60. 3, 5

61. $-4b > 72$
$$\frac{-4b}{-4} < \frac{72}{-4}$$
$$b < -18$$

62.
$$\frac{y}{12} = -7$$
$$\frac{y}{12} \cdot 12 = -7 \cdot 12$$
$$y = -84$$

63. $q = \frac{323}{-17}$
$q = -19$

64. false

65. $8x = 64$
$$\frac{8x}{8} = \frac{64}{8}$$
$$x = 8$$

66. $24 \div (9 - 3) = 24 \div 6$
$$= 4$$

5-2 Estimating Sums and Differences

Pages 230–231 Checking Your Understanding

1. Sample answers: 4.8, 7.1
2. Sample answers: to give approximate answers, to verify calculations, to detect errors in calculations.
3. Sample answer: 220 is the better estimate, since 569 and 345 were rounded to the nearest ten instead of to the nearest hundred.
4. See students' work.
5. 6
6. 13
7. 803
8. 7
9. 11
10. 33
11. 1
12. 0
13. $\frac{1}{2}$
14. b
15. a
16. Sample answer:
$34.32 + 19.51 \rightarrow 30 + 20 = 50$
$34.32 + 19.51$ is about 50.
17. Sample answer:
$159.7 - 124.8 \rightarrow 160 - 120 = 40$
$159.7 - 124.8$ is about 40.
18. Sample answer:
$6\frac{7}{10} - 3\frac{1}{6} \rightarrow 7 - 3 = 4$
$6\frac{7}{10} - 3\frac{1}{6}$ is about 4.
19. Sample answer:
$12\frac{1}{9} - 2\frac{9}{14} \rightarrow 12 - 3 = 9$
$12\frac{1}{9} - 2\frac{9}{14}$ is about 9.
20. Sample answer:
$1\frac{7}{12} + \frac{8}{19} \rightarrow 1\frac{1}{2} + \frac{1}{2} = 2$
$1\frac{7}{12} + \frac{8}{19}$ is about 2.
21. Sample answer:
$23\frac{8}{9} + 5\frac{4}{25} \rightarrow 24 + 5 = 29$
$23\frac{8}{9} + 5\frac{4}{25}$ is about 29.
22. Sample answer:
$26{,}718 - 5475 \rightarrow 27{,}000 - 5000 = 22{,}000$
About 22,000 gallons per year

Pages 231–233 Exercises

23. Sample answer:
$12.5 + 44.8 \rightarrow 15 + 45 = 60$
$12.5 + 44.8$ is about 60.

24. Sample answer:
$\$20.00 - \$15.34 \rightarrow 20.00 - 15.00 = \$5.00$
$\$20.00 - \$15.34$ is about $5.00.

25. Sample answer:
$8.6 + 11.9 \rightarrow 9 + 12 = 21$
$8.6 + 11.9$ is about 21.

26. Sample answer:
$32 - 29.75 \rightarrow 32 - 30 = 2$
$32 - 29.75$ is about 2.

27. Sample answer:
$\frac{8}{9} + \frac{1}{5} \rightarrow 1 + 0 = 1$
$\frac{8}{9} + \frac{1}{5}$ is about 1.

28. Sample answer:
$\frac{11}{15} + \frac{7}{8} \rightarrow 1 + 1 = 2$
$\frac{11}{15} + \frac{7}{8}$ is about 2.

29. Sample answer:
$6\frac{9}{10} + \frac{2}{5} \rightarrow 7 + \frac{1}{2} = 7\frac{1}{2}$
$6\frac{9}{10} + \frac{2}{5}$ is about $7\frac{1}{2}$.

30. Sample answer:
$\frac{17}{20} + 8\frac{3}{4} \rightarrow 1 + 9 = 10$
$\frac{17}{20} + 8\frac{3}{4}$ is about 10.

31. Sample answer:
$\frac{4}{5} - \frac{1}{10} \rightarrow 1 - 0 = 1$
$\frac{4}{5} - \frac{1}{10}$ is about 1.

32. Sample answer:
$\frac{7}{9} - \frac{13}{18} \rightarrow 1 - 1 = 0$
$\frac{7}{9} - \frac{13}{18}$ is about 0.

33. Sample answer:
$18\frac{1}{8} - 12\frac{1}{2} \rightarrow 18 - 13 = 5$
$18\frac{1}{8} - 12\frac{1}{2}$ is about 5.

34. Sample answer:
$11\frac{89}{100} - 4\frac{1}{7} \rightarrow 12 - 4 = 8$
$11\frac{89}{100} - 4\frac{1}{7}$ is about 8.

35. Sample answer:
$125.8 - 22.4 \rightarrow 130 - 20 = 110$
$125.8 - 22.4$ is about 110.

36. Sample answer:
$16.432 + 11.910 \rightarrow 16 + 12 = 28$
$16.432 + 11.910$ is about 28.

37. Sample answer:
$32\frac{8}{10} - 4\frac{3}{8} \rightarrow 33 - 4\frac{1}{2} = 28\frac{1}{2}$
$32\frac{8}{10} - 4\frac{3}{8}$ is about $28\frac{1}{2}$.

38. Sample answer:
$\frac{65}{131} + \frac{3}{35} \rightarrow \frac{1}{2} + 0 = \frac{1}{2}$
$\frac{65}{131} + \frac{3}{35}$ is about $\frac{1}{2}$.

39. Sample answer:
$22\frac{2}{95} - 28\frac{3}{75} \rightarrow 22 + 28 = 50$
$22\frac{2}{95} + 28\frac{3}{75}$ is about 50.

40. Sample answer:

$145\frac{4}{5} - 121\frac{2}{15} \rightarrow 146 - 121 = 25$

$145\frac{4}{5} - 121\frac{2}{15}$ is about 25.

41. Sample answer:

$2.89 + 1.29 + 0.79 \rightarrow$
$3.00 + 1.00 + 1.00 = 5.00$
The purchase price is about $5.00.

42. Sample answer:

$1.29 + 0.89 + 1.59 \rightarrow$
$1.00 + 1.00 + 2.00 = 4.00$
The purchase price is about $4.00.

43. Sample answer:

$10.00 - (4.19 + 2.79) \rightarrow$
$10.00 - (4.00 + 3.00) = 10.00 - 7.00 = 3.00$
The change amount is about $3.00.

44. Sample answer:

$20.00 - (13.89 + 2.89) \rightarrow$
$20.00 - (14.00 + 3.00) = 20.00 - 17.00 = 3.00$
The change amount is about $3.00.

45. Sample answer:

$10.00 - (0.89 + 1.29 + 0.69) \rightarrow$
$10.00 - (1.00 + 1.00 + 1.00) = 10.00 - 3.00 = 7.00$
No, the change should be about $7.00.

46. See students' work.

47. Sample answer: $11\frac{1}{10} + 1\frac{7}{15}$

48. paper

49. $41.29 + 18.25 \rightarrow 41 + 18 = 59.00$

50. a. Sample answer:

$95.60 + 41.75 + 150.95 + 125.16 \rightarrow$
$96.00 + 42.00 + 151.00 + 125.00 = 414.00$

b. $500.00 - 414.00 = 86.00$

51. $\frac{3}{10} + \frac{2}{5} \rightarrow$ more than half

52. $-0.88 = -\frac{88}{100} = -\frac{22}{25}$

53. $\frac{26}{100} = \frac{13}{50}$

54.
$$364 = w - 84$$
$$364 + 84 = w - 84 + 84$$
$$448 = w$$

55. $48 \div (-3) = -16$

56. none

57. false

58. $12n = 48$ What number
$12(4) = 48$ times 12 is 48?
$n = 4$

59. a. $2(6.25 + 2.25)$ or $2(6.25) + 2(2.25)$

b. $2(6.25 + 2.25) = 2(8.50)$
$= 17.00$

60. $(11 + 9) \div (3 - 1) = 20 \div 2$
$= 10$

Pages 232–233 Earth Watch

• Sample answer:

$250.8 \rightarrow 300$
$248.2 \rightarrow 200$
$239.5 \rightarrow 200$
$252.8 \rightarrow 300$
$271.1 \rightarrow 300$
$280.8 \rightarrow 300$
$295.1 \rightarrow 300$
$310.6 \rightarrow 300$
$314.5 \rightarrow 300$
$+\ 265.2 \rightarrow +\ 300$
2800

about 28 million kilograms

• temps below -80°C; no

• Sample answer: Through United Nations involvement, countries that have signed treaty Agenda 21 of the Montreal Protocol have been prohibited to produce CFCs and are forbidden to purchase CFCs or products containing them from nations that had not agreed to the treaty by January 1, 1996. This revised version of the treaty replaced the original draft, which had the year 2000 as its target date and only required the countries to cut their production in half. More than 100 have agreed to the treaty.

The expected results of the treaty are to find alternatives to CFCs for products and to replenish the depleting ozone layer. It is expected to take 100 years for the ozone layer to recover.

5-3 Adding and Subtracting Decimals

Page 236 Checking Your Understanding

1. commutative:
$12.3 + (8.3 + 2.5) = 12.3 + (2.5 + 8.3)$
associative:
$12.3 + (8.3 + 2.5) = (12.3 + 8.3) + 2.5$

2. -7.398

3. Both are correct because adding 2.9 is the same as subtracting -2.9.

4. 10.5   **5.** 3.68   **6.** 7.36

7. -4.91   **8.** 17.293   **9.** 77.33

10. $a = 41.3 + 0.28$
$$\begin{array}{r} 41.30 \\ +\ 0.28 \\ \hline 41.58 \end{array}$$
$a = 41.58$

11. $b = -9.6 + 3.2$
$b = -|9.6 - 3.2|$
$$\begin{array}{r} 9.6 \\ -\ 3.2 \\ \hline 6.4 \end{array}$$
$b = -6.4$

12. $34.2 - 43.0 = c$
$-43.0 + 34.2 = c$
$-|43.0 - 34.2| = c$
$$\begin{array}{r} 43.0 \\ -\ 34.2 \\ \hline 8.8 \end{array}$$
$c = -8.8$

13. $t = 81.9 - 38$
$$\begin{array}{r} 81.9 \\ -\ 38.0 \\ \hline 43.9 \end{array}$$
$t = 43.9$

14. $4.7x + 2x = (4.7 + 2.0)x$
$= 6.7x$

15. $5.3m - 1.4m - 8m = (5.3 - 1.4 - 8.0)m$
$= (5.3 - 9.4)m$
$= -4.1m$

16. Commuter rail: $349.5 - 330.8 = +18.7$
Heavy rail: $2279.0 - 2189.0 = +90.0$
Light rail: $232.9 - 224.9 = +8.0$
Bus/trolley: $5403.4 - 5412.1 = -8.7$

Pages 237–238   Exercises

17. $a = 4.3 + 9.8$
4.3
$\underline{+\ 9.8}$
14.1
$a = 14.1$

18. $x = 31.92 + 14.2$
31.92
$\underline{+14.20}$
46.12
$x = 46.12$

19. $15.3 - 13.8 = m$
15.3
$\underline{-13.8}$
1.5
$m = 1.5$

20. $85.3 - 37.07 = r$
85.30
$\underline{-37.07}$
48.23
$r = 48.23$

21. $72.47 - 9.039 = b$
72.470
$\underline{-\ 9.039}$
63.431
$b = 63.431$

22. $c = 0.735 - 0.3879$
0.7350
$\underline{-0.3879}$
0.3471
$c = 0.3471$

23. $-7.5 + 9.8 = x$
9.8
$\underline{-7.5}$
2.3
$x = 2.3$

24. $7.4 + (-3.9) = y$
$7.4 - 3.9 = y$
7.4
$\underline{-3.9}$
3.5
$y = 3.5$

25. $z = -13.9 + (-12.5)$
13.9
$\underline{+12.5}$
26.4
$z = -26.4$

26. $k = -3.91 - (-0.6)$
$k = -3.91 + 0.6$
$k = -|3.91 - 0.6|$
3.91
$\underline{-0.60}$
3.31
$k = -3.31$

27. $a = -34.1 + (-17.63)$
34.10
$\underline{+17.63}$
51.73
$a = -51.73$

28. $y = -18.12 - (-7.3)$
$y = -18.12 + 7.3$
$y = -|18.12 - 7.3|$
18.12
$\underline{-\ 7.30}$
10.82
$y = -10.82$

29. $5.3m + 7m = (5.3 + 7.0)m$
$= 12.3m$

30. $47.9w - 31.8w = (47.9 - 31.8)w$
$= 16.1w$

31. $0.3y + 4.1y + 2.5y = (0.3 + 4.1 + 2.5)y$
$= 6.9y$

32. $27y - 4.7y - 13.8y = (27.0 - 4.7 - 13.8)y$
$= (27.0 - 18.5)y$
$= 8.5y$

33. $3.5x - 5 + 8x = 3.5x + 8x - 5$
$= (3.5 + 8.0)x - 5$
$= 11.5x - 5$

34. $6.93 + (3.1 + 4.07)m = 6.93 + (3.10 + 4.07)m$
$= 6.93 + 7.17m$

35. $b + x = 8.07 + 21.33$
$= 29.4$

36. $a - y = 5.3 - 0.7$
$= 4.6$

37. $x - (b + y) = 21.33 - (8.07 + 0.7)$
$= 21.33 - (8.07 + 0.70)$
$= 21.33 - 8.77$
$= 12.56$

38. $b + x + y = 8.07 + 21.33 + 0.7$
$= 8.07 + 21.33 + 0.70$
$= 30.1$

39. $a + b - y = 5.3 + 8.07 - 0.7$
$= 5.30 + 8.07 - 0.70$
$= 13.37 - 0.70$
$= 12.67$

40. $(x - b) + a = (21.33 - 8.07) + 5.3$
$= (21.33 - 8.07) + 5.30$
$= 13.26 + 5.30$
$= 18.56$

41. $45 + 11.2 - 9.35 = 24.45$
She will have 24.45 ft left for the third side. She cannot use all 24.45 ft for the third side because the third side must be less than 20.55 ft.

42. men: $169.9 - 161.7 = 8.2$ lb.
women: $135.7 - 127.2 = 8.5$ lb.

43. $201.9 + 176.6 = 378.5$

44. $13.2 - 2.6 = 10.6$
10.6 million tons discarded

45. a. $78.7 - 54.4 = 24.3$
24.3 bags per 10,000 passengers
   b. Sample answer: Bad weather causes changes in flight schedules.

46. $P = 2.4 + 4.0 + 3.2$
$P = 9.6$ cm

47. $\$1.89 + \$4.39 + \$1.27 + \$2.04 \rightarrow$
$2 + 4 + 1 + 2 = \$9.00$
yes, $10 will be enough to pay the bill.

48. p^4

49. $19 < 17 + a$
$19 - 17 < 17 + a - 17$
$2 < a$

50. $\$435 - \$120 = \$315$

51. $b = -121 \div 11$
$b = -11$

52. $|-10| > 9$

53. $|8| + |-4| = 8 + 4$
$= 12$

54. $2m - n = 2(8) - 5$
$= 16 - 5$
$= 11$

Adding and Subtracting Like Fractions

Page 239   Your Turn

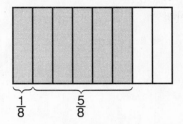

$$\underbrace{}_{\frac{1}{8}}\qquad\underbrace{}_{\frac{5}{8}}$$

a. 6; They are the same.

b. 8; They are the same.

c. $\frac{6}{8}$

d. The numerator is the sum of the numerators and the denominator is the same as the denominators of the addends.

Pages 241–242   Checking your Understanding

1. associative and commutive properties of addition.

2.

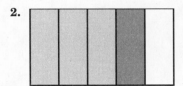

3. $\frac{33}{7} = 4\frac{5}{7}$

4. See students' work.

5. $\frac{4}{7} + \frac{5}{7} = m$
$\quad\ \ \frac{9}{7} = m$
$\quad 1\frac{2}{7} = m$

6. $1\frac{2}{19} + \frac{17}{19} = a$
$\quad 1 + \left(\frac{2}{19} + \frac{17}{19}\right) = a$
$\quad\qquad 1 + \frac{19}{19} = a$
$\quad\qquad\quad 1 + 1 = a$
$\quad\qquad\qquad\ 2 = a$

7. $\frac{19}{24} - \frac{11}{24} = r$
$\quad\ \ \frac{8}{24} = r$
$\quad\ \ \frac{1}{3} = r$

8. $-\frac{19}{30} + \frac{7}{30} = z$
$\quad -\frac{12}{30} = z$
$\quad\ -\frac{2}{5} = z$

9. $x + z = \frac{3}{8} + \frac{5}{8}$
$\qquad\quad = \frac{8}{8}$
$\qquad\quad = 1$

10. $z - y = \frac{5}{8} - \frac{7}{8}$
$\qquad\quad = -\frac{2}{8}$
$\qquad\quad = -\frac{1}{4}$

11. a. $\frac{6}{25} + \frac{3}{25} = \frac{9}{25}$

b. $\frac{3}{10} - \frac{1}{10} = \frac{2}{10}$ or $\frac{1}{5}$ of each dollar

Pages 242–243   Exercises

12. $\frac{5}{7} + \frac{1}{7} = b$
$\quad\ \ \frac{6}{7} = b$

13. $m = \frac{11}{15} - \frac{8}{15}$
$\quad m = \frac{3}{15}$
$\quad m = \frac{1}{5}$

14. $a = \frac{19}{31} - \frac{8}{31}$
$\quad a = \frac{11}{31}$

15. $\frac{19}{27} - \frac{7}{27} = r$
$\quad\ \ \frac{12}{27} = r$
$\quad\ \ \ \frac{4}{9} = r$

16. $1\frac{13}{16} - 1\frac{5}{16} = x$
$(1 - 1) + \left(\frac{13}{16} - \frac{5}{16}\right) = x$
$\qquad\qquad\quad \frac{8}{16} = x$
$\qquad\qquad\quad\ \frac{1}{2} = x$

17. $\frac{13}{18} + \frac{11}{18} = a$
$\quad\ \ \frac{24}{18} = a$
$\quad 1\frac{6}{18} = a$
$\quad 1\frac{1}{3} = a$

18. $m = 1\frac{9}{16} + \frac{15}{16}$
$\quad m = 1 + \left(\frac{9}{16} + \frac{15}{16}\right)$
$\quad m = 1 + \frac{24}{16}$
$\quad m = 1 + 1\frac{8}{16}$
$\quad m = 1 + 1\frac{1}{2}$
$\quad m = 2\frac{1}{2}$

19. $1\frac{16}{21} - \frac{9}{21} = y$
$\quad 1 + \left(\frac{16}{21} - \frac{9}{21}\right) = y$
$\qquad\quad 1 + \frac{7}{21} = y$
$\qquad\quad 1 + \frac{1}{3} = y$
$\qquad\qquad 1\frac{1}{3} = y$

20. $p = -\frac{19}{27} + \left(-\frac{7}{27}\right)$
$\quad p = -\frac{26}{27}$

21. $1\frac{5}{12} + \frac{11}{12} = z$
$\quad 1 + \left(\frac{5}{12} + \frac{11}{12}\right) = z$
$\qquad\quad 1 + \frac{16}{12} = z$
$\qquad\quad 1 + 1\frac{4}{12} = z$
$\qquad\quad 1 + 1\frac{1}{3} = z$
$\qquad\qquad 2\frac{1}{3} = z$

22. $\frac{9}{20} - \frac{17}{20} = c$
$\quad -\frac{8}{20} = c$
$\quad\ -\frac{2}{5} = c$

23. $1\frac{19}{41} + \left(-\frac{19}{41}\right) = w$
$\quad 1\frac{19}{41} - \frac{19}{41} = w$
$\quad 1 + \left(\frac{19}{41} - \frac{19}{41}\right) = w$
$\qquad\qquad 1 + 0 = w$
$\qquad\qquad\quad 1 = w$

24. $a + b = \frac{5}{12} + \frac{7}{12}$
$\qquad\quad = \frac{12}{12}$
$\qquad\quad = 1$

25. $b - c = \frac{7}{12} - \frac{1}{12}$
$\qquad\quad = \frac{6}{12}$
$\qquad\quad = \frac{1}{2}$

26. $a + c = \frac{5}{12} + \frac{1}{12}$
$\qquad\quad = \frac{6}{12}$
$\qquad\quad = \frac{1}{2}$

27. $b + c = \frac{7}{12} + \frac{1}{12}$
$\qquad\quad = \frac{8}{12}$
$\qquad\quad = \frac{2}{3}$

28. $c - a = \frac{1}{12} - \frac{5}{12}$
$\qquad\quad = -\frac{4}{12}$
$\qquad\quad = -\frac{1}{3}$

29. $a - b = \frac{5}{12} - \frac{7}{12}$
$\qquad\quad = -\frac{2}{12}$
$\qquad\quad = -\frac{1}{6}$

30. $4\frac{1}{3}x + \frac{2}{3} - 3\frac{1}{3} = \left(4\frac{1}{3} + \frac{2}{3} - 3\frac{1}{3}\right)x$
$\qquad\qquad\qquad = \left(4\frac{3}{3} - 3\frac{1}{3}\right)x$
$\qquad\qquad\qquad = \left[(4 - 3) + \left(\frac{3}{3} - \frac{1}{3}\right)\right]x$
$\qquad\qquad\qquad = \left(1 + \frac{2}{3}\right)x$
$\qquad\qquad\qquad = 1\frac{2}{3}x$

31. $-4\frac{1}{4}r + \left(-2\frac{3}{4}\right)r + 5r = \left(-4\frac{1}{4} - 2\frac{3}{4} + 5\right)r$

$\qquad = \left(-6\frac{4}{4} + 5\right)r$

$\qquad = (-7 + 5)r$

$\qquad = -2r$

32. $5\frac{1}{7}m + \left(-3\frac{3}{7}\right)m + 1\frac{2}{7}m = 5\frac{1}{7}m + 1\frac{2}{7}m + \left(-3\frac{3}{7}\right)m$

$\qquad = \left(5\frac{1}{7} + 1\frac{2}{7} - 3\frac{3}{7}\right)m$

$\qquad = \left(6\frac{3}{7} - 3\frac{3}{7}\right)m$

$\qquad = \left[(6 - 3) + \left(\frac{3}{7} - \frac{3}{7}\right)\right]m$

$\qquad = (3 + 0)m$

$\qquad = 3m$

33. $6\frac{3}{5}a - 3\frac{4}{5}a - 2\frac{2}{5}a = \left(6\frac{3}{5} - 3\frac{4}{5} - 2\frac{2}{5}\right)a$

$\qquad = \left(6\frac{3}{5} - 5\frac{6}{5}\right)a$

$\qquad = \left(6\frac{3}{5} - 6\frac{1}{5}\right)a$

$\qquad = \left[(6 - 6) + \left(\frac{3}{5} - \frac{1}{5}\right)\right]a$

$\qquad = \left(0 + \frac{2}{5}\right)a$

$\qquad = \frac{2}{5}a$

34. $5\frac{5}{6}y + 3\frac{5}{6}y - 2\frac{1}{6}y = \left(5\frac{5}{6} + 3\frac{5}{6} - 2\frac{1}{6}\right)y$

$\qquad = \left(8\frac{10}{6} - 2\frac{1}{6}\right)y$

$\qquad = \left(9\frac{4}{6} - 2\frac{1}{6}\right)y$

$\qquad = \left[(9 - 2) + \left(\frac{4}{6} - \frac{1}{6}\right)\right]y$

$\qquad = \left(7 + \frac{3}{6}\right)y$

$\qquad = \left(7 + \frac{1}{2}\right)y$

$\qquad = 7\frac{1}{2}y$

35. $3\frac{5}{9}b - 2\frac{4}{9}b - \frac{7}{9} = \left(3\frac{5}{9} - 2\frac{4}{9} - \frac{7}{9}\right)b$

$\qquad = \left(3\frac{5}{9} - 2\frac{11}{9}\right)b$

$\qquad = \left(3\frac{5}{9} - 3\frac{2}{9}\right)b$

$\qquad = \left[(3 - 3) + \left(\frac{5}{9} - \frac{2}{9}\right)\right]b$

$\qquad = \left(0 + \frac{3}{9}\right)b$

$\qquad = \frac{3}{9}b$

$\qquad = \frac{1}{3}b$

36. Sample answer: $\frac{x}{8} + \frac{y}{8}$

37. Sample answer: $\frac{2x}{5} - \frac{1}{5}$

38. $\frac{1}{20} + \frac{2}{20} + \frac{3}{20} + \ldots + \frac{17}{20} + \frac{18}{20} + \frac{19}{20} = 9\frac{1}{2}$
See students' work.

39. $5 \text{ ft} - 54\frac{5}{8} \text{ in.} = 60 \text{ in.} - 54\frac{5}{8} \text{ in.}$

$\qquad = 59\frac{8}{8} \text{ in.} - 54\frac{5}{8} \text{ in.}$

$\qquad = (59 - 54) + \left(\frac{8}{8} - \frac{5}{8}\right)$

$\qquad = 5 + \frac{3}{8}$

$\qquad = 5\frac{3}{8} \text{ inches}$

40. $\frac{3}{8} + \frac{5}{8} = \frac{8}{8}$ or 1 inch

41. $2\frac{5}{8} + \frac{7}{8} = 2\frac{12}{8}$

$\qquad = 3\frac{4}{8}$

$\qquad = 3\frac{1}{2}$ yards

42. $\$38.78 - \$25.59 = \$13.19$

43. a. $\frac{2.5}{17} = \frac{25}{170}$ or $\frac{5}{34}$

b. money received so far: 2.5

$\qquad\qquad$ 0.5

$\qquad\qquad$ 0.5

$\qquad\qquad$ 1.3

$\qquad\qquad$ 3.0

$\qquad\qquad \underline{+6.2}$

$\qquad\qquad$ 14.0

Montgomery County is contributing $\frac{0.5}{14.0}$ or $\frac{1}{28}$.

44. $\qquad \frac{d}{6} < -14$

$\qquad \frac{d}{6} \cdot 6 < -14 \cdot 6$

$\qquad\qquad d < -84$

45. $\qquad c - 12 \geq -25$

$\qquad c - 12 + 12 \geq -25 + 12$

$\qquad\qquad c \geq -13$

46. $\qquad P = 2(\ell + w)$

$\qquad\quad 42 = 2(x + 6)$

$\qquad\quad 42 = 2x + 12$

$\qquad 42 - 12 = 2x + 12 - 12$

$\qquad\quad 30 = 2x$

$\qquad\quad \frac{30}{2} = \frac{2x}{2}$

$\qquad\quad 15 = x$

47. $-8a + (-17a) - (-3a) = -8a - 17a + 3a$

$\qquad = (-8 - 17 + 3)a$

$\qquad = (-25 + 3)a$

$\qquad = -22a$

48. Identity property of multiplication

5-5	Adding and Subtracting Unlike Fractions

Page 244   Your Turn

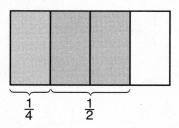

$\frac{1}{4} \qquad \frac{1}{2}$

a. $\frac{3}{4}$ $\qquad$ **b.** 4 $\qquad$ **c.** $\frac{1}{4} + \frac{2}{4} = \frac{3}{4}$

Pages 245–246   Checking Your Understanding

1. Rename them using the LCD.

2. Adding or subtracting the numerators without having a common denominator would be meaningless.

3. Sample answer: A carpet layer needs $12\frac{1}{2}$ square yards of carpet for one room and $18\frac{3}{4}$ square yards for another room. How much carpet is needed in all?

4. Keri; Hank didn't find a common denominator.

5. $\frac{3}{4} - \frac{1}{2} = \frac{1}{4}$

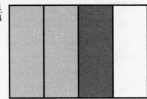

6. $\frac{1}{3} + \frac{5}{6} = h$

$\frac{2}{6} + \frac{5}{6} = h$

$\frac{7}{6} = h$

$1\frac{1}{6} = h$

7. $m = \frac{3}{4} - \frac{5}{8}$

$m = \frac{6}{8} - \frac{5}{8}$

$m = \frac{1}{8}$

8. $t = \frac{3}{5} + \frac{3}{10}$

$t = \frac{6}{10} + \frac{3}{10}$

$t = \frac{9}{10}$

9. $n = \frac{3}{8} - \frac{1}{2}$

$n = \frac{3}{8} - \frac{4}{8}$

$n = -\frac{1}{8}$

10. $\frac{7}{12} - \frac{2}{3} = g$

$\frac{7}{12} - \frac{8}{12} = g$

$-\frac{1}{12} = g$

11. $\frac{3}{7} + \frac{5}{14} = w$

$\frac{6}{14} + \frac{5}{14} = w$

$\frac{11}{14} = w$

12. a. $\frac{23}{50} + \frac{8}{25} = \frac{23}{50} + \frac{16}{50}$

$= \frac{39}{50}$

b. $\frac{7}{50} - \frac{3}{100} = \frac{14}{100} - \frac{3}{100}$

$= \frac{11}{100}$

Pages 246–247   Exercises

13. $x = \frac{1}{6} + \frac{7}{18}$

$x = \frac{3}{18} + \frac{7}{18}$

$x = \frac{10}{18}$

$x = \frac{5}{9}$

14. $m = \frac{4}{7} + \frac{9}{14}$

$m = \frac{8}{14} + \frac{9}{14}$

$m = \frac{17}{14}$

$m = 1\frac{3}{14}$

15. $\frac{5}{12} - \frac{1}{2} = d$

$\frac{5}{12} - \frac{6}{12} = d$

$-\frac{1}{12} = d$

16. $y = \frac{6}{7} - \frac{5}{21}$

$y = \frac{18}{21} - \frac{5}{21}$

$y = \frac{13}{21}$

17. $r = \frac{9}{26} + \frac{3}{13}$

$r = \frac{9}{26} + \frac{6}{26}$

$r = \frac{15}{26}$

18. $b = \frac{11}{12} + \frac{3}{4}$

$b = \frac{11}{12} + \frac{9}{12}$

$b = \frac{20}{12}$

$b = 1\frac{8}{12}$

$b = 1\frac{2}{3}$

19. $p = 4\frac{1}{3} - 2\frac{1}{2}$

$p = 4\frac{2}{6} - 2\frac{3}{6}$

$p = 3\frac{8}{6} - 2\frac{3}{6}$

$p = 1\frac{5}{6}$

20. $k = \frac{7}{8} + \frac{3}{16}$

$k = \frac{14}{16} + \frac{3}{16}$

$k = \frac{17}{16}$

$k = 1\frac{1}{16}$

21. $5\frac{1}{3} - 2\frac{1}{6} = m$

$5\frac{2}{6} - 2\frac{1}{6} = m$

$3\frac{1}{6} = m$

22. $\frac{5}{7} - \frac{10}{21} = a$

$\frac{15}{21} - \frac{10}{21} = a$

$\frac{5}{21} = a$

23. $9\frac{3}{4} - 5\frac{1}{2} = d$

$9\frac{3}{4} - 5\frac{2}{4} = d$

$4\frac{1}{4} = d$

24. $x = 7\frac{1}{3} - 3\frac{1}{2}$

$x = 7\frac{2}{6} - 3\frac{3}{6}$

$x = 6\frac{8}{6} - 3\frac{3}{6}$

$x = 3\frac{5}{6}$

25. $y = 12\frac{3}{7} + 4\frac{1}{21}$

$y = 12\frac{9}{21} + 4\frac{1}{21}$

$y = 16\frac{10}{21}$

26. $19\frac{3}{8} - 4\frac{3}{4} = s$

$19\frac{3}{8} - 4\frac{6}{8} = s$

$18\frac{11}{8} - 4\frac{6}{8} = s$

$14\frac{5}{8} = s$

27. $8\frac{9}{10} + 1\frac{1}{6} = r$

$8\frac{27}{30} + 1\frac{5}{30} = r$

$9\frac{32}{30} = r$

$10\frac{2}{30} = r$

$10\frac{1}{15} = r$

28. $b = \frac{1}{3} + \frac{2}{35}$

$b = \frac{35}{105} + \frac{6}{105}$

$b = \frac{41}{105}$

29. $\frac{7}{10} - \frac{8}{9} = c$

$\frac{63}{90} - \frac{80}{90} = c$

$-\frac{17}{90} = c$

30. $18\frac{6}{7} + 2\frac{3}{5} = a$

$18\frac{30}{35} + 2\frac{21}{35} = a$

$20\frac{51}{35} = a$

$21\frac{16}{35} = a$

31. $x + z = \frac{5}{8} + 2\frac{7}{12}$

$= \frac{15}{24} + 2\frac{14}{24}$

$= 2\frac{29}{24}$

$= 3\frac{5}{24}$

32. $z + y = 2\frac{7}{12} + \left(-\frac{3}{4}\right)$

$= 2\frac{7}{12} - \frac{3}{4}$

$= 2\frac{7}{12} - \frac{9}{12}$

$= 1\frac{19}{12} - \frac{9}{12}$

$= 1\frac{10}{12}$

$= 1\frac{5}{6}$

33. $y - x = -\frac{3}{4} - \frac{5}{8}$

$= -\frac{6}{8} - \frac{5}{8}$

$= -\frac{11}{8}$

$= -1\frac{3}{8}$

34. $x + y + z = \frac{5}{8} + \left(-\frac{3}{4}\right) + 2\frac{7}{12}$

$\qquad = \frac{5}{8} + \frac{3}{4} + 2\frac{7}{12}$

$\qquad = \frac{5}{8} + 2\frac{7}{12} - \frac{3}{4}$

$\qquad = \frac{15}{24} + 2\frac{14}{24} - \frac{18}{24}$

$\qquad = 2\frac{29}{24} - \frac{18}{24}$

$\qquad = 2\frac{11}{24}$

35. $z - x + y = 2\frac{7}{12} - \frac{5}{8} + \left(-\frac{3}{4}\right)$

$\qquad = 2\frac{7}{12} - \frac{5}{8} - \frac{3}{4}$

$\qquad = 2\frac{14}{24} - \frac{33}{24}$

$\qquad = 1\frac{38}{24} - \frac{33}{24}$

$\qquad = 1\frac{5}{24}$

36. $z + x - y = 2\frac{7}{12} + \frac{5}{8} - \left(-\frac{3}{4}\right)$

$\qquad = 2\frac{7}{12} + \frac{5}{8} + \frac{3}{4}$

$\qquad = 2\frac{14}{24} + \frac{15}{24} + \frac{18}{24}$

$\qquad = 2\frac{47}{24}$

$\qquad = 3\frac{23}{24}$

37. Sample answer: $\frac{1}{18} + \frac{1}{6}$

38.
$$\begin{array}{rcl} \frac{5}{8} & = & \frac{5}{8} \\ 5\frac{1}{2} & = & 5\frac{4}{8} \\ \frac{3}{4} & = & \frac{6}{8} \\ +\frac{7}{8} & = & +\frac{7}{8} \\ \hline & & 5\frac{22}{8} = 7\frac{6}{8} \text{ or } 7\frac{3}{4} \text{ in.} \end{array}$$

39. $\frac{1}{6} - \frac{1}{17} = \frac{17}{102} - \frac{6}{102}$

$\qquad = \frac{11}{102}$

40. $5\frac{1}{3}b + 3\frac{2}{3}b - 2\frac{1}{3}b = \left(5\frac{1}{3} + 3\frac{2}{3} - 2\frac{1}{3}\right)b$

$\qquad = \left(8\frac{3}{3} - 2\frac{1}{3}\right)b$

$\qquad = \left[(8 - 2) + \left(\frac{3}{3} - \frac{1}{3}\right)\right]b$

$\qquad = \left(6 + \frac{2}{3}\right)b$

$\qquad = 6\frac{2}{3}b$

41. $\frac{t^3}{s^2}$

42. $p = \frac{\ell \cdot w}{15}$

$\qquad p = \frac{18 \cdot 5}{15}$

$\qquad p = \frac{90}{15}$

$\qquad p = 6$

43. $b = -40 \div 8$

$\qquad b = -5$

44. $-8(3)(-2) = 48$

45. $y = 9 - (-4)$

$\qquad y = 9 + 4$

$\qquad y = 13$

46. $-11, -3, -1, 9, 12$

47. $3x + 15x = (3 + 15)x$

$\qquad = 18x$

Page 247 Self Test

1. Let $N = -0.1666\ldots$ Then $10N = -1.666\ldots$
and $100N = -16.666\ldots$

$$\begin{array}{r} 100N = -16.666\ldots \\ -\ 10N = \ -1.666\ldots \\ \hline 90N = -15 \\ N = -\frac{15}{90} \\ N = -\frac{1}{6} \end{array}$$

Therefore, $-0.1\overline{6} = -\frac{1}{6}$

2. $2.98 = 2\frac{98}{100} = 2\frac{49}{50}$

3. Let $N = 1.444\ldots$ Then $10N = 14.444\ldots$

$$\begin{array}{r} 10N = 14.444\ldots \\ -\ 1N = \ 1.444\ldots \\ \hline 9N = 13 \\ N = \frac{13}{9} \\ N = 1\frac{4}{9} \end{array}$$

4. Sample answer:
$\$50.00 - \$37.52 \rightarrow 50 - 38 = \$12.00$
$\$50.00 - \$37.52$ is about $\$12.00$.

5. Sample answer:
$\frac{8}{9} + \frac{1}{15} \rightarrow 1 + 0 = 1$

6. Sample answer:
$\frac{9}{11} - \frac{5}{12} \rightarrow 1 - \frac{1}{2} = \frac{1}{2}$

7. $r = 5.4 + 9.12$
$$\begin{array}{r} 5.40 \\ +\ 9.12 \\ \hline 14.52 \end{array}$$
$r = 14.52$

8. $90.6 - 33.1 = k$
$$\begin{array}{r} 90.6 \\ -\ 33.1 \\ \hline 57.5 \end{array}$$
$k = 57.5$

9. $m = 17.4 - (-13.2)$
$m = 17.4 + 13.2$
$$\begin{array}{r} 17.4 \\ +\ 13.2 \\ \hline 30.6 \end{array}$$
$m = 30.6$

10. $\frac{8}{10} + \frac{3}{10} = a$

$\qquad \frac{11}{10} = a$

$\qquad 1\frac{1}{10} = a$

11. $b = 4\frac{6}{7} + \frac{2}{7}$

$\qquad b = 4 + \left(\frac{6}{7} + \frac{2}{7}\right)$

$\qquad b = 4 + \frac{8}{7}$

$\qquad b = 4 + 1\frac{1}{7}$

$\qquad b = 5\frac{1}{7}$

12. $8\frac{5}{35} - 2\frac{8}{35} = d$

$\qquad 7\frac{40}{35} - 2\frac{8}{35} = d$

$\qquad (7 - 2) + \left(\frac{40}{35} - \frac{8}{35}\right) = d$

$\qquad 5 + \frac{32}{35} = d$

$\qquad 5\frac{32}{35} = d$

13. $10 - \frac{1}{2} - \frac{3}{4} = \frac{40}{4} - \frac{2}{4} - \frac{3}{4}$

$\qquad = \frac{40}{4} - \frac{5}{4}$

$\qquad = \frac{35}{4}$

$\qquad = 8\frac{3}{4}$ inches

Page 249   Checking Your Understanding

1. addition property of equality

2. Sample answer: add 8.9 to each side to isolate the x.

3. Sample answer: $6.9 + 8.5 \neq 14.7$

4.
$$\frac{7}{6} = m + \frac{5}{12}$$
$$\frac{7}{6} - \frac{5}{12} = m + \frac{5}{12} - \frac{5}{12}$$
$$\frac{14}{12} = \frac{5}{12} = m$$
$$\frac{9}{12} = m$$
$$\frac{3}{4} = m$$

Check: $\frac{7}{6} = m + \frac{5}{12}$
$$\frac{7}{6} \stackrel{?}{=} \frac{3}{4} + \frac{5}{12}$$
$$\frac{7}{6} \stackrel{?}{=} \frac{9}{12} + \frac{5}{12}$$
$$\frac{7}{6} = \frac{14}{12} ✔$$

5.
$$\frac{2}{3} + r = \frac{3}{5}$$
$$\frac{2}{3} + r - \frac{2}{3} = \frac{3}{5} - \frac{2}{3}$$
$$r = \frac{9}{15} - \frac{10}{15}$$
$$r = -\frac{1}{15}$$

Check: $\frac{2}{3} + r = \frac{3}{5}$
$$\frac{2}{3} + \left(-\frac{1}{15}\right) \stackrel{?}{=} \frac{3}{5}$$
$$\frac{10}{15} + \left(-\frac{1}{15}\right) \stackrel{?}{=} \frac{3}{5}$$
$$\frac{9}{15} = \frac{3}{5} ✔$$

6.
$$7\frac{1}{2} = x - 5\frac{2}{3}$$
$$7\frac{1}{2} + 5\frac{2}{3} = x - 5\frac{2}{3} + 5\frac{2}{3}$$
$$7\frac{3}{6} + 5\frac{4}{6} = x$$
$$12\frac{7}{6} = x$$
$$13\frac{1}{6} = x$$

Check: $7\frac{1}{2} = x - 5\frac{2}{3}$
$$7\frac{1}{2} \stackrel{?}{=} 13\frac{1}{6} - 5\frac{2}{3}$$
$$7\frac{1}{2} \stackrel{?}{=} 13\frac{1}{6} - 5\frac{4}{6}$$
$$7\frac{1}{2} \stackrel{?}{=} 12\frac{7}{6} - 5\frac{4}{6}$$
$$7\frac{1}{2} = 7\frac{3}{6} ✔$$

7.
$$m - 4.1 = -9.38$$
$$m - 4.1 + 4.1 = -9.38 + 4.1$$
$$m = -5.28$$

Check: $m - 4.1 = -9.38$
$$-5.28 - 4.1 \stackrel{?}{=} -9.38$$
$$-9.38 = -9.38 ✔$$

8.
$$y + 7.2 = 21.9$$
$$y + 7.2 - 7.2 = 21.9 - 7.2$$
$$y = 14.7$$

Check: $y + 7.2 = 21.9$
$$14.7 + 7.2 \stackrel{?}{=} 21.9$$
$$21.9 = 21.9 ✔$$

9.
$$x - 1.5 = 1.75$$
$$x - 1.5 + 1.5 = 1.75 + 1.5$$
$$x = 3.25$$

Check: $x - 1.5 = 1.75$
$$3.25 - 1.5 \stackrel{?}{=} 1.75$$
$$1.75 = 1.75 ✔$$

10.
$$a - 1\frac{1}{3} = 4\frac{1}{6}$$
$$a - 1\frac{1}{3} + 1\frac{1}{3} = 4\frac{1}{6} + 1\frac{1}{3}$$
$$a = 4\frac{1}{6} + 1\frac{2}{6}$$
$$a = 5\frac{3}{6}$$
$$a = 5\frac{1}{2}$$

Check: $a - 1\frac{1}{3} = 4\frac{1}{6}$
$$5\frac{1}{2} - 1\frac{1}{3} \stackrel{?}{=} 4\frac{1}{6}$$
$$5\frac{3}{6} - 1\frac{2}{6} \stackrel{?}{=} 4\frac{1}{6}$$
$$4\frac{1}{6} = 4\frac{1}{6} ✔$$

11.
$$-13.7 = b - 5$$
$$-13.7 + 5 = b - 5 + 5$$
$$-8.7 = b$$

Check: $-13.7 = b - 5$
$$-13.7 \stackrel{?}{=} -8.7 - 5$$
$$-13.7 = -13.7 ✔$$

12.
$$y + 3.17 = -3.17$$
$$y + 3.17 - 3.17 = -3.17 - 3.17$$
$$y = -6.34$$

Check: $y + 3.17 = -3.17$
$$-6.24 + 3.17 \stackrel{?}{=} -3.17$$
$$-3.17 = -3.17 ✔$$

13. $26{,}397.3 - 26{,}375.4 = 21.9$ miles

Page 250   Exercises

14.
$$y + 3.5 = 14.9$$
$$y + 3.5 + 3.5 = 14.9 - 3.5$$
$$y = 11.4$$

Check: $y + 3.5 = 14.9$
$$11.4 + 3.5 \stackrel{?}{=} 14.9$$
$$14.9 = 14.9 ✔$$

15.
$$r - 8.5 = -2.1$$
$$r - 8.5 + 8.5 = -2.1 + 8.5$$
$$r = 6.4$$

Check: $r - 8.5 = -2.1$
$$6.4 - 8.5 \stackrel{?}{=} -2.1$$
$$-2.1 = -2.1 ✔$$

16.
$$a - \frac{3}{5} = \frac{5}{6}$$
$$a - \frac{3}{5} + \frac{3}{5} = \frac{5}{6} + \frac{3}{5}$$
$$a = \frac{25}{30} + \frac{18}{30}$$
$$a = \frac{43}{30}$$
$$a = 1\frac{13}{30}$$

Check: $a - \frac{3}{5} = \frac{5}{6}$

$1\frac{13}{30} - \frac{3}{5} \stackrel{?}{=} \frac{5}{6}$

$1\frac{13}{30} - \frac{18}{30} \stackrel{?}{=} \frac{5}{6}$

$\frac{43}{30} - \frac{18}{30} \stackrel{?}{=} \frac{5}{6}$

$\frac{25}{30} = \frac{5}{6}$ ✔

17. $b - 1\frac{1}{2} = 14\frac{1}{4}$

$b - 1\frac{1}{2} + 1\frac{1}{2} = 14\frac{1}{4} + 1\frac{1}{2}$

$b = 14\frac{1}{4} + 1\frac{2}{4}$

$b = 15\frac{3}{4}$

Check: $b - 1\frac{1}{2} = 14\frac{1}{4}$

$15\frac{3}{4} - 1\frac{1}{2} \stackrel{?}{=} 14\frac{1}{4}$

$15\frac{3}{4} - 1\frac{2}{4} \stackrel{?}{=} 14\frac{1}{4}$

$14\frac{1}{4} = 14\frac{1}{4}$ ✔

18. $a + 7.1 = 4.7$

$a + 7.1 - 7.1 = 4.7 - 7.1$

$a = -2.4$

Check: $a + 7.1 = 4.7$

$-2.4 + 7.1 \stackrel{?}{=} 4.7$

$4.7 = 4.7$ ✔

19. $b - 5.3 = 8.1$

$b - 5.3 + 5.3 = 8.1 + 5.3$

$b = 13.4$

Check: $b - 5.3 = 8.1$

$13.4 - 5.3 \stackrel{?}{=} 8.1$

$8.1 = 8.1$ ✔

20. $y + 1\frac{1}{3} = 3\frac{1}{18}$

$y + 1\frac{1}{3} - 1\frac{1}{3} = 3\frac{1}{18} - 1\frac{1}{3}$

$y = 3\frac{1}{18} - 1\frac{6}{18}$

$y = 2\frac{19}{18} - 1\frac{6}{18}$

$y = 1\frac{13}{18}$

Check: $y + 1\frac{1}{3} = 3\frac{1}{18}$

$1\frac{13}{18} + 1\frac{1}{3} \stackrel{?}{=} 3\frac{1}{18}$

$1\frac{13}{18} + 1\frac{6}{18} \stackrel{?}{=} 3\frac{1}{18}$

$2\frac{19}{18} \stackrel{?}{=} 3\frac{1}{18}$

$3\frac{1}{18} = 3\frac{1}{18}$ ✔

21. $m + \frac{7}{12} = -\frac{5}{18}$

$m + \frac{7}{12} - \frac{7}{12} = -\frac{5}{18} - \frac{7}{12}$

$m = -\frac{10}{36} - \frac{21}{36}$

$m = -\frac{31}{36}$

Check: $m + \frac{7}{12} = -\frac{5}{8}$

$-\frac{31}{36} + \frac{7}{12} \stackrel{?}{=} -\frac{5}{8}$

$-\frac{31}{36} + \frac{21}{36} \stackrel{?}{=} -\frac{5}{8}$

$\frac{10}{36} = -\frac{5}{8}$ ✔

22. $x + \frac{5}{8} = 7\frac{1}{2}$

$x + \frac{5}{8} - \frac{5}{6} = 7\frac{1}{2} - \frac{5}{8}$

$x = 7\frac{4}{8} - \frac{5}{8}$

$x = 6\frac{12}{8} - \frac{5}{8}$

$x = 6\frac{7}{8}$

Check: $x + \frac{5}{8} = 7\frac{1}{2}$

$6\frac{7}{8} + \frac{5}{8} \stackrel{?}{=} 7\frac{1}{2}$

$6\frac{12}{8} \stackrel{?}{=} 7\frac{1}{2}$

$7\frac{4}{8} = 7\frac{1}{2}$ ✔

23. $k - \frac{3}{8} = 1\frac{3}{5}$

$k - \frac{3}{8} + \frac{3}{8} = 1\frac{3}{5} + \frac{3}{8}$

$k = 1\frac{24}{40} + \frac{15}{40}$

$k = 1\frac{39}{40}$

Check: $k - \frac{3}{8} = 1\frac{3}{5}$

$1\frac{39}{40} - \frac{3}{8} \stackrel{?}{=} 1\frac{3}{5}$

$1\frac{39}{40} - \frac{15}{40} \stackrel{?}{=} 1\frac{3}{5}$

$1\frac{24}{40} = 1\frac{3}{5}$ ✔

24. $n + 1.4 = 0.72$

$n + 1.4 - 1.4 = 0.72 - 1.4$

$n = -0.68$

Check: $n + 1.4 = 0.72$

$-0.68 + 1.4 \stackrel{?}{=} 0.72$

$0.72 = 0.72$ ✔

25. $d - (-31.4) = 28.6$

$d + 31.4 = 28.6$

$d + 31.4 - 31.4 = 28.6 - 31.4$

$d = -2.8$

Check: $d - (-31.4) = 28.6$

$-2.8 - (-31.4) \stackrel{?}{=} 28.6$

$-2.8 + 31.4 \stackrel{?}{=} 28.6$

$28.6 = 28.6$ ✔

26. $w - 0.04 = 1.2$

$w - 0.04 + 0.04 = 1.2 + 0.04$

$w = 1.24$

Check: $w - 0.04 = 1.2$

$1.24 - 0.04 \stackrel{?}{=} 1.2$

$1.2 = 1.2$ ✔

27. $d + (-7.03) = 0.98$

$d - 7.03 = 0.98$

$d - 7.03 + 7.03 = 0.98 + 7.03$

$d = 8.01$

Check: $d + (-7.03) = 0.98$

$8.01 + (-7.03) \stackrel{?}{=} 0.98$

$0.98 = 0.98$ ✔

28.
$$5\tfrac{3}{10} + z = 2\tfrac{2}{3}$$
$$5\tfrac{3}{10} + z - 5\tfrac{3}{10} = 2\tfrac{2}{3} - 5\tfrac{3}{10}$$
$$z = 2\tfrac{20}{30} - 5\tfrac{9}{30}$$
$$z = \tfrac{80}{30} - \tfrac{159}{30}$$
$$z = -\tfrac{79}{30}$$
$$z = -2\tfrac{19}{30}$$

Check: $\quad 5\tfrac{3}{10} + z = 2\tfrac{2}{3}$
$$5\tfrac{3}{10} + \left(-2\tfrac{19}{30}\right) \stackrel{?}{=} 2\tfrac{2}{3}$$
$$5\tfrac{9}{30} + \left(-2\tfrac{19}{30}\right) \stackrel{?}{=} 2\tfrac{2}{3}$$
$$4\tfrac{39}{30} - 2\tfrac{19}{30} \stackrel{?}{=} 2\tfrac{2}{3}$$
$$2\tfrac{20}{30} \stackrel{?}{=} 2\tfrac{2}{3} \checkmark$$

29.
$$v - 4\tfrac{7}{9} = 8\tfrac{1}{6}$$
$$v - 4\tfrac{7}{9} + 4\tfrac{7}{9} = 8\tfrac{1}{6} + 4\tfrac{7}{9}$$
$$v = 8\tfrac{3}{18} + 4\tfrac{14}{18}$$
$$v = 12\tfrac{17}{18}$$

Check: $v - 4\tfrac{7}{9} = 8\tfrac{1}{6}$
$$12\tfrac{17}{18} - 4\tfrac{7}{9} \stackrel{?}{=} 8\tfrac{1}{6}$$
$$12\tfrac{17}{18} - 4\tfrac{14}{18} \stackrel{?}{=} 8\tfrac{1}{6}$$
$$8\tfrac{3}{18} = 8\tfrac{1}{6} \checkmark$$

30.
$$501.1 = y - 9.32$$
$$501.1 + 9.32 = y - 9.32 + 9.32$$
$$510.42 = y$$

Check: $501.1 = y - 9.32$
$$501.1 \stackrel{?}{=} 510.42 - 9.32$$
$$501.1 = 501.1 \checkmark$$

31.
$$\tfrac{1}{312} + t = \tfrac{5}{78}$$
$$\tfrac{1}{312} + t - \tfrac{1}{312} = \tfrac{5}{78} - \tfrac{1}{312}$$
$$t = \tfrac{20}{312} - \tfrac{1}{312}$$
$$t = \tfrac{19}{312}$$

Check: $\quad \tfrac{1}{312} + t = \tfrac{5}{78}$
$$\tfrac{1}{312} + \tfrac{19}{312} \stackrel{?}{=} \tfrac{5}{78}$$
$$\tfrac{20}{312} = \tfrac{5}{78} \checkmark$$

32. Sample answer: 6, 1.2

33.
$$684.0 + x = 1372.2$$
$$684.0 + x - 684.0 = 1372.2 - 684.0$$
$$x = 688.2 \text{ million barrels}$$

34.
$$75.5° + 60.3° + x = 180.0°$$
$$135.8° + x = 180.0°$$
$$135.8° + x - 135.8° = 180.0° - 135.8°$$
$$x = 44.2°$$

35. $1.65 - 1.26 = 0.39$
0.39 million or 390,000 metric tons

36. $\tfrac{1}{4} + \tfrac{1}{4} = \tfrac{2}{4}$ or $\tfrac{1}{2}$

37.
$$y = \tfrac{7}{8} + 4\tfrac{1}{24}$$
$$y = \tfrac{21}{24} + 4\tfrac{1}{24}$$
$$y = 4\tfrac{22}{24}$$
$$y = 4\tfrac{11}{12}$$

38. $420ab^3 = 2 \cdot 210 \quad \cdot \quad a \cdot b^3$
$$= 2 \cdot 2 \cdot 105 \quad \cdot \quad a \cdot b \cdot b \cdot b$$
$$= 2 \cdot 2 \cdot 3 \cdot 35 \cdot a \cdot b \cdot b \cdot b$$
$$= 2 \cdot 2 \cdot 3 \cdot 5 \cdot 7 \cdot a \cdot b \cdot b \cdot b$$

39.
$$\tfrac{d}{6} \geq -14$$
$$\tfrac{d}{6} \cdot 6 \geq -14 \cdot 6$$
$$d \geq -84$$

40. $A = \ell \cdot w$
$$A = 6 \cdot 4$$
$$A = 24 \text{ in}^2$$

41.
$$x + 5 = 23$$
$$x + 5 - 5 = 23 - 5$$
$$x = 18$$

42. $5'11" - 5'\,9" = 2$ inches

43. $\dfrac{90}{x} = 6$ $\quad$ What number
$\dfrac{90}{15} = 6$ $\quad$ times 6 is 90?
$$x = 15$$

5-7 $\quad$ **Solving Inequalities**

Page 253 $\quad$ Checking Your Understanding

1. The same procedure is used to solve both types of inequalities. You may have to rename fractions in order to solve inequalities involving rational numbers.

2. Sample answer: Sharon earns $65.50 plus tips each week delivering pizzas. How much will she have to make in tips to make more than $89.75?

3. $n > 3.4$

4.
$$m - 2\tfrac{3}{4} \geq \tfrac{7}{12}$$
$$m - 2\tfrac{3}{4} + 2\tfrac{3}{4} \geq \tfrac{7}{12} + 2\tfrac{3}{4}$$
$$m \geq \tfrac{7}{12} + 2\tfrac{9}{12}$$
$$m \geq 2\tfrac{16}{12}$$
$$m \geq 3\tfrac{4}{12}$$
$$m \geq 3\tfrac{1}{3}$$

Check: Try 4, a number greater than or equal to $3\tfrac{1}{3}$.
$$m - 2\tfrac{3}{4} \geq \tfrac{7}{12}$$
$$4 - 2\tfrac{3}{4} \stackrel{?}{\geq} \tfrac{7}{12}$$
$$\tfrac{16}{4} - \tfrac{11}{4} \stackrel{?}{\geq} \tfrac{7}{12}$$
$$\tfrac{5}{4} \geq \tfrac{7}{12} \checkmark$$

5. $x + \frac{5}{6} \le 3\frac{3}{5}$

$x + \frac{5}{6} - \frac{5}{6} \le 3\frac{3}{5} - \frac{5}{6}$

$x \le 3\frac{18}{30} - \frac{25}{30}$

$x \le 2\frac{48}{30} - \frac{25}{30}$

$x \le 2\frac{23}{30}$

Check: Try 0, a number less than or equal to $2\frac{23}{30}$.

$x + \frac{5}{6} \le 3\frac{3}{5}$

$0 + \frac{5}{6} \overset{?}{\le} 3\frac{3}{5}$

$\frac{5}{6} \le 3\frac{3}{5}$ ✔

6. $\frac{5}{9} < 1\frac{1}{2} + y$

$\frac{5}{9} - 1\frac{1}{2} < 1\frac{1}{2} + y - 1\frac{1}{2}$

$\frac{10}{18} - 1\frac{9}{18} < y$

$\frac{10}{18} - \frac{27}{18} < y$

$-\frac{17}{18} < y$

Check: Try 1, a number greater than $-\frac{17}{18}$.

$\frac{5}{9} < 1\frac{1}{2} + y$

$\frac{5}{9} \overset{?}{<} 1\frac{1}{2} + 1$

$\frac{5}{9} < 2\frac{1}{2}$ ✔

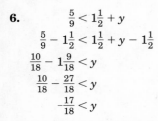

7. $x - 1.4 \le 7.9$

$x - 1.4 + 1.4 \le 7.9 + 1.4$

$x \le 9.3$

Check: Try 9, a number less than or equal to 9.3.

$x - 1.4 \le 7.9$

$9 - 1.4 \overset{?}{\le} 7.9$

$7.6 \le 7.9$

8. $n - 3.7 \ge 7.2$

$n - 3.7 + 3.7 \ge -7.2 + 3.7$

$n \ge -3.5$

Check: Try -1, a number greater than or equal to -3.5.

$n - 3.7 \ge -7.2$

$-1 - 3.7 \overset{?}{\ge} -7.2$

$-4.7 \ge -7.2$ ✔

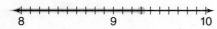

9. $y + 5.2 < 7.12$

$y + 5.2 - 5.2 < 7.12 - 5.2$

$y < 1.92$

Check: Try 1.5, a number less than 1.92.

$y + 5.2 < 7.12$

$1.5 + 5.2 \overset{?}{<} 7.12$

$6.7 < 7.12$ ✔

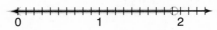

10. $2.5 + x > 36$

$2.5 + x - 2.5 > 36 - 2.5$

$x > 33.5$

more than 33.5 million

Pages 253–254 Exercises

11. $r + 7.5 \le 13.2$

$r + 7.5 - 7.5 \le 13.2 - 7.5$

$r \le 5.7$

Check: Try 4, a number less than or equal to 5.7.

$r + 7.5 \le 13.2$

$4 + 7.5 \overset{?}{\le} 13.2$

$11.5 \le 13.2$ ✔

12. $x + 4.2 \ge -7.3$

$x + 4.2 - 4.2 \ge -7.3 - 4.2$

$x \ge -11.5$

Check: Try -10, a number greater than or equal to -11.5.

$x + 4.2 \ge -7.3$

$-10 + 4.2 \overset{?}{\ge} -7.3$

$-5.8 \ge -7.3$ ✔

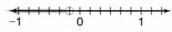

13. $y + \frac{3}{4} < \frac{7}{12}$

$y + \frac{3}{4} - \frac{3}{4} < \frac{7}{12} - \frac{3}{4}$

$y < \frac{7}{12} - \frac{9}{12}$

$y < -\frac{2}{12}$

$y < -\frac{1}{6}$

Check: Try -1, a number less than $-\frac{1}{6}$.

$y + \frac{3}{4} < \frac{7}{12}$

$-1 + \frac{3}{4} \overset{?}{<} \frac{7}{12}$

$-\frac{4}{4} + \frac{3}{4} \overset{?}{<} \frac{7}{12}$

$-\frac{1}{4} < \frac{7}{12}$ ✔

14.
$$a - 2\frac{2}{3} \geq 8\frac{5}{6}$$
$$a - 2\frac{2}{3} + 2\frac{2}{3} \geq 8\frac{5}{6} + 2\frac{2}{3}$$
$$a \geq 8\frac{5}{6} + 2\frac{4}{6}$$
$$a \geq 10\frac{9}{6}$$
$$a \geq 11\frac{3}{6}$$
$$a \geq 11\frac{1}{2}$$

Check: Try 12, a number greater than or equal to $11\frac{1}{2}$.
$$a - 2\frac{2}{3} \geq 8\frac{5}{6}$$
$$12 - 2\frac{2}{3} \stackrel{?}{\geq} 8\frac{5}{6}$$
$$\frac{36}{6} - \frac{8}{3} \stackrel{?}{\geq} 8\frac{5}{6}$$
$$\frac{28}{3} \stackrel{?}{\geq} 8\frac{5}{6}$$
$$9\frac{1}{3} \geq 8\frac{5}{6} ✔$$

15.
$$m - 3.1 < 7.4$$
$$m - 3.1 + 3.1 < 7.4 + 3.1$$
$$m < 10.5$$

Check: Try 10, a number less than 10.5.
$$m - 3.1 < 7.4$$
$$10 - 3.1 \stackrel{?}{<} 7.4$$
$$6.9 < 7.4 ✔$$

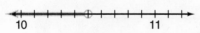

16.
$$b - 8.9 > \text{-}7.2$$
$$b - 8.9 + 8.9 > \text{-}7.2 + 8.9$$
$$b > 1.7$$

Check: Try 2, a number greater than 1.7.
$$b - 8.9 > \text{-}7.2$$
$$2 - 8.9 \stackrel{?}{>} \text{-}7.2$$
$$\text{-}6.9 > \text{-}7.2 ✔$$

17.
$$d - 1\frac{2}{3} < 1\frac{1}{6}$$
$$d - 1\frac{2}{3} + 1\frac{2}{3} < 1\frac{1}{6} + 1\frac{2}{3}$$
$$d < 1\frac{1}{6} + 1\frac{4}{6}$$
$$d < 2\frac{5}{6}$$

Check: Try 1, a number less than $2\frac{5}{6}$.
$$d - 1\frac{2}{3} < 1\frac{1}{6}$$
$$1 - 1\frac{2}{3} \stackrel{?}{<} 1\frac{1}{6}$$
$$\text{-}\frac{2}{3} < 1\frac{1}{6} ✔$$

18.
$$q - \frac{5}{12} \leq \frac{7}{18}$$
$$q - \frac{5}{12} + \frac{5}{12} \leq \frac{7}{18} + \frac{5}{12}$$
$$q \leq \frac{14}{36} + \frac{15}{36}$$
$$q \leq \frac{29}{36}$$

Check: Try $\frac{1}{2}$, a number less than or equal to $\frac{29}{36}$.
$$q - \frac{5}{12} \leq \frac{7}{18}$$
$$\frac{1}{2} - \frac{5}{12} \stackrel{?}{\leq} \frac{7}{18}$$
$$\frac{6}{12} - \frac{5}{12} \stackrel{?}{\leq} \frac{7}{18}$$
$$\frac{1}{12} \leq \frac{7}{18} ✔$$

19.
$$r + \frac{7}{8} \leq 2\frac{3}{4}$$
$$r + \frac{7}{8} - \frac{7}{8} \leq 2\frac{3}{4} - \frac{7}{8}$$
$$r \leq 2\frac{6}{8} - \frac{7}{8}$$
$$r \leq 1\frac{14}{8} - \frac{7}{8}$$
$$r \leq 1\frac{7}{8}$$

Check: Try 1, a number less than or equal to $1\frac{7}{8}$.
$$r + \frac{7}{8} \leq 2\frac{3}{4}$$
$$1 + \frac{7}{8} \stackrel{?}{\leq} 2\frac{3}{4}$$
$$1\frac{7}{8} \leq 2\frac{3}{4} ✔$$

20.
$$z - 1\frac{1}{2} \geq 4\frac{5}{9}$$
$$z - 1\frac{1}{2} + 1\frac{1}{2} \geq 4\frac{5}{9} + 1\frac{1}{2}$$
$$z \geq 4\frac{10}{18} + 1\frac{9}{18}$$
$$z \geq 5\frac{19}{18}$$
$$z \geq 6\frac{1}{18}$$

Check: Try 7, a number greater than or equal to $6\frac{1}{8}$.
$$z - 1\frac{1}{2} \geq 4\frac{5}{9}$$
$$7 - 1\frac{1}{2} \stackrel{?}{\geq} 4\frac{5}{9}$$
$$5\frac{1}{2} \geq 4\frac{5}{9} ✔$$

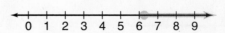

21.
$$\frac{3}{4} \leq \text{-}1\frac{1}{2} + w$$
$$\frac{3}{4} + 1\frac{1}{2} \leq \text{-}1\frac{1}{2} + w + 1\frac{1}{2}$$
$$\frac{3}{4} + 1\frac{2}{4} \leq w$$
$$1\frac{5}{4} \leq w$$
$$2\frac{1}{4} \leq w$$

Check: Try 3, a number greater than or
equal to $2\frac{1}{4}$.

$$\frac{3}{4} \le -1\frac{1}{2} + w$$
$$\frac{3}{4} \overset{?}{\le} -1\frac{1}{2} + 3$$
$$\frac{3}{4} \overset{?}{\le} -1\frac{1}{2} + \frac{6}{2}$$
$$\frac{3}{4} \overset{?}{\le} -\frac{3}{2} + \frac{6}{2}$$
$$\frac{3}{4} \le \frac{3}{2} \checkmark$$

22.
$$13.5 \le 18.3 + k$$
$$13.5 - 18.3 \le 18.3 + k - 18.3$$
$$-4.8 \le k$$

Check: Try -4, a number greater than or equal
to -4.8.
$$13.5 \le 18.3 + k$$
$$13.5 \overset{?}{\le} 18.3 - 4$$
$$13.5 \le 14.3 \checkmark$$

23.
$$h - 9.76 < 6.2$$
$$h - 9.76 + 9.76 < 6.2 + 9.76$$
$$h < 15.96$$

Check: Try 14, a number less than 15.96.
$$h - 9.76 < 6.2$$
$$14 - 9.76 \overset{?}{<} 6.2$$
$$4.24 < 6.2 \checkmark$$

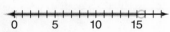

24.
$$7\frac{6}{11} + f > 2\frac{14}{15}$$
$$7\frac{6}{11} + f - 7\frac{6}{11} > 2\frac{14}{15} - 7\frac{6}{11}$$
$$f > 2\frac{154}{165} - 7\frac{90}{165}$$
$$f > \frac{484}{165} - \frac{1245}{165}$$
$$f > -\frac{761}{165}$$
$$f > -4\frac{101}{165}$$

Check: Try 0, a number greater than $-4\frac{101}{165}$.
$$7\frac{6}{11} + f > 2\frac{14}{15}$$
$$7\frac{6}{11} + 0 \overset{?}{>} 2\frac{14}{15}$$
$$7\frac{6}{11} > 2\frac{14}{15} \checkmark$$

25.
$$u - 9.03 \le 0.8$$
$$u - 9.03 + 9.03 \le 0.8 + 9.03$$
$$u \le 9.83$$

Check: Try 7, a number less than or equal to 9.83.
$$u - 9.03 \le 0.8$$
$$7 - 9.03 \overset{?}{\le} 0.8$$
$$-2.03 \le 0.8 \checkmark$$

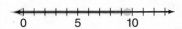

26.
$$n - 289.90 < 479.21$$
$$n - 289.90 + 289.90 < 479.21 + 289.90$$
$$n < 769.11$$

Check: Try 600, a number less than 769.11.
$$n - 289.90 < 479.21$$
$$600 - 289.90 \overset{?}{<} 479.21$$
$$310.1 < 479.21 \checkmark$$

27.
$$\frac{17}{18} + t > \frac{107}{108}$$
$$\frac{17}{18} + t - \frac{17}{18} > \frac{107}{108} - \frac{17}{18}$$
$$t > \frac{107}{108} - \frac{102}{108}$$
$$t > \frac{5}{108}$$

Check: Try 1, a number greater than $\frac{5}{108}$.
$$\frac{17}{18} + t > \frac{107}{108}$$
$$\frac{17}{18} + 1 > \frac{107}{108}$$
$$1\frac{17}{18} > \frac{107}{108}$$

28.
$$0.027 + k \le 0.00013$$
$$0.027 + k - 0.027 \le 0.00013 - 0.027$$
$$k \le -0.02687$$

Check: Try -1, a number less than or equal
to -0.02687.
$$0.027 + k \le 0.00013$$
$$0.027 - 1 \overset{?}{\le} 0.00013$$
$$-0.973 \le 0.00013$$

29. x is between 0 and 1 or x is less than -1.

30.
$$\$19.95 + s \le \$30.00$$
$$\$19.95 + s - \$19.95 \le \$30.00 - \$19.95$$
$$s \le \$10.05$$

31. $9.4 + 9.3 + 9.8 + 8.9 + x > 47.1$
$$37.4 + x > 47.1$$
$$37.4 + x - 37.4 > 47.1 - 37.4$$
$$x > 9.7$$

32. See students' work.

33. a. Sample answer: The average salary of a high
school graduate is slightly less than half of the
average salary of a college graduate.

b. Sample answer: No; if it was that low the
inequality would be written differently. The
inequality means that it is less than but close to
one-half.

34. $14\frac{3}{8} + 9\frac{1}{2} = 14\frac{3}{8} + 9\frac{4}{8}$

$\qquad\qquad = 23\frac{7}{8}$

So, $s < 23\frac{7}{8}$

35. $x + 3\frac{1}{2} = 7\frac{1}{4}$

$x + 3\frac{1}{2} - 3\frac{1}{2} = 7\frac{1}{4} - 3\frac{1}{2}$

$x = 7\frac{1}{4} - 3\frac{2}{4}$

$x = 6\frac{5}{4} - 3\frac{2}{4}$

$x = 3\frac{3}{4}$

36. $3a^{-2}$

37. $46:\boxed{2} \cdot 23$

$72:\boxed{2} \cdot 2 \cdot 2 \cdot 3 \cdot 2$

The GCF is 2.

38. $P = 2(\ell + w)$ $\qquad A = \ell \cdot w$

$P = 2(15 + 8)$ $\qquad A = 15 \cdot 8$

$P = 2(23)$ $\qquad\quad A = 120$ sq ft

$P = 46$ ft

39. $2a(-3b)(5c) = -30abc$

40. $w < 25$

41. a. Los Angeles

b. $55.8 - 35.8 = 20$ cents

Pages 255–256   Checking Your Understanding

1. Inductive reasoning is based upon past experience; deductive reasoning is based upon a given rule.

2. inductive reasoning

3. deductive; This uses a rule to draw a conclusion about a specific case.

4. See students' work.

5. Sample answer: inductive
See students' explanations.

6. Sample answer: deductive
See students' explanations.

7. Sample answer: inductive
See students' explanations.

Pages 256–257   Exercises

8. deductive; even integers are divisible by 2 by definition

9. 3,   6,   9,   12,   15,   18,   21

$\quad\;$ +3 +3 +3 +3 +3 +3

10. $n \cdot n = 196$

$14 \cdot 14 = 196$

$n = 14$

11. In each product, the numbers count up until the number of ones in the base is reached then the numbers count down to 1. So, $1111^2 = 1,234,321$.

12. $4 \times (5 - 2) + 7 = 19$

13. a. ground you; deductive

b. No, there could be another reason.

14. Use the strategy of eliminate possibilities. Make a table of possible numbers of Chicken Littles. Systematically cross off numbers that can be purchased.

Begin with all of the multiples of 6, 9, and 20, since these numbers can be purchased by buying a number of same-size boxes. Then cross off all combinations that can be purchased by buying one box of 6 and a number of boxes of 9. That is 15, 24, 33, and so on. Continue crossing off numbers that represent different numbers of boxes of different sizes.

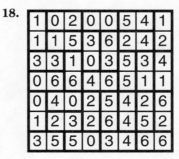

The circled numbers in the chart above are numbers of Chicken Littles that cannot be purchased. Crossed-off numbers indicate numbers that can be purchased using some combination of boxes.

Since you can buy 81 Chicken Littles, you can buy $81 + 20$ or 101 Chicken Littles by adding a box of 20 to the combination for 81. This logic can be extended to show that any number of Chicken Littles over 100 can be purchased. Thus, the greatest number of Chicken Littles that cannot be purchased is 43.

15. a. Each number being multiplied by 11 is increased by one. The product is the number being multiplied by 11 repeated. Therefore, 11×10 would be written as 1010.

b. $11 \times 10 = 110$

c. Inductive reasoning does not always work so it would not be wise to use it to prove something.

16. deductive

17. Look at the diagonal pattern. The piece needed should be pink.

18.

1	0	2	0	0	5	4	1
1	1	5	3	6	2	4	2
3	3	1	0	3	5	3	4
0	6	6	4	6	5	1	1
0	4	0	2	5	4	2	6
1	2	3	2	6	4	5	2
3	5	5	0	3	4	6	6

19. $\quad z - 4.71 \le -3.8$

$z - 4.71 + 4.71 \le -3.8 + 4.71$

$\qquad\qquad\quad z \le 0.91$

20.
$$a - 9\frac{5}{6} = 2\frac{3}{24}$$
$$a - 9\frac{5}{6} + 9\frac{5}{6} = 2\frac{3}{24} + 9\frac{5}{6}$$
$$a = 2\frac{3}{24} + 9\frac{20}{24}$$
$$a = 11\frac{23}{24}$$

21. $78: 2 \cdot 3 \cdot 13$
$35: 5 \cdot 7$
The GCF is 1.

22. $s = 3f - 21$
$s = 3(11) - 21$
$s = 33 - 21$
$s = 12$

23. $|-6| + |4| = 6 + 4$
$= 10$

Page 257   From the Funny Papers

1. Inductive; see students' explanations.
2. No; Milk doesn't boil down to nothing.

5-9   Integration: Discrete Mathematics Arithmetic Sequences

Page 258   Your Turn

a. 4400 feet or about $\frac{4}{5}$ miles

b. The distance increases by 1100 feet or $\frac{1}{5}$ mile with each second.

c. Add 1100 feet (or $\frac{1}{5}$ mile) to the previous distance.

Page 260   Checking Your Understanding

1. Sample answer; 1, 3, 5, 7, 9, . . .
2. Each term is the sum of the previous term and the common difference.
3. Find the difference between each pair of consecutive terms. If they are all the same, the sequence is arithmetic.
4. See students' work.

5. 2   5   8   11   14
$+3$ $+3$ $+3$ $+3$
Yes; 17, 20, 23

6. 5   9   13   17   21
$+4$ $+4$ $+4$ $+4$
Yes; 25, 29, 33

7. 17   16   14   11   7
-1 -2 -3 -4
No; 2, -4, -11

8. $\frac{3}{2}$ 2 $\frac{5}{2}$ 3
$+\frac{1}{2}$ $+\frac{1}{2}$ $+\frac{1}{2}$
Yes; $\frac{7}{2}$, 4, $\frac{9}{2}$

9. 3   5   8   12   17
$+2$ $+3$ $+4$ $+5$
No; 23, 30, 38

10. 15   25   40   60   85
$+10$ $+15$ $+20$ $+25$
No; 115, 150, 190

11. a. 9.95, 12.90, 15.85, 18.80, 21.75, 24.70
$+10$ $+15$ $+20$ $+25$ $+30$

b. $\$9.95 + 9(\$2.95) = \$9.95 + \$26.55$
$= \$36.50$

Pages 261–262   Exercises

12. 0.75   1.5   2.25   3
$+0.75$ $+0.75$ $+0.75$
Yes; 3.75, 4.5, 5.25

13. 4.5   4.0   3.5   3.0
-0.5 -0.5 -0.5
Yes; 2.5, 2.0, 1.5

14. 0   1100   2200   3300
$+1100$ $+1100$ $+1100$
Yes; 4400, 5500, 6600

15. 1, 4, 9, 16
$1^2, 2^2, 3^2, 4^2$
No; 25, 36, 49

16. 1   1   1   1   1
$+0$ $+0$ $+0$ $+0$
Yes; 1, 1, 1

17. 1   2   4   8   16
$\times 2$ $\times 2$ $\times 2$ $\times 2$
No; 32, 64, 128

18. 7   10   13   16
$+3$ $+3$ $+3$
Yes; 19, 22, 25

19. 91   82   73   64
-9 -9 -9
Yes; 55, 46, 37

20. 83   77   71   65
-6 -6 -6
Yes; 59, 53, 47

21. 19   15   11   7
-4 -4 -4
Yes; 3, -1, -5

22. 0.1   0.3   0.9   2.7
$\times 3$ $\times 3$ $\times 3$
No; 8.1, 24.3, 72.9

23. 5.47   6.49   7.51   8.53
$+1.02$ $+1.02$ $+1.02$
Yes; 9.55, 10.57, 11.59

24. 10   12   15   19   24
$+2$ $+3$ $+4$ $+5$
No; 30, 37, 45

25. 11   14   19   26   35
$+3$ $+5$ $+7$ $+9$
No; 46, 59, 74

26. 1 $\frac{1}{2}$ $\frac{1}{3}$ $\frac{1}{4}$
1^{-1} 2^{-1} 3^{-1} 4^{-1}
No; $\frac{1}{5}, \frac{1}{6}, \frac{1}{7}$

27. $\frac{3}{4}, \frac{4}{5}, \frac{5}{6}, \frac{6}{7} \cdots \frac{x}{x+1}$
No; $\frac{7}{8}, \frac{8}{9}, \frac{9}{10}$

28. 35   32   29   26   23,   20
-3 -3 -3 -3 -3

29. 7,   18,   29,   40, + . . .
$+11$ $+11$ $+11$
7; 11

30. $a + (n - 1)d = 2 + (25 - 1)2$
$\qquad\qquad\qquad = 2 + (24)2$
$\qquad\qquad\qquad = 2 + 48$
$\qquad\qquad\qquad = 50$

31. 100, 125, 150, 175, 200, 225
$\qquad$ +25 +25 +25 +25 +25

32.

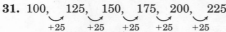

33. a. Sample answer:
10 miles = 10·5280 or 52, 800 feet
Each second, the light travels 1100 feet.
Thus, the light will travel 52,800 feet in
52,800 ÷ 1100 or 48 seconds.

b. $d = \frac{1}{5}t$

34. a. $\frac{1}{2}, \frac{1}{4}, \frac{1}{8}, \frac{1}{16}, \frac{1}{32}, \frac{1}{64}, \frac{1}{128}, \frac{1}{256}, \frac{1}{512}, \frac{1}{1024}$

b. No; each term is half of the previous term so there is no common difference.

c. 1

35. 32, 64, 96, 128, 160, 192, 224, 256, 288, 320, + ...
$\qquad$ +32 +32 +32 +32 +32 +32 +32 +32 +32

At the end of 10 seconds, the sandbag will be falling 320 feet/second.

36. a.

Mercury	25	26	27	28	29	30	31	32
Water	27.2	28.33	29.46	30.59	31.72	32.85	33.98	35.11

b. 27.2; 1.13

c. 32.85 feet

37. deductive
38. $x \cdot 125^{-1}$ or $x \cdot 5^{-3}$

39. $(x^6)(x^9) = x^{15}$

40. Quadrant III

41.

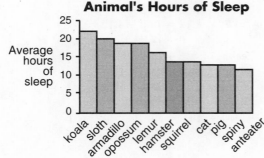

Animal's Hours of Sleep

Average hours of sleep (y-axis): 0, 5, 10, 15, 20, 25

koala, sloth, armadillo, opossum, lemur, hamster, squirrel, cat, pig, spiny anteater

42. $35 - m = 16$ or $35 - 16 = m$

Math Lab: Fibonacci Sequence

Page 263 Your Turn
1, 1, 2, 3, 5, 8, 13, 21, 34, 55

1. 13; See students' work.

2. 144, 8

3. 2, 5, 13, 34, . . .
The sequence is the 3rd, 5th, 7th, . . . terms of the Fibonacci sequence.

4. The Fibonacci numbers are found in spirals of pineapples. Since the scales of a pineapple are hexagonal, the spirals run in three distinct directions. Usually five rows run up the pineapple. Eight rows run more steeply down, and thirteen spirals run very steeply up the pineapple.

The seeds of a mature sunflower form two distinct spirals. One goes clockwise and the other goes counterclockwise. The number of spirals going one way and the number of spirals going the other way are usually adjacent Fibonacci numbers.

Chapter 5 Study Guide and Assessment

Page 265 Understanding and Using Vocabulary
1. B. rational number
2. H. inductive reasoning
3. I. scale
4. D. Commutative property of addition
5. C. integers
6. F. deductive reasoning
7. A. Identity property of addition

Pages 266–168 Skills and Concepts
8. Rational
9. Integer, Rationals
10. Whole, Integer, Rational
11. none

12. $3.25 = 3\frac{25}{100} = 3\frac{1}{4}$

13. $-9.45 = -9\frac{45}{100} = -9\frac{9}{20}$

14. $0.40 = \frac{40}{100} = \frac{2}{5}$
15. $-0.13 = -\frac{13}{100}$

16. Let $N = 0.727272 \ldots$ Then $100N = 72.727272 \ldots$
$\qquad 100N = 72.727272 \ldots$
$\qquad \underline{- \; 1N = 0.727272 \ldots}$
$\qquad\quad 99N = 72$
$\qquad\qquad N = \frac{72}{99}$
$\qquad\qquad N = \frac{8}{11}$
Therefore, $0.\overline{72} = \frac{8}{11}$.

17. Let $N = 4.24242424 \ldots$
Then $100N = 424.242424 \ldots$
$\qquad 100N = 424.242424 \ldots$
$\qquad \underline{- \; 1N = 4.242424 \ldots}$
$\qquad\quad 99N = 420$

$N = \frac{420}{99}$

$N = 4\frac{24}{99}$ or $4\frac{8}{33}$

18. Let $N = 0.0666\ldots$ Then $10N = 0.666\ldots$
and $100N = 6.666\ldots$

$100N = 6.666\ldots$
$\underline{-10N = 0.666\ldots}$
$90N = 6$

$N = \frac{6}{90}$ or $\frac{1}{15}$

Therefore $0.0\overline{6} = \frac{1}{15}$.

19. $8.89 = 8\frac{89}{100}$

20. Sample answer:
$53.6 + 41.2 \rightarrow 50 + 40 = 90$
$53.6 + 41.2$ is about 90.

21. Sample answer:
$4.99 + 3.29 \rightarrow 5 + 3 = 8$
$4.99 + 3.29$ is about 8.

22. Sample answer:
$325.44 - 249.25 \rightarrow 325 - 250 = 75$
$325.44 - 249.25$ is about 75.

23. Sample answer:
$50.00 - 39.89 \rightarrow 50 - 40 = 10$
$50.00 - 39.89$ is about 10.

24. Sample answer:
$\frac{11}{12} + \frac{6}{10} \rightarrow 1 + \frac{1}{2} = 1\frac{1}{2}$
$\frac{11}{12} + \frac{6}{10}$ is about $1\frac{1}{2}$.

25. Sample answer:
$\frac{24}{25} + \frac{1}{11} \rightarrow 1 + 0 = 1$
$\frac{24}{25} + \frac{1}{11}$ is about 1.

26. Sample answer:
$18\frac{1}{10} - 3\frac{1}{9} \rightarrow 18 - 3 = 15$
$18\frac{1}{10} - 3\frac{1}{9}$ is about 15.

27. Sample answer:
$24\frac{4}{7} - 22\frac{1}{6} \rightarrow 24\frac{1}{2} - 22 = 2\frac{1}{2}$
$24\frac{4}{7} - 22\frac{1}{6}$ is about $2\frac{1}{2}$.

28. $t = 8.5 + 42.25$

$\begin{array}{r} 42.25 \\ +\ 8.50 \\ \hline 50.75 \end{array}$

$t = 50.75$

29. $9.43 - (1.8) = p$
$9.43 + 1.8 = p$

$\begin{array}{r} 9.43 \\ +\ 1.80 \\ \hline 11.23 \end{array}$

$p = 11.23$

30. $j = -7.43 + 5.34$
$j = -|7.43 - 5.34|$

$\begin{array}{r} 7.43 \\ -\ 5.34 \\ \hline 2.09 \end{array}$

$j = -2.09$

31. $m = 17.19 - 24.87$
$m = -24.87 + 17.19$
$m = -|24.87 - 17.19|$

$\begin{array}{r} 24.87 \\ -\ 17.19 \\ \hline 7.68 \end{array}$

$m = -7.68$

32. $y = 13.983 + 4.52$

$\begin{array}{r} 13.983 \\ +\ 4.520 \\ \hline 18.503 \end{array}$

$y = 18.503$

33. $-8.52 - 9.43 = d$
$-8.52 + (-9.43) = d$

$\begin{array}{r} 9.43 \\ +\ 8.52 \\ \hline 17.95 \end{array}$

$d = -17.95$

34. $w = \frac{4}{7} + \frac{6}{7}$

$w = \frac{10}{7}$

$w = 1\frac{3}{7}$

35. $t = 5\frac{2}{9} + 8\frac{5}{9}$

$t = (5 + 8) + \left(\frac{2}{9} + \frac{5}{9}\right)$

$t = 13 + \frac{7}{9}$

$t = 13\frac{7}{9}$

36. $7\frac{4}{7} + \left(-2\frac{5}{7}\right) = s$

$7\frac{4}{7} - 2\frac{5}{7} = s$

$6\frac{11}{7} - 2\frac{5}{7} = s$

$(6 - 2) + \left(\frac{11}{7} - \frac{5}{7}\right) = s$

$4 + \frac{6}{7} = s$

$4\frac{6}{7} = s$

37. $\frac{7}{8} - \frac{5}{8} = b$

$\frac{2}{8} = b$

$\frac{1}{4} = b$

38. $k = 5\frac{1}{5} - 4\frac{4}{5}$

$k = 4\frac{6}{5} - 4\frac{4}{5}$

$k = (4 - 4) + \left(\frac{6}{5} - \frac{4}{5}\right)$

$k = 0 + \frac{2}{5}$

$k = \frac{2}{5}$

39. $\frac{4}{15} - \frac{13}{15} = y$

$-\frac{9}{15} = y$

$-\frac{3}{5} = y$

40. $\frac{3}{7} + \frac{11}{14} = q$

$\frac{6}{14} + \frac{11}{14} = q$

$\frac{17}{14} = q$

$1\frac{3}{14} = q$

41. $s = \frac{7}{15} - \frac{16}{30}$

$s = \frac{14}{30} - \frac{16}{30}$

$s = -\frac{2}{30}$

$s = -\frac{1}{15}$

42. $6\frac{4}{5} + 1\frac{3}{4} = h$

$6\frac{16}{20} + 1\frac{15}{20} = h$

$7\frac{31}{20} = h$

$8\frac{11}{20} = h$

43. $4\frac{1}{6} - \left(-2\frac{3}{4}\right) = m$

$4\frac{1}{6} + 2\frac{3}{4} = m$

$4\frac{4}{24} + 2\frac{18}{24} = m$

$6\frac{22}{24} = m$

$6\frac{11}{12} = m$

44. $1\frac{2}{5} + \frac{1}{3} = a$

$1\frac{6}{15} + \frac{5}{15} = a$

$1\frac{11}{15} = a$

45. $9\frac{5}{12} - 4\frac{7}{18} = h$

$9\frac{15}{36} - 4\frac{14}{36} = h$

$5\frac{1}{36} = h$

46. $v - 4.72 = 7.52$
$v - 4.72 + 4.72 = 7.52 - 4.72$
$v = 12.24$

Check: $v - 4.72 = 7.52$

$12.24 - 4.72 \overset{?}{=} 7.52$

$7.52 = 7.52$ ✔

47. $s + (-13.5) = -22.3$
$s - 13.5 = -22.3$
$s - 13.5 + 13.5 = -22.3 + 13.5$
$s = -8.8$

Check: $s + (-13.5) = -22.3$

$-8.8 + (-13.5) \overset{?}{=} -22.3$

$-22.3 = -22.3$ ✔

48. $x + \frac{3}{4} = -1\frac{2}{5}$

$x + \frac{3}{4} - \frac{3}{4} = -1\frac{2}{5} - \frac{3}{4}$

$x = -1\frac{8}{20} - \frac{15}{20}$

$x = -1\frac{23}{20}$

$x = -2\frac{3}{20}$

Check: $x + \frac{3}{4} = -1\frac{2}{5}$

$-2\frac{3}{20} + \frac{3}{4} \stackrel{?}{=} -1\frac{2}{5}$

$-2\frac{3}{20} + \frac{15}{20} \stackrel{?}{=} -1\frac{2}{5}$

$-\frac{43}{20} + \frac{15}{20} \stackrel{?}{=} -1\frac{2}{5}$

$-\frac{28}{20} \stackrel{?}{=} -1\frac{2}{5}$

$-1\frac{8}{20} = -1\frac{2}{5}$ ✔

49. $b - \frac{5}{8} = 1\frac{3}{16}$

$b - \frac{5}{8} + \frac{5}{8} = 1\frac{3}{16} + \frac{5}{8}$

$b = 1\frac{3}{16} + \frac{10}{16}$

$b = 1\frac{13}{16}$

Check: $b - \frac{5}{8} = 1\frac{3}{16}$

$1\frac{13}{16} - \frac{5}{8} \stackrel{?}{=} 1\frac{3}{16}$

$1\frac{13}{16} - \frac{10}{16} \stackrel{?}{=} 1\frac{3}{16}$

$1\frac{3}{16} = 1\frac{3}{16}$ ✔

50. $z - (-5.8) = 1.36$

$z + 5.8 = 1.36$

$z + 5.8 - 5.8 = 1.36 - 5.8$

$z = -4.44$

Check: $z - (-5.8) = 1.36$

$-4.44 - (-5.8) \stackrel{?}{=} 1.36$

$-4.44 + 5.8 \stackrel{?}{=} 1.36$

$1.36 = 1.36$ ✔

51. $k - \frac{4}{9} = 1\frac{7}{18}$

$k - \frac{4}{9} + \frac{4}{9} = 1\frac{7}{18} + \frac{4}{9}$

$k = 1\frac{7}{18} + \frac{8}{18}$

$k = 1\frac{15}{18}$

$k = 1\frac{5}{6}$

Check: $k - \frac{4}{9} = 1\frac{7}{18}$

$1\frac{5}{6} - \frac{4}{9} \stackrel{?}{=} 1\frac{7}{18}$

$1\frac{15}{18} - \frac{8}{18} \stackrel{?}{=} 1\frac{7}{18}$

$1\frac{7}{18} = 1\frac{7}{18}$ ✔

52. $w + \frac{7}{12} \geq \frac{5}{18}$

$w + \frac{7}{12} - \frac{7}{12} \geq \frac{5}{18} - \frac{7}{12}$

$w \geq \frac{10}{36} - \frac{21}{36}$

$w \geq -\frac{11}{36}$

Check: Try 0, a number greater than or equal to $-\frac{11}{36}$.

$w + \frac{7}{12} \geq \frac{5}{18}$

$0 + \frac{7}{12} \stackrel{?}{\geq} \frac{5}{18}$

$\frac{7}{12} \geq \frac{5}{18}$ ✔

53. $f - 3\frac{1}{4} \leq \frac{7}{8}$

$f - 3\frac{1}{4} + 3\frac{1}{4} \leq \frac{7}{8} + 3\frac{1}{4}$

$f \leq \frac{7}{8} + 3\frac{2}{8}$

$f \leq 3\frac{9}{8}$

$f \leq 4\frac{1}{8}$

Check: Try 3, a number less than or equal to $4\frac{1}{8}$.

$f - 3\frac{1}{4} \leq \frac{7}{8}$

$3 - 3\frac{1}{4} \stackrel{?}{\leq} \frac{7}{8}$

$-\frac{1}{4} \leq \frac{7}{8}$ ✔

54. $31.6 < -5.25 + g$

$31.6 + 5.26 < -5.26 + g + 5.26$

$36.86 < g$

Check: Try 37, a number greater than 36.86.

$31.6 < -5.26 + g$

$31.6 \stackrel{?}{<} -5.26 + 37$

$31.6 < 31.74$ ✔

55. $q - (-6.7) > 12$

$q + 6.7 > 12$

$q + 6.7 - 6.7 > 12 - 6.7$

$q > 5.3$

Check: Try 6, a number greater than 5.3.

$q - (-6.7) > 12$

$6 - (-6.7) \stackrel{?}{>} 12$

$6 + 6.7 \stackrel{?}{>} 12$

$12.7 > 12$ ✔

56. $w - 4.32 \leq 1.234$

$w - 4.32 + 4.32 \leq 1.234 + 4.32$

$w \leq 5.554$

Check: Try 4, a number less than or equal to 5.5554.

$w - 4.32 \leq 1.234$

$4 - 4.32 \stackrel{?}{\leq} 1.234$

$-0.32 \leq 1.234$ ✔

57.
$$m + 7.17 > 1.019$$
$$m + 7.17 - 7.17 > 1.019 - 7.17$$
$$m > -6.151$$
Check: Try -6, a number greater than -6.151.
$$m + 7.17 > 1.019$$
$$-6 + 7.17 \overset{?}{>} 1.019$$
$$1.17 > 1.019 ✔$$

58.
$$\frac{7}{6} + c \geq 3\frac{5}{24}$$
$$\frac{7}{6} + c - \frac{7}{6} \geq 3\frac{5}{24} - \frac{7}{6}$$
$$c \geq 3\frac{5}{24} - \frac{28}{24}$$
$$c \geq 2\frac{29}{24} - \frac{28}{24}$$
$$c \geq 2\frac{1}{24}$$
Check: Try 3, a number greater than or equal to $2\frac{1}{24}$.
$$\frac{7}{6} + c \geq 3\frac{5}{24}$$
$$\frac{7}{6} + 3 \overset{?}{\geq} 3\frac{5}{24}$$
$$3\frac{7}{6} \overset{?}{\geq} 3\frac{5}{24}$$
$$4\frac{1}{6} \geq 3\frac{5}{24} ✔$$

59.
$$a - \left(-\frac{3}{10}\right) \leq 1\frac{1}{5}$$
$$a + \frac{3}{10} \leq 1\frac{1}{5}$$
$$a + \frac{3}{10} - \frac{3}{10} \leq 1\frac{1}{5} - \frac{3}{10}$$
$$a \leq 1\frac{2}{10} - \frac{3}{10}$$
$$a \leq \frac{12}{10} - \frac{3}{10}$$
$$a \leq \frac{9}{10}$$
Check: Try 0, a number less than or equal to $\frac{9}{10}$.
$$a - \left(-\frac{3}{10}\right) \leq 1\frac{1}{5}$$
$$0 - \left(-\frac{3}{10}\right) \overset{?}{\leq} 1\frac{1}{5}$$
$$\frac{3}{10} \leq 1\frac{1}{15} ✔$$

60. 75 90 105
+15 +15
Yes; 120, 135, 150

61. 45 37 29 21
-8 -8 -8
Yes; 13, 5, -3

62. 0.0625 0.125 0.25
×2 ×2
No; 0.5, 1, 2

63. $\frac{10}{11}, \frac{9}{8}, \frac{7}{6}, \cdots \frac{x}{x-1}$
No; $\frac{4}{5}, \frac{2}{3}, \frac{0}{1}$

64. 67 58 49 40
-9 -9 -9
Yes; 31, 22, 13

Page 268 Applications and Problem Solving

65. a. $\frac{35}{1200}$ or $\frac{7}{240}$
b. Rational, it is a fraction.

66. $186.7 - 113.9 = 72.8$ million

67. 4 ft = 48 inches
$$48 - 41\frac{3}{8} = 47\frac{8}{8} - 41\frac{3}{8}$$
$$= (47 - 41) + \left(\frac{8}{8} - \frac{3}{8}\right)$$
$$= 6 + \frac{5}{8}$$
$$= 6\frac{5}{8} \text{ inches}$$

68. deductive reasoning, a rule used to make a conclusion about a specific case.

69. a. 25 units
b. The lengths are the squares of 1, 2, 3, ... It is not an arithmetic sequence because there is no common difference.

Page 269 Alternative Assessment

1. a. $\frac{18 \text{ inches}}{36 \text{ feet}} = \frac{18 \text{ inches}}{432 \text{ inches}} = \frac{1}{24}$
b. Rational, it is a fraction.

2.

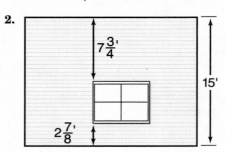

2. a. $15 - 7\frac{3}{4} - 2\frac{7}{8} \rightarrow 15 - 8 - 3 = 4$
The windows are about 4 feet tall.
b. $15 - 7\frac{3}{4} - 2\frac{7}{8} = 15 - 7\frac{6}{8} - 2\frac{7}{8}$
$$= 15 - 9\frac{13}{8}$$
$$= 15 - 10\frac{5}{8}$$
$$= \frac{120}{8} - \frac{85}{8}$$
$$= \frac{35}{8}$$
$$= 4\frac{3}{8}$$
The windows are exactly $4\frac{3}{8}$ feet tall.

3.

6.72 + 4.14 + 4.14 = 15
The front of the house is 15 feet wide.

4. Area (yard) = Area (house and yard) − Area (house)
Area (yard) = 43,560 − 1023.5
Area (yard) = 42,536.5 sq ft

5. Deductive; he used a rule to draw a conclusion about a specific case.

6. Sample answer:
1, 3, 5, 7 feet from the front

Page 269   Thinking Critically

- Sample answer: If you forgot the amount of your paycheck that was deposited in your checking account, you would want to underestimate the amount to find the estimated balance.
- Sample answer: You come closer to the actual answer when you round to the nearest tenth because the rounded number is closer to the actual number than if it were rounded to the nearest whole number.

Page 269   Portfolio

See students' work.

Page 269   Self Evaluation

See students' work.

| 6-1 |

Writing Fractions as Decimals

Page 277   Checking Your Understanding

1. Fractions represent division problems.

2. Terminating decimals have a zero remainder; repeating decimals have a pattern that repeats without end. Check students' examples.

3. $0.6 = 0.60$ and $0.\overline{6} = 0.66\ldots$; $0.\overline{6}$ is greater.

4. Juanita, $\frac{2}{3} = \frac{10}{15}$, $\frac{3}{5} = \frac{9}{15}$ and $\frac{10}{15} > \frac{9}{15}$.

5.
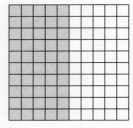

0.5

$\frac{1}{5}$

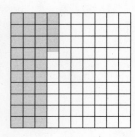

$\frac{1}{3}$

0.25

a. 0.5

b. $\frac{1}{5}$

c. $\frac{1}{5}$, 0.25, $\frac{1}{3}$, 0.45, 0.5

6.
$$\frac{5}{9} \to 9\overline{)5.000}$$
$$\underline{-45}$$
$$50$$
$$\underline{-45}$$
$$50$$
$$\underline{-45}$$
$$5$$
$$\frac{5}{9} = 0.\overline{5}$$
(quotient 0.555)

7. $2\frac{2}{3} = 2 + \frac{2}{3}$
$$\frac{2}{3} \to 3\overline{)2.000}$$
$$\underline{-18}$$
$$20$$
$$\underline{-18}$$
$$20$$
$$\underline{-18}$$
$$2$$
(quotient 0.666)
$$2 + 0.\overline{6} = 2.\overline{6}$$
$$2\frac{2}{3} \to 2.\overline{6}$$

8. $-3\frac{1}{8} = -\left(3 + \frac{1}{8}\right)$
$$\frac{1}{8} \to 8\overline{)1.000}$$
$$\underline{-8}$$
$$20$$
$$\underline{-16}$$
$$40$$
$$\underline{-40}$$
$$0$$
(quotient 0.125)
$$-(3 + 0.125) = -3.125$$
$$-3\frac{1}{8} = -3.125$$

9.
$$\frac{1}{8} \to 8\overline{)1.000}$$
$$\underline{-8}$$
$$20$$
$$\underline{-16}$$
$$40$$
$$\underline{-40}$$
$$0$$
(quotient 0.125)
$$\frac{1}{8} = 0.125$$

10. $\frac{1}{2} = 0.5$
$\frac{1}{3} = 0.\overline{3}$
$\frac{1}{2}$ is greater

11. $-\frac{3}{4} = -.075$
$-\frac{7}{8} = -0.825$
$-\frac{3}{4}$ is greater

12. $\frac{3}{8} = 0.375$
$\frac{10}{33} = 0.\overline{30}$
$\frac{3}{8}$ is greater

13. $-\frac{3}{4} = -0.75$
$-\frac{3}{4}$ is greater

14. On Monday, the stock closed at $16\frac{5}{8}$ or 16.625.

On Friday, the stock closed at $16\frac{3}{4}$ or 16.75. Therefore, the stock closed at a higher price on Friday.

Pages 277–279   Exercises

15. $\frac{7}{10} \to 10\overline{)7.0}$
$$\underline{-70}$$
$$0$$
$$\frac{7}{10} = 0.7$$
(quotient 0.7)

16. $-\frac{1}{3} \to -3\overline{)1.000}$
$$\underline{-9}$$
$$10$$
$$\underline{-9}$$
$$10$$
$$\underline{-9}$$
$$1$$
(quotient 0.333)
$$-\frac{1}{3} = -0.\overline{3}$$

17. $\frac{1}{2} \to 2\overline{)1.0}$
$$\underline{10}$$
$$0$$
$$\frac{1}{2} = 0.5$$
(quotient 0.5)

18. $-1\frac{1}{4} = -\left(1 + \frac{1}{4}\right)$
$$\frac{1}{4} \to 4\overline{)1.00}$$
$$\underline{-8}$$
$$20$$
$$\underline{-20}$$
$$0$$
(quotient 0.25)
$$-(1 + 0.25) = -1.25$$
$$-1\frac{1}{4} = -1.25$$

19. $\frac{14}{20} \to 20\overline{)14.0}$
$$\underline{-140}$$
$$0$$
$$\frac{14}{20} = 0.7$$
(quotient 0.7)

20. $-\frac{2}{9} \to 9\overline{)2.000}$
$$\underline{-18}$$
$$20$$
$$\underline{-18}$$
$$20$$
$$\underline{-18}$$
$$2$$
(quotient 0.222)
$$-\frac{2}{9} = -0.\overline{2}$$

21. $\frac{5}{16} \rightarrow 16\overline{)5.0000}$

$$\begin{array}{r} 0.3125 \\ \underline{-48} \\ 20 \\ \underline{-16} \\ 40 \\ \underline{-32} \\ 80 \\ \underline{-80} \\ 0 \end{array}$$

$\frac{5}{16} = 0.3125$

22. $\frac{21}{25} \rightarrow 25\overline{)21.00}$

$$\begin{array}{r} 0.84 \\ \underline{-20\,0} \\ 100 \\ \underline{-100} \\ 0 \end{array}$$

$\frac{21}{25} = 0.84$

23. $-3\frac{4}{11} \rightarrow -\left(3 + \frac{4}{11}\right)$

$\frac{4}{11} \rightarrow 11\overline{)4.0000}$

$$\begin{array}{r} 0.3636 \\ \underline{-3\,3} \\ 70 \\ \underline{-66} \\ 40 \\ \underline{-33} \\ 70 \\ \underline{-66} \\ 3 \end{array}$$

$-(3 + 0.\overline{36}) = -3.\overline{36}$

$-3\frac{4}{11} = -3.\overline{36}$

24. $\frac{23}{45} \rightarrow 45\overline{)23.000}$

$$\begin{array}{r} 0.511 \\ \underline{-22\,5} \\ 50 \\ \underline{-45} \\ 50 \\ \underline{-45} \\ 5 \end{array}$$

$\frac{23}{45} = 0.51\overline{1}$

25. $-4\frac{5}{16} = -\left(4 + \frac{5}{16}\right)$

$\frac{5}{16} \rightarrow 16\overline{)5.0000}$

$$\begin{array}{r} 0.3125 \\ \underline{-48} \\ 20 \\ \underline{-16} \\ 40 \\ \underline{-32} \\ 80 \\ \underline{-80} \\ 0 \end{array}$$

$-(4 + 0.3125) = -4.3125$

$-4\frac{5}{16} = 4.3125$

26. $\frac{31}{40} \rightarrow 40\overline{)31.000}$

$$\begin{array}{r} 0.775 \\ \underline{-28\,0} \\ 300 \\ \underline{-280} \\ 200 \\ \underline{-200} \\ 0 \end{array}$$

$\frac{31}{40} = 0.775$

27. $5\frac{1}{5} > 5.18$ because $5.2 > 5.18$

28. $7.56 > 7\frac{12}{25}$ because $7.56 > 7.48$

29. $-3.45 < 3\frac{2}{3}$ because $-3.45 < 3.\overline{6}$

30. $-1\frac{1}{20} < 1.01$ because $-1.05 < 1.01$

31. $\frac{7}{8} < \frac{8}{9}$ because $\frac{63}{72} < \frac{64}{72}$

32. $\frac{2}{5} > \frac{1}{3}$ because $\frac{6}{15} > \frac{5}{15}$

33. $3\frac{4}{7} < 3\frac{5}{8}$ because $3\frac{32}{56} < 3\frac{35}{56}$

34. $2\frac{5}{8} < 2\frac{2}{3}$ because $2\frac{15}{24} < 2\frac{16}{24}$

35. $-\frac{11}{14} > -\frac{13}{16}$ because $-\frac{176}{224} > -\frac{182}{224}$

36. $\frac{9}{11} < \frac{19}{23}$ because $\frac{207}{253} < \frac{209}{253}$

37. $1\frac{4}{5} < 1.857$ because $1.8 < 1.857$

38. $-5\frac{1}{12} > -5.09$ because $-5.08\overline{3} > -5.09$

39. $.7777777$

40. 0.7777777

41. 0.7777778

42. $.78$

43. $\frac{1}{3} = 0.\overline{3}$, $\frac{1}{4} = 0.25$, $\frac{7}{10} = 0.7$, $\frac{4}{5} = 0.8$,

$\frac{5}{12} = 0.41\overline{6}$, $\frac{4}{7} = 0.\overline{571428}$, $\frac{3}{25} = 0.12$

a. terminating: $\frac{1}{4}, \frac{7}{10}, \frac{4}{5}, \frac{3}{25}$;

repeating: $\frac{1}{3}, \frac{5}{12}, \frac{4}{7}$

b. $3 = 1 \times 3$

$4 = 2 \times 2$

$10 = 2 \times 5$

$5 = 1 \times 5$

$12 = 2 \times 2 \times 3$

$7 = 1 \times 7$

$25 = 5 \times 5$

c. 2 and 5; see students' work.

44. Sample answer: $\frac{3}{5}$ and $\frac{2}{3}$; see students' explanations.

45. $\frac{1}{3} \rightarrow 3\overline{)1.00}$

$$\begin{array}{r} 0.33 \\ \underline{-9} \\ 10 \\ \underline{-9} \\ 1 \end{array}$$

$\frac{1}{3} = 0.33$

46. yes, $\frac{6000}{6500} = 0.9231$

47. $82\frac{3}{8} = 82 + \frac{3}{8}$

$\frac{3}{8} \rightarrow 8\overline{)3.000}$

$$\begin{array}{r} 0.375 \\ \underline{-2\,4} \\ 60 \\ \underline{-56} \\ 40 \\ \underline{-40} \\ 0 \end{array}$$

$82 + 0.375 = 82.375$

$82\frac{3}{8} = \$82.38$

$46\frac{7}{8} = 46 + \frac{7}{8}$

$\frac{7}{8} \rightarrow 8\overline{)7.000}$

$$\begin{array}{r} 0.875 \\ \underline{-6\,4} \\ 60 \\ \underline{-56} \\ 40 \\ \underline{-40} \\ 0 \end{array}$$

$46 + 0.875 = 46.875$

$46\frac{7}{8} = \$46.88$

$36\frac{3}{4} = 36 + \frac{3}{4}$

$\frac{3}{4} \rightarrow 4\overline{)3.00}$

$$\begin{array}{r} 0.75 \\ \underline{-2\,8} \\ 20 \\ \underline{-20} \\ 0 \end{array}$$

$36 + 0.75 = 36.75$

$36\frac{3}{4} = \$36.75$

48. "It happens:" $\frac{2}{5} = \frac{10}{25}$

"It could happen:" $\frac{7}{25} = \frac{7}{25}$

"No way:" $\frac{8}{25} = \frac{8}{25}$

Most people responded "It happens."

49. $88, \underset{-6}{\frown} 82, \underset{-6}{\frown} 76, \underset{-6}{\frown} 70, \underset{-6}{\frown} 64, \underset{-6}{\frown} 58, \underset{-6}{\frown} 52$

50.
$$t - 3\frac{1}{4} = \frac{7}{2}$$
$$t - 3\frac{1}{4} + 3\frac{1}{4} = \frac{7}{12} + 3\frac{1}{4}$$
$$t = \frac{14}{4} + 3\frac{1}{4}$$
$$t = 3\frac{15}{4}$$
$$t = 6\frac{3}{4}$$

51. b^{11}

52.

Number	divisible by 2?	divisible by 3?	divisible by 6?
103	no	no	no
104	yes	no	no
107	no	no	no
108	yes	yes	yes

Sample answer: 108

53. $P = 2(\ell + w)$
$P = 2(6 + 4)$
$P = 2(10)$
$P = 20$ feet

54. $-7, -6, 0, 15, 20$

55. $r > 7$ or $r \geq 8$

56.
$$13 + y = 25$$
$$13 + y - 13 = 25 - 13$$
$$y = 12$$

57.
$3t = 81$ What number
$3(27) = 81$ times 3 is 81?
$t = 27$

6-2

Estimating Products and Quotients

Page 282 Checking Your Understanding

1. Sample answer: an estimate lets you check for possible errors in entering numbers into the calculator.

2. Sample answer: 36 and 6; $36 \div 6 = 6$

3. less than

4. See students' work.

5. $\left(1\frac{1}{8}\right)\left(3\frac{1}{4}\right) \to 1 \cdot 3 = 3$
Since both factors are greater than those used in the estimate, choice c is the most reasonable.

6. $49 \times \frac{2}{5} \to 50 \times \frac{2}{5} = 20$
Choice a is the most reasonable.

7. $\$24.99 \div 4 \to \$24 \div 4 = \$6$
Since \$24.99 was rounded down to estimate, the actual quotient will be greater than 6. Choice d is the best answer.

8. Sample answer:
$40 \times \frac{2}{9} \to 40 \times \frac{1}{4} = 10$
$40 \times \frac{2}{9}$ is about 10.

9. Sample answer:
$17.8 \div 3.2 \to$
$18 \div 3 = 6$
$17.8 \div 3.2$ is about 6.

10. Sample answer:
$\frac{5}{12} \times 44 \to \frac{1}{2} \times 44 = 22$
$\frac{5}{12} \times 44$ is about 22.

11. Sample answer:
$8.4 \div 0.95 \to$
$8 \div 1 = 8$
$8.4 \div 0.95$ is about 8.

12. Sample answer:
$75.4 \div 9.8 \to$
$70 \div 10 = 7$
$75.4 \div 9.8$ is about 7.

13. Sample answer:
$20\frac{1}{9} \times \frac{1}{4} \to 20 \times \frac{1}{4} = 5$
$20\frac{1}{9} \times \frac{1}{4}$ is about 5.

14. $P = 2(\ell + w)$
$\ell \approx 6, w \approx 3$
$P \approx 2(6 + 3)$
$P \approx 18$
The perimeter is less than 20 meters.

Page 282–283 Exercises

15. Sample answer:
$15.93 \times 9.8 \to$
$16 \times 10 = 160$
15.93×9.8 is about 160.

16. Sample answer:
$2.94 \cdot 1.8 \to$
$3 \cdot 2 = 6$
$2.94 \cdot 1.8$ is about 6.

17. Sample answer:
$8.1 \div 2.2 \to 8 \div 2 = 4$
$8.1 \div 2.2$ is about 4.

18. Sample answer:
$47.6 \div 7.8 \to$
$48 \div 8 = 6$
$47.6 \div 7.8$ is about 6.

19. Sample answer:
$15.2 \div 2.7 \to$
$15 \div 3 = 5$
$15.2 \div 2.7$ is about 5.

20. Sample answer:
$(84.2)(3.9) \to$
$(80)(4) = 320$
$(84.2)(3.9)$ is about 320.

21. Sample answer:
$\frac{1}{4} \cdot 9 \to \frac{1}{4} \cdot 8 = 2$
$\frac{1}{4} \cdot 9$ is about 2.

22. Sample answer:
$\left(\frac{1}{3}\right)(14) \to \left(\frac{1}{3}\right)(15) = 5$
$\left(\frac{1}{3}\right)(14)$ is about 5.

23. Sample answer:
$\frac{3}{8} \times 17 \to \frac{1}{3} \times 18 = 6$
$\frac{3}{8} \times 17$ is about 6.

24. Sample answer:
$\frac{9}{19} \times 120 \to$
$\frac{1}{2} \times 120 = 60$
$\frac{9}{19} \times 120$ is about 60.

25. Sample answer:
$\frac{11}{20} \times 41 \to$
$\frac{1}{2} \times 40 = 20$
$\frac{11}{20} \times 41$ is about 20.

26. Sample answer:
$75 \div 6\frac{7}{8} \to$
$70 \div 7 = 10$
$75 \div 6\frac{7}{8}$ is about 10.

27. Sample answer:
$\frac{31}{40} \times 200 \to$
$\frac{3}{4} \times 200 = 150$
$\frac{31}{40} \times 200$ is about 150.

28. Sample answer:
$146 \div 13\frac{1}{15} \to$
$156 \div 13 = 12$
$146 \div 13\frac{1}{15}$ is about 12.

29. Sample answer:
$43.8 \div 9.2 \to$
$45 \div 9 = 5$
$43.8 \div 9.2$ is about 5.

30. Sample answer:
$\frac{5}{6} \times 10 \to \frac{4}{6} \times 12 = 8$
$\frac{5}{6} \times 10$ is about 8.

31. Sample answer:
$27.26 \div 2.6 \to$
$30 \div 3 = 10$
$27.26 \div 26$ is about 10.

32. a. $80 \div 0.5 = 160$
$6 \div 0.5 = 12$
$1.5 \div 0.5 = 3$

b. $10 \div 0.1 = 100$
$2 \div 0.1 = 20$
$6.5 \div 0.1 = 65$

c. $4 \div 0.25 = 16$
$20 \div 0.25 = 80$
$1.1 \div 0.25 = 4.4$

d. The quotients of the numbers divided by 0.5 are the dividend multiplied by 2. The quotients of the numbers divided by 0.1 are the dividend multiplied by 10. The quotients of the numbers divided by 0.25 are the dividend multiplied by 4.

e. $14 \div 0.48 = 28$ **f.** $5 \div 0.12 = 50$

g. $12 \div 0.23 = 48$ **h.** $2\frac{1}{5} \div 0.25 = 8$

i. $21.2 \div 0.085 = 212$ **j.** $3\frac{1}{4} \div 0.51 = 6$

33. If the numbers were rounded up, the actual answer is less than the estimate. If the numbers were rounded down, the product is greater than the estimate.

34.

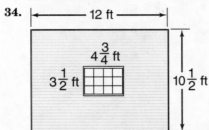

34. a. Round up for waste. She will need about 110 square feet of wallpaper.

b. $110 \div 51 \rightarrow 100 \div 50 = 2$
Since the numbers were rounded down, the quotient is greater than the estimate. Therefore, she should purchase 3 rolls of wallpaper.

35. $\frac{3}{50} \times 248{,}709{,}873 \rightarrow \frac{3}{50} \times 250{,}000{,}000 = 15{,}000{,}000$
$\frac{3}{50} \times 248{,}709{,}873$ is about $15{,}000{,}000$.

36. a. $37 \times \$107.25 \rightarrow 40 \times 110 = \$4400$

b. $\$1000 \div \$107.25 \rightarrow 1000 \div 110$ is about 9.

37. $\frac{1}{8} \times 37 \rightarrow \frac{1}{8} \times 40 = 5$ mph

38. $\frac{3}{8} \rightarrow 8)\overline{3.000}$
$\quad\quad\quad 0.375$
$\quad\quad\quad -2\,4$
$\quad\quad\quad\;\; 60$
$\quad\quad\quad -56$
$\quad\quad\quad\;\; 40$
$\quad\quad\quad -40$
$\quad\quad\quad\;\;\; 0$
$\frac{3}{8} = 0.375$

39. $\frac{6}{7} + \frac{5}{14} = s$
$\frac{12}{14} + \frac{5}{14} = s$
$\frac{17}{14} = s$
$1\frac{3}{14} = s$

40. $\frac{4}{6} = \frac{2}{3}$

41. $\quad -14 + c = 13$
$-14 + c + 14 = 13 + 14$
$\quad\quad\quad\quad c = 27$

42. $-13 + 6 = -(|13 - 6|)$
$\quad\quad\quad\quad = -7$

43. $|-6| - |-4| = 6 - 4$
$\quad\quad\quad\quad\quad = 2$

44. $\frac{r}{9} = 15$
$r = 15 \cdot 9$
$r = 135$

6-3 Multiplying Fractions

Page 284

a. See students' work.

b. See students' work.

c. $\frac{3}{5} \cdot \frac{1}{4} = \frac{3}{20}$

d. See students' work.

Pages 286–287 Checking Your Understanding

1. Yellow shading is $\frac{3}{4}$, blue shading is $\frac{1}{2}$, green shading is the product, $\frac{3}{8}$.

2. Jamal; Penny cancelled incorrectly.

3. D; see students' work.

4. a. See students' work.

b. See students' work.

5. d; $\frac{1}{6} \cdot \left(-\frac{3}{5}\right) = -\frac{3}{30}$ or $-\frac{1}{10}$

6. b; $\left(\frac{1}{2}\right)^2 = \frac{1}{2} \cdot \frac{1}{2} = \frac{1}{4}$

7. $\frac{3}{4} \cdot \frac{2}{3} = a$
$\frac{\overset{1}{\cancel{3}} \cdot \overset{1}{\cancel{2}}}{\underset{2}{\cancel{4}} \cdot \underset{1}{\cancel{3}}} = a$
$\frac{1 \cdot 1}{2 \cdot 1} = a$
$\frac{1}{2} = a$

8. $b = \frac{1}{2}\left(-\frac{5}{6}\right)$
$b = \frac{1 \cdot -5}{2 \cdot 6}$
$b = \frac{-5}{12}$

9. $c = \frac{8}{12} \cdot \frac{4}{6}$
$c = \frac{\overset{4}{\cancel{8}} \cdot \overset{1}{\cancel{4}}}{\underset{3}{\cancel{12}} \cdot \underset{3}{\cancel{6}}}$
$c = \frac{4 \cdot 1}{3 \cdot 3}$
$c = \frac{4}{9}$

10. $x = \left(3\frac{1}{2}\right)4$
$x = \left(\frac{7}{2}\right)\frac{4}{1}$
$x = \left(\frac{7}{\cancel{2}}\right)\frac{\overset{2}{\cancel{4}}}{1}$
$x = \frac{7 \cdot 2}{1 \cdot 1}$
$x = \frac{14}{1}$
$x = 14$

11. $m = \frac{8}{15}(-45)$
$m = \frac{8}{15}\left(-\frac{45}{1}\right)$
$m = \frac{8}{\underset{1}{\cancel{15}}}\left(-\frac{\overset{3}{\cancel{45}}}{1}\right)$
$m = \frac{8 \cdot -3}{1 \cdot 1}$
$m = \frac{-24}{1}$
$m = -24$

12. $\left(-\frac{4}{5}\right)^2 = p$
$\left(-\frac{4}{5}\right)\left(-\frac{4}{5}\right) = p$
$\frac{16}{25} = p$

13. $xy = \frac{3}{5} \cdot \frac{5}{8}$

$= \frac{3 \cdot \cancel{5}^{1}}{\cancel{5}_{1} \cdot 8}$

$= \frac{3 \cdot 1}{1 \cdot 8}$

$= \frac{3}{8}$

14. $2a = 2 \cdot \frac{2}{3}$

$= \frac{2}{1} \cdot \frac{2}{3}$

$= \frac{2 \cdot 2}{1 \cdot 3}$

$= \frac{4}{3}$

$= 1\frac{1}{3}$

15. $x^2 = \left(\frac{3}{5}\right)^2$

$= \left(\frac{3}{5}\right)\left(\frac{3}{5}\right)$

$= \frac{9}{25}$

16. $ay = \frac{2}{5} \cdot \frac{5}{8}$

$= \frac{\cancel{2}^{1} \cdot 5}{3 \cdot \cancel{8}_{4}}$

$= \frac{1 \cdot 5}{3 \cdot 4}$

$= \frac{5}{12}$

17. a. $8\left(\frac{19}{40}\right) = \left(\frac{8}{1}\right)\left(\frac{19}{40}\right)$

$= \frac{\cancel{8}^{1}}{1}\left(\frac{19}{\cancel{40}_{5}}\right)$

$= \frac{1 \cdot 19}{1 \cdot 5}$

$= \frac{19}{5}$

$= 3\frac{4}{5}$ or 3.8¢

b. $\left(1\frac{1}{4}\right)\left(22\frac{1}{2}\right) = \left(\frac{5}{4}\right)\left(\frac{45}{2}\right)$

$= \frac{5 \cdot 45}{4 \cdot 2}$

$= \frac{225}{8}$

$= 28\frac{1}{8}$

$= 28$ years, 1.5 months

c. Answers will vary.

Pages 287–288   Exercises

18. $\frac{3}{4} \cdot \left(-\frac{1}{3}\right) = b$

$\frac{\cancel{3}^{1}}{4} \cdot \left(-\frac{1}{\cancel{3}_{1}}\right) = b$

$\frac{1 \cdot -1}{4 \cdot -1} = b$

$-\frac{1}{4} = b$

19. $\frac{1}{2} \cdot \frac{2}{7} = t$

$\frac{1 \cdot \cancel{2}^{1}}{\cancel{2}_{1} \cdot 7} = t$

$\frac{1 \cdot 1}{1 \cdot 7} = t$

$\frac{1}{7} = t$

20. $k = -\frac{5}{6}\left(-\frac{2}{5}\right)$

$k = -\frac{\cancel{5}^{1}}{\cancel{6}_{3}}\left(-\frac{\cancel{2}^{1}}{\cancel{5}_{1}}\right)$

$k = \frac{-1 \cdot -1}{3 \cdot 1}$

$k = \frac{1}{3}$

21. $d = -4\left(\frac{3}{8}\right)$

$d = -\frac{4}{1}\left(\frac{3}{8}\right)$

$d = -\frac{\cancel{4}^{1}}{1}\left(\frac{3}{\cancel{8}_{2}}\right)$

$d = -\frac{1 \cdot 3}{1 \cdot 2}$

$d = -\frac{3}{2}$

$d = -1\frac{1}{2}$

22. $(-7)\left(-2\frac{1}{3}\right) = h$

$\left(-\frac{7}{1}\right)\left(-\frac{7}{3}\right) = h$

$\frac{49}{3} = h$

$16\frac{1}{3} = h$

23. $c = 1\frac{4}{5} \cdot \left(-2\frac{1}{2}\right)$

$c = \frac{9}{5} \cdot \left(-\frac{5}{2}\right)$

$c = \frac{9}{\cancel{5}_{1}} \cdot \left(-\frac{\cancel{5}^{1}}{2}\right)$

$c = \frac{9 \cdot -1}{1 \cdot 2}$

$c = \frac{-9}{2}$

$c = -4\frac{1}{2}$

24. $v = 2\frac{5}{6} \cdot 3\frac{1}{3}$

$v = \frac{17}{6} \cdot \frac{10}{3}$

$v = \frac{17 \cdot \cancel{10}^{5}}{\cancel{6}_{3} \cdot 3}$

$v = \frac{17 \cdot 5}{3 \cdot 3}$

$v = \frac{85}{9}$

$v = 9\frac{4}{9}$

25. $s = \left(2\frac{1}{4}\right)\left(-\frac{4}{3}\right)$

$s = \left(\frac{9}{4}\right)\left(-\frac{4}{3}\right)$

$s = \left(\frac{\cancel{9}^{3}}{\cancel{4}_{1}}\right)\left(-\frac{\cancel{4}^{1}}{\cancel{3}_{1}}\right)$

$s = \frac{3 \cdot -1}{1 \cdot 1}$

$s = \frac{-3}{1}$

$s = -3$

26. $\left(-9\frac{3}{5}\right)\left(\frac{5}{12}\right) = y$

$\left(-\frac{48}{5}\right)\left(\frac{5}{12}\right) = y$

$\left(-\frac{\cancel{48}^{4}}{\cancel{5}_{1}}\right)\left(\frac{\cancel{5}^{1}}{\cancel{12}_{1}}\right) = y$

$\frac{-4 \cdot 1}{1 \cdot 1} = y$

$-\frac{4}{1} = y$

$-4 = y$

27. $\left(-3\frac{1}{5}\right)\left(7\frac{1}{2}\right) = w$

$\left(-\frac{16}{5}\right)\left(\frac{15}{2}\right) = w$

$\left(-\frac{\cancel{16}^{8}}{\cancel{5}_{1}}\right)\left(\frac{\cancel{15}^{3}}{\cancel{2}_{1}}\right) = w$

$\frac{-8 \cdot 3}{1 \cdot 1} = w$

$-\frac{24}{1} = w$

$-24 = w$

28. $m = (9)\left(-1\frac{5}{6}\right)$

$m = \left(\frac{9}{1}\right)\left(-\frac{11}{6}\right)$

$m = \left(\frac{\cancel{9}^{3}}{1}\right)\left(-\frac{11}{\cancel{6}_{2}}\right)$

$m = \frac{3 \cdot -11}{1 \cdot 2}$

$m = -\frac{33}{2}$

$m = -16\frac{1}{2}$

29. $p = \left(-\frac{3}{5}\right)^2$

$p = \left(-\frac{3}{5}\right)\left(-\frac{3}{5}\right)$

$p = \frac{9}{25}$

30. $r = \left(\frac{7}{11}\right)^2$

$r = \left(\frac{7}{11}\right)\left(\frac{7}{11}\right)$

$r = \frac{49}{121}$

31. $\left(-\frac{9}{10}\right)^2 \cdot 8 = f$

$\left(-\frac{9}{10}\right)\left(-\frac{9}{10}\right) \cdot 8 = f$

$\frac{81}{100} \cdot \frac{8}{1} = f$

$\frac{81}{\cancel{100}_{25}} \cdot \frac{\cancel{8}^{2}}{1} = f$

$\frac{81 \cdot 2}{25 \cdot 1} = f$

$\frac{162}{25} = f$

$6\frac{12}{25} = f$

32. $\left(\frac{5}{7}\right)^2 = n$

$\left(\frac{5}{7}\right)\left(\frac{5}{7}\right) = n$

$\frac{25}{49} = n$

33. $\frac{4}{9} \cdot \frac{3}{5} = \frac{4 \cdot \cancel{3}^{1}}{\cancel{9}_{3} \cdot 5}$

$= \frac{4 \cdot 1}{3 \cdot 5}$

$= \frac{4}{15}$

34. $\frac{5}{8}(36) = \frac{5}{8}\left(\frac{36}{1}\right)$

$= \frac{5 \cdot 36}{8 \cdot 1}$

$= \frac{180}{8}$

$= 22\frac{4}{8}$ or $22\frac{1}{2}$

35. $ay = \left(-\frac{1}{3}\right)\left(-3\frac{1}{6}\right)$

$= \left(-\frac{1}{3}\right)\left(-\frac{19}{6}\right)$

$= \frac{19}{18}$

$= 1\frac{1}{18}$

36. $2a^2 = 2\left(-\frac{1}{3}\right)^2$

$= 2\left(-\frac{1}{3}\right)\left(-\frac{1}{3}\right)$

$= 2\left(\frac{1}{9}\right)$

$= \frac{2}{1}\left(\frac{1}{9}\right)$

$= \frac{2}{9}$

37. $b(x + a) = \frac{3}{4}\left[1\frac{2}{5} + \left(-\frac{1}{3}\right)\right]$

$= \frac{3}{4}\left[\frac{7}{5} + \left(-\frac{1}{3}\right)\right]$

$= \frac{3}{4}\left[\frac{21}{15} + \left(-\frac{5}{15}\right)\right]$

$= \frac{3}{4} \cdot \frac{16}{15}$

$= \frac{\overset{1}{\cancel{3}} \cdot \overset{4}{\cancel{16}}}{\underset{1}{\cancel{4}} \cdot \underset{5}{\cancel{15}}}$

$= \frac{1 \cdot 4}{1 \cdot 5}$

$= \frac{4}{5}$

38. $3a - 5x = 3\left(-\frac{1}{3}\right) - 5\left(1\frac{2}{5}\right)$

$= \frac{3}{1}\left(-\frac{1}{3}\right) - \frac{5}{1}\left(\frac{7}{5}\right)$

$= \frac{\overset{1}{\cancel{3}}}{1}\left(-\frac{1}{\cancel{3}}\right) - \frac{\overset{1}{\cancel{5}}}{1}\left(\frac{7}{\cancel{5}}\right)$

$= \frac{1 \cdot -1}{1 \cdot 1} - \frac{1 \cdot 7}{1 \cdot 1}$

$= \frac{-1}{1} - \frac{7}{1}$

$= -1 - 7$

$= -8$

39. $a^2(b + 2) = \left(-\frac{1}{3}\right)^2\left(\frac{3}{4} + 2\right)$

$= \left(-\frac{1}{3}\right)\left(-\frac{1}{3}\right)\left(2\frac{3}{4}\right)$

$= \left(\frac{1}{9}\right)\left(\frac{11}{4}\right)$

$= \frac{11}{36}$

40. $-a(a - b) = -\left(-\frac{1}{3}\right)\left(-\frac{1}{3} - \frac{3}{4}\right)$

$= \left(\frac{1}{3}\right)\left(-\frac{4}{12} - \frac{9}{12}\right)$

$= \left(\frac{1}{3}\right)\left(-\frac{13}{12}\right)$

$= -\frac{13}{36}$

41. $\frac{7}{2} \times \frac{6}{3}$ or $\frac{6}{2} \times \frac{7}{3}$; Use the greatest numbers as numerators and the least as denominators.

42. a. Sample answer: $\frac{2}{3} \times \frac{3}{5} \times \frac{7}{3}$

b. Yes; rearrange the numerators and denominators.

43. $\frac{1}{4} \cdot 15 = \frac{1}{4} \cdot \frac{15}{1}$

$= \frac{15}{4}$

$= 3\frac{3}{4}$ hours

44. $45 \cdot 3\frac{1}{4} = \frac{45}{1} \cdot \frac{13}{4}$ $45 \cdot 1\frac{2}{3} = \frac{45}{1} \cdot \frac{5}{3}$

$= \frac{45 \cdot 13}{1 \cdot 4}$ $= \frac{45 \cdot 5}{1 \cdot 3}$

$= \frac{585}{4}$ $= \frac{225}{3}$

$= 146\frac{1}{4}$ $= 75$

$146\frac{1}{4}$ oz cider   75 oz garlic powder

45. a. 1 point $= \frac{1}{72}$ inch.

So, 12 points $= \frac{12}{72}$ or $\frac{1}{6}$ inch.

Since 12 points make one pica, one pica equals $\frac{1}{6}$ inch. Thus, there are 6 picas in an inch.

b. How many picas are equal to $\frac{3}{4}$ inch?

$\frac{1}{6} \cdot x = \frac{3}{4}$

$\frac{1}{6} \cdot \frac{x}{1} = \frac{3}{4}$

$\frac{x}{6} = \frac{3}{4}$

$\frac{x}{6} \cdot 6 = \frac{3}{4} \cdot 6$

$x = \frac{18}{4}$

$x = 4\frac{2}{4}$

$x = 4\frac{1}{2}$ picas

c. $2\frac{3}{4} \times 6 \times 5\frac{1}{2} = \frac{11}{4} \times \frac{6}{1} \times \frac{11}{2}$

$= \frac{11}{4} \times \frac{24}{4} \times \frac{22}{4}$

$= \frac{5808}{64}$

$= 90.75$

about 91 characters

46. African $= \frac{3}{5} \cdot \frac{1}{4}$ Modern $= \frac{3}{5} \cdot \frac{2}{3}$

$= \frac{3 \cdot 1}{5 \cdot 4}$ $= \frac{\overset{1}{\cancel{3}} \cdot 3}{5 \cdot \cancel{3}}$

$= \frac{3}{20}$ $= \frac{1 \cdot 2}{5 \cdot 1}$

$= \frac{2}{5}$

Ballet $= \frac{3}{5} \cdot \frac{1}{2}$

$= \frac{\overset{1}{\cancel{3}} \cdot 1}{5 \cdot \underset{4}{\cancel{12}}}$

$= \frac{1 \cdot 1}{5 \cdot 4}$

$= \frac{1}{20}$

47. $\frac{13}{28} \times 30 \rightarrow \frac{1}{2} \times 30 = 15$

48. no; $7 + 1 + 3 = 11$

49. $72 = 2 \cdot 36$
$= 2 \cdot 2 \cdot 18$
$= 2 \cdot 2 \cdot 2 \cdot 9$
$= 2 \cdot 2 \cdot 2 \cdot 3 \cdot 3$

50. $f + (-3) > 8$
$f - 3 > 8$
$f - 3 + 3 > 8 + 3$
$f > 11$

51. $-4(-x)(-5y) = -4(-5)(-x)y$
$= -20xy$

52. $y + 57 = 180$
$y + 57 - 57 = 180 - 57$
$y = 123°$

53. $18 \div 3 + 18 \div 2 = 6 + 18 \div 2$
$= 6 + 9$
$= 15$

54. No, it should be about 40.

Page 289   Your Turn

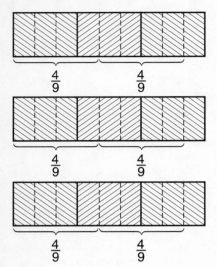

$$\underbrace{\qquad}_{\frac{4}{9}}\quad\underbrace{\qquad}_{\frac{4}{9}}$$

$$\underbrace{\qquad}_{\frac{4}{9}}\quad\underbrace{\qquad}_{\frac{4}{9}}$$

$$\underbrace{\qquad}_{\frac{4}{9}}\quad\underbrace{\qquad}_{\frac{4}{9}}$$

a. 6
b. 6

Pages 291–292   Checking Your Understanding

1. Sample answer: reciprocals are numbers whose product is 1. $\frac{4}{7}$ and $\frac{7}{4}$ are reciprocals.

2. Dividing by a number is the same as multiplying by the reciprocal.

3. Sample answer: $5 \div \frac{3}{8} = y$

4. 0; $0 = \frac{0}{1}$, but since division by 0 is undefined, $\frac{1}{0}$ is meaningless. 0 has no reciprocal.

5. The quotient is greater because dividing by the number is the same as multiplying by the reciprocal. If a number is between 0 and 1, its reciprocal will be greater than it is.

6. yes; $7 \cdot \frac{1}{7} = 1$

7. no; $\left(-\frac{2}{3}\right)\left(-1\frac{1}{2}\right) = \frac{3}{5}$

8. no; $\left(5\frac{2}{3}\right)\left(\frac{17}{3}\right) = 32\frac{1}{9}$

9. yes; $(1.4)\left(\frac{5}{7}\right) = 1$

10. $\frac{1}{2} \div \frac{6}{7} = \frac{1}{2} \times \frac{7}{6}$
$= \frac{7}{12}$

11. $-\frac{3}{4} \div \frac{3}{4} = -\frac{3}{4} \times \frac{4}{3}$
$= -\frac{12}{12}$
$= -1$

12. $\frac{7}{9} \div \frac{2}{3} = \frac{7}{9} \times \frac{3}{2}$
$= \frac{21}{18}$
$= 1\frac{3}{18}$
$= 1\frac{1}{6}$

13. $5 \div \left(-1\frac{1}{3}\right) = \frac{5}{1} \div \left(-\frac{4}{3}\right)$
$= \frac{5}{1} \times \left(-\frac{3}{4}\right)$
$= -\frac{15}{4}$
$= -3\frac{3}{4}$

14. $2\frac{3}{5} \div 3\frac{6}{7} = \frac{13}{5} \div \frac{27}{7}$
$= \frac{13}{5} \times \frac{7}{27}$
$= \frac{91}{135}$

15. $-8 \div \left(-22\frac{4}{5}\right) = -\frac{8}{1} \div \left(-\frac{114}{5}\right)$
$= -\frac{8}{1} \times \left(-\frac{5}{114}\right)$
$= \frac{40}{114}$
$= \frac{20}{57}$

16. $x \div y = 1\frac{1}{2} \div \frac{1}{2}$
$= \frac{3}{2} \div \frac{1}{2}$
$= \frac{3}{2} \times \frac{2}{1}$
$= \frac{6}{2}$
$= 3$

17. $c \div d + e = \frac{2}{3} \div 1\frac{1}{2} + \frac{1}{6}$
$= \frac{2}{3} \div \frac{3}{2} + \frac{1}{6}$
$= \frac{2}{3} \times \frac{2}{3} + \frac{1}{6}$
$= \frac{4}{9} + \frac{1}{6}$
$= \frac{8}{18} + \frac{3}{18}$
$= \frac{11}{18}$

18. 2 feet 8 inches equals $2\frac{8}{12}$ or $2\frac{2}{3}$.
$16 \div 2\frac{2}{3} = \frac{16}{1} \div \frac{8}{3}$
$= \frac{16}{1} \times \frac{3}{8}$
$= \frac{48}{8}$
$= 6$ boards

Pages 292–293   Exercises

19. $-\frac{3}{7}$
20. $\frac{1}{8}$
21. $\frac{5}{8}$
22. $-\frac{7}{23}$

23. $\frac{2}{3}$
24. $-\frac{5}{2}$
25. $\frac{y}{x}$
26. $\frac{n}{m}$

27. $r = -\frac{3}{5} \div \frac{5}{9}$
$r = -\frac{3}{5} \times \frac{9}{5}$
$r = -\frac{27}{25}$
$r = -1\frac{2}{25}$

28. $u = -1\frac{1}{9} \div \frac{2}{3}$
$u = -\frac{10}{9} \div \frac{2}{3}$
$u = -\frac{10}{9} \times \frac{3}{2}$
$u = -\frac{30}{18}$
$u = -1\frac{12}{18}$
$u = -1\frac{2}{3}$

29. $-8 \div \frac{4}{5} = t$
$-\frac{8}{1} \div \frac{4}{5} = t$
$-\frac{8}{1} \times \frac{5}{4} = t$
$-\frac{40}{4} = t$
$-10 = t$

30. $6 \div \frac{1}{3} = m$
$\frac{6}{1} \div \frac{1}{3} = m$
$\frac{6}{1} \times \frac{3}{1} = m$
$\frac{18}{1} = m$
$18 = m$

31. $2\frac{1}{4} \div \left(-1\frac{1}{2}\right) = h$
$\frac{9}{4} \div \left(-\frac{3}{2}\right) = h$
$\frac{9}{4} \times \left(-\frac{2}{3}\right) = h$
$-\frac{18}{12} = h$
$-1\frac{6}{12} = h$
$-1\frac{1}{2} = h$

32. $-2\frac{3}{7} \div \left(-4\frac{4}{7}\right) = d$
$-\frac{17}{7} \div \left(-\frac{32}{7}\right) = d$
$-\frac{17}{7} \times \left(-\frac{7}{32}\right) = d$
$\frac{119}{224} = d$
$\frac{17}{32} = d$

33. $12 \div \frac{4}{9} = c$

$\frac{12}{1} \div \frac{4}{9} = c$

$\frac{12}{1} \times \frac{9}{4} = c$

$\frac{108}{4} = c$

$27 = c$

34. $-10 \div \frac{3}{8} = f$

$\frac{-10}{1} \div \frac{3}{8} = f$

$\frac{-10}{1} \times \frac{8}{3} = f$

$\frac{-80}{3} = f$

$-26\frac{2}{3} = f$

35. $z = 24 \div \frac{7}{10}$

$z = \frac{24}{1} \div \frac{7}{10}$

$z = \frac{24}{1} \times \frac{10}{7}$

$z = \frac{240}{7}$

$z = 34\frac{2}{7}$

36. $q = -2 \div \left(-\frac{1}{3}\right)$

$q = -\frac{2}{1} \div \left(-\frac{1}{3}\right)$

$q = -\frac{2}{1} \times \left(-\frac{3}{1}\right)$

$q = \frac{6}{1}$

$q = 6$

37. $s = -3\frac{1}{4} \div 2\frac{1}{6}$

$s = -\frac{13}{4} \div \frac{13}{6}$

$s = -\frac{13}{4} \times \frac{6}{13}$

$s = -\frac{78}{52}$

$s = -1\frac{26}{52}$

$s = -1\frac{1}{2}$

38. $7\frac{1}{2} \div 1\frac{1}{5} = n$

$\frac{15}{2} \div \frac{6}{5} = n$

$\frac{15}{2} \times \frac{5}{6} = n$

$\frac{75}{12} = n$

$6\frac{3}{12} = n$

$6\frac{1}{4} = n$

39. $m = -\frac{16}{17} \div \left(-\frac{12}{35}\right)$

$m = \frac{16}{7} \left(-\frac{35}{12}\right)$

$m = \frac{560}{84}$

$m = 6\frac{56}{84}$

$m = 6\frac{2}{3}$

40. $a = \frac{21}{30} \div \frac{7}{15}$

$a = \frac{21}{30} \times \frac{15}{7}$

$a = \frac{315}{210}$

$a = 1\frac{105}{210}$

$a = 1\frac{1}{2}$

41. $12\frac{1}{4} \div \left(-\frac{14}{3}\right) = j$

$\frac{49}{4} \div \left(-\frac{14}{3}\right) = j$

$\frac{49}{4} \times \left(-\frac{3}{14}\right) = j$

$-\frac{147}{56} = j$

$-2\frac{35}{56} = j$

$-2\frac{5}{8} = j$

42. $a \div b = \frac{2}{3} \div 1\frac{1}{3}$

$= \frac{2}{3} \div \frac{4}{3}$

$= \frac{2}{3} \times \frac{3}{4}$

$= \frac{6}{12}$

$= \frac{1}{2}$

43. $r \div s = -\frac{8}{9} \div \frac{7}{18}$

$= -\frac{8}{9} \times \frac{18}{7}$

$= -\frac{144}{63}$

$= -2\frac{18}{63}$

$= -2\frac{2}{7}$

44. $a^2 \div b^2 = \left(-\frac{3}{4}\right)^2 \div \left(1\frac{1}{3}\right)^2$

$= \left(-\frac{3}{4}\right)^2 \div \left(\frac{4}{3}\right)^2$

$= \left(-\frac{3}{4}\right)\left(-\frac{3}{4}\right) \div \left(\frac{4}{3}\right)\left(\frac{4}{3}\right)$

$= \frac{9}{16} \div \frac{16}{9}$

$= \frac{9}{16} \times \frac{9}{16}$

$= \frac{81}{256}$

45. $m + n \div p = \frac{2}{3} + 1\frac{1}{3} \div \frac{1}{9}$

$= \frac{2}{3} + \frac{4}{3} \div \frac{1}{9}$

$= \frac{2}{3} + \frac{4}{3} \times \frac{9}{1}$

$= \frac{2}{3} + \frac{36}{3}$

$= \frac{38}{3}$

$= 12\frac{2}{3}$

46. a. $\frac{3}{4} \div \frac{1}{2} = \frac{3}{4} \times \frac{2}{1}$

$= \frac{6}{4}$

$= \frac{3}{2}$

$\frac{3}{4} \div \frac{1}{4} = \frac{3}{4} \times \frac{4}{1}$

$= \frac{12}{4}$

$= 3$

$\frac{3}{4} \div \frac{1}{8} = \frac{3}{4} \times \frac{8}{1}$

$= \frac{24}{4}$

$= 6$

$\frac{3}{4} \div \frac{1}{12} = \frac{3}{4} \times \frac{12}{1}$

$= \frac{36}{4}$

$= 9$

b. The quotient gets larger.

c. The quotient would get smaller.

47. $50 \div 2\frac{1}{3} = \frac{50}{1} \div \frac{7}{3}$

$= \frac{50}{1} \times \frac{3}{7}$

$= \frac{150}{7}$

$= 21\frac{3}{7}$

She can make 21 uniforms plus extra fabric remaining.

48. 2; see students' work.

49. $12 \div 1\frac{1}{2} = \frac{12}{1} \div \frac{3}{2}$

$= \frac{12}{1} \times \frac{2}{3}$

$= \frac{24}{3}$

$= 8$ days

50. $\frac{3}{5} \cdot \frac{2}{7} = a$

$\frac{3 \cdot 2}{5 \cdot 7} = a$

$\frac{6}{35} = a$

51. $\frac{2}{5} > 0.25$ because

$0.4 > 0.25$

52. $1\frac{3}{4} + 3\frac{1}{4} = (1 + 3) + \left(\frac{3}{4} + \frac{1}{4}\right)$

$= 4 + \frac{4}{4}$

$= 4 + 1$

$= 5$ pounds

53. $30 = \boxed{2} \cdot \boxed{3} \cdot 5$

$12 = \boxed{2} \cdot 2 \cdot \boxed{3}$

The GCF is $2 \cdot 3$ or 6.

54. $x - 395 = 510$

$x - 395 + 395 = 510 + 395$

$x = \$905$

55. Quadrant II **56.** true

57. $h + 12h + 23 = 1h + 12h + 23$

$= (1 + 12)h + 23$

$= 13h + 23$

6-5A

Math Lab: Multiplying and Dividing Decimals

Page 294

1. 24 squares; 24 hundredths or 0.24
2. 2; 2; They are the same.
3.

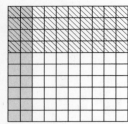

0.4 × 0.2 = 0.08, each square represents one one-hundredth.

4. 5 groups
5. 5
6.

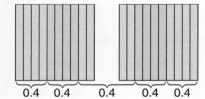

| 0.4 | 0.4 | 0.4 | 0.4 | 0.4 | 0.4 |

6-5

Multiplying and Dividing Decimals

Page 295   Your Turn

15.6 × 38 = 592.8
15.6 × 3.8 = 59.28
15.6 × 0.38 = 5.928
15.5 × 0.038 = .5928

a. The numbers are the same, but the decimal point moves one place to the left in the second factor in each successive problem.

b. The numbers are the same, but the decimal point moves one place to the left in each successive problem.

c. 0.05928; The decimal point moved one place to the left from the previous problem.

d. The number of digits after the decimal point in the product is the sum of the number of digits after the decimal point in the factors.

Pages 297–298   Checking Your Understanding

1. There will be five places. The first factor has hundredths (2 places), the second factor has thousandths (3 places).

   2 + 3 = 5 places.

2. Find the estimate.
3. Sample answer: 4.93 and 1.7

4. **a.** (1.2)(3)

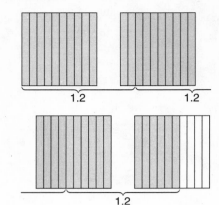

1.2   1.2

1.2

(1.2)(3) = 3.6

b. (1.2)(0.3)

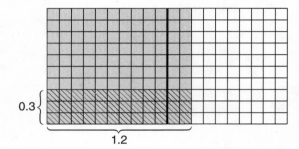

0.3

1.2

(1.2)(0.3) = 0.36

c. 4.8 ÷ 4

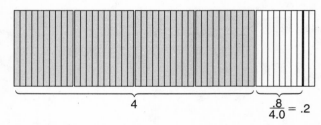

4                    $\frac{8}{4.0}$ = .2

Divide region into 4 equal parts.

4.8 ÷ 4 = 1.2

d. 4.8 ÷ 0.4

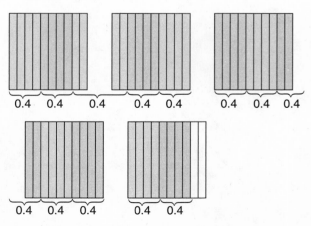

| 0.4 | 0.4 | 0.4 | 0.4 | 0.4 | 0.4 | 0.4 | 0.4 |

| 0.4 | 0.4 | 0.4 | 0.4 | 0.4 |

4.8 ÷ 0.4 = 12

5. 1.44   **6.** 0.18   **7.** 0.7   **8.** 21

9. $x = (-0.2)(-3.1)$

$$\begin{array}{r} -0.2 \\ \times\ -3.1 \\ \hline 0\,2 \\ 0\,6\,0 \\ \hline 0.62 \end{array}$$

$x = 0.62$

10. $y = (1.2)(-0.05)$

$$\begin{array}{r} -0.05 \\ \times\ 1.2 \\ \hline 0\,1\,0 \\ 0\,0\,5\,0 \\ \hline -0.060 \end{array}$$

$y = -0.06$

11. $s = 27 \div (-0.3)$

$$0.3\,\overline{)27.0}$$

$$\begin{array}{r} 90. \\ 3\overline{)270.} \\ -27 \\ \hline 0 \\ -0 \\ \hline 0 \end{array}$$

$s = -90$

12. $t = 0.4 \div 2$

$$\begin{array}{r} 0.2 \\ 2\overline{)0.4} \\ -4 \\ \hline 0 \end{array}$$

$t = 0.2$

13. $ac = (15.7)(1.6)$
$ = 25.12$

14. $5c \div b = 5(1.6) \div 0.4$
$ = 8 \div 0.4$
$ = 20$

15. Inverse property of multiplication

16. Commutative property of multiplication

17. $0.65\,\overline{)45.50}$

$$\begin{array}{r} 70. \\ 65\overline{)4550.} \\ -455 \\ \hline 0 \\ -0 \\ \hline 0 \end{array}$$

70 pounds

Pages 298–299   Exercises

18. $g = (-6.5)(0.13)$

$$\begin{array}{r} 0.13 \\ \times\ -6.5 \\ \hline 0\,6\,5 \\ 0\,7\,8\,0 \\ \hline 0.845 \end{array}$$

$g = -0.845$

19. $k = (0.47)(3.01)$

$$\begin{array}{r} 0.47 \\ \times\ 3.01 \\ \hline 0\,4\,7 \\ 1\,4\,1\,0\,0 \\ \hline 1.4147 \end{array}$$

$k = 1.4147$

20. $-14.9(-0.56) = n$

$$\begin{array}{r} -14.9 \\ \times\ -0.5\,6 \\ \hline 8\,9\,4 \\ 7\,4\,5\,0 \\ \hline 8.3\,4\,4 \end{array}$$

$n = 8.344$

21. $7.45(-0.75) = t$

$$\begin{array}{r} 7.45 \\ \times\ -0.75 \\ \hline 37\,25 \\ 5\,21\,50 \\ \hline -5.58\,75 \end{array}$$

$t = -5.5875$

22. $x = (0.001)(7.09)$

$$\begin{array}{r} 0.0001 \\ \times\ 7.09 \\ \hline 00\,09 \\ 0\,007\,00 \\ \hline 0.007\,09 \end{array}$$

$x = 0.00709$

23. $b = (1.03)(-6.4)$

$$\begin{array}{r} 1.03 \\ \times\ -6.4 \\ \hline 412 \\ 6180 \\ \hline 6.592 \end{array}$$

$b = -6.592$

24. $r = 14.4 \div (0.16)$

$$0.16\,\overline{)14.40}$$

$$\begin{array}{r} 90. \\ 16\overline{)1440.} \\ -144 \\ \hline 0 \\ -0 \\ \hline 0 \end{array}$$

$r = 90$

25. $q = 0.384 \div 1.2$

$$1.2\,\overline{)0.384}$$

$$\begin{array}{r} 0.32 \\ 12\overline{)3.84} \\ -36 \\ \hline 24 \\ -24 \\ \hline 0 \end{array}$$

$q = 0.32$

26. $-85 \div (-1.7) = k$

$$1.7\,\overline{)85.0}$$

$$\begin{array}{r} 50. \\ 17\overline{)850.} \\ -85 \\ \hline 0 \\ -0 \\ \hline 0 \end{array}$$

$k = 50$

27. $-0.51 \div 0.03 = g$

$$0.03\,\overline{)0.51}$$

$$\begin{array}{r} 17. \\ 3\overline{)51.} \\ -3 \\ \hline 21 \\ -21 \\ \hline 0 \end{array}$$

$g = -17$

28. $s = -15.3 \div (-9)$

$$\begin{array}{r} 1.7 \\ 9\overline{)15.3} \\ -9 \\ \hline 63 \\ -63 \\ \hline 0 \end{array}$$

$s = 1.7$

29. $h = 2.92 \div 0.002$

$$0.002\,\overline{)2.920}$$

$$\begin{array}{r} 1460. \\ 2\overline{)2920.} \\ -2 \\ \hline 9 \\ -8 \\ \hline 12 \\ -12 \\ \hline 0 \\ -0 \\ \hline 0 \end{array}$$

$h = 1460$

30.

$$\begin{array}{r} 0.03 \\ \times\ 7.5 \\ \hline 0\,1\,5 \\ 0\,2\,1\,0 \\ \hline 0.225 \end{array}$$

31. $9.4\,\overline{)52.64}$

$$\begin{array}{r} 5.6 \\ 94\overline{)526.4} \\ -470 \\ \hline 564 \\ -564 \\ \hline 0 \end{array}$$

32. $3y^2 = 3(0.4)^2$
$ = 3(0.16)$
$ = 0.48$

33. $ab = (-1.5)(10)$
$ = -15$

34. $\dfrac{5t}{s} = \dfrac{5(6.2)}{2.5}$
$\phantom{\dfrac{5t}{s}} = \dfrac{31}{2.5}$
$\phantom{\dfrac{5t}{s}} = 12.4$

35. $n^2 \div q = (2.2)^2 \div 4$
$ = (2.2)(2.2) \div 4$
$ = 4.84 \div 4$
$ = 1.21$

36. $12y \div z = 12(9.8) \div 6.4$
$ = 117.6 \div 6.4$
$ = 18.375$

37. $(x + 4)(x - 2) = (1.8 + 4)(1.8 - 2)$
$ = (5.8)(-0.2)$
$ = -1.16$

38. Commutative property of multiplication

39. Identity property of multiplication

40. Inverse property of multiplication

41. Associative property of multiplication

42. Identity property of multiplication

43. Commutative property of multiplication

44. Estimate: $8 \times 3 = 24$
$$(8.01)(3.33) = w$$
$$26.7 = w$$

45. Estimate: $\frac{1}{2} \times 5 = \frac{-5}{2}$ or -2.5
$$(-0.56)(4.59) = r$$
$$-2.6 = r$$

46. Estimate: $-8 \times -0.03 = 0.24$
$$-8.022(-0.03) = y$$
$$0.24 = y$$

47. Estimate: $90 \div (-9) = -10$
$$c = 90.5 \div (-8.9)$$
$$c = -10.2$$

48. Estimate: $94 \div 2 = 47$
$$f = 93.702 \div 2.4$$
$$f = 39.0$$

49. Estimate: $0.2 \div 2 = 0.1$
$$z = -0.36 \div (-2.1)$$
$$z = 0.2$$

50. a. 1.2, 1.2

   b. 1.8, 0.9

51. $13.5\overline{)2.4\!\cdot\!5}$ $19.5\overline{)3.5\!\cdot\!9}$

$$
\begin{array}{r}
0.181 \\
135\overline{)24.500} \\
-13\,5 \\
\hline
1\,100 \\
-10\,80 \\
\hline
200 \\
-135 \\
\hline
65
\end{array}
\qquad
\begin{array}{r}
0.184 \\
195\overline{)35.900} \\
-19\,5 \\
\hline
16\,40 \\
-15\,60 \\
\hline
800 \\
-780 \\
\hline
20
\end{array}
$$

Muesli; muesli 18.1¢ per oz;
frosted corn flakes 18.4¢ per oz

52.
$$
\begin{array}{r}
2702.7 \\
\times \quad 25 \\
\hline
13513\,5 \\
54054\,0 \\
\hline
67{,}567.5
\end{array}
$$
67,567.5 pesos

53.
$$
\begin{array}{r}
0.8 \\
\times 4 \\
\hline
3.2
\end{array}
$$
\$3.2 billion

54. $\frac{5}{11} \div \frac{10}{11} = \frac{5}{11} \times \frac{11}{10}$
$$= \frac{55}{110}$$
$$= \frac{1}{2}$$

55. $3\frac{4}{9} \cdot \frac{3}{4} = h$
$$\frac{31}{9} \cdot \frac{3}{4} = h$$
$$\frac{31 \cdot \overset{1}{\cancel{3}}}{\underset{3}{\cancel{9}} \cdot 4} = h$$
$$\frac{31 \cdot 1}{3 \cdot 4} = h$$
$$\frac{31}{12} = h$$
$$2\frac{7}{12} = h$$

56. $b - 1.6 \le 4.3$
$$b - 1.6 + 1.6 \le 4.3 + 1.6$$
$$b \le 5.9$$

57. integers,
rationals

58. $8 = -\frac{b}{11}$
$$8 \cdot (-11) = -\frac{b}{11} \cdot (-11)$$
$$-88 = b$$

59. $x + 2931 = 3245$
$$x + 2931 - 2931 = 3245 - 2931$$
$$x = 314$$
The total of the checks is \$314.

60. $93° - 86° = 7°F$

61. commutative property of addition

62. $18 \div (18 - 6 \cdot 2) = 18 \div (18 - 12)$
$$= 18 \div 6$$
$$= 3$$

Page 299   Self Test

1. $\frac{7}{8} \rightarrow$
$$
\begin{array}{r}
0.875 \\
8\overline{)7.000} \\
-64 \\
\hline
60 \\
-56 \\
\hline
40 \\
-40 \\
\hline
0
\end{array}
$$
$$\frac{7}{8} = 0.875$$

2. $-1\frac{2}{3} = -\left(1 + \frac{2}{3}\right)$
$$\frac{2}{3} \rightarrow
\begin{array}{r}
0.666 \\
3\overline{)2.000} \\
-1\,8 \\
\hline
20 \\
-18 \\
\hline
2
\end{array}$$
$$-(1 + 0.\overline{6}) = -1.\overline{6}$$
$$-1\frac{2}{3} = -1.\overline{6}$$

3. $-\frac{8}{11} \rightarrow$
$$
\begin{array}{r}
0.7272 \\
11\overline{)8.0000} \\
-7\,7 \\
\hline
30 \\
-22 \\
\hline
80 \\
-77 \\
\hline
30 \\
-22 \\
\hline
8
\end{array}
$$
$$-\frac{8}{11} = -0.\overline{72}$$

4. $2\frac{1}{8} = 2 + \frac{1}{8}$ $2.125 + x = 75.50$
$$\qquad\qquad 2.125 + x - 2.125 = 75.50 - 2.125$$
$$\qquad\qquad\qquad\qquad x = 73.375$$
$$\frac{1}{8} \rightarrow
\begin{array}{r}
0.125 \\
8\overline{)1.000} \\
-8 \\
\hline
20 \\
-16 \\
\hline
40 \\
-40 \\
\hline
0
\end{array}$$
$$2 + 0.125 = 2.125$$
On Tuesday, the closing price was \$73.38.

5. Sample answer:
$$\frac{2}{3} \times 25 \rightarrow \frac{2}{3} \times 24 = 16$$
$$\frac{2}{3} \times 25 \text{ is about } 16.$$

6. Sample answer:
$$3.85 \times 6 \rightarrow 4 \times 6 = 24$$
$$3.85 \times 6 \text{ is about } 24.$$

7. Sample answer:
$$6.2 \div 2.1 \rightarrow 6 \div 2 = 3$$
$$6.2 \div 2.1 \text{ is about } 3.$$

8. $x = \frac{1}{4}\left(-\frac{3}{8}\right)$

$x = -\frac{3}{32}$

9. $y = -9 \div \frac{3}{8}$

$y = -\frac{9}{1} \div \frac{3}{8}$

$y = -\frac{9}{1} \times \frac{8}{3}$

$y = -\frac{72}{3}$

$y = -24$

10. $w = (0.5)(1.46)$

$$\begin{array}{r} 1.46 \\ \times\ 0.5 \\ \hline .730 \end{array}$$

$w = 0.73$

6-6A | Math Lab: Mean, Median, and Mode

Page 300

1–8. See students' work

6-6 | Integration: Statistics Measures of Central Tendency

Page 304   Checking Your Understanding

1. Sample answer: The mean of 7.0 for both networks best represents the data. It shows that, overall, the ratings for the two networks were about the same.

2. Sample answers: 6 7 7 8, yes;
5 6 8 9, no

3. a. Answers will vary.

b. Recently minted coins should have greater number.

c. Same as b.

4. 3, 4, 5, 7, 9, 11, 23, 37

mean: $\frac{3 + 4 + 5 + 7 + 9 + 11 + 23 + 37}{8} = 12.4$

median: $\frac{7 + 9}{2} = 8$

mode: none

5. 8, 11, 12, 12, 33, 35, 45, 47, 62

mean: $\frac{8 + 11 + 12 + 12 + 33 + 35 + 45 + 47 + 62}{9} = 29.4$

median: 33

mode: 12

6. 25.00, 25.98, 30.00, 45.36, 45.36

mean: $\frac{25.00 + 25.98 + 30.00 + 45.36 + 45.36}{5} = 34.3$

median: 30.0

mode: 45.4

7. 78, 78, 105, 116, 125

mean: $\frac{78 + 78 + 105 + 116 + 125}{5} = 100.4$

median: 105

mode: 78

8. $\frac{50(59) + 30(72) + 15(84) + 5(93)}{100}$

$= \frac{2950 + 2160 + 1260 + 465}{100} = 68.35$

Pages 305–306   Exercises

9. 22, 32, 45, 45, 63, 64, 78

mean: $\frac{22 + 32 + 45 + 45 + 63 + 64 + 78}{7} = 49.9$

median: 45

mode: 45

10. 12, 22, 26, 26, 41, 44, 53, 63

mean: $\frac{12 + 22 + 26 + 26 + 41 + 44 + 53 + 63}{8} = 35.9$

median: $\frac{26 + 41}{2} = 33.5$

mode: 26

11. 3.6, 3.6, 5.2, 6.5, 7.2, 7.2, 9.0

mean: $\frac{3.6 + 3.6 + 5.2 + 6.5 + 7.2 + 7.2 + 9.0}{7} = 6.0$

median: 6.5

mode: 3.6 and 7.2

12. 0.2, 0.6, 0.7, 0.7, 0.7, 0.9, 1.4, 1.4

$\frac{0.2 + 0.6 + 0.7 + 0.7 + 0.7 + 0.9 + 1.4 + 1.4}{8} = 0.8$

median: 0.7

mode: 0.7

13. 86, 94, 100, 105, 113, 113, 120

mean: $\frac{86 + 94 + 100 + 105 + 113 + 113 + 120}{7} = 104.4$

median: 105

mode: 113

14. 2.3, 2.9, 3.0, 3.6, 3.6, 4.1

mean: $\frac{2.3 + 2.9 + 3.0 + 3.6 + 3.6 + 4.1}{6} = 3.3$

median: $\frac{3.0 + 3.6}{2} = 3.3$

mode: 3.6

15. 0.4, 0.7, 0.8, 0.9, 1.1, 1.6

mean: $\frac{0.4 + 0.7 + 0.8 + 0.9 + 1.1 + 1.6}{6} = 0.9$

median: $\frac{0.8 + 0.9}{2} = 0.9$

mode: none

16. 1.2, 3.4, 3.4, 4.5, 4.8, 5.6, 7.6, 8.8

mean: $\frac{1.2 + 3.4 + 3.4 + 4.5 + 4.8 + 5.6 + 7.6 + 8.8}{8} = 4.9$

median: $\frac{4.5 + 4.8}{2} = 4.7$

mode: 3.4

17. mean: $\frac{2136}{25} = 85.4$

18. 73, 74, 76, 78, 78, 83, 83, 84, 85, 85, 86, 86, 86, 86, 88, 88, 88, 89, 90, 90, 90, 92, 92, 93, 93

median: 86

19. mode: 86

20. a. mean: $\frac{93 + 86 + 84 + 92 + 85}{5} = 88$

b. It raises it.

21. a. 84, 85, 86, 92, 93
median: 86

b. no effect

22. a. mean: $\frac{90 + 88 + 83 + 76 + 90}{5} = 85.4$

b. no effect

23. a. mode: 90

b. no effect

24. It will be raised.

25.
$$\frac{83 + 85 + 93 + 78 + 86 + s}{6} = 86$$
$$\frac{425 + s}{6} = 86$$
$$6 \cdot \frac{425 + s}{6} = 86 \cdot 6$$
$$425 + s = 516$$
$$425 + s - 425 = 516 - 425$$
$$s = 91$$

Lakesha must earn a 91.

26. The mayor's IQ was less than the mean IQ in Glasshouse City and greater than the mean IQ in Stonethrowers.

27. Sample answer: 2, 4, 6, 8, 8, 10, 12, 14

28. a. 1983: 76.7, 81.0, 88.6, 91.2, 91.6, 93.4, 99.5, 102.5

mean:
$$\frac{76.7 + 81.0 + 88.6 + 91.2 + 91.6 + 93.4 + 99.5 + 102.5}{8}$$
$$= 90.6$$

median: $\frac{91.2 + 91.6}{2} = 91.4$

mode: none

1992: 90.3, 91.6, 94.2, 94.6, 94.6, 96.0, 104.7, 105.6

mean:
$$\frac{90.3 + 91.6 + 94.2 + 94.6 + 94.6 + 96.0 + 104.7 + 105.6}{8}$$
$$= 96.5$$

median: 94.6

mode: 94.6

b. Sample answers: The situation has improved from 1983 to 1993, but women still earn less than men for the same work.

29. See students' work.

30. a. mean:
$$\frac{380 + 450 + 465 + 789 + 800 + 815 + 1000 + 1400 + 1800 + 1820}{10}$$
$$= \$971.90$$

median: $\frac{800 + 815}{2} = \$807.50$

mode: none

b. mean

31. $w = (-3.2)(4.057)$

$$\begin{array}{r} 4.057 \\ \times\ -3.2 \\ \hline 8114 \\ 12\,1710 \\ \hline 12.9824 \end{array}$$

$w = -12.9824$

32. $\frac{36a^3b}{52a^1b^2} = \frac{\overset{9}{\cancel{36}} \cdot \overset{1}{\cancel{a}} \cdot a \cdot a \cdot \overset{1}{\cancel{b}}}{\underset{13}{\cancel{52}} \cdot \underset{1}{\cancel{a}} \cdot \underset{1}{\cancel{b}} \cdot b}$

$= \frac{9a^2}{13b}$

33. $-3y \geq 72$

$\frac{-3y}{-3} \leq \frac{72}{-3}$

$y \leq -24$

34. $-2200 + (-1325) = -3525$

The submarine is 3525 feet below sea level.

35. Multiplication property of zero

36. a. $9g$

b. $9g = 9(5)$

$= 45$

Page 307 Your Turn

1. 5.55, 5.75

2. 210.22, 190

3. -16.36, -15

4. 0.29, 1.35

5. mean: $\frac{30.7 + 68.7 + 133.9 + 192.2 + 16.2 + 0}{6} = 73.6$

0, 16.2, 30.7, 68.7, 133.9, 192.2

median: $\frac{30.7 + 68.7}{2} = 49.7$

6. when there is an odd number of data pieces

7. The mean is affected more by very large or very small numbers. So the median is a better representation if the data have extreme values. If the data are more closely clustered, the mean is a good representation.

6-7 Solving Equations and Inequalities

Page 310 Checking Your Understanding

1. Divide each side by 0.3.

2. **a.** Answers will vary.

   b. Multiplication property of equality

3. Divide each side by $\frac{1}{4}$ or multiply each side by 4.

4. $x \leq -2$

5. Divide each side by 0.6;

$0.6n = -9$

$\frac{0.6n}{0.6} = \frac{-9}{0.6}$

$n = -15$

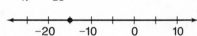

6. Divide each side by 4.1;

$4.1p = 16.4$

$\frac{4.1p}{4.1} = \frac{16.4}{4.1}$

$p = 4$

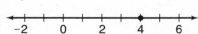

7. Divide each side by 0.3;

$-2.7 < 0.3f$

$\frac{-2.7}{0.3} < \frac{0.3f}{0.3}$

$-9 < f$

8. Multiply each side by $-\frac{3}{2}$ and reverse the order symbol;

$$-\frac{2}{3}x > 6$$
$$\left(-\frac{3}{2}\right)\left(-\frac{2}{3}\right)x < 6\left(-\frac{3}{2}\right)$$
$$x < -9$$

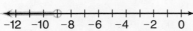

9. Multiply each side by $\frac{6}{5}$;

$$\frac{5}{6}y = \frac{3}{5}$$
$$\frac{6}{5} \cdot \frac{5}{6}y = \frac{3}{5} \cdot \frac{6}{5}$$
$$y = \frac{18}{25}$$

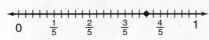

10. Multiply each side by -4.6 and reverse the order symbol.

$$\frac{r}{-4.6} \geq 0.01$$
$$(-4.6)\left(\frac{r}{-4.6}\right) \leq 0.01(-4.6)$$
$$r \leq -0.046$$

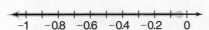

11. $2.5x = 15$
$$\frac{2.5x}{2.5} = \frac{15}{2.5}$$
$$x = 6 \text{ cm}$$

Page 311 Exercises

12. $7y < 3.5$
$$\frac{7y}{7} < \frac{3.5}{7}$$
$$y < 0.5$$

Check: Try 0.3, a number less than 0.5
$$7y < 3.5$$
$$7(0.3) \overset{?}{<} 3.5$$
$$2.1 < 3.5 \checkmark$$

13. $-3y = 1.5$
$$\frac{-3y}{-3} = \frac{1.5}{-3}$$
$$y = -0.5$$

Check: $\quad -3y = 1.5$
$$-3(-0.5) \overset{?}{=} 1.5$$
$$1.5 = 1.5 \checkmark$$

14. $\quad 5a > -7\frac{1}{2}$
$$5a > -\frac{15}{2}$$
$$\frac{1}{5} \cdot 5a > -\frac{15}{2} \cdot \frac{1}{5}$$
$$a > -\frac{15}{10}$$
$$a > -1\frac{1}{2}$$

Check: Try 0, a number greater than $-1\frac{1}{2}$
$$5a > -7\frac{1}{2}$$
$$5 \cdot 0 \overset{?}{>} -7\frac{1}{2}$$
$$0 > -7\frac{1}{2} \checkmark$$

15. $\quad \frac{1}{4}x = 4\frac{1}{8}$
$$\frac{1}{4}x = \frac{33}{8}$$
$$4 \cdot \frac{1}{4}x = \frac{33}{8} \cdot 4$$
$$x = \frac{132}{8}$$
$$x = 16\frac{1}{2}$$

Check: $\quad \frac{1}{4}x = 4\frac{1}{8}$
$$\frac{1}{4} \cdot 16\frac{1}{2} \overset{?}{=} 4\frac{1}{8}$$
$$\frac{1}{4} \cdot \frac{33}{2} \overset{?}{=} 4\frac{1}{8}$$
$$\frac{33}{8} = 4\frac{1}{8} \checkmark$$

16. $\quad -\frac{1}{8}r = \frac{1}{4}$
$$(-8)\left(-\frac{1}{8}\right)r = \frac{1}{4}(-8)$$
$$r = -\frac{8}{4}$$
$$r = -2$$

Check: $\quad -\frac{1}{8}r = \frac{1}{4}$
$$\left(-\frac{1}{8}\right)(-2) \overset{?}{=} \frac{1}{4}$$
$$\frac{1}{8}\left(\frac{2}{1}\right) \overset{?}{=} \frac{1}{4}$$
$$\frac{2}{8} = \frac{1}{4} \checkmark$$

17. $\quad \frac{x}{3.2} < -4.5$
$$(3.2)\frac{x}{3.2} < -4.5(3.2)$$
$$x < -14.4$$

Check: Try -15, a number less than -14.4.
$$\frac{x}{3.2} < -4.5$$
$$\frac{-15}{3.2} \overset{?}{<} -4.5$$
$$-4.69 < -4.5 \checkmark$$

18. $\quad \frac{7}{8}r \leq 1.4$
$$\left(\frac{8}{7}\right)\frac{7}{8}r \leq 1.4\left(\frac{8}{7}\right)$$
$$r \leq 1.6$$

Check: Try 1, a number less than or equal to 1.6.
$$\frac{7}{8}r \leq 1.4$$
$$\frac{7}{8} \cdot 1 \overset{?}{\leq} 1.4$$
$$\frac{7}{8} \leq 1.4 \checkmark$$

19. $\quad -15 = 2\frac{2}{5}x$
$$-15 = \frac{12}{5}x$$
$$-15 \cdot \frac{5}{12} = \frac{5}{12} \cdot \frac{12}{5}x$$
$$-\frac{75}{12} = x$$
$$-6\frac{1}{4} = x$$

Check: $-15 = 2\frac{2}{5}x$
$$-15 \overset{?}{=} 2\frac{2}{5}\left(-6\frac{1}{4}\right)$$
$$-15 \overset{?}{=} \frac{12}{5}\left(-\frac{25}{4}\right)$$
$$-15 = -15 \checkmark$$

20. $-6.7b = 14.07$
$$\frac{-6.7b}{-6.7} = \frac{14.07}{-6.7}$$
$$b = -2.1$$

Check: $\quad -6.7b = 14.07$
$$-6.7(-2.1) \overset{?}{=} 14.07$$
$$14.07 = 14.07 \checkmark$$

21. $\frac{p}{7.1} = -0.5$

$(7.1)\frac{p}{7.1} = -0.5(7.1)$

$p = -3.55$

Check: $\frac{p}{7.1} = -0.5$

$\frac{-3.55}{7.1} \overset{?}{=} -0.5$

$-0.5 = -0.5$ ✔

22. $\frac{1}{3}d = -0.36$

$(3)\frac{1}{3}d = -0.36(3)$

$d = -1.08$

Check: $\frac{1}{3}d = -0.36$

$\frac{1}{3}(-1.08) \overset{?}{=} -0.36$

$-0.36 = -0.36$ ✔

23. $-1.3z \geq 1.69$

$\frac{-1.3z}{-1.3} \leq \frac{1.69}{-1.3}$

$z \leq -1.3$

Check: Try -2, a number less than or equal to -1.3.

$-1.3z \geq 1.69$

$-1.3(-2) \overset{?}{\geq} 1.69$

$2.6 \geq 1.69$ ✔

24. $\frac{3}{4}y > 1\frac{4}{5}$

$\frac{3}{4}y > \frac{9}{5}$

$\frac{4}{3} \cdot \frac{3}{4}y > \frac{9}{5} \cdot \frac{4}{3}$

$y > \frac{36}{15}$

$y > 2\frac{2}{5}$

Check: Try 3, a number greater than $2\frac{2}{5}$.

$\frac{3}{4}y > 1\frac{4}{5}$

$\frac{3}{4}(3) \overset{?}{>} 1\frac{4}{5}$

$\frac{9}{4} \overset{?}{>} 1\frac{4}{5}$

$2\frac{1}{4} > 1\frac{4}{5}$ ✔

25. $-7\frac{1}{2}x = 5\frac{1}{4}$

$\frac{-15}{2}x = \frac{21}{4}$

$\left(-\frac{2}{15}\right)\left(-\frac{15}{2}\right)x = \frac{21}{4}\left(-\frac{2}{15}\right)$

$x = -\frac{42}{60}$

$x = -\frac{7}{10}$

Check: $-7\frac{1}{2}x = 5\frac{1}{4}$

$\left(-7\frac{1}{2}\right)\left(-\frac{7}{10}\right) \overset{?}{=} 5\frac{1}{4}$

$\left(-\frac{15}{2}\right)\left(-\frac{7}{10}\right) \overset{?}{=} 5\frac{1}{4}$

$\frac{105}{20} \overset{?}{=} 5\frac{1}{4}$

$5\frac{1}{4} = 5\frac{1}{4}$ ✔

26. $-2h > 4.6$

$\frac{22h}{-2} < \frac{4.6}{-2}$

$h < -2.3$

Check: Try -3, a number less than -2.3.

$-2h > 4.6$

$-2(-3) \overset{?}{>} 4.6$

$6 > 4.6$ ✔

27. $-0.05x = -0.95$

$\frac{-0.05x}{-0.05} = \frac{-0.95}{-0.05}$

$x = 19$

Check: $-0.05x = -0.95$

$-0.05(19) \overset{?}{=} -0.95$

$-0.95 = -0.95$ ✔

28. $\frac{x}{-2.5} \leq 3.2$

$(-2.5)\left(\frac{x}{-2.5}\right) \geq 3.2(-2.5)$

$x \geq -8$

Check: Try -5, number greater than or equal to -8.

$\frac{x}{-2.5} \leq 3.2$

$\frac{-5}{-2.5} \overset{?}{\leq} 3.2$

$2 \leq 3.2$ ✔

29. $7x < 1\frac{4}{10}$

$7x < \frac{14}{10}$

$\frac{1}{7} \cdot 7x < \frac{14}{10} \cdot \frac{1}{7}$

$x < \frac{14}{70}$

$x < \frac{1}{5}$

Check: Try 0, a number less than $\frac{1}{5}$.

$7x < 1\frac{4}{10}$

$7 \cdot 0 \overset{?}{<} 1\frac{4}{10}$

$0 < 1\frac{4}{10}$ ✔

30. $-\frac{1}{4}c = 3.4$

$(-4)\left(-\frac{1}{4}\right)c = 3.4(-4)$

$c = -13.6$

31. $\frac{4}{5}y < \frac{3}{8}$

$\frac{5}{4} \cdot \frac{4}{5}y < \frac{3}{8} \cdot \frac{5}{4}$

$y < \frac{15}{32}$

32. $-12.6p \geq 28.98$

$\frac{-12.6p}{12.6} \leq \frac{29.98}{-12.6}$

$p \leq -2.3$

33. Answers will vary.

34. $A = \frac{1}{2}bh$

$18 < \frac{1}{2}(2.5)h$

$18 < 1.25h$

$\frac{18}{1.25} < \frac{1.25h}{1.25}$

$14.4 < h$

35. $\frac{1}{3}(\$24.99) = \$8.33$

The shirt is on sale for $24.99 − 8.33$ or $16.66.

36. a. $\frac{1}{3}x > 332$

$3 \cdot \frac{1}{3}x > 332 \cdot 3$

$x > 996$

more than 996 people

b. Sample answer: 1000; because it is more than 996 and is a round number. Also, if the size of the group was much larger than 1000, say 1500, it would be reported that less than $\frac{1}{4}$ of those polled had tried Indian or Thai food.

37. $\frac{93 + 86 + 84 + 92 + 85 + 93}{6} = 88.8$

38. $\frac{28}{45} \rightarrow 45\overline{)28.000}$

$\underline{-27\,0}$

$1\,00$

$\underline{-90}$

100

$\underline{-90}$

1

$\frac{28}{45} = 0.6\overline{2}$

39. $\frac{6}{7} + \frac{5}{14} = s$

$\frac{12}{14} + \frac{5}{14} = s$

$\frac{17}{14} = s$

$1\frac{3}{14} = s$

40. $15c = 3 \cdot 5 \cdot c$

$12cd = 2 \cdot 2 \cdot 3 \cdot c \cdot d$

The LCM is $2 \cdot 2 \cdot 3 \cdot 5 \cdot c \cdot d$ or $60cd$

41. $a = (-12)(3)$

$a = -36$

42. Associative property of multiplication

6-8

Integration: Discrete Mathematics Geometric Sequences

Pages 314–315 Checking Your Understanding

1. The number by which a term is multiplied to get the next term.

2. Geometric sequences have common factors and arithmetic sequences have common addends.

3. Sample answer: $\frac{1}{4}, \frac{1}{40}, \frac{1}{400}$

4. Generation 9: 128×2 or 256

5. a. See students' work.

b. See students' work.

c. 16 more, 32 total

d. $1, 2, 4, 8, 16, 32, \ldots$

Yes, the common ratio is 2.

---

6. $1 \xrightarrow{\times 3} 3 \xrightarrow{\times 3} 9 \xrightarrow{\times 3} 27$

Yes, 3; 81, 243, 729

7. $2 \xrightarrow{+2} 4 \xrightarrow{+2} 6 \xrightarrow{+2} 8$

no

8. $1 \xrightarrow{-4} -3 \xrightarrow{+8} 5 \xrightarrow{-12} -7$

no

9. $81 \xrightarrow{\times \frac{1}{3}} 27 \xrightarrow{\times \frac{1}{3}} 9 \xrightarrow{\times \frac{1}{3}} 3$

yes, $\frac{1}{3}$; $1, \frac{1}{3}, \frac{1}{9}$

10. $10 \xrightarrow{+4} 14 \xrightarrow{+4} 18 \xrightarrow{+4} 22$

no

11. $\frac{1}{2} \xrightarrow{\times 2} 1 \xrightarrow{\times 2} 2 \xrightarrow{\times 2} 4$

yes, 2; 8, 16, 32

12. $a \cdot r^{(n-1)} = (-5) \cdot (-2)^{4-1}$

$= (-5) \cdot (-2)^3$

$= (-5) \cdot (-8)$

$= 40$

13.

Generation 1	1	) ×2
Generation 2	2	) ×2
Generation 3	4	) ×2
Generation 4	8	) ×2
Generation 5	16	) ×2
Generation 6	32	) ×2
Generation 7	64	) ×2
Generation 8	128	) ×2
Generation 9	256	) ×2
Generation 10	512	) ×2
Generation 11	1024	) ×2
Generation 12	2048	) ×2

Pages 315–316 Exercises

14. $-5 \xrightarrow{\times(-\frac{1}{5})} 1 \xrightarrow{\times(-\frac{1}{5})} -\frac{1}{5} \xrightarrow{\times(-\frac{1}{5})} \frac{1}{25}$

yes, $-\frac{1}{5}$; $-\frac{1}{25}, \frac{1}{625}, -\frac{1}{3125}$

15. $24 \xrightarrow{\times \frac{1}{2}} 12 \xrightarrow{\times \frac{1}{2}} 6 \xrightarrow{\times \frac{1}{2}} 3$

yes, $\frac{1}{2}$; $\frac{3}{2}, \frac{3}{4}, \frac{3}{8}$

16. $9 \xrightarrow{-6} 3 \xrightarrow{-6} -3 \xrightarrow{-6} -9$

no

17. $144 \xrightarrow{\times \frac{1}{12}} 12 \xrightarrow{\times \frac{1}{12}} 1 \xrightarrow{\times \frac{1}{12}} \frac{1}{12}$

yes, $\frac{1}{12}$; $\frac{1}{144}, \frac{1}{1728}, \frac{1}{20,736}$

18. $-14 \xrightarrow{\times(-\frac{1}{2})} 7 \xrightarrow{\times(-\frac{1}{7})} -1 \xrightarrow{\times(-\frac{1}{7})} \frac{1}{7}$

no

19. $\frac{1}{2} \xrightarrow{\times \frac{1}{2}} \frac{1}{4} \xrightarrow{\times \frac{1}{2}} \frac{1}{8} \xrightarrow{\times \frac{1}{2}} \frac{1}{16}$

yes, $\frac{1}{2}$; $\frac{1}{32}, \frac{1}{64}, \frac{1}{128}$

20. $-8 \xrightarrow{\times -2} 16 \xrightarrow{\times -2} -32 \xrightarrow{\times -2} 64$

yes, -2; $-128, 256, -512$

21. $7 \xrightarrow{\times -2} -14 \xrightarrow{\times -2} 28 \xrightarrow{\times -2} -56$

yes, -2; $112, -224, 448$

22. $25 \xrightarrow{\times \frac{1}{5}} 5 \xrightarrow{\times \frac{1}{5}} 1 \xrightarrow{\times \frac{1}{5}} \frac{1}{5}$

yes, $\frac{1}{5}$; $\frac{1}{25}, \frac{1}{125}, \frac{1}{625}$

23. $2\frac{1}{2} \xrightarrow{-2} \frac{1}{2} \xrightarrow{-2} -1\frac{1}{2}$

no

24. $-\frac{1}{4} \xrightarrow{\times 2} -\frac{1}{2} \xrightarrow{\times 2} -1 \xrightarrow{\times 2} -2$

yes, 2; $-4, -8, -16$

25. $1 \xrightarrow{+0} 1 \xrightarrow{+1} 2 \xrightarrow{+1} 3 \xrightarrow{+2} 5$

no

26. $18 \xrightarrow{\times(-\frac{1}{3})} -6 \xrightarrow{\times(-\frac{1}{3})} 2 \xrightarrow{\times(-\frac{1}{3})} -\frac{2}{3}$

yes, $-\frac{1}{3}$; $\frac{2}{9}, -\frac{2}{27}, \frac{2}{81}$

27. $\underset{\times\frac{1}{4}}{\overset{24}{\frown}}\ \underset{\times\frac{1}{4}}{\overset{6}{\frown}}\ \underset{\times\frac{1}{4}}{\overset{\frac{3}{2}}{\frown}}\ \overset{\frac{3}{8}}{}$

yes, $\frac{1}{4}$; $\frac{3}{32}$, $\frac{3}{128}$, $\frac{3}{512}$

28. $\underset{+2}{\overset{5}{\frown}}\ \underset{+2}{\overset{7}{\frown}}\ \underset{+2}{\overset{9}{\frown}}\ \underset{+2}{\overset{11}{\frown}}\ \overset{13}{}$

no

29. $2(-2) = -4$; $-4(-2) = 8$; $8(-2) = -16$; $-16(-2) = 32$
2, -4, 8, -16, 32

30. $-6\left(\frac{2}{3}\right) = -4$; $-4\left(\frac{2}{3}\right) = -\frac{8}{3}$; $-\frac{8}{3}\left(\frac{2}{3}\right) = -\frac{16}{9}$
-6, -4, $-\frac{8}{3}$, $-\frac{16}{9}$, ...

31. $80\left(\frac{5}{4}\right) = 100$; $100\left(\frac{5}{4}\right) = 125$
80, 100, 125

32. $a \cdot r^{(n-1)} = (-14)\left(\frac{1}{4}\right)^{9-1}$
$= (-14)\left(\frac{1}{4}\right)^{8}$
$= (-14)\left(\frac{1}{65,536}\right)$
$= -\frac{14}{65,536}$
$= -\frac{7}{32,768}$

33. $1 \cdot 7^1 = \quad\quad 7$
$1 \cdot 7^2 = \quad\quad 49$
$1 \cdot 7^3 = \quad\quad 343$
$1 \cdot 7^4 = \quad\quad 2,401$
$1 \cdot 7^5 = \quad\quad 16,807$
$1 \cdot 7^6 = \quad 117,649$
$1 \cdot 7^7 = \quad 823,543$
$1 \cdot 7^8 = 5,764,801$
7, 9, 3, 1, 7, 9, 3, 1, ... ; 1

34. a. When you multiply by a number less than 1, the term decreases.

b. The term increases.

35. a. 1.3

b. $\underset{\times 1.3}{\overset{10}{\frown}}\ \underset{\times 1.3}{\overset{13}{\frown}}\ \underset{\times 1.3}{\overset{16.9}{\frown}}\ \underset{\times 1.3}{\overset{21.97}{\frown}}\ \underset{\times 1.3}{\overset{28.561}{\frown}}\ \overset{37.1293}{}$

In 2030, the population of Florida will be 37,129,300.

36. $\underset{\times 1\frac{1}{10}}{\overset{\$1250}{\frown}}\ \underset{\times 1\frac{1}{10}}{\overset{\$1375}{\frown}}\ \underset{\times 1\frac{1}{10}}{\overset{\$1512.5}{\frown}}\ \overset{\$1663.75}{}$

After 3 years, the face value is $1663.75.

37. $\underset{\times 3}{\overset{1}{\frown}}\ \underset{\times 3}{\overset{3}{\frown}}\ \underset{\times 3}{\overset{9}{\frown}}\ \overset{27}{}$
$1 + 3 + 9 + 27 = 40$

38. $3 \times 3 \times 3 \times 3 \times 3 = 243$
243 players participate.

39. $\frac{5}{9}k = 15$
$\frac{9}{5} \cdot \frac{5}{9}k = 15 \cdot \frac{9}{5}$
$k = 27$

40. $d = 119 - 9.8$
$\begin{array}{r} 119.0 \\ -\ 9.8 \\ \hline 109.2 \end{array}$
$d = 109.2$

41. $\frac{3^3}{3^7} = 3^{3-7}$
$= 3^{-4}$
$= \frac{1}{3^4}$
$= \frac{1}{81}$

42. $A = b \cdot b$
$= b^2$

43. $t = \frac{120}{24}$
$t = 5$

44. $5x + 3x + 1 = (5 + 3)x + 1$
$= 8x + 1$

45. $6.5 + 12 \div 3 = 6 \cdot 5 + 4$
$= 30 + 4$
$= 34$

46. $\underset{+1}{\overset{8}{\frown}}\ \underset{+2}{\overset{9}{\frown}}\ \underset{+3}{\overset{11}{\frown}}\ \underset{+4}{\overset{14}{\frown}}\ \underset{+5}{\overset{18}{\frown}}\ \underset{+6}{\overset{23}{\frown}}\ \overset{29}{}$

6-9 Scientific Notation

Pages 318–319 Checking Your Understanding

1. a–b. Answers will vary. Write the decimal point after the first nonzero digit and multiply this number by a power of ten that represents the places the decimal was moved. The sign of the power is negative if moved from the left and positive if moved from the right.

2. Answers will vary. Numbers that are small, < 1, have negative exponents because they must be multiplied by a number < 1 in scientific notation. Numbers that are large, > 1, have positive exponents because they must be multiplied by a number > 1.

3. See students' work.

4. No; 23.45 is not between 1 and 10.

5. yes

6. No; 0.23 is not between 1 and 10.

7. $8490 = 8.490 \times 10^3$

8. $0.000045 = 4.5 \times 10^{-5}$

9. $847.9 = 8.479 \times 10^2$

10. $5.2 \times 10^5 = 5.2 \times 100,000$
$= 520,000$

11. $6.1 \times 10^4 = 6.1 \times 10,000$
$= 61,000$

12. $9.34 \times 10^{-2} = 9.34 \times \left(\frac{1}{10}\right)^2$
$= 9.34 \times \frac{1}{100}$
$= 0.0934$

13. $60 \times 60 \times 24 \times 365.25 = 31,557,600$ seconds in a year;
$(31,557,600)(3.00 \times 10^5)$ or about 9.47×10^{12} km

Pages 319–320 Exercises

14. $5,894,000 = 5.894 \times 10^6$

15. $0.0059 = 5.9 \times 10^{-3}$

16. $269,000 = 2.69 \times 10^5$

17. $0.00015 = 1.5 \times 10^{-4}$

18. $80,000,000 = 8.0 \times 10^7$

19. $0.0000000498 = 4.98 \times 10^{-8}$

20. $2,598,960 = 2.59896 \times 10^6$

21. $701,000,000 = 7.01 \times 10^8$

22. $0.001 = 1.0 \times 10^{-3}$

23. $5.6 \times 10^{-6} = 5.6 \times \left(\frac{1}{10}\right)^6$

$\qquad = 5.6 \times \frac{1}{1,000,000}$

$\qquad = 0.0000056$

24. $1.399 \times 10^2 = 1.399 \times 100$

$\qquad = 139.9$

25. $9.001 \times 10^{-3} = 9.001 \times \left(\frac{1}{10}\right)^3$

$\qquad = 9.001 \times \frac{1}{1000}$

$\qquad = 0.009001$

26. $7.8 \times 10^{11} = 7.8 \times 100,000,000,000$

$\qquad = 780,000,000,000$

27. $5.985 \times 10^{-5} = 5.985 \times \left(\frac{1}{10}\right)^5$

$\qquad = 5.985 \times \frac{1}{100,000}$

$\qquad = 0.00005985$

28. $4.054 \times 10^1 = 4.054 \times 10$

$\qquad = 40.54$

29. $1.454 \times 10^3 = 1.454 \times 1000$

$\qquad = 1454$ feet

30. $3.5 \times 10^{-8} = 3.5 \times \left(\frac{1}{10}\right)^8$

$\qquad = 3.5 \times \frac{1}{100,000,000}$

$\qquad = 0.000000035$

31. $5 \times 10^{-5} = 5 \times \left(\frac{1}{10}\right)^5$

$\qquad = 5 \times \frac{1}{100,000}$

$\qquad = 0.00005$

32. $(4 \times 10^4) + (8 \times 10^3) + (3 \times 10^2) + (9 \times 10^1) +$ (6×10^0)

$\qquad = (4 \times 10,000) + (8 \times 1000) + (3 \times 100) +$ $(9 \times 10) + (6 \times 1)$

$\qquad = 48,396$

33. $(7 \times 10^8) + (8 \times 10^4) + (3 \times 10^0)$

$\qquad = (7 \times 100,000,000) + (8 \times 10,000) + (3 \times 1)$

$\qquad = 700,080,003$

34. $(6 \times 10^0) + (4 \times 10^{-3}) + (3 \times 10^{-5})$

$\qquad = (6 \times 1) + \left(4 \times \frac{1}{1000}\right) + \left(3 \times \frac{1}{100,000}\right)$

$\qquad = 6.00403$

35. 3.14

36. 0.000002 or 2.0×10^{-6}

37. a. Bezymianny

b. Ngauruhoe

c. Bezymianny; Santa Maria; Agung; Mount St. Helens tied with Hekla 1947; Hekla, 1970; Ngauruhoe

38. 9 $\overset{-3}{\curvearrowright}$ 1 $\overset{-\frac{1}{3}}{\curvearrowright}$

$\qquad \times\left(-\frac{1}{3}\right) \quad \times\left(-\frac{1}{3}\right) \quad \times\left(-\frac{1}{3}\right)$

yes; $-\frac{1}{3}, \frac{1}{9}, -\frac{1}{27}, \frac{1}{81}$

39. $x + \frac{2}{3} \geq 3$

$\qquad x + \frac{2}{3} - \frac{2}{3} \geq 3 - \frac{2}{3}$

$\qquad x \geq \frac{3}{1} - \frac{2}{3}$

$\qquad x \geq \frac{9}{3} - \frac{2}{3}$

$\qquad x \geq \frac{7}{3}$

$\qquad x \geq 2\frac{1}{3}$

40. $-3\frac{1}{5} - \left(-\frac{2}{5}\right) = a$

$\qquad -3\frac{1}{5} + \frac{2}{5} = a$

$\qquad -\frac{16}{5} + \frac{2}{5} = a$

$\qquad -\frac{14}{5} = a$

$\qquad -2\frac{4}{5} = a$

41. $\frac{b}{7} = \frac{-91}{7}$

$\qquad = -13$

42. $x + 7 = 19$ $\qquad$ What number
$\quad 12 + 7 = 19$ $\qquad$ plus 7 is 19?
$\qquad x = 12$

43. $b + 3$

Page 320   The Shape of Things to Come

- See students' work
- Sample answer: By connecting the zinc and copper needles with a wire, an electric circuit is formed. Thus, as the electrons on the negative zinc needle flow to the positive copper needle, the lightbulb begins to glow.
- Sample answer: In alkaline batteries, electricity is produced by chemical action. In living batteries, the energy is released by single-celled microbes.

Chapter 6   Study Guide and Assessment

Page 321   Understanding and Using Vocabulary

1. true
2. false; "The median is the number in the middle when the data are arranged in order" or "The mode is the number that occurs most frequently in a set of data."
3. false; Each term in a geometric sequence increases or decreases by a common ratio.
4. true
5. false; A decimal is called a terminating decimal because the digits terminate.
6. false; Compatible numbers are rounded so that they fit together.
7. true
8. true
9. false; It is possible to have a set of numerical data with no mode.
10. false; The inverse property of multiplication says that every number, except zero, has a multiplicative inverse. Zero has no multiplicative inverse.

11. $\frac{5}{8} \to 8\overline{)5.000}$

$$
\begin{array}{r}
0.625 \\
8\overline{)5.000} \\
\underline{-4\,8} \\
20 \\
\underline{-16} \\
40 \\
\underline{-40} \\
0
\end{array}
$$

$\frac{5}{8} = 0.625$

12. $\frac{6}{9} \to 9\overline{)6.000}$

$$
\begin{array}{r}
0.666 \\
9\overline{)6.000} \\
\underline{-5\,4} \\
60 \\
\underline{-54} \\
60 \\
\underline{-54} \\
6
\end{array}
$$

$\frac{6}{9} = 0.\overline{6}$

13. $\frac{17}{40} \to 40\overline{)17.000}$

$$
\begin{array}{r}
0.425 \\
40\overline{)17.000} \\
\underline{-16\,0} \\
1\,00 \\
\underline{-80} \\
200 \\
\underline{-200} \\
0
\end{array}
$$

$\frac{17}{40} = 0.425$

14. $\frac{2}{25} \to 25\overline{)2.00}$

$$
\begin{array}{r}
0.08 \\
25\overline{)2.00} \\
\underline{-0} \\
200 \\
\underline{-200} \\
0
\end{array}
$$

$\frac{2}{25} = 0.08$

15. $\frac{4}{15} \to 15\overline{)4.000}$

$$
\begin{array}{r}
0.266 \\
15\overline{)4.000} \\
\underline{-3\,0} \\
1\,00 \\
\underline{-90} \\
100 \\
\underline{-90} \\
10
\end{array}
$$

$\frac{4}{15} = 0.2\overline{6}$

16. $\frac{7}{12} \to 12\overline{)7.0000}$

$$
\begin{array}{r}
0.5833 \\
12\overline{)7.0000} \\
\underline{-6\,0} \\
1\,00 \\
\underline{-96} \\
40 \\
\underline{-36} \\
40 \\
\underline{-36} \\
4
\end{array}
$$

$\frac{7}{12} = .058\overline{3}$

17. $\frac{9}{10} \cdot 21 \to 1 \cdot 21 = 21$

18. $8.36 \div 16.53 \to 8 \div 16 = 0.5$

19. $9 \div 1\frac{1}{5} \to 9 \div 1 = 9$

20. $18.17 \times 6.19 \to 20 \times 6 = 120$

21. $-\frac{5}{9} \cdot \frac{8}{25} = n$

$-\frac{\overset{1}{\cancel{5}}}{9} \cdot \frac{8}{\underset{5}{\cancel{25}}} = n$

$-\frac{1}{9} \cdot \frac{8}{5} = n$

$-\frac{8}{45} = n$

22. $6\frac{2}{3} \cdot \frac{1}{2} = t$

$\frac{20}{3} \cdot \frac{1}{2} = t$

$\frac{20}{6} = t$

$3\frac{2}{6} = t$

$3\frac{1}{3} = t$

23. $w = -3\left(\frac{6}{15}\right)$

$w = -\frac{18}{15}$

$w = -1\frac{3}{15}$

$w = -1\frac{1}{5}$

24. $-7\left(\frac{8}{21}\right) = d$

$-\frac{\overset{1}{\cancel{7}}}{1}\left(\frac{8}{\underset{3}{\cancel{21}}}\right) = d$

$-\frac{8}{3} = d$

$-2\frac{2}{3} = d$

25. $g = \left(\frac{4}{5}\right)^3$

$g = \left(\frac{4}{5}\right)\left(\frac{4}{5}\right)\left(\frac{4}{5}\right)$

$g = \frac{64}{125}$

26. $q = \frac{2}{5} \cdot \frac{7}{8}$

$q = \frac{\overset{1}{\cancel{2}}}{5} \cdot \frac{7}{\underset{4}{\cancel{8}}}$

$q = \frac{7}{20}$

27. $a \div b = \frac{1}{4} \div \frac{2}{6}$

$ = \frac{1}{4} \times \frac{6}{2}$

$ = \frac{6}{8}$

$ = \frac{3}{4}$

28. $bc \div f = \left(-\frac{8}{15}\right)(3) \div 1\frac{1}{2}$

$ = -\frac{24}{15} \div 1\frac{1}{2}$

$ = -\frac{24}{15} \div \frac{3}{2}$

$ = -\frac{24}{15} \times \frac{2}{3}$

$ = -\frac{48}{45}$

$ = -1\frac{3}{45}$

$ = -1\frac{1}{15}$

29. $\frac{x}{y} = \dfrac{\frac{8}{12}}{-6}$

$\phantom{\frac{x}{y}} = \dfrac{\frac{8}{12}}{\frac{-6}{1}}$

$\phantom{\frac{x}{y}} = \frac{8}{12} \times \left(-\frac{1}{6}\right)$

$\phantom{\frac{x}{y}} = -\frac{8}{72}$

$\phantom{\frac{x}{y}} = -\frac{1}{9}$

30. $\frac{gh}{8} = \dfrac{\left(3\frac{2}{7}\right)\left(-5\frac{1}{3}\right)}{8}$

$\phantom{\frac{gh}{8}} = \dfrac{\left(\frac{23}{7}\right)\left(-\frac{16}{3}\right)}{8}$

$\phantom{\frac{gh}{8}} = \dfrac{-\frac{368}{21}}{\frac{8}{1}}$

$\phantom{\frac{gh}{8}} = -\frac{368}{21} \times \frac{1}{8}$

$\phantom{\frac{gh}{8}} = -\frac{\overset{46}{\cancel{368}}}{21} \times \frac{1}{\underset{1}{\cancel{8}}}$

$\phantom{\frac{gh}{8}} = -\frac{46}{21}$

$\phantom{\frac{gh}{8}} = -2\frac{4}{21}$

31. $4 \times 7.07 = y$

$$
\begin{array}{r}
7.07 \\
\times\quad 4 \\
\hline
28.28
\end{array}
$$

$y = 28.28$

32. $k = -1.25 \times 12$

$$
\begin{array}{r}
-1.25 \\
\times 12 \\
\hline
250 \\
1250 \\
\hline
15.00
\end{array}
$$

$k = -15$

33. $b = 62.9 \div 1000$

$$
\begin{array}{r}
0.0629 \\
1000\overline{)62.9000} \\
\underline{-60\,00} \\
2\,900 \\
\underline{-2\,000} \\
9000 \\
\underline{-9000} \\
0
\end{array}
$$

$b = 0.0629$

34. $2.65 \cdot 3.46 = x$

$$
\begin{array}{r}
2.65 \\
\times 3.46 \\
\hline
1590 \\
10600 \\
79500 \\
\hline
9.1690
\end{array}
$$

$x = 9.169$

35. $0.7 \div 2.4 = d$

$2.4 \overline{)0.7}$

$$
\begin{array}{r}
0.29166 \\
24\overline{)7.00000} \\
\underline{-4\ 8} \\
2\ 20 \\
\underline{-2\ 16} \\
40 \\
\underline{-24} \\
160 \\
\underline{-144} \\
160 \\
\underline{-144} \\
16
\end{array}
$$

$d = 0.291\overline{6}$

36. $-25.9 \div 2.8 = s$

$2.8 \overline{)25.9}$

$$
\begin{array}{r}
9.25 \\
28\overline{)259.00} \\
\underline{-252} \\
70 \\
\underline{-56} \\
140 \\
\underline{-140} \\
0
\end{array}
$$

$s = -9.25$

37. $n = 5.3 \cdot (-9)$

$$
\begin{array}{r}
5.3 \\
\underline{\times -9} \\
47.7
\end{array}
$$

$n = -47.7$

38. $f = 1.3 \div 100$

$$
\begin{array}{r}
0.013 \\
100\overline{)1.300} \\
\underline{-1\ 00} \\
300 \\
\underline{-300} \\
0
\end{array}
$$

$f = 0.013$

39. 16, 17, 18, 18, 19, 21, 21, 25, 25, 26

mean: $\dfrac{16 + 17 + 18 + 18 + 19 + 21 + 21 + 25 + 25 + 26}{10} =$ 20.6

median: $\dfrac{19 + 21}{2} = 20$

mode: 18, 21, and 25

40. 2.6, 3.1, 3.4, 4.3, 4.9, 5.7, 6.8

mean: $\dfrac{2.6 + 3.1 + 3.4 + 4.3 + 4.9 + 5.7 + 6.8}{7} = 4.4$

median: 4.3

mode: none

41. 0, 9, 14, 14, 22, 26

mean: $\dfrac{0 + 9 + 14 + 14 + 22 + 26}{6} = 14.17$

median: 14

mode: 14

42. 2.7, 4.6, 5.4, 6.2, 8.0

mean: $\dfrac{2.7 + 4.6 + 5.4 + 6.2 + 8.0}{5} = 5.38$

median: 5.4

mode: none

43. $8.67k = 78.03$

$\dfrac{8.67k}{8.67} = \dfrac{78.03}{8.67}$

$k = 9$

Check: $8.67k = 78.03$

$8.67(9) \stackrel{?}{=} 78.03$

$78.03 = 78.03$ ✔

44. $6.3a \leq 52.92$

$\dfrac{6.3a}{6.3} \leq \dfrac{52.92}{6.3}$

$a \leq 8.4$

Check: Try 7, a number less than or equal to 8.4.

$6.3a \leq 52.92$

$6.3(7) \stackrel{?}{\leq} 52.92$

$44.1 \leq 52.92$ ✔

45. $-\dfrac{1}{4}r = 3$

$\left(-\dfrac{4}{1}\right)\left(-\dfrac{1}{4}\right)r = 3\left(-\dfrac{4}{1}\right)$

$r = -12$

Check: $-\dfrac{1}{4}r = 3$

$-\dfrac{1}{4}(-12) \stackrel{?}{=} 3$

$3 = 3$ ✔

46. $4.5 < -\dfrac{5}{8}f$

$\left(-\dfrac{8}{5}\right)4.5 > -\dfrac{5}{8}f\left(-\dfrac{8}{5}\right)$

$-7.2 > f$

Check: Try -8, a number greater than -7.2.

$4.5 < -\dfrac{5}{8}f$

$4.5 \stackrel{?}{<} -\dfrac{5}{8}(-8)$

$4.5 < 5$ ✔

47. $-25 \geq 6.25n$

$\dfrac{-25}{6.25} \geq \dfrac{6.25n}{6.25}$

$-4 \geq n$

Check: Try -5, a number less than or equal to -4.

$-25 \geq 6.25n$

$-25 \stackrel{?}{\geq} 6.25(-5)$

$-25 \geq -31.25$ ✔

48. $3x = 55.8$

$\dfrac{3x}{3} = \dfrac{55.8}{3}$

$x = 18.6$

Check: $3x = 55.8$

$3(18.6) \stackrel{?}{=} 55.8$

$55.8 = 55.8$ ✔

49. $8x = 42.4$

$\dfrac{8x}{8} = \dfrac{42.4}{8}$

$x = 5.3$

Check: $8x = 42.4$

$8(5.3) \stackrel{?}{=} 42.4$

$42.4 = 42.4$ ✔

50. $2.6v > 19.76$

$\dfrac{2.6v}{2.6} > \dfrac{19.76}{2.6}$

$v > 7.6$

Check: Try 8, a number greater than 7.6.

$2.6v > 19.76$

$2.6(8) \stackrel{?}{>} 19.76$

$20.8 > 19.76$ ✔

51. 6.6 5.7 4.9

-0.9 -0.8

no

52. 3 9 27

$\times 3$ $\times 3$

yes; 3; 81, 243, 729

53. 0.5 2 3.5 5

$+1.5$ $+1.5$ $+1.5$

no

54. $\dfrac{1}{4}$ $\dfrac{1}{2}$ 1 2

$\times 2$ $\times 2$ $\times 2$

yes; 2; 4, 8, 16

55. 17 13 18 14 19

-4 $+5$ -4 $+5$

no

56. $13{,}490{,}000 = 1.349 \times 10^7$

57. $0.00000674 = 6.74 \times 10^{-6}$

58. $0.00032 = 3.2 \times 10^{-4}$

59. $5810 = 5.81 \times 10^3$

60. $4.24 \times 10^2 = 4.24 \times 100$
$= 424$

61. $5.72 \times 10^4 = 5.72 \times 10,000$
$= 57,200$

62. $3.347 \times 10^{-1} = 3.347 \times \left(\frac{1}{10}\right)^1$
$= 3.347 \times \frac{1}{10}$
$= 0.3347$

63. $2.02 \times 10^8 = 2.02 \times 100,000,000$
$= 202,000,000$

Page 324   Applications and Problem Solving

64. $0.34 < \frac{44}{112}$ because
$0.34 < 0.39$; Therefore, the Unified team had a greater portion of their medals as gold.

65. $24 \times 5\frac{1}{2} = \frac{24}{1} \times \frac{11}{2}$
$= \frac{264}{2}$
$= 132$¢ or \$1.32

66. a. $2546 + 3282 + 1092 + 724 + 568 +$
$\dfrac{900 + 10,085 + 130 + 6896 + 989}{10} = 2,721.2$ thousand

b. 130, 568, 724, 900, 989, 1092,
2546, 3282, 6896, 10,085
median: $\frac{989 + 1092}{2} = 1,040.5$ thousand

c. none

67. $273.6 \div 18$

$$
\begin{array}{r}
15.3 \\
18\overline{)273.6} \\
-18 \\
\hline
93 \\
-90 \\
\hline
36 \\
-36 \\
\hline
0
\end{array}
$$

15.3 times

68. $80,663,217.42 = 8.066321742 \times 10^7$

Page 325   Alternative Assessment

1. $92\frac{3}{4} = 92 + \frac{3}{4}$

$$
\frac{3}{4} \rightarrow
\begin{array}{r}
0.75 \\
4\overline{)3.00} \\
-2\,8 \\
\hline
20 \\
-20 \\
\hline
0
\end{array}
$$

$92 + 0.75 = 92.75$
$92\frac{3}{4} = \$92.75$

2. $6\left(55\frac{3}{8}\right) = 6\left(\frac{443}{8}\right)$
$= \frac{\overset{3}{\cancel{6}}}{1}\left(\frac{443}{\underset{4}{\cancel{8}}}\right)$
$= \frac{1329}{4}$
$= 332.25$

It would cost \$332.25 to buy 6 shares of Sony stock.

3. $951 \div 39\frac{5}{8} = 951 \div \frac{317}{8}$
$= 951 \times \frac{8}{317}$
$= \frac{\overset{3}{\cancel{951}}}{1} \times \frac{8}{\underset{1}{\cancel{317}}}$
$= \frac{24}{1}$
$= 24$

4.

Stock	Price per share	Dollars
McDonalds	$39\frac{5}{8}$	39.63
Wendy's	19	19.00
Sony	$55\frac{3}{8}$	55.38
Nike	$92\frac{3}{4}$	92.75

mean: $\frac{39.63 + 19.00 + 55.38 + 92.75}{4} = \$51.69$

5. 19.00, 39.63, 55.38, 92.75
median: $\frac{39.63 + 55.38}{2} = \$47.50$

6. $32\left(17\frac{3}{4}\right) = 32\left(\frac{71}{4}\right)$
$= \frac{\overset{8}{\cancel{32}}}{1}\left(\frac{71}{\underset{1}{\cancel{4}}}\right)$
$= 568$

32 shares of Wendy's stock at $17\frac{3}{4}$ per share cost \$568.00.

$32(19) = 608$
32 shares of Wendy's stock at 19 per share cost \$608.00.

$\$608.00 - \$568.00 = \$40.00$
You would make \$40.00.

7. a. See students' work.

b. See students' work.

Page 325   Thinking Critically

- faster, smaller margin of error
- 1 meter = 1×10^2 or 100 centimeters
  size of an atom = 1×10^{-10} or $\frac{1}{10,000,000,000}$ centimeters

$\frac{1 \times 10^{-10}}{1 \times 10^2} = \frac{10^{-10}}{10^2}$
$= 10^{-10-2}$
$= 10^{-12}$
$= 1 \times 10^{-12}$ or 0.000000000001 meters

Page 325   Portfolio
- See students' work

Page 325   Self Evaluation
- See students' work

Ongoing Assessment

Pages 326–327

1. C; $\$532.16 \div 12 \rightarrow 540 \div 12 = \$45.00$

2. A; $15 + 12 + 12 = 39$ feet

3. B; $\$1.39 + \$2.89 + \$0.58 + \$1.19 \rightarrow$
$1 + 3 + 1 + 1 = \$6$

4. B; $m + mp = 12 + 12(10)$
$= 12 + 120$
$= 132$

5. A; $3.2y = 80$
$\frac{3.2y}{3.2} = \frac{80}{3.2}$
$y = 25$

6. C; $\frac{8}{11} \not< \frac{7}{13}$ because
$.72 \not< .54$

7. A; $82 + g > 170$

8. D; 739.4
$\underline{-256.8}$
482.6 mi

9. A; $\frac{a^2}{a^4} = a^{2-4}$
$= a^{-2}$

10. B; $\$42.50$
$\underline{\times\ 2.5}$
21250
$\underline{85000}$
$106.250 \rightarrow \$106.25$

11. $\frac{a}{-5} < 1$
$(-5)\frac{a}{-5} > 1(-5)$
$a > -5$

12. $0.36 = \frac{36}{100} = \frac{9}{25}$

13. $60x^2y = \boxed{2} \cdot \boxed{2} \cdot \boxed{3} \cdot 5 \cdot \boxed{x} \cdot x \cdot \boxed{y}$
$24x^3y^2 = \boxed{2} \cdot \boxed{2} \cdot 2 \cdot \boxed{3} \cdot \boxed{x} \cdot x \cdot x \cdot \boxed{y} \cdot y$
$84xy^4 = \boxed{2} \cdot \boxed{2} \cdot \boxed{3} \cdot 7 \cdot \boxed{x} \cdot \boxed{y} \cdot y \cdot y \cdot \boxed{y} \cdot y$
The GCF is $2 \cdot 2 \cdot 3 \cdot x \cdot y$ or $12xy$.

14. See students' work.

15. $3\frac{1}{4} - 2\frac{5}{8} = 3\frac{2}{8} - 2\frac{5}{8}$
$= 2\frac{10}{8} - 2\frac{5}{8}$
$= \frac{5}{8}$ yards

16. $85° - x = 37°$
$85° - x + x = 37° + x$
$85° = 37° + x - 37°$
$85° - 37° = 37° + x - 37°$
$48° = x$

17. $\frac{25}{40} = \frac{5}{8}$

18. $5\left(2\frac{5}{8}\right) = 5\left(\frac{21}{8}\right)$
$= \frac{105}{8}$
$= 13\frac{1}{8}$ gallons

19. See students' work.

20. 56°F, 58°F, 58°F, 60°F, 62°F, 63°F, 70°F
mean: $\frac{56 + 58 + 58 + 60 + 62 + 63 + 70}{7} = 61°F$
median: 60°F
The mean is the arithmetic average and the median is the middle number.

21. Sample answer: $0.01001000100001\ldots$

Chapter 7   Solving Equations and Inequalities

Problem-Solving Strategy: Work Backward

Page 330   Your Turn

Operation	Begin with a designed square.	Rotate 45° clockwise.	Remove thin line.	Rotate 45° clockwise.	Remove thick line.
Result					

a. Undoing the steps used to assemble the designed square.

b. Sample answer: Paint thick line. Rotate counterclockwise 45°. Paint thin line. Rotate counterclockwise 135°.

Page 331   Checking Your Understanding

1. Sample answer: When you have the final result after a sequence of known operations and you want to know the starting point.

2. Sample answer: Reverse the order.

3. See students' work.

4. See students' work.

5. Half of the milk and the can weigh 9 ounces. All of the milk and the can weigh 15 ounces. Thus, half of the milk weighs $15 - 9$ or 6 ounces. All of the milk would weigh 2×6 or 12 ounces. So, the can weighs $15 - 12$ or 3 ounces.

6.

$$\text{The final answer is 32.} \longrightarrow 32$$
$$\textit{Undo} \text{ the 1 that was} \longrightarrow \underline{+ \ 1}$$
$$\text{subtracted from the result.} \qquad 33$$
$$\textit{Undo} \text{ divided by 5.} \longrightarrow \underline{\times \ 5}$$
$$165$$

The number is 165.

7. Mr. Gentry sold one third of his stock for $2700. So, the total value of his stock was $3 \times \$2700$ or $8100. Since Mr. and Mrs. Gentry each own an equal number of shares, the total value of their stock was $\$8100 + \$8100$ or $16,200.

8.

$$\text{The final answer is 41.} \longrightarrow 41$$
$$\textit{Undo} \text{ the 5 that was added} \longrightarrow \underline{- \ 5}$$
$$\text{to the number.} \qquad 36$$
$$\textit{Undo} \text{ the 3 that the number} \longrightarrow \underline{\div \ 3}$$
$$\text{was multiplied by.} \qquad 12$$

The number is 12.

9.

$$\text{Chris had } \$1.50 \longrightarrow 1.50$$
$$\textit{Undo} \text{ the dollar that he lent} \longrightarrow \underline{+1.00}$$
$$\text{to Bill.} \qquad 2.50$$
$$\textit{Undo} \text{ the half that he had} \longrightarrow \underline{\times \ \ 2}$$
$$\text{spent on lunch.} \qquad 5.00$$

Chris started with $5.00.

10. $\$1.25 \times 44 = \$55.00$
The driver collected $55.00

11.

Day	Number of People Told
Mon.	3
Tues.	$3(3) = 9$
Wed.	$9(3) = 27$
Thurs.	$27(3) = 81$
Fri.	$81(3) = 243$
Sat.	$243(3) = 729$

729 people will hear the joke on Saturday.

12.

Time	Weight (lbs)
After 8 hours	$\frac{5}{16}$
After 7 hours	$\frac{5}{16}(2) = \frac{10}{16}$ or $\frac{5}{8}$
After 6 hours	$\frac{5}{8}(2) = \frac{10}{8}$ or $1\frac{1}{4}$
After 5 hours	$\frac{10}{8}(2) = \frac{20}{8}$ or $2\frac{1}{2}$
After 4 hours	$\frac{20}{8}(2) = \frac{40}{8}$ or 5
After 3 hours	$5(2) = 10$
After 2 hours	$10(2) = 20$
After 1 hour	$20(2) = 40$
After 0 hours	$40(2) = 80$

At the beginning, the ice sculpture weighed 80 pounds.

13. 29.8.92 and 2.9.92

14.

	Al	Bart	Carlos
After 4th Round	8	8	8
After 3rd Round	4	4	16
After 2nd Round	2	14	8
After 1st Round	13	7	4

Al: 13 points; Bart: 7 points; Carlos: 4 points

15. $6.789 \times 10^{-7} = 6.789 \times \left(\frac{1}{10}\right)^7$
$$= 6.789 \times \frac{1}{10,000,000}$$
$$= 0.0000006789$$

16. $1.68 - 1.40 = 0.28$
0.28 million or 280,000

17. whole numbers, integers, rational

18. $ab \div (-7) = (49)(-2) \div (-7)$
$$= -98 \div (-7)$$
$$= 14$$

19. $[4(3 + 8) \div (4 - 2)] + 9 = [4(11) \div (4 - 2)] + 9$
$$= [4(11) \div 2] + 9$$
$$= [44 \div 2] + 9$$
$$= 22 + 9$$
$$= 31$$

Math Lab: Two-Step Equations

Page 333   Your Turn

1. See students' work; –3
2. See students' work; 3
3. See students' work; 4
4. See students' work; –1
5. See students' work; 2
6. See students' work; –2
7. Sample answer: You undo operations to find the value of x.
8. Sample answer: Turn two cups upside down to represent negative $2x$.

7-2

Solving Two-Step Equations

Pages 335–336   Checking Your Understanding

1. Sample answer: The order of operations is used in reverse order.
2. **a.** Answers will vary. By following the reverse order of operations, Kelsey is correct. Both students will get the correct answer.
   b. Sample answer: Dana's method will involve the use of fractions while Kelsey's method will involve integers. Kelsey's method is easier.
3. Sample answer: Dawn now has 15 meters of rope. She cut five meters off of the amount she started with and cut the remaining rope into three equal pieces. How long was each of the three pieces?
4. **a.** 2

   b.
   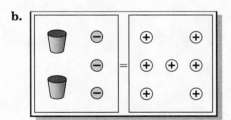

   $$2x - 3 = 7$$
   $$2x - 3 + 3 = 7 + 3$$
   $$2x = 10$$
   $$\frac{2x}{2} = \frac{10}{2}$$
   $$x = 5$$

5. $$2n - 5 = 21$$
   $$2n - 5 + 5 = 21 + 5$$
   $$2n = 26$$
   $$\frac{2n}{2} = \frac{26}{2}$$
   $$n = 13$$
   Check: $2n - 5 = 21$
   $$2(13) - 5 \stackrel{?}{=} 21$$
   $$26 - 5 \stackrel{?}{=} 21$$
   $$21 = 21 \checkmark$$

6. $$3 + \frac{t}{2} = 35$$
   $$3 + \frac{t}{2} - 3 = 35 - 3$$
   $$\frac{t}{2} = 32$$
   $$2 \cdot \frac{t}{2} = 32 \cdot 2$$
   $$t = 64$$
   Check: $3 + \frac{t}{2} = 35$
   $$3 + \frac{64}{2} \stackrel{?}{=} 35$$
   $$3 + 32 \stackrel{?}{=} 35$$
   $$35 = 35 \checkmark$$

7. $$7.5r + 2 = -28$$
   $$7.5r + 2 - 2 = -28 - 2$$
   $$7.5r = -30$$
   $$\frac{7.5r}{7.5} = \frac{-30}{7.5}$$
   $$r = -4$$
   Check: $7.5r + 2 = -28$
   $$7.5(-4) + 2 \stackrel{?}{=} 28$$
   $$-30 + 2 \stackrel{?}{=} -28$$
   $$-28 = -28 \checkmark$$

8. $$3(x + 5) = 9$$
   $$3x + 15 = 9$$
   $$3x + 15 - 15 = 9 - 15$$
   $$3x = -6$$
   $$\frac{3x}{3} = \frac{-6}{3}$$
   $$x = -2$$
   Check: $3(x + 5) = 9$
   $$3(-2 + 5) \stackrel{?}{=} 9$$
   $$3(3) \stackrel{?}{=} 9$$
   $$9 = 9 \checkmark$$

9. $$-2.5(a + 2a) = 22.5$$
   $$-2.5a + (-5a) = 22.5$$
   $$-7.5a = 22.5$$
   $$\frac{-7.5a}{-7.5} = \frac{22.5}{-7.5}$$
   $$a = -3$$
   Check: $-2.5(a + 2a) = 22.5$
   $$-2.5[-3 + 2(-3)] \stackrel{?}{=} 22.5$$
   $$-2.5[-3 + (-6)] \stackrel{?}{=} 22.5$$
   $$-2.5(-9) \stackrel{?}{=} 22.5$$
   $$22.5 = 22.5 \checkmark$$

10. $$\frac{a + 5}{2} = 10.5$$
    $$2\left(\frac{a + 5}{2}\right) = 2(10.5)$$
    $$a + 5 = 21$$
    $$a + 5 - 5 = 21 - 5$$
    $$a = 16$$
    Check: $\frac{a + 5}{2} = 10.5$
    $$\frac{16 + 5}{2} \stackrel{?}{=} 10.5$$
    $$\frac{21}{2} \stackrel{?}{=} 10.5$$
    $$10.5 = 10.5 \checkmark$$

11.
$$32 + 29w = 177$$
$$32 + 29w - 32 = 177 - 32$$
$$29w = 145$$
$$\frac{29w}{29} = \frac{145}{29}$$
$$w = 5$$

Judi had to pay for 5 additional ounces. So, the package weighed 6 ounces.

Pages 336–337   Exercises

12.
$$85 = 4d + 5$$
$$85 - 5 = 4d + 5 - 5$$
$$80 = 4d$$
$$\frac{80}{4} = \frac{4d}{4}$$
$$20 = d$$
Check: $85 = 4d + 5$
$$85 \stackrel{?}{=} 4(20) + 5$$
$$85 \stackrel{?}{=} 80 + 5$$
$$85 = 85 \checkmark$$

13.
$$2r - 7 = 1$$
$$2r - 7 + 7 = 1 + 7$$
$$2r = 8$$
$$\frac{2r}{2} = \frac{8}{2}$$
$$r = 4$$
Check: $2r - 7 = 1$
$$2(4) - 7 \stackrel{?}{=} 1$$
$$8 - 7 \stackrel{?}{=} 1$$
$$1 = 1 \checkmark$$

14.
$$4 - 2b = -8$$
$$4 - 2b - 4 = -8 - 4$$
$$-2b = -12$$
$$\frac{-2b}{-2} = \frac{-12}{-2}$$
$$b = 6$$
Check: $4 - 2b = -8$
$$4 - 2(6) \stackrel{?}{=} -8$$
$$4 - 12 \stackrel{?}{=} -8$$
$$-8 = -8 \checkmark$$

15.
$$-8 - t = -25$$
$$-8 - t + 8 = -25 + 8$$
$$-t = -17$$
$$-1(-t) = -1(-17)$$
$$t = 17$$
Check: $-8 - t = -25$
$$-8 - 17 \stackrel{?}{=} -25$$
$$-25 = -25 \checkmark$$

16.
$$-4y + 3 = 19$$
$$-4y + 3 - 3 = 19 - 3$$
$$-4y = 16$$
$$\frac{-4y}{-4} = \frac{16}{-4}$$
$$y = -4$$
Check: $-4y + 3 = 19$
$$-4(-4) + 3 \stackrel{?}{=} 19$$
$$16 + 3 \stackrel{?}{=} 19$$
$$19 = 19 \checkmark$$

17.
$$1.8 = 0.6 - y$$
$$1.8 - 0.6 = 0.6 - y - 0.6$$
$$1.2 = -y$$
$$-1(1.2) = -1(-y)$$
$$-1.2 = y$$
Check: $1.8 = 0.6 - y$
$$1.8 \stackrel{?}{=} 0.6 - (-1.2)$$
$$1.8 \stackrel{?}{=} 0.6 + 1.2$$
$$1.8 = 1.8 \checkmark$$

18.
$$19 = 7 + \frac{b}{7}$$
$$19 - 7 = 7 + \frac{b}{7} - 7$$
$$12 = \frac{b}{7}$$
$$7(12) = 7\left(\frac{b}{7}\right)$$
$$84 = b$$
Check: $19 = 7 + \frac{b}{7}$
$$19 \stackrel{?}{=} 7 + \frac{84}{7}$$
$$19 \stackrel{?}{=} 7 + 12$$
$$19 = 19 \checkmark$$

19.
$$-12 + \frac{j}{4} = 9$$
$$-12 + \frac{j}{4} + 12 = 9 + 12$$
$$\frac{j}{4} = 21$$
$$4\left(\frac{j}{4}\right) = 4(21)$$
$$j = 84$$
Check: $-12 + \frac{j}{4} = 9$
$$-12 + \frac{84}{4} \stackrel{?}{=} 9$$
$$-12 + 21 \stackrel{?}{=} 9$$
$$9 = 9 \checkmark$$

20.
$$-3 = -31 + \frac{c}{6}$$
$$-3 + 31 = -31 + \frac{c}{6} + 31$$
$$28 = \frac{c}{6}$$
$$6(28) = 6\left(\frac{c}{6}\right)$$
$$168 = c$$
Check: $-3 = -31 + \frac{c}{6}$
$$-3 \stackrel{?}{=} -31 + \frac{168}{6}$$
$$-3 \stackrel{?}{=} -31 + 28$$
$$-3 = -3 \checkmark$$

21.
$$8 = \frac{h}{-3} + 19$$
$$8 - 19 = \frac{h}{-3} + 19 - 19$$
$$-11 = \frac{h}{-3}$$
$$-3(-11) = -3\left(\frac{h}{-3}\right)$$
$$33 = h$$
Check: $8 = \frac{h}{-3} + 19$
$$8 \stackrel{?}{=} \frac{33}{-3} + 19$$
$$8 \stackrel{?}{=} -11 + 19$$
$$8 = 8 \checkmark$$

22. $\frac{-4x}{3} = 24$

$3\left(\frac{-4x}{3}\right) = 3(24)$

$-4x = 72$

$\frac{-4x}{-4} = \frac{72}{-4}$

$x = -18$

Check: $\frac{-4x}{3} = 24$

$\frac{-4(-18)}{3} \stackrel{?}{=} 24$

$\frac{72}{3} \stackrel{?}{=} 24$

$24 = 24 \checkmark$

23. $13 + \frac{-p}{3} = -4$

$13 + \frac{-p}{3} - 13 = -4 - 13$

$\frac{-p}{3} = -17$

$3\left(\frac{-p}{3}\right) = 3(-17)$

$-p = -51$

$-1(-p) = -1(-51)$

$p = 51$

Check: $13 + \frac{-p}{3} = -4$

$13 + \frac{-51}{3} \stackrel{?}{=} -4$

$13 + -17 \stackrel{?}{=} -4$

$-4 = -4 \checkmark$

24. $\frac{3}{4}n - 3 = 9$

$\frac{3}{4}n - 3 + 3 = 9 + 3$

$\frac{3}{4}n = 12$

$\frac{4}{3}\left(\frac{3}{4}\right)n = \frac{4}{3}(12)$

$n = 16$

Check: $\frac{3}{4}n - 3 = 9$

$\frac{3}{4}(16) - 3 \stackrel{?}{=} 9$

$12 - 3 \stackrel{?}{=} 9$

$9 = 9 \checkmark$

25. $\frac{y}{3} + 6 = -45$

$\frac{y}{3} + 6 - 6 = -45 - 6$

$\frac{y}{3} = -51$

$3\left(\frac{y}{3}\right) = 3(-51)$

$y = -153$

Check: $\frac{y}{3} + 6 = -45$

$\frac{-153}{3} + 6 \stackrel{?}{=} -45$

$-51 + 6 \stackrel{?}{=} -45$

$-45 = -45 \checkmark$

26. $\frac{c}{-4} - 8 = -42$

$\frac{c}{-4} - 8 + 8 = -42 + 8$

$\frac{c}{-4} = -34$

$-4\left(\frac{c}{-4}\right) = -4(-34)$

$c = 136$

Check: $\frac{c}{-4} - 8 = -42$

$\frac{136}{-4} - 8 \stackrel{?}{=} -42$

$-34 - 8 \stackrel{?}{=} -42$

$-42 = -42 \checkmark$

27. $\frac{n - 10}{5} = 2.5$

$5\left(\frac{n - 10}{5}\right) = 5(2.5)$

$n - 10 = 12.5$

$n - 10 + 10 = 12.5 + 10$

$n = 22.5$

Check: $\frac{n - 10}{5} = 2.5$

$\frac{22.5 - 10}{5} \stackrel{?}{=} 2.5$

$\frac{12.5}{5} \stackrel{?}{=} 2.5$

$2.5 = 2.5 \checkmark$

28. $16 = \frac{-8 + s}{-7}$

$-7(16) = -7\left(\frac{-8 + s}{-7}\right)$

$-112 = -8 + s$

$-112 + 8 = -8 + s + 8$

$-104 = s$

Check: $16 = \frac{-8 + s}{-7}$

$16 \stackrel{?}{=} \frac{-8 + (-104)}{-7}$

$16 \stackrel{?}{=} \frac{-112}{-7}$

$16 = 16 \checkmark$

29. $\frac{-d - (-5)}{7} = 14$

$\frac{-d + 5}{7} = 14$

$\frac{7(-d + 5)}{7} = 7(14)$

$-d + 5 = 98$

$-d + 5 - 5 = 98 - 5$

$-d = 93$

$-1(-d) = -1(93)$

$d = -93$

Check: $\frac{-d - (-5)}{7} = 14$

$\frac{-(-93) - (-5)}{7} \stackrel{?}{=} 14$

$\frac{93 + 5}{7} \stackrel{?}{=} 14$

$\frac{98}{7} \stackrel{?}{=} 14$

$14 = 14 \checkmark$

30. $\frac{6 + c}{-13} = -3$

$-13\left(\frac{6 + c}{-13}\right) = -13(-3)$

$6 + c = 39$

$6 + c - 6 = 39 - 6$

$c = 33$

Check: $\frac{6 + c}{-13} = -3$

$\frac{6 + 33}{-13} \stackrel{?}{=} -3$

$\frac{39}{-13} \stackrel{?}{=} -3$

$-3 = -3 \checkmark$

31. $\frac{n}{2} \div (-3) = 5$

$\quad\quad \frac{n}{2} - 3 = 5$

$\quad \frac{n}{2} - 3 + 3 = 5 + 3$

$\quad\quad\quad \frac{n}{2} = 8$

$\quad\quad 2\left(\frac{n}{2}\right) = 2(8)$

$\quad\quad\quad\quad n = 16$

Check: $\frac{n}{2} + (-3) = 5$

$\quad\quad \frac{16}{2} + (-3) \overset{?}{=} 5$

$\quad\quad\quad 8 + (-3) \overset{?}{=} 5$

$\quad\quad\quad\quad\quad\quad 5 = 5 \checkmark$

32. $\quad\quad 4.7 = 1.2 - 7m$

$\quad 4.7 - 1.2 = 1.2 - 7m - 1.2$

$\quad\quad\quad 3.5 = -7m$

$\quad\quad\quad \frac{3.5}{-7} = \frac{-7m}{-7}$

$\quad\quad -0.5 = m$

Check: $4.7 = 1.2 - 7m$

$\quad\quad 4.7 \overset{?}{=} 1.2 - 7(-0.5)$

$\quad\quad 4.7 \overset{?}{=} 1.2 + 3.5$

$\quad\quad 4.7 = 4.7 \checkmark$

33. Sample answer: $6x + 3 = 2$

$\quad\quad 6x + 3 = 2$

$\quad 6x + 3 - 3 = 2 - 3$

$\quad\quad\quad 6x = -1$

$\quad\quad\quad \frac{6x}{6} = \frac{-1}{6}$

$\quad\quad\quad\quad x = -\frac{1}{6}$

34. $\quad\quad 8 + 4d = 28$

$\quad 8 + 4d - 8 = 28 - 8$

$\quad\quad\quad 4d = 20$

$\quad\quad\quad \frac{4d}{4} = \frac{20}{4}$

$\quad\quad\quad\quad d = 5$ more days

35. $4P + 5O_2 \rightarrow P_4O_{10}$

36. $\quad\quad 18x + 54 = 305.89$

$\quad 18x + 54 - 54 = 305.89 - 54$

$\quad\quad\quad 18x = 251.89$

$\quad\quad\quad \frac{18x}{18} = \frac{251.89}{18}$

$\quad\quad\quad\quad x = 13.994$

The carpet is about $13.99 per square yard.

37. $\quad\quad 2x + 33 = 213$

$\quad 2x + 33 - 33 = 213 - 33$

$\quad\quad\quad 2x = 180$

$\quad\quad\quad \frac{2x}{2} = \frac{180}{2}$

$\quad\quad\quad\quad x = 90$

90 people from the United Kingdom have won Nobel prizes.

38. Shantal wants to have
$100 left over. $\longrightarrow$ $\quad$ 100
Undo $30 that will be $\longrightarrow$ $\quad + \; 30$
spent on souvenirs. $\quad\quad\quad\quad\quad\quad$ 130
Undo the three-fourths that $\longrightarrow$ $\times \;\; 3$
will be spent on hotel, car, $\quad\quad\quad\quad$ 390
and food. (130 is $\frac{1}{4}$ of the $\quad\quad +130$
remaining money.) $\quad\quad\quad\quad\quad\quad$ 520
Undo the cost of the $\longrightarrow$ $\quad +156$
plane ticket. $\quad\quad\quad\quad\quad\quad\quad$ 676

Shantal should start with $676 in her vacation budget.

39. $16.43 > 16\frac{3}{7}$ because
$16.43 > 16.429$.

40. $\quad\quad c - \frac{3}{5} > 14\frac{2}{9}$

$\quad\quad\quad c - \frac{3}{5} > \frac{128}{9}$

$\quad c - \frac{3}{5} + \frac{3}{5} > \frac{128}{9} + \frac{3}{5}$

$\quad\quad\quad\quad c > \frac{640}{45} + \frac{27}{45}$

$\quad\quad\quad\quad c > \frac{667}{45}$

$\quad\quad\quad\quad c > 14\frac{37}{45}$

41. $y \cdot y \cdot y = y^3$

42. $|18| - |-4| = 18 - 4$
$\quad\quad\quad\quad\quad = 14$

43. $\quad x - (-17) > 29$
$\quad 11 - (-17) \overset{?}{>} 29$
$\quad\quad\quad 28 \overset{?}{>} 29 \quad$ false

44. a. estimate; the problem says *about*

b. Explore—We know the average amount that was spent on eating out in 1994. We need to find the average amount that was spent in a month.

Plan—Divide the average amount that was spent in 1994 by 12 to find the average amount that was spent in a month. Since an exact answer is not necessary, solve by using estimation.

Solve—$1644 ÷ 12 → 1680 ÷ 12 = 140
The average family spent about $140 each month on eating out.

Examine—The actual answer is $137. So the estimate of $140 per month is reasonable.

7-3	Writing Two-Step Equations

Page 339   Checking Your Understanding

1. Sample answer: Read the problem; define a variable; write an equation; solve the equation; check the solution.

2. a. Pick: 8
$\quad\quad 8 \times 2 = 16$
$\quad\quad 16 + 30 = 46$
$\quad\quad 46 \div 2 = 23$
$\quad\quad 23 - 8 = 15$

b. Pick: 12   Pick: 25

$12 \times 2 = 24$ $25 \times 2 = 50$
$24 + 30 = 54$ $50 + 30 = 80$
$54 \div 2 = 27$ $80 \div 2 = 40$
$27 - 12 = 15$ $40 - 25 = 15$

c. Let n = any number
$$[(n \times 2 + 30) \div 2] - n = [(2n + 30 \div 2] - n$$
$$= [2n \div 2 + 30 \div 2] - n$$
$$= [n + 15] - n$$
$$= 15$$

3. Let x = number
$$17 - 2x = 5$$
$$17 - 2x - 17 = 5 - 17$$
$$-2x = -12$$
$$\frac{-2x}{-2} = \frac{-12}{-2}$$
$$x = 6$$
The number is 6.

4. Let n = number
$$3n + 2n + 1 = 6$$
$$5n + 1 = 6$$
$$5n + 1 - 1 = 6 - 1$$
$$5n = 5$$
$$\frac{5n}{5} = \frac{5}{5}$$
$$n = 1$$
The number is 1.

5. a. $2682 = 4d - 354$

    b.
$$2682 = 4d - 354$$
$$2682 + 354 = 4d - 354 + 354$$
$$3036 = 4d$$
$$\frac{3036}{4} = \frac{4d}{4}$$
$$759 = d$$
759 thousand dogs can "sing."

Pages 339–340   Exercises

6. A; $4 + 3x = 18$

7. C; $18 = 7 + 2n$

8. B; $4n - 15 = 92$

9. E; $10 - 3x = 45$

10. Let x = number
$$3x - 4 = 17$$
$$3x - 4 + 4 = 17 + 4$$
$$3x = 21$$
$$\frac{3x}{3} = \frac{21}{3}$$
$$x = 7$$
The number is 7.

11. Let n = number
$$\frac{n + 6}{7} = 5$$
$$7\left(\frac{n + 6}{7}\right) = 7(5)$$
$$n + 6 = 35$$
$$n + 6 - 6 = 35 - 6$$
$$n = 29$$
The number is 29.

12. Let c = number
$$20 + 2c = -30$$
$$20 + 2c - 20 = -30 - 20$$
$$2c = -50$$
$$\frac{2c}{2} = \frac{-50}{2}$$
$$c = -25$$
The number is -25.

13. Let c = number
$$\frac{c}{-4} - 8 = -42$$
$$\frac{c}{-4} - 8 + 8 = -42 + 8$$
$$\frac{c}{-4} = -34$$
$$-4\left(\frac{c}{-4}\right) = -4(-34)$$
$$c = 136$$
The number is 136.

14. Let x = number
$$2x - 9 = 16$$
$$2x - 9 + 9 = 16 + 9$$
$$2x = 25$$
$$\frac{2x}{2} = \frac{25}{2}$$
$$x = 12.5$$
The number is 12.5.

15.
$$5x - 10 = 145$$
$$5x - 10 + 10 = 145 + 10$$
$$5x = 155$$
$$\frac{5x}{5} = \frac{155}{5}$$
$$x = 31$$
The number is 31.

16. Answers will vary.

17. Let x = length of one side.
$x - 2$ = length of second side.
$x + 2$ = length of third side.
$$x + (x - 2) + (x + 2) = 27$$
$$x + x - 2 + x + 2 = 27$$
$$3x = 27$$
$$\frac{3x}{3} = \frac{27}{3}$$
$$x = 9 \text{ yd}$$
The lengths of the sides of the triangle are 7 yd, 9 yd, and 11 yd.

18. If $2x$ is an even integer, the next consecutive even integer is $2x + 2$. Their sum is $2x + (2x + 2)$.

19. a. $2w + 50 = 130$

    b.
$$2w + 50 = 130$$
$$2w + 50 - 50 = 130 - 50$$
$$2w = 80$$
$$\frac{2w}{2} = \frac{80}{2}$$
$$w = 40$$
The width of the garden is 40 feet.

20. a. Let $n, (n + 1), (n + 2)$ = the other members' places.
$$5 + n + (n + 1) + (n + 2) = 35$$

b. $5 + n + (n + 1) + (n + 2) = 35$

$\quad 5 + n + n + 1 + n + 2 = 35$

$\qquad\qquad\qquad\quad 3n + 8 = 35$

$\quad 3n + 8 - 8 = 35 - 8$

$\qquad\qquad\qquad\quad 3n = 27$

$\qquad\qquad\qquad\quad \frac{3n}{3} = \frac{27}{3}$

$\qquad\qquad\qquad\qquad n = 9$

The other three members finished in 9th, 10th, and 11th place.

21. $\qquad 8 + \frac{2}{5}n = 28$

$8 + \frac{2}{5}n - 8 = 28 - 8$

$\qquad\quad \frac{2}{5}n = 20$

$\frac{5}{2}\left(\frac{2}{5}\right)n = \frac{5}{2}(20)$

$\qquad\qquad n = 50$

22. Sample answer: 110

23. $\qquad y - 19 = 53$

$y - 19 + 19 = 53 + 19$

$\qquad\qquad\quad y = 72$

24. Students should use guess and check.

Number of coins	Change for $1.00?
20	yes; $8(10¢) + 2(5¢) + 10(1¢)$
47	yes; $5(10¢) + 2(5¢) + 40(1¢)$
77	no

The least positive number of coins that is impossible to give as change for a dollar is 77.

25. associative property of addition

Page 340 From the Funny Papers

1. See students' work.

2. $y = 4(20) + 7$

3. $y = 4(20) + 7$

$\ y = 80 + 7$

$\ y = 87$

7-4 Integration: Geometry
Circles and Circumference

Page 341 Your Turn

a. about 3.14; Answers will vary.

b. Answers will vary. π and your mean should be close.

Page 341 Your Turn

1. Sample answer: The radius of a circle is one-half its diameter.

2. $3.14, \frac{22}{7}$

3. Sample answer: Multiply the diameter times π, or 2 times the radius times π.

4. a diameter

5. Sample answer: Multiply the diameter by 3 or the radius by 6.

---

6. $C = \pi d$

$\ C = \pi \cdot 3$

$\ C \approx 9.42$ ft

7. $C = 2\pi r$

$\ C = 2 \cdot \pi \cdot 1.8$

$\ C \approx 11.31$ cm

8. $C = \pi d$

$\ C \approx \frac{22}{7} \cdot 5\frac{1}{4}$

$\ C \approx \frac{\cancel{22}^{11}}{\cancel{7}_1} \cdot \frac{\cancel{21}^{3}}{\cancel{4}_2}$

$\ C \approx \frac{33}{2}$

$\ C \approx 16\frac{1}{2}$ in.

9. $C = 2\pi r$

$\ C = 2 \cdot \pi \cdot 1.75$

$\ C = 10.99$ m

10. $C = \pi d$

$\ C \approx 27\pi$

$\ C \approx 84.82$ in.

After 10 rotations the distance traveled will be 84.82×10 or about 848.2 in.

Pages 343–344 Exercises

11. $C = \pi d$

$\ C = \pi \cdot 4$

$\ C \approx 12.57$ cm

12. $C = 2\pi r$

$\ C = 2 \cdot \pi \cdot 7$

$\ C \approx 44$ m

13. $C = 2\pi r$

$\ C = 2 \cdot \pi \cdot 5\frac{1}{2}$

$\ C \approx 34.56$ ft

14. $C = \pi d$

$\ C = \pi \cdot 9$

$\ C \approx 28.27$ in.

15. $C = \pi d$

$\ C = \pi \cdot 14$

$\ C \approx 43.96$ mm

16. $C = 2\pi r$

$\ C = 2 \cdot \pi \cdot 34$

$\ C \approx 213.63$ ft

17. $C = \pi d$

$\ C = \pi \cdot 18.8$

$\ C \approx 59.032$ m

18. $C = 2\pi r$

$\ C = 2 \cdot \pi \cdot 0.5$

$\ C \approx 3.14$ m

19. $C = 2\pi d$

$\ C = 2 \cdot \pi \cdot 1.3$

$\ C \approx 8.164$ yd

20. $C = \pi d$

$\ C = \pi \cdot 13\frac{1}{2}$

$\ C \approx 42.39$ in.

21. $C = \pi d$

$\ C \approx \frac{22}{7} \cdot 2\frac{1}{3}$

$\ C \approx \frac{22}{\cancel{7}_1} \cdot \frac{\cancel{7}^{1}}{3}$

$\ C \approx \frac{22}{3}$

$\ C \approx 7\frac{1}{3}$ ft

22. $C = 2\pi r$

$\ C = 2 \cdot \pi \cdot 4\frac{1}{2}$

$\ C \approx 28.27$ km

23. $\quad C = 628$ cm

$\ 2\pi r = 628$

$\quad\ r \approx 100$ cm

Choice C is correct.

24. $r = 30$cm

$\ C = 2\pi(30)$

$\ C = 190$ cm

Choice D is correct.

25. $2r = 28$ cm

$\ C = 2\pi r$

$\ C = 28\pi$

$\ C \approx 88$ cm

Choice B is correct.

26. $C = 47.728$ cm

$\ C = 2\pi d$

$\ d \approx 15.2$ cm

Choice A is correct.

27. $\qquad C = 2\pi r$

$\ 4.082 = 2\pi r$

$\ \frac{4.082}{2\pi} = \frac{2\pi r}{2\pi}$

$\quad 0.65 = r$

The radius is 0.65 m.

28. $\quad C = 2\pi r$

$\quad\ \pi = 2\pi r$

$\quad \frac{\pi}{2\pi} = \frac{2\pi r}{2\pi}$

$\quad\ \frac{1}{2} = r$

The radius is $\frac{1}{2}$ unit.

29. $C = 2\pi r$
$C = 2 \cdot \frac{22}{7} \cdot \frac{7}{22}$
$C = 2$
The circumference is 2 units.

30. A 145° angle intersects an arc of the circle that has a length that is $\frac{145}{360}$ or $\frac{29}{72}$ of the circumference.
$C = \pi d$
$C = \pi \cdot 8$
$C = 25.12$ ft
So, the length of the arc is $\frac{29}{72}(25.12)$ or about 10.12 ft.

31. $C = \pi d$
$C = \pi \cdot 76$
$C = 238.76$ m
In one revolution, you would travel about 238.76 m.

32. a. 14 in. + 2(5.4 in.) = 24.8 in.
$C = \pi d$
$C = \pi \cdot 24.8$
$C = 77.91$ in.
The car will travel about 77.91 in. or about 6.49 ft.

b. 1 mile = 5280 ft; So, the tire will turn $\frac{5280}{6.49}$ or about 813.56 times.

c. It would take 813.56 × 50,000 or about 40,678,000 turns to travel 50,000 miles.

33. a. The perimeter of the square is longer.

b. Sample answer: The perimeter of a square is 4 times the length of one side. The circumference of a circle is approximately 3.14 times the diameter. 4 > 3.14.

34. Archimedes was the first to calculate a value of π. In 1992, two mathematicians extended the digits of π to 2,160,000,000 decimal places.

35. Let x = number of visitors
$2x + 0.1 = 7.5$
$2x + 0.1 - 0.1 = 7.5 - 0.1$
$2x = 7.4$
$\frac{2x}{2} = \frac{7.4}{2}$
$x = 3.7$
3.7 million visitors go to the Metropolitan Museum each year.

36. $\frac{x}{-1.7} \geq 6.8$
$-1.7\left(\frac{x}{-1.7}\right) \leq -1.7(6.8)$
$x \leq -11.56$

37. $220pq^2 = 2 \cdot 110 \cdot p \cdot q^2$
$= 2 \cdot 2 \cdot 55 \cdot p \cdot q \cdot q$
$= 2 \cdot 2 \cdot 5 \cdot 11 \cdot p \cdot q \cdot q$

38. $-4 + m \geq -3$
$-4 + m + 4 \geq -3 + 4$
$m \geq 1$

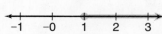

39. $|-13| > |7|$

40. $18z + 7(2 + 3z) = 18z + 7(2) + 7(3z)$
$= 18z + 14 + 21z$
$= 18z + 21z + 14$
$= (18 + 21)z + 14$
$= 39z + 14$

7-5A | **Equations with Variables on Each Side**

Page 345 Your Turn

1. See students' work; −8
2. See students' work; −2
3. See students' work; 4
4. See students' work; 4
5. See students' work; 1
6. See students' work; −4
7. Sample answer: No; The result is the same.
8. Sample answer: Use upside down cups to model negative variables. Place two cups and three positive counters on the left side of the mat and one cup and 5 negative counters on the right side. Take one cup from each side. Add three zero pairs to the right side. Add three negative counters to each side and remove the zero pairs on the left side. The result shows that $-x = -8$. Thus, $x = 8$.

7-5 | **Solving Equations with Variables on Each Side**

Page 346 Your Turn

a. −40
b. It converts the Fahrenheit temperature to Celsius.

Page 348 Checking Your Understanding

1. Sample answer: Subtract $7p$ from each side. Divide each side by −5.
2. Sample answer: Subtraction property of equality.
3. a. $2x - 1 = x - 4$
$2x - x - 1 = x - x - 4$
$x - 1 = -4$
$x - 1 + 1 = -4 + 1$
$x = -3$

b. See students' work; $x = 2$
c. See students' work; $\varnothing$

4. Sample answer: Subtract $2k$ from each side; Subtract 15 from each side.
$12k + 15 = 35 + 2k$
$12k - 2k + 15 = 35 + 2k - 2k$
$10k + 15 = 35$
$10k + 15 - 15 = 35 - 15$
$10k = 20$
$\frac{10k}{10} = \frac{20}{10}$
$k = 2$

Check: $12k + 15 = 35 + 2k$

$12(2) + 15 \stackrel{?}{=} 35 + 2(2)$

$24 + 15 \stackrel{?}{=} 35 + 4$

$39 = 39$ ✔

5. Sample answer: Add 1 to each side; subtract $3x$ from each side.

$3x + 2 = 4x - 1$

$3x + 2 + 1 = 4x - 1 + 1$

$3x + 3 = 4x$

$3x - 3x + 3 = 4x - 3x$

$3 = x$

Check: $3x + 2 = 4x - 1$

$3(3) + 2 \stackrel{?}{=} 4(3) - 1$

$9 + 2 \stackrel{?}{=} 12 - 1$

$11 = 11$ ✔

6. Sample answer: Simplify the right side to $-9b$; Add $9b$ to each side.

$3b + 8 = -10b + b$

$3b + 8 = -9b$

$3b + 9b + 8 = -9b + 9b$

$12b + 8 = 0$

$12b + 8 - 8 = 0 - 8$

$12b = -8$

$\frac{12b}{12} = \frac{-8}{12}$

$b = \frac{-2}{3}$

Check: $3b + 8 = -10b + b$

$3\left(-\frac{2}{3}\right) + 8 \stackrel{?}{=} -10\left(-\frac{2}{3}\right) + \left(-\frac{2}{3}\right)$

$-2 + 8 \stackrel{?}{=} \frac{20}{3} + \left(-\frac{2}{3}\right)$

$6 \stackrel{?}{=} \frac{18}{3}$

$6 = 6$ ✔

7. Sample answer: Simplify the left side to $3a + 66$; subtract $3a$ from each side.

$3(a + 22) = 12a + 30$

$3a + 66 = 12a + 30$

$3a - 3a + 66 = 12a - 3a + 30$

$66 = 9a + 30$

$66 - 30 = 9a + 30 - 30$

$36 = 9a$

$\frac{36}{9} = \frac{9a}{9}$

$4 = a$

Check: $3(a + 22) = 12a + 30$

$3(4 + 22) \stackrel{?}{=} 12(4) + 30$

$3(26) \stackrel{?}{=} 48 + 30$

$78 = 78$ ✔

8. Sample answer: Subtract $2k$ from each side; subtract 10 from each side.

$3k + 10 = 2k - 21$

$3k - 2k + 10 = 2k - 2k - 21$

$k + 10 = -21$

$k + 10 - 10 = -21 - 10$

$k = -31$

Check: $3k + 10 = 2k - 21$

$3(-31) + 10 \stackrel{?}{=} 2(-31) - 21$

$-93 + 10 \stackrel{?}{=} -62 - 21$

$-83 = -83$ ✔

9. Sample answer: Add n to each side; subtract 4 from each side.

$n + 4 = -n + 10$

$n + n + 4 = -n + n + 10$

$2n + 4 = 10$

$2n + 4 - 4 = 10 - 4$

$2n = 6$

$\frac{2n}{2} = \frac{6}{2}$

$n = 3$

Check: $n + 4 = -n + 10$

$3 + 4 \stackrel{?}{=} -3 + 10$

$7 = 7$ ✔

10. If w = width, then length = $3w + 4$.

$P = 2w + 2\ell$

$32 = 2w + 2(3w + 4)$

$32 = 2w + 6w + 8$

$32 = 8w + 8$

$32 - 8 = 8w + 8 - 8$

$24 = 8w$

$\frac{24}{8} = \frac{8w}{8}$

$3 = w$

The width is 3 ft and the length is $3(3) + 4$ or 13 ft.

Pages 348–350　Exercises

11. $6n - 42 = 4n$

$6n - 6n - 42 = 4n - 6n$

$-42 = -2n$

$\frac{-42}{-2} = \frac{-2n}{-2}$

$21 = n$

Check: $6n - 42 = 4n$

$6(21) - 42 \stackrel{?}{=} 4(21)$

$126 - 42 \stackrel{?}{=} 84$

$84 = 84$ ✔

12. $8 - 3g = -2 - 2g$

$8 + 2 - 3g = -2 + 2 + 2g$

$10 - 3g = 2g$

$10 - 3g + 3g = 2g + 3g$

$10 = 5g$

$\frac{10}{5} = \frac{5g}{5}$

$2 = g$

Check: $8 - 3g = -2 + 2g$

$8 - 3(2) \stackrel{?}{=} -2 + 2(2)$

$8 - 6 \stackrel{?}{=} -2 + 4$

$2 = 2$ ✔

13. $3(k + 2) = 12$

$3k + 6 = 12$

$3k + 6 - 6 = 12 - 6$

$3k = 6$

$\frac{3k}{3} = \frac{6}{3}$

$k = 2$

Check: $3(k + 2) = 12$

$3(2 + 2) \stackrel{?}{=} 12$

$3(4) \stackrel{?}{=} 12$

$12 = 12$ ✔

14. $\frac{4}{7}y - 8 = \frac{2}{7}y + 10$

$\frac{4}{7}y - 8 + 8 = \frac{2}{7}y + 10 + 8$

$\frac{4}{7}y = \frac{2}{7}y + 18$

$\frac{4}{7}y - \frac{2}{7}y = \frac{2}{7}y - \frac{2}{7}y + 18$

$\frac{2}{7}y = 18$

$\frac{7}{2}\left(\frac{2}{7}\right)y = \frac{7}{2}(18)$

$y = 63$

Check: $\frac{4}{7}y - 8 = \frac{2}{7}y + 10$

$\frac{4}{7}(63) - 8 \stackrel{?}{=} \frac{2}{7}(63) + 10$

$36 - 8 \stackrel{?}{=} 18 + 10$

$28 = 28$ ✔

15. $6 - 8x = 20x + 20$

$6 - 20 - 8x = 20x + 20 - 20$

$-14 - 8x = 20x$

$-14 - 8x + 8x = 20x + 8x$

$-14 = 28x$

$\frac{-14}{28} = \frac{28x}{28}$

$-0.5 = x$

Check: $6 - 8x = 20x + 20$

$6 - 8(-0.5) \stackrel{?}{=} 20(-0.5) + 20$

$6 + 4 \stackrel{?}{=} -10 + 20$

$10 = 10$ ✔

16. $13 - t = -t + 7$

$13 - t + t = -t + t + 7$

$13 = 7$

This sentence is never true. The solution is $\varnothing$.

17. $3n + 7 = 7n - 13$

$3n + 7 - 7 = 7n - 13 - 7$

$3n = 7n - 20$

$3n - 7n = 7n - 7n - 20$

$-4n = -20$

$\frac{-4n}{-4} = \frac{-20}{-4}$

$n = 5$

Check: $3n + 7 = 7n - 13$

$3(5) + 7 \stackrel{?}{=} 7(5) - 13$

$15 + 7 \stackrel{?}{=} 35 - 13$

$22 = 22$ ✔

18. $7b - 3 = -b + 4$

$7b - 3 + 3 = -b + 4 + 3$

$7b = -b + 7$

$7b + b = -b + b + 7$

$8b = 7$

$\frac{8b}{8} = \frac{7}{8}$

$b = 0.875$

Check: $7b - 3 = -b + 4$

$7(0.875) - 3 \stackrel{?}{=} -0.875 + 4$

$6.125 - 3 \stackrel{?}{=} -0.875 + 4$

$3.125 = 3.125$ ✔

19. $2 + 7(d + 1) = 9 + 7d$

$2 + 7d + 7 = 9 + 7d$

$9 + 7d = 9 + 7d$

This sentence is always true.
The solution set is all numbers.

20. $2a - 1 = 3.5a - 3$

$2a - 1 + 1 = 3.5a - 3 + 1$

$2a = 3.5a - 2$

$2a - 3.5a = 3.5a - 3.5a - 2$

$-1.5a = -2$

$\frac{-1.5a}{-1.5} = \frac{-2}{-1.5}$

$a = 1\frac{0.5}{1.5}$

$a = 1\frac{1}{3}$

$a = \frac{4}{3}$

Check: $2a - 1 = 3.5a - 3$

$2\left(\frac{4}{3}\right) - 1 \stackrel{?}{=} 3.5\left(\frac{4}{3}\right) - 3$

$\frac{8}{3} - 1 \stackrel{?}{=} \frac{14}{3} - 3$

$\frac{8}{3} - \frac{3}{3} \stackrel{?}{=} \frac{14}{3} - \frac{9}{3}$

$\frac{5}{3} = \frac{5}{3}$ ✔

21. $5m + 4 = 7(m+1) - 2m$

$5m + 4 = 7m + 7 - 2m$

$5m + 4 = 5m + 7$

$5m - 5m + 4 = 5m - 5m + 7$

$4 = 7$

This sentence is never true.
The solution is $\varnothing$.

22. $12x - 24 = -14x + 28$

$12x + 14x - 24 = -14x + 14x + 28$

$26x - 24 = 28$

$26x - 24 + 24 = 28 + 24$

$26x = 52$

$\frac{26x}{26} = \frac{52}{26}$

$x = 2$

Check: $12x - 24 = -14x + 28$

$12(2) - 24 \stackrel{?}{=} -14(2) + 28$

$24 - 24 \stackrel{?}{=} -28 + 28$

$0 = 0$ ✔

23. $2(f - 3) + 5 = 3(f - 1)$

$2f - 6 + 5 = 3f - 3$

$2f - 1 = 3f - 3$

$2f - 3f - 1 = 3f - 3f - 3$

$-1f - 1 = -3$

$-1f - 1 + 1 = -3 + 1$

$-1f = -2$

$-1(-1f) = -1(-2)$

$f = 2$

Check: $2(f - 3) + 5 = 3(f - 1)$

$2(2 - 3) + 5 \stackrel{?}{=} 3(2 - 1)$

$2(-1) + 5 \stackrel{?}{=} 3(1)$

$-2 + 5 \stackrel{?}{=} 3$

$3 = 3$ ✔

24. $4[z + 3(z - 1)] = 36$

$4[z + 3z - 3] = 36$

$4[4z - 3] = 36$

$16z - 12 = 36$

$16z - 12 + 12 = 36 + 12$

$16z = 48$

$\frac{16z}{16} = \frac{48}{16}$

$z = 3$

Check: $4[z + 3(z - 1)] = 36$

$$4[3 + 3(3 - 1)] \overset{?}{=} 36$$
$$4[3 + 3(3 - 1)] \overset{?}{=} 36$$
$$4[3 + 3(2)] \overset{?}{=} 36$$
$$4[3 + 6] \overset{?}{=} 36$$
$$4[9] \overset{?}{=} 36$$
$$36 = 36 ✔$$

25. $-3(4b - 10) = \frac{1}{2}(-24b + 60)$

$$-12b + 30 = -12b + 30$$

This sentence is always true.
The solution set is all numbers.

26. $\frac{3}{4}a + 16 = 2 - \frac{1}{8}a$

$$\frac{3}{4}a + \frac{1}{8}a + 16 = 2 - \frac{1}{8}a + \frac{1}{8}a$$
$$\frac{6}{8}a + \frac{1}{8}a + 16 = 2$$
$$\frac{7}{8}a + 16 = 2$$
$$\frac{7}{8}a + 16 - 16 = 2 - 16$$
$$\frac{7}{8} = -14$$
$$\frac{8}{7}\left(\frac{7}{8}\right)a = \frac{8}{7}(-14)$$
$$a = -16$$

Check: $\frac{3}{4}a + 16 = 2 - \frac{1}{8}a$

$$\frac{3}{4}(-16) + 16 \overset{?}{=} 2 - \frac{1}{8}(-16)$$
$$-12 + 16 \overset{?}{=} 2 + 2$$
$$4 = 4 ✔$$

27. $\frac{d}{0.4} = 2d + 1.24$

$$0.4\left(\frac{d}{0.4}\right) = 0.4(2d + 1.24)$$
$$d = 0.8d + 0.496$$
$$d - 0.8d = 0.8d - 0.8d + 0.496$$
$$0.2d = 0.496$$
$$\frac{0.2d}{0.2} = \frac{0.496}{0.2}$$
$$d = 2.48$$

Check: $\frac{d}{0.4} = 2d + 1.24$

$$\frac{2.48}{0.4} \overset{?}{=} 2(2.48) + 1.24$$
$$6.2 \overset{?}{=} 4.96 + 1.24$$
$$6.2 = 6.2 ✔$$

28. $\frac{a - 6}{12} = \frac{a - 2}{4}$

$$12\left(\frac{a - 6}{12}\right) = 12\left(\frac{a - 2}{4}\right)$$
$$a - 6 = 3(a - 2)$$
$$a - 6 = 3a - 6$$
$$a - 3a - 6 = 3a - 6 - 3a$$
$$-2a - 6 = -6$$
$$-2a - 6 + 6 = -6 + 6$$
$$-2a = 0$$
$$\frac{-2a}{-2} = \frac{0}{-2}$$
$$a = 0$$

Check: $\frac{a - 6}{12} = \frac{a - 2}{4}$

$$\frac{0 - 6}{12} \overset{?}{=} \frac{0 - 2}{4}$$
$$-\frac{6}{12} \overset{?}{=} -\frac{2}{4}$$
$$-\frac{1}{2} = -\frac{1}{2} ✔$$

29.
$$P = 2w + 2\ell$$
$$460 = 2w + 2(w + 30)$$
$$460 = 2w + 2w + 60$$
$$460 = 4w + 60$$
$$460 - 60 = 4w + 60 - 60$$
$$400 = 4w$$
$$\frac{400}{4} = \frac{4w}{4}$$
$$100 = w$$

The width is 100 m and the length is 100 + 30 or 130 m.

30.
$$P = 2w + 2\ell$$
$$440 = 2w + 2(3w - 60)$$
$$440 = 2w + 6w - 120$$
$$440 = 8w - 120$$
$$440 + 120 = 8w - 120 + 120$$
$$560 = 8w$$
$$\frac{560}{8} = \frac{8w}{8}$$
$$70 = w$$

The width is 70 yd and the length is 3(70) − 60 or 150 yd.

31.
$$P = 2w + 2\ell$$
$$110 = 2w + 2(2w - 20)$$
$$110 = 2w + 4w - 40$$
$$110 = 6w - 40$$
$$110 + 40 = 6w - 40 + 40$$
$$150 = 6w$$
$$\frac{150}{6} = \frac{6w}{6}$$
$$25 = w$$

The width is 25 ft and the length is 2(25) − 20 or 30 ft.

32. Let x = number
$$2x = 6x - 220$$
$$2x - 6x = 6x - 6x - 220$$
$$-4x = -220$$
$$\frac{-4x}{-4} = \frac{-220}{-4}$$
$$x = 55$$

The number is 55.

33. Let y = number
$$3y - 14 = y$$
$$3y - 3y - 14 = y - 3y$$
$$-14 = -2y$$
$$\frac{-14}{-2} = \frac{-2y}{-2}$$
$$7 = y$$

The number is 7.

34. Let a = cost of apple
Let b = cost of banana
Let c = cost of orange
We know that $a = 2c$, $c + b = a + 10$, and $2c = 15 + b$ or $b = 2c - 15$.

Use substitution,
$$c + b = a + 10$$
$$c + (2c - 15) = 2c + 10$$
$$c + 2c - 15 = 2c + 10$$
$$3c - 15 = 2c + 10$$
$$3c - 2c - 15 = 2c - 2c + 10$$
$$c - 15 = 10$$
$$c - 15 + 15 = 10 + 15$$
$$c = 25$$

So, an orange costs 25¢, an apple costs $2 \times 25¢$ or 50¢, and a banana costs $2(25¢) - 15¢$ or 35¢.

35. a. $199,000 - 700x$

b. $165,000 + 3700x$

c. $199,000 - 700x = 165,000 + 3700x$

d.
$$199,000 - 700x = 165,000 + 3700x$$
$$199,000 - 700x + 700x = 165,000 + 3700x + 700x$$
$$199,000 = 165,000 + 4400x$$
$$199,000 - 165,000 = 165,000 - 165,000 + 4400x$$
$$34,000 = 4400x$$
$$\frac{34,000}{4400} = \frac{4400x}{4400}$$
$$7.73 = x$$

The population of the two cities will be the same in about 8 years.

36. a. $b = 212 - \frac{A}{550}$

b. $b = 212 - \frac{A}{550}$
$b = 212 - \frac{5280}{550}$
$b = 212 - 9.6$
$b = 202.4°\text{F}$

c. $b = 212 - \frac{A}{550}$
$b = 212 - \left(\frac{-282}{550}\right)$
$b = 212 + 0.513$
$b = 212.513°\text{F}$

37. a. Let x = sales ($)
Plan 1: $2 + 0.10x$
Plan 2: $3 + 0.05x$
$$2 + 0.10x = 3 + 0.05x$$
$$100(2 + 0.10x) = 100(3 + 0.05x)$$
$$200 + 10x = 300 + 5x$$
$$200 + 10x - 5x = 300 + 5x - 5x$$
$$200 + 5x = 300$$
$$200 + 5x - 200 = 300 - 200$$
$$5x = 100$$
$$\frac{5x}{5} = \frac{100}{5}$$
$$x = \$20$$

b. See students' work.

38. $c = \pi d$
$18 = \pi \cdot d$
$\frac{18}{\pi} = \frac{\pi d}{\pi}$
$5.7 \approx d$

The diameter is about 5.7 in.

39. $3x + 3 = 99$
$3x + 3 - 3 = 99 - 3$
$3x = 96$
$\frac{3x}{3} = \frac{96}{3}$
$x = 32$

40. $15 \div \frac{3}{7} = n$
$\frac{15}{1} \times \frac{7}{3} = n$
$\frac{105}{3} = n$
$35 = n$

41. $\frac{36}{126} = \frac{\overset{1}{\cancel{2}} \cdot \overset{}{2} \cdot \overset{1}{\cancel{3}} \cdot \overset{1}{\cancel{3}}}{\underset{1}{\cancel{2}} \cdot \underset{1}{\cancel{3}} \cdot \underset{1}{\cancel{3}} \cdot 7}$
$= \frac{2}{7}$

42. $A = \ell w$
$65 = 13 \cdot w$
$\frac{65}{13} = \frac{13w}{13}$
$5 = w$

43. $n - 10 = 42$
$n = 42 + 10$
$n = 52$

44. $7m = 56$
$7(8) = 56$
$m = 8$

What number times 7 is 56?

Page 350 Self Test

1. Balance in the check register ⟶ $973.88
Undo the deposit. ⟶ $\underline{-497.92}$
475.96
Undo the checks. ⟶ 13.85
19.72
$\underline{+\ 59.66}$
569.19

The bank statement should say that $569.19 is in her account.

2.
$$12 - z = 28$$
$$12 - z - 12 = 28 - 12$$
$$-z = 16$$
$$-1(-z) = -1(16)$$
$$z = -16$$

3.
$$9 - 4z = 57$$
$$9 - 4z - 9 = 57 - 9$$
$$-4z = 48$$
$$\frac{-4z}{-4} = \frac{48}{-4}$$
$$z = -12$$

4.
$$\frac{d-5}{7} = 14$$
$$7\left(\frac{d-5}{7}\right) = 7(14)$$
$$d - 5 = 98$$
$$d - 5 + 5 = 98 + 5$$
$$d = 103$$

5. Let x = number
$$4x - 12 = 18$$
$$4x - 12 + 12 = 18 + 12$$
$$4x = 30$$
$$\frac{4x}{4} = \frac{30}{4}$$
$$x = 7\frac{2}{4}$$
$$x = 7\frac{1}{2}$$

The number is $7\frac{1}{2}$.

6. Let x = number
$$6x - 8 = 10$$
$$6x - 8 + 8 = 10 + 8$$
$$6x = 18$$
$$\frac{6x}{6} = \frac{18}{6}$$
$$x = 3$$

The number is 3.

7. $C = 2\pi r$
$6.398 = 2 \cdot \pi \cdot r$
$\frac{6.398}{2\pi} = \frac{2\pi r}{2\pi}$
$1.02 \approx r$

8. $C = \pi d$
$C = \pi \cdot 16.2$
$C \approx 50.89$ in.

9. If w = width, then length = $3w - 75$.

$$P = 2w + 2\ell$$
$$370 = 2w + 2(3w - 75)$$
$$370 = 2w + 6w - 150$$
$$370 = 8w - 150$$
$$370 + 150 = 8w - 150 + 150$$
$$520 = 8w$$
$$\frac{520}{8} = \frac{8w}{8}$$
$$65 = w$$

The width is 65 yd and the length is $3(65) - 75$ or 120 yd.

7-6

Solving Multi-Step Inequalities

Page 351   Your Turn

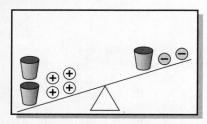

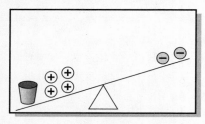

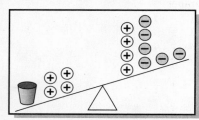

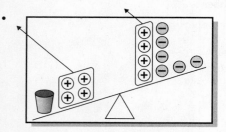

a. $4 + x > -2$

b. Sample answer: So that 4 positive counters can be removed from each side.

c. $x > -6$

d. Substitute numbers greater and less than -6 for each cup into the original inequality.

Page 353   Checking Your Understanding

1. Sample answer: Substitute numbers greater and less than 340.2 for m.

2. Sample answer: Tinesha is correct because simplifying the grouping symbols will make it easier to multiply.

3.

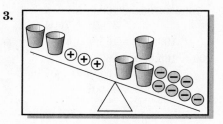

4. $x + 1 < 2x + (-4); 5 < x$

5.
$$3x + 2 \le 23$$
$$3x + 2 - 2 \le 23 - 2$$
$$3x \le 21$$
$$\frac{3x}{3} \le \frac{21}{3}$$
$$x \le 7$$

Check: Try 0, a number less than or equal to 7.
$$3x + 2 \le 23$$
$$3(0) + 2 \overset{?}{\le} 23$$
$$0 + 2 \overset{?}{\le} 23$$
$$2 \le 23 \; ✔$$

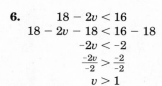

6.
$$18 - 2v < 16$$
$$18 - 2v - 18 < 16 - 18$$
$$-2v < -2$$
$$\frac{-2v}{-2} > \frac{-2}{-2}$$
$$v > 1$$

Check: Try 2, a number greater than 1.
$$18 - 2v < 16$$
$$18 - 2(2) \overset{?}{<} 16$$
$$18 - 4 \overset{?}{<} 16$$
$$14 < 16 \; ✔$$

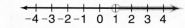

7.
$$2k + 7 > 13 - k$$
$$2k + k + 7 > 13 - k + k$$
$$3k + 7 > 13$$
$$3k + 7 - 7 > 13 - 7$$
$$3k > 6$$
$$\frac{3k}{3} > \frac{6}{3}$$
$$k > 2$$

Check: Try 5, a number greater than 2.
$$2k + 7 > 13 - k$$
$$2(5) + 7 \overset{?}{>} 13 - 5$$
$$10 + 7 \overset{?}{>} 13 - 5$$
$$17 > 8 \; ✔$$

8.
$$y + 1 \geq 5y + 5$$
$$y - 5y + 1 \geq 5y - 5y + 5$$
$$-4y + 1 \geq 5$$
$$-4y + 1 - 1 \geq 5 - 1$$
$$-4y \geq 4$$
$$\frac{-4y}{-4} \leq \frac{4}{-4}$$
$$y \leq -1$$

Check: Try -3, a number less than or equal to -1.
$$y + 1 \geq 5y + 5$$
$$-3 + 1 \overset{?}{\geq} 5(-3) + 5$$
$$-3 + 1 \overset{?}{\geq} -15 + 5$$
$$-2 \geq -10$$

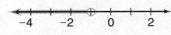

9.
$$-3(m - 2) > 12$$
$$-3m + 6 > 12$$
$$-3m + 6 - 6 > 12 - 6$$
$$-3m > 6$$
$$\frac{-3m}{-3} < \frac{6}{-3}$$
$$m < -2$$

Check: Try -4, a number less than -2.
$$-3(m - 2) > 12$$
$$-3(-4 - 2) \overset{?}{>} 12$$
$$-3(-6) \overset{?}{>} 12$$
$$18 > 12 \ \checkmark$$

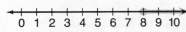

10.
$$-5 \leq \frac{x}{4} - 7$$
$$-5 + 7 \leq \frac{x}{4} - 7 + 7$$
$$2 \leq \frac{x}{4}$$
$$4(2) \leq 4\left(\frac{x}{4}\right)$$
$$8 \leq x$$

Check: Try 12, a number greater than or equal to 8.
$$-5 \leq \frac{x}{4} - 7$$
$$-5 \overset{?}{\leq} \frac{12}{4} - 7$$
$$-5 \overset{?}{\leq} 3 - 7$$
$$-5 \leq -4 \ \checkmark$$

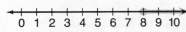

11.
$$2d + 65 \leq 90$$
$$2d + 65 - 65 \leq 90 - 65$$
$$2d \leq 25$$
$$\frac{2d}{2} \leq \frac{25}{2}$$
$$d \leq 12.5$$

Sample answer: If Heather can find CDs that cost no more than $12.50 each, she can buy the shoes and two CDs.

12.
$$2x + 9 > 25$$
$$2x + 9 - 9 > 25 - 9$$
$$2x > 16$$
$$\frac{2x}{2} > \frac{16}{2}$$
$$x > 8$$

Check: Try 10, a number greater than 8.
$$2x + 9 > 25$$
$$2(10) + 9 \overset{?}{>} 25$$
$$20 + 9 \overset{?}{>} 25$$
$$29 > 25 \ \checkmark$$

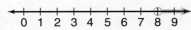

13.
$$-2u + 3 \leq 11$$
$$-2u + 3 - 3 \leq 11 - 3$$
$$-2u \leq 8$$
$$\frac{-2u}{-2} \geq \frac{8}{-2}$$
$$u \geq -4$$

Check: Try -1, a number greater than or equal to -4.
$$-2u + 3 \leq 11$$
$$-2(-1) + 3 \overset{?}{\leq} 11$$
$$2 + 3 \overset{?}{\leq} 11$$
$$5 \leq 11 \ \checkmark$$

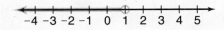

14.
$$16 < 18 - 2n$$
$$16 - 18 < 18 - 2n - 18$$
$$-2 < -2n$$
$$\frac{-2}{-2} > \frac{-2n}{-2}$$
$$1 > n$$

Check: Try 0, a number less than 1.
$$16 < 18 - 2n$$
$$16 \overset{?}{<} 18 - 2(0)$$
$$16 \overset{?}{<} 18 - 0$$
$$16 < 18 \ \checkmark$$

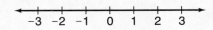

15.
$$2x - 5 < 2x - 9$$
$$2x - 2x - 5 < 2x - 2x - 9$$
$$-5 < -9$$

This sentence is never true.
The solution is $\varnothing$.

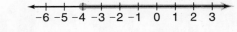

16.
$$1.2z - 2 > 7 + 0.9z$$
$$1.2z - 0.9z - 2 > 7 + 0.9z - 0.9z$$
$$0.3z - 2 > 7$$
$$0.3z - 2 + 2 > 7 + 2$$
$$0.3z > 9$$
$$\frac{0.3z}{0.3} > \frac{9}{0.3}$$
$$z > 30$$

Check: Try 32, a number greater than 30.

$1.2z - 2 > 7 + 0.9z$

$1.2(32) - 2 \stackrel{?}{>} 7 + 0.9(32)$

$38.4 - 2 \stackrel{?}{>} 7 + 28.8$

$36.4 > 35.8$ ✓

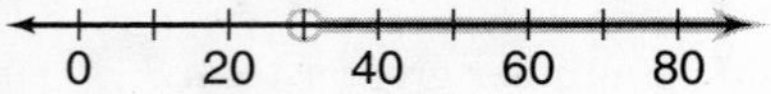

17. $3(j - 1) \geq -12$

$3j - 3 \geq -12$

$3j - 3 + 3 \geq -12 + 3$

$3j \geq -9$

$\frac{3j}{3} \geq \frac{-9}{3}$

$j \geq -3$

Check: Try -2, a number greater than or equal to -3.

$3(j - 1) \geq -12$

$3(-2 - 1) \stackrel{?}{\geq} -12$

$3(-3) \stackrel{?}{\geq} -12$

$-9 \geq -12$ ✓

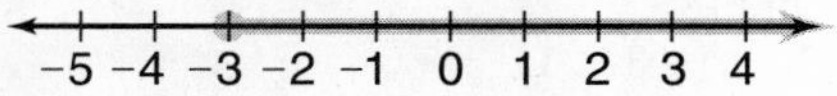

18. $\frac{m}{3} - 7 > 11$

$\frac{m}{3} - 7 + 7 > 11 + 7$

$\frac{m}{3} > 18$

$3\left(\frac{m}{3}\right) > 3(18)$

$m > 54$

Check: Try 57, a number greater than 54.

$\frac{m}{3} - 7 > 11$

$\frac{57}{3} - 7 \stackrel{?}{>} 11$

$19 - 7 \stackrel{?}{>} 11$

$12 > 11$ ✓

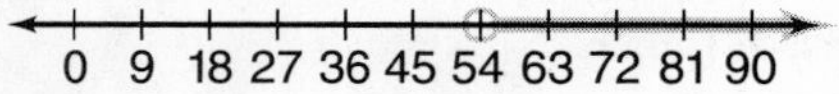

19. $36 + \frac{k}{5} \geq 51$

$36 + \frac{k}{5} - 36 \geq 51 - 36$

$\frac{k}{5} \geq 15$

$5\left(\frac{k}{5}\right) \geq 5(15)$

$k \geq 75$

Check: Try 80, a number greater than or equal to 75.

$36 + \frac{k}{5} \geq 51$

$36 + \frac{80}{5} \stackrel{?}{\geq} 51$

$36 + 16 \stackrel{?}{\geq} 51$

$52 \geq 51$ ✓

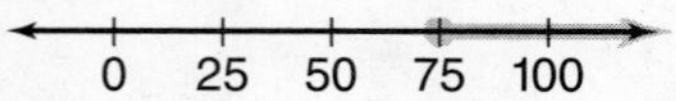

20. $\frac{2x}{9} - 2 < -4$

$\frac{2x}{9} - 2 + 2 < -4 + 2$

$\frac{2x}{9} < -2$

$\frac{9}{2}\left(\frac{2}{9}\right)x < \frac{9}{2}(-2)$

$x < -9$

Check: Try -18, a number less than -9.

$\frac{2x}{9} - 2 < -4$

$\frac{2(-18)}{9} - 2 \stackrel{?}{<} -4$

$-4 - 2 \stackrel{?}{<} -4$

$-6 < -4$ ✓

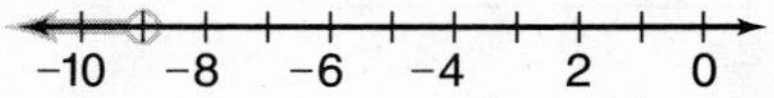

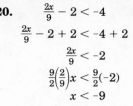

21. $0.47 < \frac{t}{-9} + 0.6$

$0.47 - 0.6 < \frac{t}{-9} + 0.6 - 0.6$

$-0.13 < \frac{t}{-9}$

$-9(-0.13) > -9\left(\frac{t}{-9}\right)$

$1.17 > t$

Check: Try 0, a number less than 1.17.

$0.47 < \frac{t}{-9} + 0.6$

$0.47 \stackrel{?}{<} \frac{0}{-9} + 0.6$

$0.47 \stackrel{?}{<} 0 + 0.6$

$0.47 < 0.6$ ✓

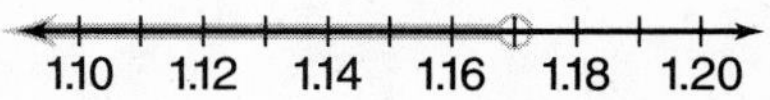

22. $-4.4 > \frac{b}{-5} - 4.8$

$-4.4 + 4.8 > \frac{b}{-5} - 4.8 + 4.8$

$0.4 > \frac{b}{-5}$

$-5(0.4) < -5\left(\frac{b}{-5}\right)$

$-2 < b$

Check: Try 0, a number greater than -2.

$-4.4 > \frac{b}{-5} - 4.8$

$-4.4 \stackrel{?}{>} \frac{0}{-5} - 4.8$

$-4.4 \stackrel{?}{>} 0 - 4.8$

$-4.4 > -4.8$ ✓

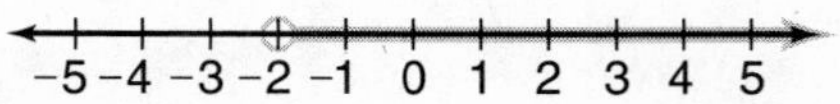

23. $12 - \frac{5z}{4} < 37$

$12 - \frac{5z}{4} - 12 < 37 - 12$

$-\frac{5z}{4} < 25$

$-\frac{4}{5}\left(-\frac{5}{4}\right)z > -\frac{4}{5}(25)$

$z > -20$

Check: Try 4, a number greater than -20.

$$12 - \frac{5z}{4} < 37$$

$$12 - \frac{5(4)}{4} \overset{?}{<} 37$$

$$12 - 5 \overset{?}{<} 37$$

$$7 < 37 \checkmark$$

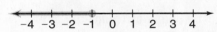

24. $\frac{n - 11}{2} \leq -6$

$$2\left(\frac{n - 11}{2}\right) \leq 2(-6)$$

$$n - 11 \leq -12$$

$$n - 11 + 11 \leq -12 + 11$$

$$n \leq -1$$

Check: Try -3, a number less than or equal to -1.

$$\frac{n - 11}{2} \leq -6$$

$$\frac{-3 - 11}{2} \overset{?}{\leq} -6$$

$$\frac{-14}{2} \overset{?}{\leq} -6$$

$$-7 \leq -6 \checkmark$$

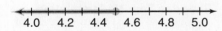

25. $1.3x + 6.7 \geq 3.1x - 1.4$

$$1.3x - 3.1x + 6.7 \geq 3.1x - 3.1x - 1.4$$

$$-1.8x + 6.7 \geq 1.4$$

$$-1.8x + 6.7 - 6.7 \geq -1.4 - 6.7$$

$$-1.8x \geq -8.1$$

$$\frac{-1.8x}{-1.8} \leq \frac{-8.1}{-1.8}$$

$$x \leq 4.5$$

Check: Try 0, a number less than or equal to 4.5.

$$1.3x + 6.7 \geq 3.1x - 1.4$$

$$1.3(0) + 6.7 \overset{?}{\geq} 3.1(0) - 1.4$$

$$0 + 6.7 \overset{?}{\geq} 0 - 1.4$$

$$6.7 \geq -1.4 \checkmark$$

(number line: 4.0 4.2 4.4 4.6 4.8 5.0)

26. $-5x + 3 < 3x + 23$

$$-5x - 3x + 3 < 3x - 3x + 23$$

$$-8x + 3 < 23$$

$$-8x + 3 - 3 < 23 - 3$$

$$-8x < 20$$

$$\frac{-8x}{-8} > \frac{20}{-8}$$

$$x > -2.5$$

Check: Try 1, a number greater than -2.5.

$$-5x + 3 < 3x + 23$$

$$-5(1) + 3 \overset{?}{<} 3(1) + 23$$

$$-5 + 3 \overset{?}{<} 3 + 23$$

$$-2 < 26 \checkmark$$

(number line: -3.0 -2.8 -2.6 -2.4 -2.2 -2.0)

27. $-5(k + 4) \geq 3(k - 4)$

$$-5k - 20 \geq 3k - 12$$

$$-5k - 3k - 20 \geq 3k - 3k - 12$$

$$-8k - 20 \geq -12$$

$$-8k - 20 + 20 \geq -12 + 20$$

$$-8k \geq 8$$

$$\frac{-8k}{-8} \leq \frac{8}{-8}$$

$$k \leq -1$$

Check: Try -2, a number less than or equal to -1.

$$-5(k + 4) \geq 3(k - 4)$$

$$-5(-2 + 4) \overset{?}{\geq} 3(-2 - 4)$$

$$-5(-2) \overset{?}{\geq} 3(-6)$$

$$-10 \geq -18 \checkmark$$

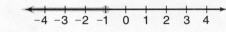

28. $8c - (c - 5) > c + 17$

$$8c - c + 5 > c + 17$$

$$7c + 5 > c + 17$$

$$7c - c + 5 > c - c + 17$$

$$6c + 5 > 17$$

$$6c + 5 - 5 > 17 - 5$$

$$6c > 12$$

$$\frac{6c}{6} > \frac{12}{6}$$

$$c > 2$$

Check: Try 3, a number greater than 2.

$$8c - (c - 5) > c + 17$$

$$8(3) - (3 - 5) \overset{?}{>} 3 + 17$$

$$24 - (-2) \overset{?}{>} 20$$

$$24 + 2 \overset{?}{>} 20$$

$$26 > 20 \checkmark$$

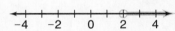

29. $\frac{c + 8}{4} < \frac{5 - c}{9}$

$$36\left(\frac{c + 8}{4}\right) < 36\left(\frac{5 - c}{9}\right)$$

$$9(c + 8) < 4(5 - c)$$

$$9c + 72 < 20 - 4c$$

$$9c + 4c + 72 < 20 - 4c + 4c$$

$$13c + 72 < 20$$

$$13c + 72 - 72 < 20 - 72$$

$$13c < -52$$

$$\frac{13c}{13} < \frac{-52}{13}$$

$$c < -4$$

Check: Try -5, a number less than -4.

$$\frac{c + 8}{4} < \frac{5 - c}{9}$$

$$\frac{-5 + 8}{4} \overset{?}{<} \frac{5 - (-5)}{9}$$

$$\frac{-5 + 8}{4} \overset{?}{<} \frac{5 + 5}{9}$$

$$\frac{3}{4} < \frac{10}{9} \checkmark$$

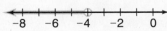

30.
$$\frac{2(n+1)}{7} \geq \frac{n+4}{5}$$
$$35\left[\frac{2(n+1)}{7}\right] \geq 35\left(\frac{n+4}{5}\right)$$
$$5[2(n+1)] \geq 7(n+4)$$
$$5(2n+2) \geq 7(n+4)$$
$$10n+10 \geq 7n+28$$
$$10n-7n+10 \geq 7n-7n+28$$
$$3n+10 \geq 28$$
$$3n+10-10 \geq 28-10$$
$$3n \geq 18$$
$$\frac{3n}{3} \geq \frac{18}{3}$$
$$n \geq 6$$

Check: Try 8, a number greater than or equal to 6.
$$\frac{2(n+1)}{7} \geq \frac{n+4}{5}$$
$$\frac{2(8+1)}{7} \stackrel{?}{\geq} \frac{8+4}{5}$$
$$\frac{2(9)}{7} \stackrel{?}{\geq} \frac{12}{5}$$
$$\frac{18}{7} \stackrel{?}{\geq} \frac{12}{5}$$
$$2\frac{4}{7} \geq 2\frac{2}{5} ✔$$

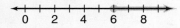

31.
$$-10 < 3x+5 < 8$$
$$-10-5 < 3x+5-5 < 8-5$$
$$-15 < 3x < 3$$
$$\frac{-15}{3} < \frac{3x}{3} < \frac{3}{3}$$
$$-5 < x < 1$$

32.
$$16\left(\frac{15+b}{2}\right) \geq 320$$
$$8(15+b) \geq 320$$
$$120+8b \geq 320$$
$$120+8b-120 \geq 320-120$$
$$8b \geq 200$$
$$\frac{8b}{8} \geq \frac{200}{8}$$
$$b \geq 25 \text{ meters}$$

33.
$$\frac{89+92+82+s}{4} \geq 90$$
$$4\left(\frac{89+92+82+s}{4}\right) \geq 4(90)$$
$$89+92+82+s \geq 360$$
$$263+s \geq 360$$
$$263+s-263 \geq 360-263$$
$$s \geq 97$$

34.
$$-75-m = 25+4m$$
$$-75-m-4m = 25+4m-4m$$
$$-75-5m = 25$$
$$-75-5m+75 = 25+75$$
$$-5m = 100$$
$$\frac{-5m}{-5} = \frac{100}{-5}$$
$$m = -20$$

35.

Number of People That Received Letter
6
$6(6) = 36$
$36(6) = 216$

216 people have received the chain letter.

36.
$$7.5x-31+13.78x = 7.5x+13.78x-31$$
$$= (7.5+13.78)x-31$$
$$= 21.28x-31$$

37. $\frac{t^{17}}{t^8} = t^9$

38.
$$17+(-13)+8 = 17+8+(-13)$$
$$= 25+(-13)$$
$$= (|25|-|-13|)$$
$$= 25-13$$
$$= 12$$

39. Let n represent the number of vacation days for Northridge High School. Then 3 more days would be represented by $n+3$.

Page 354   The Shape of Things to Come

- Aerodynamics is the study of the way gases interact with something in motion. If something is "more aerodynamic," it interacts better with the air than another object.

- Javelins were flying too far—into stands of spectators and out of stadiums. The new javelins were banned from competition.

- See students' work.

7-7   Writing Inequalities

Page 356   Checking Your Understanding

1. a. $6n-4 \leq 41$

   b. Replace n with $4\frac{1}{2}$.

2. $-7 > x > -9$

3. See students' work.

4. Let n = number
$$n-4 \leq 10$$
$$n-4+4 \leq 10+4$$
$$n \leq 14$$

5. Let n = number
$$2n-9 > 11$$
$$2n-9+9 > 11+9$$
$$2n > 20$$
$$\frac{2n}{2} > \frac{20}{2}$$
$$n > 10$$

6. Let s = number of subscriptions

$$2s + 10 \geq 40$$
$$2s + 10 - 10 \geq 40 - 10$$
$$2s \geq 30$$
$$\frac{2s}{2} \geq \frac{30}{2}$$
$$s \geq 15$$

at least 15

7. Let c = number of candy bars

$$55c + 35 \leq 200$$
$$55c + 35 - 35 \leq 200 - 35$$
$$55c \leq 165$$
$$\frac{55c}{55} \leq \frac{165}{55}$$
$$c \leq 3$$

at most 3

8. Let s = score on fifth dive

$$68.2 + 68.9 + 67.5 + 71.7 + s > 345.4$$
$$276.3 + s > 345.4$$
$$276.3 + s - 276.3 > 345.4 - 276.3$$
$$s > 69.1$$

Gao will overtake the first-place diver if her fifth-dive score is greater than 69.1

Pages 356–357 Exercises

9. Let x = number

$$4x + 4 \geq 16$$
$$4x + 4 - 4 \geq 16 - 4$$
$$4x \geq 12$$
$$\frac{4x}{4} \geq \frac{12}{4}$$
$$x \geq 3$$

10. Let n = number

$$6n - 9 \leq 33$$
$$6n - 9 + 9 \leq 33 + 9$$
$$6n \leq 42$$
$$\frac{6n}{6} \leq \frac{42}{6}$$
$$n \leq 7$$

11. Sample answer: A stove and a freezer weigh at least 260 kg. The stove weighs 155 kg. What is the freezer's weight?

12. Sample answer: Jenny has scores of 87, 92, 89 and 97 on quizzes. There will be one more quiz. What must Jenny's fifth score be to have an average score of at least of at least 90?

13.
$$3(h - 1) \geq 18$$
$$3h - 3 \geq 18$$
$$3h - 3 + 3 \geq 18 + 3$$
$$3h \geq 21$$
$$\frac{3h}{3} \geq \frac{21}{3}$$
$$h \geq 7$$

14.
$$12n - \frac{1}{20}n < 3250$$
$$\frac{240}{20}n - \frac{1}{20}n < 3250$$
$$\frac{239}{20}n < 3250$$
$$\frac{20}{239}\left(\frac{239}{20}\right)n < \frac{20}{239}(3250)$$
$$n < 271\frac{231}{239}$$

15. Let n = integer

$n + 1$ = next greater integer

$$n + (n + 1) \geq 35$$
$$n + n + 1 \geq 35$$
$$2n + 1 \geq 35$$
$$2n + 1 - 1 \geq 35 - 1$$
$$2n \geq 34$$
$$\frac{2n}{2} \geq \frac{34}{2}$$
$$n \geq 17$$

The least pair of such integers is 17, 18.

16. Let n = odd integer

$n + 2$ = next greater odd integer

$$n + (n + 2) > 136$$
$$n + n + 2 > 136$$
$$2n + 2 > 136$$
$$2n + 2 - 2 > 136 - 2$$
$$2n > 134$$
$$\frac{2n}{2} > \frac{134}{2}$$
$$n > 67$$

The least pair of such integers is 69, 71.

17. Let t = number

$$3t - 5 \geq 6$$
$$3t - 5 + 5 \geq 6 + 5$$
$$3t \geq 11$$
$$\frac{3t}{3} \geq \frac{11}{3}$$
$$t \geq \frac{11}{3}$$

18. Let n = number

$$n < 2(-n) + 5$$
$$n < -2n + 5$$
$$n + 2n < -2n + 2n + 5$$
$$3n < 5$$
$$\frac{3n}{3} < \frac{5}{3}$$
$$n < \frac{5}{3}$$

19. Let n = integer

$$39 < 12.15n + 9.348 < 75$$
$$39 - 9.348 < 12.15n + 9.348 - 9.348 < 75 - 9.348$$
$$29.652 < 12.15n < 65.652$$
$$\frac{29.652}{12.15} < \frac{12.15n}{12.15} < \frac{65.652}{12.15}$$
$$2.44 < n < 5.4$$

The integer is 3, 4, or 5.

20. a.
$$2x - 5 < 3 \quad \text{and} \quad x + 5 > 4$$
$$2x - 5 + 5 < 3 + 5 \qquad x + 5 - 5 > 4 - 5$$
$$2x < 8 \qquad\qquad x > -1$$
$$\frac{2x}{2} < \frac{8}{2}$$
$$x < 4$$

$$-1 < x < 4$$

b. $90 < m\angle A < 180$

21. $28 + 22 > c > 28 - 22$

$\qquad 50 > c > 6$

22. a. Let r = revenue

$r > \$7000 + \$1200(10)$

$r > \$7000 + \$12{,}000$

$r > \$19{,}000$

b. Revenue > Expenses

Expenses = $7000 + $1200(5)

= $7000 + $6000

= $13,000

Let x = number of acres

$5(\$100)x > \$13,000$

$\$500x > \$13,000$

$\dfrac{\$500x}{\$500} > \dfrac{\$13,000}{\$500}$

$x > 26$

The farm should be over 26 acres.

23. $\dfrac{2}{5}x - 1 > -3$

$\dfrac{2}{5}x - 1 + 1 > -3 + 1$

$\dfrac{2}{5}x > -2$

$\dfrac{5}{2}\left(\dfrac{2}{5}\right)x > \dfrac{5}{2}(-2)$

$x > -5$

24. $\dfrac{20}{27} - \dfrac{11}{27} = b$

$\dfrac{9}{27} = b$

$\dfrac{1}{3} = b$

25. a. $\dfrac{1.7}{10^{24}}$

b. 0.0000000000000000000000017

26. $6 \le \dfrac{n}{-7}$

$-7(6) \ge -7\left(\dfrac{n}{-7}\right)$

$-42 \ge n$

27. $-14 \cdot 9b = (-14 \cdot 9)b$

$= -126b$

7-8 Integration: Measurement Using the Metric System

Page 360   Checking Your Understanding

1. Sample answer: Multiply if you are changing to smaller units; divide if you are changing to larger units.

2. Sample answer: A kilometer is 1,000,000 times longer than a millimeter.

3. See students' work.

4. cm

5. mL

6. mm

7. kg

8. $0.035 \times 1000 = 35$

$0.035 \text{ m} = 35 \text{ mm}$

9. $40 \div 1000 = 0.040$

$40 \text{ mL} = 0.040 \text{ L}$

10. $3 \times 1000 = 3000$

$3 \text{ kg} = 3000 \text{ g}$

11. Ramon ran a total of 32 laps around a 400-meter track. So, he ran 32×400 or 12,800 meters.

$12,800 \div 1000 = 12.8$

$12,800 \text{ m} = 12.8 \text{ km}$

Ramon ran 12.8 kilometers.

Pages 360–361   Exercises

12. km

13. cm or m

14. mg

15. L

16. $3 \times 100 = 300$

$3 \text{ m} = 300 \text{ cm}$

17. $400 \div 1000 = 0.4$

$400 \text{ m} = 0.4 \text{ km}$

18. $30 \div 10 = 3$

$30 \text{ mm} = 3 \text{ cm}$

19. $9400 \div 1000 = 9.4$

$9400 \text{ mL} = 9.4 \text{ L}$

20. $5 \times 1000 = 5000$

$5 \text{ L} = 5000 \text{ mL}$

21. $600 \div 100 = 6$

$600 \text{ cm} = 6 \text{ m}$

22. $5000 \div 1000 = 5$

$5000 \text{ mg} = 5 \text{ g}$

23. $8 \times 1000 = 8000$

$8 \text{ kg} = 8000 \text{ g}$

24. $67 \times 1000 = 67,000$

$67 \text{ g} = 67,000 \text{ mg}$

25. $1 \times 1000 = 1000$

$1 \text{ m} = 1000 \text{ mm}$

26. $1 \times 100,000 = 100,000$

$1 \text{ km} = 100,000 \text{ cm}$

27. $0.316 \times 1000 = 316$

$0.316 \text{ kg} = 316 \text{ g}$

28. $0.035 \times 10 = 0.35$

$0.035 \text{ cm} = 0.35 \text{ mm}$

29. $0.946 \times 1000 = 946$

$0.946 \text{ L} = 946 \text{ mL}$

30. $0.019 \times 1,000,000 = 19,000$

$0.019 \text{ kg} = 19,000 \text{ mg}$

31. $6.032 \times 100,000 = 603,200$

$6.032 \text{ km} = 603,200 \text{ cm}$

32. $13 \div 1000 = 0.013$

$13 \text{ mm} = 0.13 \text{ m}$

$0.013x = 0.5$

$\dfrac{0.013x}{0.013} = \dfrac{0.5}{0.013}$

$x = 38.46$

It would take more than 38 months for hair to grow 0.5 meter.

33. $5 \text{ mm} = 0.5 \text{ cm}$

If the volumes sit on the shelf in order, the bookworm will eat through the front cover of Volume 1, the back cover of Volume 2, Volume 2, the front cover of Volume 2, the back cover of Volume 3, Volume 3, the front cover of Volume 3, and the back cover of Volume 4. It will eat $0.5 + 0.5 + 5 + 0.5 + 0.5 + 5 + 0.5 + 0.5$ or 13 cm.

34. 1 metric ton = 1000 kg

$16,427 \div 1000 = 16.427$

$16,427 \text{ kg} = 16.427 \text{ metric tons}$

Since every metric ton saves about 19 trees, 16.427 metric tons will save 16.427×19 or about 312 trees.

35. P = side 1 + side 2 + side 3

$1.6 \text{ m} = 160 \text{ cm}$

$150 \text{ mm} = 15 \text{ cm}$

$160 \text{ cm} = 40 \text{ cm} + (15 \text{ cm} + 40 \text{ cm}) + s$

$160 \text{ cm} = 40 \text{ cm} + 55 \text{ cm} + s$

$160 \text{ cm} = 95 \text{ cm} + s$

$65 \text{ cm} = s$

The lengths of the other sides are 55 cm and 65 cm.

36. a. $1893 \div 1000 = 1.893$

$1893 \text{ mL} = 1.893 \text{ L}$

$3 \text{ L} + 1.893 \text{ L} = 4.893 \text{ L}$

There are 4.893 L in the punch bowl.

b. $4.893 \text{ L} = 4893 \text{ mL}$

$4893 \div 250 = 19.572$

About 19.5 250-mL glasses of punch can be served.

37. $35 \div 1000 = 0.035$

$35 \text{ mm} = 0.035 \text{ m}$

The film is 0.035 meters wide.

38. a. $10^{-10} \times 10^3 = 10^{-7}$ $10^{-6} \times 10^3 = 10^{-3}$
         10^{-10} m $= 10^{-7}$ mm 10^{-6} m $= 10^{-3}$ mm

b. $3900 \times 10^{-7} = 0.00039$ mm
     $7700 \times 10^{-7} = 0.00077$ mm
     0.00039 to 0.00077 mm

c.   1 angstrom $= 10^{-10}$ m

         1 angstrom $= \frac{1}{10^{10}}$ m

    $10^{10}(1$ angstrom$) = 10^{10}\left(\frac{1}{10^{10}}\right)$ m

       10^{10} angstrom $= 1$ meter

           1 meter $= 10^{10}$ angstrom

     $10(1$ meter$) = 10(10^{10})$ angstrom

        10 meters $= 10^{11}$ angstrom

1 to 10 meters is 10^{10} to 10^{11} angstroms.

39. See students' work.

40. $x + (x + 1) + (x + 2) \geq 216$
       $x + x + 1 + x + 2 \geq 216$
             $3x + 3 \geq 216$
        $3x + 3 - 3 \geq 216 - 3$
               $3x \geq 213$
               $\frac{3x}{3} \geq \frac{213}{3}$
                $x \geq 71$
The three smallest such integers are 71, 72, 73.

41. $7b - 39 > 2(b - 2)$
        $7b - 39 > 2b - 4$
   $7b - 2b - 39 > 2b - 2b - 4$
        $5b - 39 > -4$
   $5b - 39 + 39 > -4 + 39$
            $5b > 35$
            $\frac{5b}{5} > \frac{35}{5}$
             $b > 7$

42. $2z - 500 = 100 - z$
   $2z + z - 500 = 100 - z + z$
         $3z - 500 = 100$
  $3z - 500 + 500 = 100 + 500$
             $3z = 600$
             $\frac{3z}{3} = \frac{600}{3}$
              $z = 200$

43. $\frac{5x}{y} = \frac{5(31.74)}{9.2}$
    $= \frac{158.7}{9.2}$
    $= 17.25$

44. mean:
$\frac{3 + 39 + 17 + 17 + 2 + 109 + 15 + 7}{8} = 26.125$ million

2, 3, 7, 15, 17, 17, 39, 109

median: $\frac{15 + 17}{2} = 16$ million

mode: 17 million

45. $\left(3\frac{1}{4}\right)\left(-6\frac{2}{5}\right) = r$
    $\left(\frac{13}{4}\right)\left(-\frac{32}{5}\right) = r$
        $-\frac{416}{20} = r$
      $-20\frac{16}{20} = r$
       $-20\frac{4}{5} = r$

46. $15x = 45$
    $\frac{15x}{15} = \frac{45}{15}$
      $x = 3$

Chapter 7   Study Guide and Assessment

Page 363   Understanding and Using Vocabulary

1. false; the basic unit of capacity is the liter.

2. true   **3.** true

4. false; the diameter is twice the radius.

5. true   **6.** true

7. true

Pages 364–366   Skills and Concepts

8. $54 = 7x - 9$
   $54 + 9 = 7x - 9 + 9$
       $63 = 7x$
       $\frac{63}{7} = \frac{7x}{7}$
         $9 = x$

Check: $54 = 7x - 9$
        $54 \stackrel{?}{=} 7(9) - 9$
        $54 \stackrel{?}{=} 63 - 9$
        $54 = 54$ ✔

9. $\frac{g}{3} + 10 = 14$
    $\frac{g}{3} + 10 - 10 = 14 - 10$
          $\frac{g}{3} = 4$
      $3\left(\frac{g}{3}\right) = 3(4)$
           $g = 12$

Check: $\frac{g}{3} + 10 = 14$
       $\frac{12}{3} + 10 \stackrel{?}{=} 14$
       $4 + 10 \stackrel{?}{=} 14$
          $14 = 14$ ✔

10. $12 = 7 - m$
   $12 - 7 = 7 - m - 7$
        $5 = -m$
   $-1(5) = -1(-m)$
      $-5 = m$

Check: $12 = 7 - m$
       $12 \stackrel{?}{=} 7 - (-5)$
       $12 \stackrel{?}{=} 7 + 5$
       $12 = 12$ ✔

11. $\frac{x}{4} - 17 = -2$
    $\frac{x}{4} - 17 + 17 = -2 + 17$
          $\frac{x}{4} = 15$
     $4\left(\frac{x}{4}\right) = 4(15)$
         $x = 60$

Check: $\frac{x}{4} - 17 = -2$
       $\frac{60}{4} - 17 \stackrel{?}{=} -2$
       $15 - 17 \stackrel{?}{=} -2$
         $-2 = -2$ ✔

12.
$$24 - y = -9$$
$$24 - y - 24 = -9 - 24$$
$$-y = -33$$
$$-1(-y) = -1(-33)$$
$$y = 33$$
Check: $24 - y = -9$
$$24 - 33 \stackrel{?}{=} -9$$
$$-9 = -9 ✔$$

13.
$$4d - 8 = -88$$
$$4d - 8 + 8 = -88 + 8$$
$$4d = -80$$
$$\frac{4d}{4} = \frac{-80}{4}$$
$$d = -20$$
Check: $4d - 8 = -88$
$$4(-20) - 8 \stackrel{?}{=} -88$$
$$-80 - 8 \stackrel{?}{=} -88$$
$$-88 = -88 ✔$$

14.
$$-2f - 37 = -11$$
$$-2f - 37 + 37 = -11 + 37$$
$$-2f = 26$$
$$\frac{-2f}{-2} = \frac{26}{-2}$$
$$f = -13$$
Check: $-2f - 37 = -11$
$$-2(-13) - 37 \stackrel{?}{=} -11$$
$$26 - 37 \stackrel{?}{=} -11$$
$$-11 = -11 ✔$$

15.
$$2.9 = 3.1 - t$$
$$2.9 - 3.1 = 3.1 - t - 3.1$$
$$-0.2 = -t$$
$$-1(-0.2) = -1(-t)$$
$$0.2 = t$$
Check: $2.9 = 3.1 - t$
$$2.9 \stackrel{?}{=} 3.1 - 0.2$$
$$2.9 = 2.9 ✔$$

16. Let n = number
$$6n + 4 = 52$$
$$6n + 4 - 4 = 52 - 4$$
$$6n = 48$$
$$\frac{6n}{6} = \frac{48}{6}$$
$$n = 8$$
The number is 8.

17. Let x = number
$$2x - 7 = 19$$
$$2x - 7 + 7 = 19 + 7$$
$$2x = 26$$
$$\frac{2x}{2} = \frac{26}{2}$$
$$x = 13$$
The number is 13.

18. Let c = number
$$600 = 15c + 15$$
$$600 - 15 = 15c + 15 - 15$$
$$585 = 15c$$
$$\frac{585}{15} = \frac{15c}{15}$$
$$39 = c$$
The number is 39.

19. Let s = salary
$$2s - 50 = 450$$
$$2s - 50 + 50 = 450 + 50$$
$$2s = 500$$
$$\frac{2s}{2} = \frac{500}{2}$$
$$s = 250$$
His old salary was $250.

20. $C = \pi d$
$$C = \pi \cdot 14\frac{2}{3}$$
$$C \approx 46.1 \text{ km}$$

21. $C = 2\pi r$
$$C = 2 \cdot \pi \cdot 3\frac{1}{2}$$
$$C \approx 22.0 \text{ in.}$$

22. $C = \pi d$
$$C = \pi \cdot 18.45$$
$$C \approx 58.0 \text{ cm}$$

23. $C = 2\pi r$
$$C = 2 \cdot \pi \cdot 4.9$$
$$C \approx 30.8 \text{ m}$$

24.
$$6n - 8 = 2n$$
$$6n - 6n - 8 = 2n - 6n$$
$$-8 = -4n$$
$$\frac{-8}{-4} = \frac{-4n}{-4}$$
$$2 = n$$
Check: $6n - 8 = 2n$
$$6(2) - 8 \stackrel{?}{=} 2(2)$$
$$12 - 8 \stackrel{?}{=} 4$$
$$4 = 4 ✔$$

25.
$$4 + 2w = 8w + 16$$
$$4 + 2w - 8w = 8w - 8w + 16$$
$$4 - 6w = 16$$
$$4 - 4 - 6w = 16 - 14$$
$$-6w = 12$$
$$\frac{-6w}{-6} = \frac{12}{-6}$$
$$w = -2$$
Check: $4 + 2w = 8w + 16$
$$4 + 2(-2) \stackrel{?}{=} 8(-2) + 16$$
$$4 - 4 \stackrel{?}{=} -16 + 16$$
$$0 = 0 ✔$$

26.
$$4m + 11 = 6 - m$$
$$4m + m + 11 = 6 - m + m$$
$$5m + 11 = 6$$
$$5m + 11 - 11 = 6 - 11$$
$$5m = -5$$
$$\frac{5m}{5} = \frac{-5}{5}$$
$$m = -1$$
Check: $4m + 11 = 6 - m$
$$4(-1) + 11 \stackrel{?}{=} 6 - (-1)$$
$$-4 + 11 \stackrel{?}{=} 6 + 1$$
$$7 = 7 ✔$$

27.
$$5(3 - k) = 20$$
$$15 - 5k = 20$$
$$15 - 15 - 5k = 20 - 15$$
$$-5k = 5$$
$$\frac{-5k}{-5} = \frac{5}{-5}$$
$$k = -1$$
Check: $5(3 - k) = 20$
$$5[3 - (-1)] \stackrel{?}{=} 20$$
$$5(3 + 1) \stackrel{?}{=} 20$$
$$5(4) \stackrel{?}{=} 20$$
$$20 = 20 ✔$$

28.
$$5(q + 2) = 2q + 1$$
$$5q + 10 = 2q + 1$$
$$5q - 2q + 10 = 2q - 2q + 1$$
$$3q + 10 = 1$$
$$3q + 10 - 10 = 1 - 10$$
$$3q = -9$$
$$\frac{3q}{3} = \frac{-9}{3}$$
$$q = -3$$

Check: $5(q + 2) = 2q + 1$
$$5(-3 + 2) \stackrel{?}{=} 2(-3) + 1$$
$$5(-1) \stackrel{?}{=} -6 + 1$$
$$-5 = -5 \ ✔$$

29.
$$\frac{2}{7}h - 10 = h - 20$$
$$\frac{2}{7}h - h - 10 = h - h - 20$$
$$\frac{2}{7}h - \frac{7}{7}h - 10 = -20$$
$$-\frac{5}{7}h - 10 = -20$$
$$-\frac{5}{7}h - 10 + 10 = -20 + 10$$
$$-\frac{5}{7}h = -10$$
$$-\frac{7}{5}\left(-\frac{5}{7}\right)h = -\frac{7}{5}(-10)$$
$$h = 14$$

Check: $\frac{2}{7}h - 10 = h - 20$
$$\frac{2}{7}(14) - 10 \stackrel{?}{=} 14 - 20$$
$$4 - 10 \stackrel{?}{=} 14 - 20$$
$$-6 = -6 \ ✔$$

30.
$$\frac{x - 5}{6} = \frac{x - 11}{2}$$
$$6\left(\frac{x - 5}{6}\right) = 6\left(\frac{x - 11}{2}\right)$$
$$x - 5 = 3(x - 11)$$
$$x - 5 = 3x - 33$$
$$x - 3x - 5 = 3x - 3x - 33$$
$$-2x - 5 = -33$$
$$-2x - 5 + 5 = -33 + 5$$
$$-2x = -28$$
$$\frac{-2x}{-2} = \frac{-28}{-2}$$
$$x = 14$$

Check: $\frac{x - 5}{6} = \frac{x - 11}{2}$
$$\frac{14 - 5}{6} \stackrel{?}{=} \frac{14 - 11}{2}$$
$$\frac{9}{6} \stackrel{?}{=} \frac{3}{2}$$
$$\frac{3}{2} = \frac{3}{2} \ ✔$$

31.
$$5n + 4 > 34$$
$$5n + 4 - 4 > 34 - 4$$
$$5n > 30$$
$$\frac{5n}{5} > \frac{30}{5}$$
$$n > 6$$

Check: Try 7, a number greater than 6.
$$5n + 4 > 34$$
$$5(7) + 4 \stackrel{?}{>} 34$$
$$35 + 4 \stackrel{?}{>} 34$$
$$39 > 34 \ ✔$$

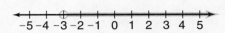

32.
$$-7m - 12 < 9$$
$$-7m - 12 + 12 < 9 + 12$$
$$-7m < 21$$
$$\frac{-7m}{-7} > \frac{21}{-7}$$
$$m > -3$$

Check: Try -1, a number greater than -3.
$$-7m - 12 < 9$$
$$-7(-1) - 12 \stackrel{?}{<} 9$$
$$7 - 12 \stackrel{?}{<} 9$$
$$-5 < 9 \ ✔$$

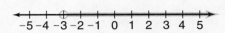

33.
$$\frac{r}{7} - 11 \le 3$$
$$\frac{r}{7} - 11 + 11 \le 3 + 11$$
$$\frac{r}{7} \le 14$$
$$7\left(\frac{r}{7}\right) \le 7(14)$$
$$r \le 98$$

Check: Try 63, a number less than or equal to 98.
$$\frac{r}{7} - 11 \le 3$$
$$\frac{63}{7} - 11 \stackrel{?}{\le} 3$$
$$9 - 11 \stackrel{?}{\le} 3$$
$$-2 \le 3 \ ✔$$

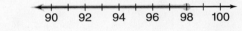

34.
$$16f > 13f + 45$$
$$16f - 13f > 13f - 13f + 45$$
$$3f > 45$$
$$\frac{3f}{3} > \frac{45}{3}$$
$$f > 15$$

Check: Try 17, a number greater than 15.
$$16f > 13f + 45$$
$$16(17) \stackrel{?}{>} 13(17) + 45$$
$$272 \stackrel{?}{>} 221 + 45$$
$$272 > 266 \ ✔$$

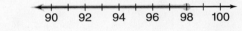

35.
$$0.52c + 14.7 > 2.48c$$
$$0.52c - 0.52c + 14.7 > 2.48c - 0.52c$$
$$14.7 > 1.96c$$
$$\frac{14.7}{1.96} > \frac{1.96c}{1.96}$$
$$7.5 > c$$

Check: Try 0, a number less than 7.5.
$$0.52c + 14.7 > 2.48c$$
$$0.52(0) + 14.7 \stackrel{?}{>} 2.48(0)$$
$$0 + 14.7 \stackrel{?}{>} 0$$
$$14.7 > 0 \ ✔$$

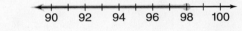

36.

$$\frac{a-5}{6} \le \frac{a+9}{8}$$

$$24\left(\frac{a-5}{6}\right) \le 24\left(\frac{a+9}{8}\right)$$

$$4(a-5) \le 3(a+9)$$

$$4a - 20 \le 3a + 27$$

$$4a - 3a - 20 \le 3a - 3a + 27$$

$$a - 20 \le 27$$

$$a - 20 + 20 \le 27 + 20$$

$$a \le 47$$

Check: Try 40, a number less than or equal to 47.

$$\frac{a-5}{6} \le \frac{a+9}{8}$$

$$\frac{40-5}{6} \overset{?}{\le} \frac{40+9}{8}$$

$$\frac{35}{6} \overset{?}{\le} \frac{49}{8}$$

$$5\frac{5}{6} \le 6\frac{1}{8} \checkmark$$

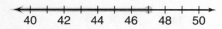

37. Let n = number

$$8n + 2 \ge 18$$

$$8n + 2 - 2 \ge 18 - 2$$

$$8n \ge 16$$

$$\frac{8n}{8} \ge \frac{16}{8}$$

$$n \ge 2$$

38. Let n = number

$$3n - 12 \le 27$$

$$3n - 12 + 12 \le 27 + 12$$

$$3n \le 39$$

$$\frac{3n}{3} \le \frac{39}{3}$$

$$n \le 13$$

39. Let x = integer

$x + 1$ = next greater integer

$$x + (x + 1) > 47$$

$$x + x + 1 > 47$$

$$2x + 1 > 47$$

$$2x + 1 - 1 > 47 - 1$$

$$2x > 46$$

$$\frac{2x}{2} > \frac{46}{2}$$

$$x > 23$$

40. Let s = number

$$4s - 8 \ge 6$$

$$4s - 8 + 8 \ge 6 + 8$$

$$4s \ge 14$$

$$\frac{4s}{4} \ge \frac{14}{4}$$

$$s \ge \frac{7}{2}$$

41. $6 \div 1000 = 0.006$
6 mm = 0.006 m

42. $8.3 \div 1000 = 0.0083$
8.3 g = 0.0083 kg

43. $43 \times 1000 = 43,000$
43 L = 43,000 mL

44. $560 \div 1000 = 0.56$
560 mg = 0.56 g

45. $3 \times 100,000 = 300,000$
3 km = 300,000 cm

46. $40 \div 1000 = 0.04$
40 mL = 0.04 L

47. $88 \times 100 = 8800$
88 m = 8800 cm

Page 366   Applications and Problem Solving

48.

A

F   B

Ⓔ   C

D

Begin with any child and count clockwise eliminating the eighth child. In order for E to be "it," Alejándro must have began the first rhyme with C.

49. $r = \frac{4(220 - a)}{5}$

$$r = \frac{4(220 - a)}{5}$$

$$r = \frac{4(176)}{5}$$

$$r = \frac{704}{5}$$

$r = 140.8$ beats per minute

50. $C = \pi d$

$$C = \pi \cdot 3.4$$

$$C \approx 10.7$$

The piece of metal was about 10.7 inches.

51. Let x = minutes

$$630x + 1500 < 12,000$$

$$630x + 1500 - 1500 < 12,000 - 1500$$

$$630x < 10,500$$

$$\frac{630x}{630} < \frac{10,500}{630}$$

$$x < 16.67$$

To stay at least 1500 feet below the ceiling, the pilot can ascend for less than 16.67 minutes.

Page 367   Alternative Assessment

1. a. Let x = amount *Raise the Titanic* lost

$$48.1 = 2x - 10.3$$

$$48.1 + 10.3 = 2x - 10.3 + 10.3$$

$$58.4 = 2x$$

$$\frac{58.4}{2} = \frac{2x}{x}$$

$$29.2 = x$$

Raise the Titanic lost 29.2 million.

b. Let n = amount *Billy Bathgate* lost

$$n + 38.1 = 2n + 5.1$$

$$n - 2n + 38.1 = 2n - 2n + 5.1$$

$$-n + 38.1 = 5.1$$

$$-n + 38.1 - 38.1 = 5.1 - 38.1$$

$$-n = -33$$

$$-1(-n) = -1(-33)$$

$$n = 33$$

Billy Bathgate lost 33 million.

c. Let r = the amount *Rambo III* lost

$$r > \frac{1}{2}(47.3) + 6.3$$

$$r > 23.65 + 6.3$$

$$r > \$29.95 \text{ million}$$

d. See students' work.

2. a. $C = \pi d$

$$C = \pi \cdot 56.25$$

$$C \approx 176.7 \text{ cm or } 1.76 \text{ m}$$

b. 56.25 cm = 0.5625 m
  0.5625 m + 1.2 m + 1.2 m = 2.9625 m
  or 296.25 cm

c. $C = \pi d$
  $C = \pi \cdot 2.9625$
  $C \approx 9.3$ meters

Page 367   Thinking Critically

Sample answer: yes, if you could remember either
formula and the relationship $2r = d$, you could always
find the circumference of a circle.

Page 367   Portfolio

See students' work.

Page 367   Self Evaluation

See students' work.

Chapter 8   Functions and Graphing

| 8-1 | **Relations and Functions** |

Pages 374–375   Checking Your Understanding

1. Sample answer: a set of ordered pairs: {(1,2), (4,5), (−3,5), (−1,4)};

a table:

x	y
1	2
4	5
−3	5
−1	4

a graph:

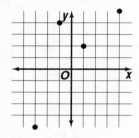

2. The domain is the set of all first coordinates while the range is the set of all second coordinates.

3. Marita is correct because each x is paired with exactly one y.

4.

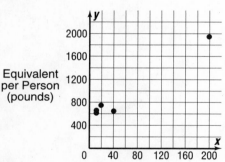

Equivalent per Person (pounds)

Annual Domestic Waste (millions of tons)

5. {−1.3, 4, −2.4}; {1, −3.9, 3.6}

6. $\left\{-\frac{1}{2}, 1\frac{1}{2}, 3, 5\frac{1}{4}\right\}; \left\{-\frac{1}{4}, -\frac{2}{3}, -\frac{2}{5}, 6\frac{2}{7}\right\}$

7. {(−1, 3), (0, 6), (4, −1), (7, 2)};
   D = {−1, 0, 4, 7}, R = {3, 6, −1, 2}

8. {(2, 4), (0, 2), (−2, 0), (−4, 2)};
   D = {2, 0, −2, −4}, R = {4, 2, 0}

9. {(−2, 1), (0, −1), (2, 2)};
   D = {−2, 0, 2}, R = {1, −1, 2}

10. {(3, 1), (0, 2), (−2, 1), (−4, −2), (1, −3)};
    D = {3, 0, −2, −4, 1}, R = {1, 2, −2, −3}

11. yes, each domain element is paired with two range values exactly one range element.

12. no, 0 is paired with two range values

13. no, 1 is paired with four range values

14. yes, each domain element is paired with exactly one range element

15. {(8, 4), (9, 3), (10, 2), (11, 1), (12, 0)}

Pages 375–377   Exercises

16. {5, −2, 2}; {−4, 3, −1}

17. {−1, 4, 2, 1}; {6, 2, 36}

18. {3.1, 7, −3.9}; {2, −4.4, −8.8}

19. {1.4, −2, 4, 6}; {3, 9.6, 4, −2.7}

20. $\left\{\frac{2}{5}, 98\frac{3}{5}, -4\right\}; \left\{\frac{3}{4}, 37\frac{1}{2}, -\frac{7}{12}\right\}$

21. $\left\{-\frac{1}{2}, 4\frac{2}{3}, -12\frac{3}{8}\right\}; \left\{\frac{1}{3}, -17, 66\right\}$

22. {(0, 5), (2, 3), (1, −4), (−3, 3), (−1, −2)};
    D = {0, 2, 1, −3, −1}, R = {5, 3, −4, −2}

23. {(−4, −2), (−2, 1), (0, 2), (1, −3), (3, 1)};
    D = {−4, −2, 0, 1, 3,}, R = {−2, 1, 2, −3}

24. {(−1, 5), (−2, 5), (−2, 4), (−2, 1), (−6, 1)};
    D = {−1, −2, −6}, R = {5, 4, 1}

25. {(5, 4), (2, 8), (−7, 9), (2, 12), (5, 14)};
    D = {5, 2, −7}, R = {4, 8, 9, 12, 14}

26. {(−2, 2), (−1, 1), (0, 1), (1, 1), (1, −1), (2, −1), (3, 1)};
    D = {−2, −1, 0, 1, 2, 3}, R = {2, 1, −1}

27. {(−3, −2), (−2, −1), (0, 0), (1, 1)};
    D = {−3, −2, 0, 1}, R = {−2, −1, 0, 1}

28. {(−3, 0), (−2, 2), (−1, 3), (0, 1), (1, −1), (1, −2), (1, −3), (3, −2)};
    D = {−3, −2, −1, 0, 1, 3}, R = {0, 2, 3, 1, −1, −2, −3}

29. yes, each element of the domain is paired with exactly one element of the range

30. yes, each element of the domain is paired with exactly one element of the range

31. no, 1 is paired with two elements of the range

32. yes, each element of the domain is paired with exactly one element of the range

33. yes, each element of the domain is paired with exactly one element of the range

34. no, 0 is paired with three elements of the range

35. no, 5 is paired with three elements of the range

36. yes, each element of the domain is paired with exactly one element of the range

37. no, 1 and 3 are each paired with two elements of the range

38. no, 1 and 2 are each paired with two elements of the range

39. no, 0 is paired with three elements of the range

40. {(0, 4), (1, 5), (2, 6), (3, 6)}; yes

41. {(5, 5), (−1, −3), (1, −2), (0, −4)}; yes

42. a. If the cars were considered the domain, then the relation is a function since each number in the domain has exactly one corresponding value in the range.

    b. If the trucks were considered the domain, then the relation would not be a function since 650 trucks is paired with two different numbers of cars.

43. a. $6.95

    b. more than $30 and less than or equal to $70

       Pre-Algebra Chapter 8

c. Yes, each x-value (total price) has exactly one y-value (shipping cost).

44. 2-liter bottle: 2 L = 2000 mL
Six-pack: 6×354 mL = 2124 mL
The six-pack has $2124 - 2000$ or 124 mL more.

45.
$$-2.2 < \frac{b}{-10} - 2.4$$
$$-2.2 + 2.4 < \frac{b}{-10} - 2.4 + 2.4$$
$$0.2 < \frac{b}{-10}$$
$$-10(0.2) > -10\left(\frac{b}{-10}\right)$$
$$-2 > b$$

46. first bounce: $\frac{2}{3}(48)$ or 32 ft
second bounce: $\frac{2}{3}(32)$ or $21\frac{1}{3}$ ft
third bounce: $\frac{2}{3}\left(21\frac{1}{3}\right)$ or $14\frac{2}{9}$ ft

47.
$$z - \frac{2}{5} \geq -2$$
$$z - \frac{2}{5} + \frac{2}{5} \geq -2 + \frac{2}{5}$$
$$z \geq -\frac{10}{5} + \frac{2}{5}$$
$$z \geq -\frac{8}{5}$$
$$z \geq -1\frac{3}{5}$$

48. $(-7y^2)(3y^3) = (-7 \cdot 3)(y^2 \cdot y^3)$
$$= -21 \cdot y^{2+3}$$
$$= -21y^5$$

49. $P = 2(\ell + w)$
$P = 2(6 + 2)$
$P = 2(8)$
$P = 16$ miles

50. Let n = number
$n - 3 = -7$
$n - 3 + 3 = -7 + 3$
$n = -4$
The number is -4.

51. Sample answer: two times the sum of a number and three.

Pages 376–377   Earth Watch

1. yes
2. The size of the catch is increasing.
3. See students' work.

8-2A   **Math Lab: Scatter Plots**

Page 378

1. Sample answer: Generally, as shoe length increases, arm span increases.
2. Answers will vary. Sample answer: Yes, arm span is about 6 times shoe length.
3. Sample answer: Because points appear to be scattered around a general area.
4. See students' work.

8-2   **Integration: Statistics
Scatter Plots**

Page 379   Your Turn

a. It appears that greater sales is related to greater advertising.
b. Two points show relatively low sales and high advertising.

Page 381   Checking Your Understanding

1. Sample answer: a scatter plot is used to analyze relationships between data.
2. Sample answer: Collect two sets of data and form ordered pairs. Then graph the ordered pairs.
3. See students' work.
4. Sample answer: The scatter plot shows the cost of cars based on the age of the cars. This scatter plot shows a negative relationship. That is, the age of the car increases as the cost goes down.
5. negative   **6.** none   **7.** positive
8. Sample answer: none
See students' explanations.
9. Sample answer: positive
See students' explanations.
10. a. It represents the winning time of 11.4 seconds in the 1964 Olympics.
b. 12.2 seconds in 1928
c. about 11.5 seconds
d. Sample answer: Generally as the year increases, the associated winning time decreases.
e. See students' work.

Pages 382–384   Exercises

11. none   **12.** positive   **13.** negative
14. a. It represents a study time of 75 minutes with a resulting test score of 87.
b. yes; positive
c. The points would be in the lower right portion of the scatter plot.
d. 14
15. Sample answer: positive
See students' explanations.
16. Sample answer: no
See students' explanations.
17. Sample answer: no
See students' explanations.
18. Sample answer: negative
See students' explanations.
19. Sample answer: negative
See students' explanations.
20. Sample answer: positive
See students' explanations.
21. Sample answer: no
See students' explanations.
22. Sample answer: positive
See students' explanations.

23.

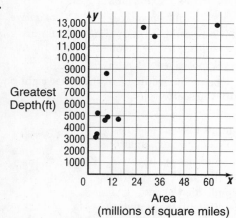

23. a. The data show a positive relationship.

   b. Sample answer: about 62 wpm

   c. Sample answer: between 3 and 4 weeks

   d. The more experience a student has the more words per minute he or she can key.

24. a. Sample answer: Both activities are dependent on cold weather.

   b. No; buying boots does not cause skiing accidents. The relationship may be that both things are caused by a third factor.

25. a.

Relationship of Year and Cost per Year

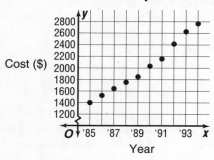

   b. yes; positive

26. a.

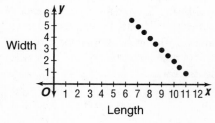

   b. The bodies of water that have the greater surface have the greater depth.

27. a.

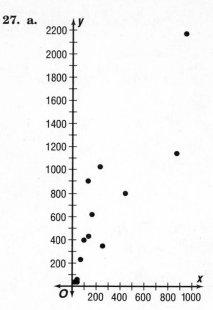

   b. yes; positive

   c. Sample answer: yes; you could estimate by using the points in the scatter plot.

   d. Sample answer: Yes; some players have more opportunities to get rebounds because of the position they play for the team.

   e. Sample answer: Yes, since more playing time provides a player with more opportunity to score points.

28.

Width	Length
1	11
1.5	10.5
2	10
2.5	9.5
3	9
4	8
4.5	7.5
5	7
5.5	6.5
6	6

There is a negative relationship between length and width.

29. {8, 4, 6, 5}, {1, 2, -4, -3, 0}

30.
$$12x - 24 = -14x + 28$$
$$12x + 14x - 24 = -14x + 14x + 28$$
$$26x - 24 = 28$$
$$26x - 24 + 24 = 28 + 24$$
$$26x = 52$$
$$\frac{26x}{26} = \frac{52}{26}$$
$$x = 2$$

31. mean: $\frac{121 + 130 + 128 + 126 + 130 + 131}{6} = 127.7$
121, 126, 128, 130, 130, 131
median: $\frac{128 + 130}{2} = 129$
mode: 130

32. 5, 6.5, 8, 9.5, 11, 12.5, 14
    +1.5 +1.5 +1.5 +1.5 +1.5 +1.5

33. $5 \cdot 17 = 85$
$1990 + 85 = 2075$

8-3 Graphing Linear Relations

Pages 387–388   Checking Your Understanding

1.

x	$0.5x$	y
10	0.5(10)	5
8	0.5(8)	4
300	0.5(300)	150

(8, 4) is a solution of $y = 0.5x$.

2. Sample answer: An equation with two variables has an infinite number of solutions because an infinite number of values can be substituted for x.

3. (0, 3) and (3, 0) are solutions of the equation. Since $0 + 3 = 3$ and $3 + 0 = 3$, the correct choice is b.

4. Sample answer: An equation whose graph is a straight line.

5. Sample answer: Find at least four solutions to the equation. Graph the points associated with the ordered pairs. Draw the line containing the four points.

6. a.

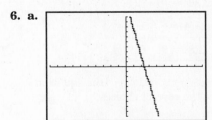

b.

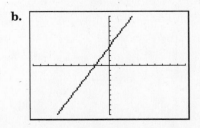

7.

(x, y)	Is $x - 3y = -7$?
(2, 4)	no; $2 - 3(4) = -10$
(2, -1)	no; $2 - 3(-1) = 5$
(2, 3)	yes; $2 - 3(3) = -7$
(-1, 2)	yes; $-1 - 3(2) = -7$

(2, 3) and (-1, 2) are solutions of the equation. So, c and d are the correct choices.

8.

x	$x + 4$	y
-1	-1 + 4	3
0	0 + 4	4
1	1 + 4	5
3	3 + 4	7

(-1, 3), (0, 4)
(1, 5), (3, 7)

9.

x	$1.5x - 2$	y
-2	1.5(-2) - 2	-5
0	1.5(0) - 2	-2
2	1.5(2) - 2	1
4	1.5(4) - 2	4

(-2, -5), (0, -2),
(2, 1), (4, 4)

10.

x	$x - 7$	y
0	0 - 7	-7
7	7 - 7	0
8	8 - 7	1
9	9 - 7	2

Answers will vary.
Sample answer:
(0, -7), (7, 0),
(8, 1), (9, 2)

11.

x	$5x + 2.8$	y
0	5(0) + 2.8	2.8
-2	5(-2) + 2.8	-7.2
2	5(2) + 2.8	12.8
-1	5(-1) + 2.8	-2.2

Answers will vary.
Sample answer:
(0, 2.8), (-2, -7.2),
(2, 12.8), (-1, -2.2)

12.

x	$-2x$	y
0	-2(0)	0
7	-2(7)	-14
-8	-2(-8)	16
1	-2(1)	-2

Answers will vary.
Sample answer:
(0, 0), (7, -14),
(-8, 16), (1, -2)

13. no   **14.** yes

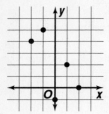 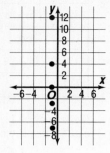

15.

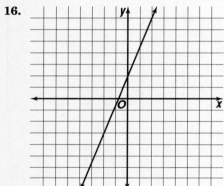

16.

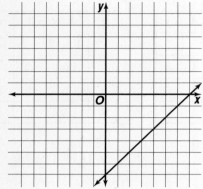

17.   **18.**

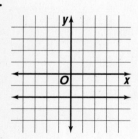 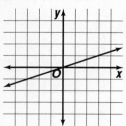

19. a. $y = 0.5x$

b.

x	$y = 0.5x$	y	(x, y)
0	$y = 0.5(0)$	0	$(0, 0)$
1	$y = 0.5(1)$	0.5	$(1, 0.5)$
2	$y = 0.5(2)$	1	$(2, 1)$
3	$y = 0.5(3)$	1.5	$(3, 1.5)$

c. Sample answer: There is no such thing as a negative number of seedlings.

d.

Tree Survival

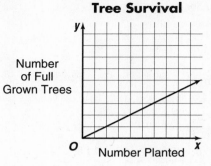

Pages 388–390 Exercises

20.

(x, y)	Is $4x + 2y = 8$?
$(2, 0)$	yes; $4(2) + 2(0) = 8$
$(0, 2)$	no; $4(0) + 2(2) = 4$
$(0.5, -3)$	no; $4(0.5) + 2(-3) = -4$
$(1, -2)$	no; $4(1) + 2(-2) = 0$

$(2, 0)$ is the solution of the equation. So, a is the correct choice.

21.

(x, y)	Is $2a - 5b = 1$?
$(-2, -1)$	yes; $2(-2) - 5(-1) = 1$
$(2, 1)$	no; $2(2) - 5(1) = -1$
$(7, 3)$	no; $2(7) - 5(3) = -1$
$(-7, -3)$	yes; $2(-7) - 5(-3) = -1$

$(-2,-1)$ and $(-7,-3)$ are solutions of the equation. So, a and d are the correct choices.

22.

(x, y)	Is $3x = 8 - y$?
$(3, 1)$	no; $3(3) \neq 8 - 1$
$(2, 2)$	yes; $3(2) = 8 - 2$
$(4, -4)$	yes; $3(4) = \div 8 - (-4)$
$(8, 0)$	no; $3(8) \neq 8 - 0$

$(2, 2)$ and $(4, -4)$ are solutions of the equation. So, b and c are the correct choices.

23.

x	2.5x	y
0	2.5(0)	0
1	2.5(1)	2.5
2	2.5(2)	5
3	2.5(3)	7.5

Answers will vary.
Sample answer:
(0, 0), (1, 2.5),
(2, 5), (3, 7.5)

24.

x	4x	y
1	4(1)	4
2	4(2)	8
3	4(3)	12
4	4(4)	16

Answers will vary.
Sample answer:
(1, 4), (2, 8),
(3, 12), (4, 16)

25.

x	3x + 7	y
0	3(0) + 7	7
1	3(1) + 7	10
2	3(2) + 7	13
3	3(3) + 7	16

Answers will vary.
Sample answer:
(0, 7), (1, 10),
(2, 13), (3, 16)

26.

x	y
0	0
1	1
2	2
3	3

Answers will vary.
Sample answer:
(0, 0), (1, 1),
(2, 2), (3, 3)

27.

x	-x - 4	y
0	-0 - 4	-4
1	-1 - 4	-5
2	-2 - 4	-6
3	-3 - 4	-7

Answers will vary.
Sample answer:
(0, -4), (1, -5),
(2, -6), (3, -7)

28.

x	10x - 1	y
0	10(0) - 1	-1
1	10(1) - 1	9
2	10(2) - 1	19
3	10(3) - 1	29

Answers will vary.
Sample answer:
(0, -1), (1, 9),
(2, 19), (3, 29)

29. Rewrite $x + y = 1$
as $y = 1 - x$.

x	1 - x	y
0	1 - 0	1
1	1 - 1	0
2	1 - 2	-1
3	1 - 3	-2

Answers will vary.
Sample answer:
(0, 1), (1, 0),
(2, -1), (3, -2)

30. Rewrite $2x + y = 10$
as $y = 10 - 2x$.

x	10 - 2x	y
0	10 - 2(0)	8
2	10 - 2(2)	6
3	10 - 2(3)	4
4	10 - 2(4)	2

Answers will vary.
Sample answer:
(0, 10), (2, 6),
(3, 4), (4, 2)

31. Rewrite $y - x = 1$
as $y = 1 + x$.

x	1 + x	y
1	1 + 1	2
3	1 + 3	4
5	1 + 5	6
6	1 + 6	7

Answers will vary.
Sample answer:
(1, 2), (3, 4),
(5, 6), (6, 7)

32.

x	$\frac{1}{3}x$	y
3	$\frac{1}{3}(3)$	1
6	$\frac{1}{3}(6)$	2
9	$\frac{1}{3}(9)$	3
12	$\frac{1}{3}(12)$	4

Answers will vary.
Sample answer:
(3, 1), (6, 2),
(9, 3), (12, 4)

33.

x	$-\frac{1}{2}x + 3$	y
0	$-\frac{1}{2}(0) + 3$	3
3	$-\frac{1}{2}(3) + 3$	1.5
4	$-\frac{1}{2}(4) + 3$	1
6	$-\frac{1}{2}(6) + 3$	0

Answers will vary.
Sample answer:
(0, 3), (3, 1.5),
(4, 1), (6, 0)

34.

x	$\frac{2}{3}x + 1$	y
0	$\frac{2}{3}(0) - 1$	-1
3	$\frac{2}{3}(3) - 1$	1
6	$\frac{2}{3}(6) - 1$	3
9	$\frac{2}{3}(9) - 1$	5

Answers will vary.
Sample answer:
(0, -1), (3, 1),
(6, 3), (9, 5)

35. Rewrite $x + y = 0$
as $y = -x$.

x	-x	y
1	-1	-1
2	-2	-2
3	-3	-3
4	-4	-4

Answers will vary.
Sample answer:
(1, 1), (2, -2),
(3, -3), (4, -4)

36.

x	y
0	5
1	5
2	5
3	5

Answers will vary.
Sample answer:
(0,5), (1,5),
(2, 5), (3, 5)

37.

x	y
-2	0
-2	1
-2	2
-2	3

Answers will vary.
Sample answer:
(-2, 0), (-2, 1)
(-2, 2), (-2, 3)

38. yes

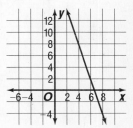

39. no

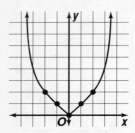

40. yes

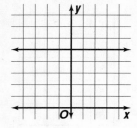

41.

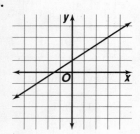

42.

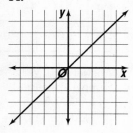

43.

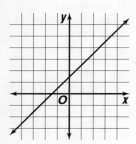

44.

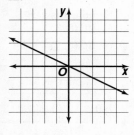

45.

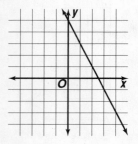

46.

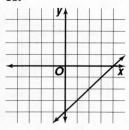

47.

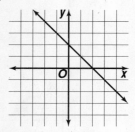

48.

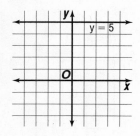

49.

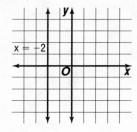

50. $x = 4 + y$

y	$4 + x$	x
0	4 + 0	4
4	4 + 4	8
6	4 + 6	10
8	4 + 8	12

Answers will vary.
Sample answer:
(4, 0), (8, 4),
(10, 6), (12, 8)

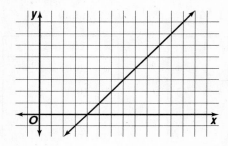

51. $x = \frac{1}{4}y$

y	$\frac{1}{4}x$	x
0	$\frac{1}{4}(0)$	0
4	$\frac{1}{4}(4)$	1
8	$\frac{1}{4}(8)$	2
12	$\frac{1}{4}(12)$	3

Answers will vary.
Sample answer:
(0, 0), (1, 4),
(2, 8), (3, 12)

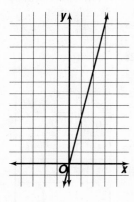

52. $4x - y = 8$

Rewrite $4x - y = 8$ as $y = -8 + 4x$.

x	$-8 + 4x$	y
0	$-8 + 4(0)$	-8
2	$-8 + 4(2)$	0
3	$-8 + 4(3)$	4
4	$-8 + 4(4)$	8

Answers will vary.
Sample answer: $(0, -8)$, $(2, 0)$, $(3, 4)$, $(4, 8)$

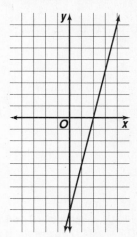

53.
$$y = cx + 1$$
$$5 = c(2) + 1$$
$$5 = 2c + 1$$
$$5 - 1 = 2c + 1 - 1$$
$$4 = 2c$$
$$\frac{4}{2} = \frac{2c}{2}$$
$$2 = c$$

54.
$$2x + ay = 4$$
$$2(-1) + a(2) = 4$$
$$-2 + 2a = 4$$
$$-2 + 2a + 2 = 4 + 2$$
$$2a = 6$$
$$\frac{2a}{2} = \frac{6}{2}$$
$$a = 3$$

55. $y = -3x$ or $3x + y = 0$

56.

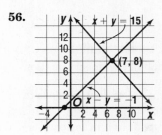

$(7, 8)$ is a solution for both $x + y = 15$ and $x - y = -1$.

57. a. Sample answer: $(1, 4)$, $(2, 8)$, $(4, 16)$, $(6, 24)$, $(8, 32)$

b.

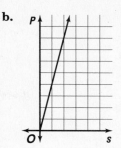

c. Length cannot have a negative value.

58. a.

x	$y = 0.21x$	y	(x,y)
1	$y = 0.21(1)$	0.21	$(1, 0.21)$
2	$y = 0.21(2)$	0.42	$(2, 0.42)$
3	$y = 0.21(3)$	0.63	$(3, 0.63)$
4	$y = 0.21(4)$	0.84	$(4, 0.84)$
5	$y = 0.21(5)$	1.05	$(5, 1.05)$

b.

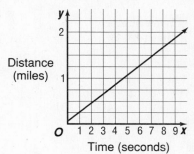

c. about 0.525 miles

59. a. $(0, 32)$, $(100, 212)$

b.

c. Find the coordinates of other points on the graph.

d. Sample answer: $(20, 68)$

60. positive

61.
$$2a - 5 > 17$$
$$2a - 5 + 5 > 17 + 5$$
$$2a > 22$$
$$\frac{2a}{2} > \frac{22}{2}$$
$$a > 11$$

62. $0.004976 = 4.976 \times 10^{-3}$

63. $2.49 \times 1.9 \rightarrow 2 \times 2$ or 4

64. $36 - 14\frac{3}{4} = \frac{144}{4} - \frac{59}{4}$

$\qquad = \frac{85}{4}$

$\qquad = 21\frac{1}{4}$ inches

65. $\frac{7^4}{7^2} = 7^{4-2}$

$\qquad = 7^2$

66. $P = 4s$

$56 = 4s$

$\frac{56}{4} = \frac{4s}{4}$

$14 = s$

14 inches

67.

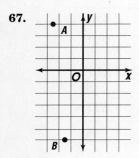

68. $4b = 36$ What number

$4(9) = 36$ times 4 is 36?

$b = 9$

69. $5n + 9n = (5 + 9)n$

$\qquad = 14n$

70. $4[12(22 - 19) - 3 \cdot 6] = 4[12(3) - 3 \cdot 6]$

$\qquad = 4[36 - 18]$

$\qquad = 4[18]$

$\qquad = 72$

Page 390   From the Funny Papers

1. No; The number used to represent the temperature in Celsius is less than the number used to represent it in Fahrenheit, but the temperature is the same.

2. 96.8°F

 8-3B   Math Lab: Graphing Parabolas

Page 391

1. Each distance is the same.

2. A parabola is the set of all points that are the same distance from a given point and a given line.

3. a.

x	$x^2 - 2$	y
-3	$(-3)^2 - 2$	7
-2	$(-2)^2 - 2$	2
-1	$(-1)^2 - 2$	-1
0	$(0)^2 - 2$	-2
1	$(1)^2 - 2$	-1
2	$(2)^2 - 2$	2
3	$(3)^2 - 2$	7

{7, 2, -1, -2, -1, 2, 7}

b. {(-3, 7), (-2, 2), (-1, -1), (0, -2), (1, -1), (2, 2), (3, 7)}

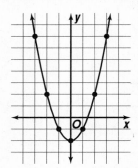

c. Sample answer: They both open upward and have their vertex on the y-axis. The graphs pass through different points on the y-axis. The graph of $y = x^2 - 2$ is narrower.

8-4   Equations as Functions

Page 392   Your Turn

a. $y = 2x - 3$

b. by working backward

Page 394   Checking Your Understanding

1. Sample answer: The graph of the linear equation $x = 1$ is a vertical line but it is not a function because the same element in the domain maps to every element in the range.

2. Sample answer: Substitute 5 for n in the equation and simplify.

3. Sample answer: $f(x) = 2x - 5$

4.

x	y
-3	-7
0	8
1	13
4	28

yes

5.

x	y
-3	10
0	1
1	2
4	17

yes

6. no; Since x has the same value for any range value, $x = 7$ is not a function.

7. $h(x) = 4 - \frac{1}{2}x$

$h(2) = 4 - \frac{1}{2}(2)$

$ = 4 - 1$

$ = 3$

8. $h(x) = 4 - \frac{1}{2}x$

$h(0) = 4 - \frac{1}{2}(0)$

$ = 4 - 0$

$ = 4$

9. $h(x) = 4 - \frac{1}{2}(x)$

$h(-4) = 4 - \frac{1}{2}(-4)$

$ = 4 + 2$

$ = 6$

10. $h(x) = 4 - \frac{1}{2}x$

$h\left(\frac{1}{2}\right) = 4 - \frac{1}{2}\left(\frac{1}{2}\right)$

$ = 4 - \frac{1}{4}$

$ = 3\frac{3}{4}$

11. $f(x) = 1500 + 80x$

$2200 = 1500 + 80x$

$2200 - 1500 = 1500 + 80x - 1500$

$700 = 80x$

$\frac{700}{80} = \frac{80x}{80}$

$8.75 = x$

Carlos will have enough money in 9 weeks.

Pages 394–395   Exercises

12.

x	y
-2	-21
0	-23
3	-26
5	-28

yes

13.

x	y
-2	8
0	16
3	28
5	36

yes

14.

x	y
-2	-180
0	undefined
3	120
5	72

yes

15.

x	y
-2	2
0	2
3	2
5	2

yes

16. no; Since x has the same value for every range value, $x = -8.8$ is not a function.

17.

x	y
-2	5
0	4
3	2.5
5	1.5

yes

18.

x	y
-2	26
0	24
3	21
5	19

yes

19.

x	y
-2	7
0	11
3	2
5	-14

yes

20. $g(x) = x^2 - 2$

$g(5) = (5)^2 - 2$

$ = 25 - 2$

$ = 23$

21. $f(x) = 5x + 3$

$f(-10) = 5(-10) + 3$

$ = -50 + 3$

$ = -47$

22. $f(x) = 5x + 3$

$f(-4) = 5(-4) + 3$

$ = -20 + 3$

$ = -17$

23. $g(x) = x^2 - 2$

$g\left(\frac{1}{2}\right) = \left(\frac{1}{2}\right)^2 - 2$

$ = \frac{1}{4} - 2$

$ = -1\frac{3}{4}$

24. $g(x) = x^2 - 2$

$g(-3.3) = (-3.3)^2 - 2$

$ = 10.89 - 2$

$ = 8.89$

25. $5[g(x)] = 5[x^2 - 2]$

$5[g(3)] = 5[(3)^2 - 2]$

$ = 5(9 - 2)$

$ = 5 \cdot 7$

$ = 35$

26. $f(x) = 5x + 3$

$f\left(\frac{1}{3}\right) = 5\left(\frac{1}{3}\right) + 3$

$ = \frac{5}{3} + 3$

$ = 1\frac{2}{3} + 3$

$ = 4\frac{2}{3}$

27. $f(x) = 5x + 3$

$f(0.25) = 5(0.25) + 3$

$ = 1.25 + 3$

$ = 4.25$

28. $f(x) = 5x + 3$

$f(2a) = 5(2a) + 3$

$ = 10a + 3$

29. $g(x) = x^2 - 2$

$g(2b) = (2b)^2 - 2$

$ = 4b^2 - 2$

30. $2[g(x)] = 2[x^2 - 2]$

$2[g(b)] = 2[b^2 - 2]$

$ = 2b^2 - 4$

31. $f[f(x)] = f[5x + 3]$

$f[f(4)] = f[5(4) + 3]$

$ = f(20 + 3)$

$ = f(23)$

$f(x) = 5x + 3$

$f(23) = 5(23) + 3$

$ = 115 + 3$

$ = 118$

32. Sample answer: The inverse is $x = 3y - 1$. It is a function since no member of the domain is paired with more than one member of the range.

157

33. a.

x	y
0	$-17\frac{7}{9}$
32	0
72	$22\frac{2}{9}$
98.6	37

$\{-17\frac{7}{9}, 0, 22\frac{2}{9}, 37\}$

b.

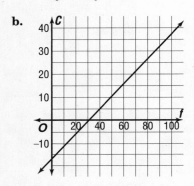

c. Yes; no member of the domain is paired with more than one member of the range.

34. a.

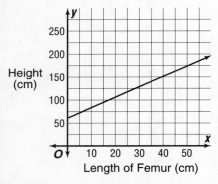

Length of Femur (cm)

b. Yes; no member of the domain is paired with more than one member of the range.

c. $h = 61.412 + 2.317x$
$h = 61.412 + 2.317(49)$
$h = 61.412 + 113.533$
$h = 174.945$
about 175 cm

35. a.

x	$y = 18x + 66.5$	y	(x, y)
1	$y = 18(1) + 66.5$	84.5	$(1, 84.5)$
5	$y = 18(5) + 66.5$	156.5	$(5, 156.5)$
10	$y = 18(10) + 66.5$	246.5	$(10, 246.5)$
15	$y = 18(15) + 66.5$	336.5	$(15, 336.5)$
20	$y = 18(20) + 66.5$	426.5	$(20, 426.5)$

b.

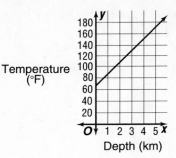

Depth (km)

c. $y = 18x + 66.5$
$y = 18(3.6) + 66.5$
$y = 64.8 + 66.5$
$y = 131.3°\text{F}$

36. $C = 2\pi r$
$C = 2 \cdot \pi \cdot 14$
$C \approx 87.92$ yards

37. $\left(-\frac{3}{4}\right)^2 = \left(-\frac{3}{4}\right)\left(-\frac{3}{4}\right)$
$= \frac{9}{16}$

38. $\frac{15rs^2}{50rs} = \frac{3 \cdot \overset{1}{\cancel{5}} \cdot \overset{1}{\cancel{r}} \cdot \overset{1}{\cancel{s}} \cdot s}{2 \cdot \underset{1}{\cancel{5}} \cdot 5 \cdot \underset{1}{\cancel{r}} \cdot \underset{1}{\cancel{s}}}$
$= \frac{3s}{10}$

39. $-3a \geq 18$
$\frac{-3a}{-3} \leq \frac{18}{-3}$
$a \leq -6$

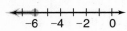

40.

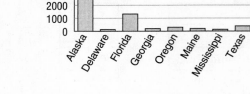

8-5 | **Problem-Solving Strategy: Draw a Graph**

Pages 397–398 Checking Your Understanding

1. Because a graph is visual, it allows you to see patterns that may not be obvious from the equation.

2. Let each axis represent a column of data. Graph points using ordered pairs of values taken from the two columns of data. Then draw a line that contains the points.

3. **a.** about 78.2 m^3 **b.** about $12.76

4. $(5, 2)$, $(11, 3.2)$

5. Let the horizontal axis represent depth in feet. Let the vertical axis represent the atmospheric pressure in pounds per square inch. Graph (0, 14.7) for 0 feet and 14.7 lb/in², (500, 237) for 500 feet and 237 lb/in², (1500, 683) for 1500 feet and 683 lb/in², (4500, 2019) for 4500 feet and 2019 lb/in². Draw the line that contains these points. Thus, about 4500 lb/in² corresponds to 10,000 feet below sea level. At 10,000 feet below sea level, the atmospheric pressure is about 4500 lb/in².

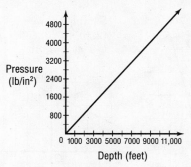

6. (600, 450), (200, 150)

7. Let the horizontal axis represent octane gas. Let the vertical axis represent cost per gallon. Graph (87, 1.03) for 87-octane gas and $1.03 per gallon and (93, 1.28) for 93-octane gas and $1.28 per gallon. Draw the line that contains these points. Thus, 1.11 corresponds to 89. The cost of 89-octane gas is $1.11 per gallon.

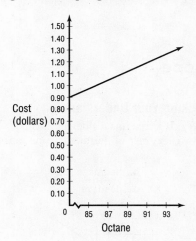

8. Let the horizontal axis represent the amount of marbles. Let the vertical axis represent the distance in centimeters that the spring stretches. Graph (1, 0.6) for 1 marble and 0.6 cm and (6, 4.0) for 6 marbles and 4.0 cm. Draw the line that contains these points. Thus, about 6.6 corresponds to 10. When 10 marbles are in the cup, the spring stretches about 6.6 centimeters.

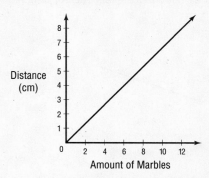

9. Let the horizontal axis represent degree days. Let the vertical axis represent natural gas. Graph (300, 85) for 300 degree days and 85 cubic meters and (700, 265) for 700 degree days and 265 cubic meters. Draw the line that contains these points. Thus, about 150 cubic meters corresponds to 450 degree days. If there are 450 degree days, a homeowner will use about 150 cubic meters of natural gas.

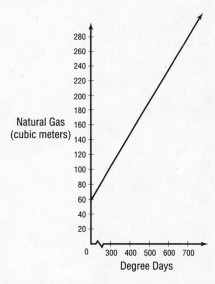

10. a. Yes, six gallons allows for about 180 miles of travel.

  b. before driving 180 miles

11. Let the horizontal axis represent height in inches. Let the vertical axis represent weight in pounds. Graph (60, 130) for 60 inches and 130 pounds and (66, 143) for 66 inches and 143 pounds. Draw the line that contains these points. Steve's 6 foot height equals 72 inches. 72 corresponds to 156 pounds. Note that $130 \div 60 = 2\frac{1}{3}$. There is an increase of $2\frac{1}{3}$ pounds for every inch of height. $72 \times 2\frac{1}{3} = 156$.

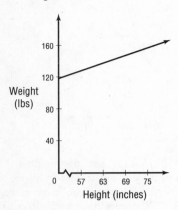

12. (2, 2)

13. $g(x) = 2x - 1$

$g\left(\frac{5}{2}\right) = 2\left(\frac{5}{2}\right) - 1$

$\qquad = 5 - 1$

$\qquad = 4$

14. $\qquad A = h \cdot \frac{1}{2}(b_1 + b_2)$

$\qquad 64 = 8 \cdot \frac{1}{2}(7 + b_2)$

$\qquad \frac{64}{8} = \frac{8 \cdot \frac{1}{2}(7 + b_2)}{8}$

$\qquad 8 = \frac{1}{2}(7 + b_2)$

$\qquad 2(8) = 2\left[\frac{1}{2}(7 + b_2)\right]$

$\qquad 16 = (7 + b_2)$

$\qquad 16 - 7 = 7 + b_2 - 7$

$\qquad 9 = b_2$

9 inches

15. $y = 4\frac{3}{4} - 5\frac{1}{6}$

$y = \frac{19}{4} - \frac{31}{6}$

$y = \frac{57}{12} - \frac{62}{12}$

$y = \frac{-5}{12}$

16. $(a^2 - b)^2 = (2^2 - 4)^2$
$\qquad\qquad\quad = (4 - 4)^2$
$\qquad\qquad\quad = 0^2$
$\qquad\qquad\quad = 0$

17. negative

Page 399   Self Test

1. D = {4, 1, 3, 6}; R = {2, 3, 4}; yes

2. D = {4, -3, 8, 7}; R = {2, 9, 5}; no

3. positive

4. a 185 pound, 6' 2" player

5.

x	4x − 2	y
2	4(2) − 2	6
1	4(1) − 2	2
0	4(0) − 2	-2
-1	4(-1) − 2	-6

Sample answer:
(2, 6), (1, 2),
(0, -2), (-1, -6)

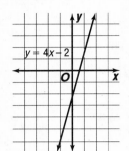

6.

x	$\frac{1}{2}x + 5$	y
2	$\frac{1}{2}(2) + 5$	6
0	$\frac{1}{2}(0) + 5$	5
-2	$\frac{1}{2}(-2) + 5$	4
-4	$\frac{1}{2}(-4) + 5$	3

Sample answer:
(2, 6), (0, 5),
(-2, 4), (-4, 3)

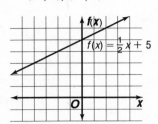

7. $f(x) = 9x - 4$
$f(6) = 9(6) - 4$
$\qquad = 54 - 4$
$\qquad = 50$

8. $f(x) = 9x - 4$
$f(0) = 9(0) - 4$
$\qquad = 0 - 4$
$\qquad = -4$

9. $f(x) = 9x - 4$
$f(-3) = 9(-3) - 4$
$\qquad = -27 - 4$
$\qquad = -31$

10. (172, 0.5), (206, 0.6)

8-6   Slope

Page 402   Checking Your Understanding

1. Sample answer: If a line has a slope of 3, this means that for every rise of 3 units, it runs to the right 1 unit.

2. a. none

   b. negative

   c. 0

   d. positive

3. Sample answer:

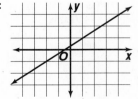

4. Sample answer: Subtract the y-values first. This is the numerator of the slope fraction. Then subtract the x-values. This is the denominator of the slope fraction.

5. Sample answer: A line that has a positive slope slants up to the right. A line that has a negative slope slants down to the right.

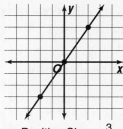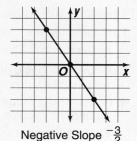

Positive Slope $\frac{3}{2}$ Negative Slope $-\frac{3}{2}$

6. slope $= \dfrac{\text{difference in } y\text{-coordinates}}{\text{difference in } x\text{-coordinates}}$

$= \dfrac{0 - (-2)}{-3 - 0}$

$= \dfrac{2}{-3} \text{ or } \dfrac{-2}{3}$

7. slope $= \dfrac{\text{difference in } y\text{-coordinates}}{\text{difference in } x\text{-coordinates}}$

$= \dfrac{3 - 0}{1 - (-2)}$

$= \dfrac{3}{3}$

$= 1$

8. slope $= \dfrac{\text{difference in } y\text{-coordinates}}{\text{difference in } x\text{-coordinates}}$

$= \dfrac{0}{\text{any number}}$

$= 0$

9. slope $= \dfrac{-2 - (-5)}{9 - 3}$

$= \dfrac{3}{6}$

$= \dfrac{1}{2}$

10. slope $= \dfrac{3 - 3}{14 - (-11)}$

$= \dfrac{0}{25}$

$= 0$

11. slope $= \dfrac{-2 - (-5)}{-1 - 2}$

$= \dfrac{3}{-3}$

$= -1$

12. slope $= \dfrac{-4 - (-3)}{-6 - (-8)}$

$= \dfrac{-1}{2}$

13. slope $= \dfrac{\text{rise}}{\text{run}}$

$= \dfrac{16}{4}$

$= 4$

Pages 403–404   Exercises

14. slope $= \dfrac{5 - 2}{-7 - (-8)}$

$= \dfrac{3}{1}$

$= 3$

15. slope $= \dfrac{4 - 2}{-4 - (-2)}$

$= \dfrac{2}{-2}$

$= -1$

16. slope $= \dfrac{5 - 2}{5 - 3}$

$= \dfrac{3}{2}$

17. slope $= 0$

18. no slope

19. slope $= \dfrac{-3 - (-2)}{-3 - (-8)}$

$= \dfrac{-1}{5}$

20. slope $= \dfrac{-4 - (-2)}{-2 - 4}$

$= \dfrac{-2}{-6}$

$= \dfrac{1}{3}$

21. slope $= \dfrac{-6 - (-2)}{7 - 5}$

$= \dfrac{-4}{2}$

$= -2$

22. Sample answer: The larger the absolute value of the slope of a line, the steeper the slant of the line.

23. Sample answer: Both graphs slant up to the right.

24. slope $= \dfrac{4 - 6}{3 - 4}$

$= \dfrac{-2}{-1}$

$= 2$

25. slope $= \dfrac{6 - 9}{-3 - (-5)}$

$= \dfrac{-3}{2}$

26. slope $= \dfrac{3 - 3}{2 - (-1)}$

$= \dfrac{0}{3}$

$= 0$

27. slope $= \dfrac{-3 - 4}{1 - 5}$

$= \dfrac{-7}{-4}$

$= \dfrac{7}{4}$

28. slope $= \dfrac{-4 - (-1)}{7 - 9}$

$= \dfrac{-3}{-2}$

$= \dfrac{3}{2}$

29. slope $= \dfrac{-2 - (-3)}{5 - 4}$

$= \dfrac{1}{1}$

$= 1$

30. slope $= \dfrac{0 - 0.75}{0 - 0.5}$

$= \dfrac{-0.75}{-0.5}$

$= 1.5$

31. slope $= \dfrac{-1 - (-4)}{5 - (-3)}$

$= \dfrac{3}{8}$

32. slope $= \dfrac{1 - (-1)}{\frac{3}{4} - \frac{3}{4}}$

$= \text{none}$

33. slope $= \dfrac{5\frac{1}{4} - 6}{3\frac{1}{2} - 2\frac{1}{2}}$

$= \dfrac{-\frac{3}{4}}{1}$

$= -\dfrac{3}{4}$

34. Sample answer: The slopes are negative reciprocals of each other. That is, the product of their slopes is -1.

35. slope $= \dfrac{\text{riser}}{\text{tread}}$

$= \dfrac{8}{12}$

$= \dfrac{2}{3}$

36. a. The section of the graph that has the steepest slant up to the right.

b. horizontal line segment

c. a decrease in consumption

37. The road declines 0.00895 feet vertically for every 1 ft traveled horizontally. So, the vertical change is 0.00895×8941 or about 80 feet. Therefore, the elevation of the eastern end of the tunnel is $11,160 - 80$ or 11,080 feet.

38. Let the horizontal axis represent time in hours. Let the vertical axis represent distance in kilometers. Graph (2, 160) for 2 hours and 160 km. Graph (5, 400) for 5 hours (3 more hours than 2 hours) and 400 km. Draw the line that contains these points. Thus, 560 km corresponds to 7 hours. This is 2 more hours of travel time.

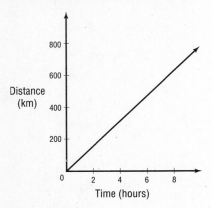

39. $7.45(12) = 89.4$
The ham should be baked for 89 minutes or 1 hour 29 minutes.

40. 24.7

41. Since $57 = 3 \cdot 19$, 57 is composite.

42. $a + (-7) = 8$
$a - 7 = 8$
$a - 7 + 7 = 8 + 7$
$a = 15$

43. $6(5 + 9) \div 7 = 6(14) \div 7$
$= 84 \div 7$
$= 12$

44. One third of those remaining were planning, so two-thirds were cleaning.
$\frac{2}{3}x = 18$
$\frac{3}{2} \cdot \frac{2}{3}x = \frac{3}{2} \cdot 18$
$x = 27$

The 27 people who remained were half of those who attended the meeting. So, 2(27) or 54 people attended the meeting.

8-6B   Math Lab: Circles and Slope

Page 405

1. See students' work.
2. The slope should be about 3.
3. The point should be on the line.
4. Sample answer: The slope should equal π because the change in y is the circumference and the change in x is the diameter and circumference divided by diameter is π. The slope is about 3.14.

8-7   Intercepts

Pages 408–409   Checking Your Understanding

1. Sample answer: The x-intercept is 4. The y-intercept is 2. The slope is $-\frac{1}{2}$.

2. Graph (-3, 0) and (0, 1). Draw the line that contains the two points.

3. To find the x-intercept, let $y = 0$ and solve for x. To find the y-intercept, let $x = 0$ and solve for y. For $y = -\frac{1}{2}x + 8$, the x-intercept is 16 and the y-intercept is 8.

4. See students' graphs. It should be a horizontal line.

5. In 1940, the time was 431 minutes.

6. Plot the y-intercept on the y-axis. From this point, use the slope to rise and run to find the coordinate on the line. Then connect these two points.

7. **a–c.** See students' work.

8. -2, 1

9. 1.5, 3

10. Let $y = 0$:
$y = x - 8$
$0 = x - 8$
$0 + 8 = x - 8 + 8$
$8 = x$
The x-intercept is 8.
Let $x = 0$:
$y = x - 8$
$y = 0 - 8$
$y = -8$
The y-intercept is -8.

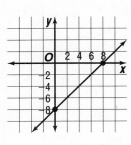

11. Let $y = 0$:
$y = x + 6$
$0 = x + 6$
$0 - 6 = x + 6 - 6$
$-6 = x$
The x-intercept is -6.
Let $x = 0$:
$y = x + 6$
$y = 0 + 6$
$y = 6$
The y-intercept is 6.

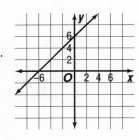

12. Let $y = 0$:
$y = -2x - 1$
$0 = -2x - 1$
$0 + 1 = -2x - 1 + 1$
$1 = -2x$
$-\frac{1}{2} = x$
The x-intercept is $-\frac{1}{2}$.
Let $x = 0$:
$y = -2x - 1$
$y = -2(0) - 1$
$y = 0 - 1$
$y = -1$
The y-intercept is -1.

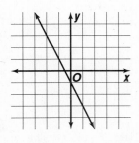

13. Let $y = 0$:
$$y = 6 - 9x$$
$$0 = 6 - 9x$$
$$0 - 6 = 6 - 9x - 6$$
$$-6 = -9x$$
$$\frac{2}{3} = x$$
The x-intercept is $\frac{2}{3}$.

Let $x = 0$:
$$y = 6 - 9x$$
$$y = 6 - 9(0)$$
$$y = 6 - 0$$
$$y = 6$$
The y-intercept is 6.

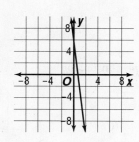

14. $y = 2x + 1$
slope $= m = 2$
Let $x = 0$:
$$y = 2x + 1$$
$$y = 2(0) + 1$$
$$y = 1$$
The y-intercept is $(0, 1)$.

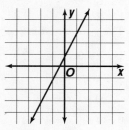

15. $y = -7x - 4$
slope $= m = -7$
Let $x = 0$:
$$y = -7x - 4$$
$$y = -7(0) - 4$$
$$y = -4$$
The y-intercept is $(0, -4)$.

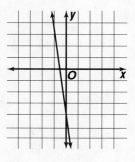

16. a. Let $y = 0$:
$$y = 60x + 40$$
$$0 = 60x + 40$$
$$0 - 40 = 60x + 40 - 40$$
$$-40 = 60x$$
$$-\frac{2}{3} = x$$
The x-intercept is $-\frac{2}{3}$.

Let $x = 0$
$$y = 60x + 40$$
$$y = 60(0) + 40$$
$$y = 0 + 40$$
$$y = 40$$
The y-intercept is 40.

b.

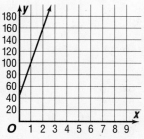

Distance (miles)

Time (hours)

c.
$$y = 60x + 40$$
$$400 = 60x + 40$$
$$400 - 40 = 60x + 40 - 40$$
$$360 = 60x$$
$$6 = x$$
6 hours

Pages 409–410   Exercises

17. 5, -5   **18.** 1, -2   **19.** -2, -1
20. 1, 4   **21.** 2, -4   **22.** 3, 2

23. Let $y = 0$:
$$y = x - 2$$
$$0 = x - 2$$
$$0 + 2 = x - 2 + 2$$
$$2 = x$$
The x-intercept is 2.

Let $x = 0$:
$$y = x - 2$$
$$y = 0 - 2$$
$$y = -2$$
The y-intercept is -2.

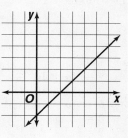

24. Let $y = 0$:
$$y = x + 1$$
$$0 = x + 1$$
$$0 - 1 = x + 1 - 1$$
$$-1 = x$$
The x-intercept is -1.

Let $x = 0$:
$$y = x + 1$$
$$y = 0 + 1$$
$$y = 1$$
The y-intercept is 1.

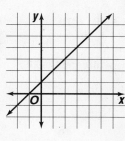

25. Let $y = 0$:
$$y = x - 4$$
$$0 = x - 4$$
$$0 + 4 = x - 4 + 4$$
$$4 = x$$
The x-intercept is 4.

Let $x = 0$:
$$y = x - 4$$
$$y = 0 - 4$$
$$y = -4$$
The y-intercept is -4.

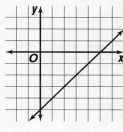

26. Let $y = 0$:
$$y = 2x - 1$$
$$0 = 2x - 1$$
$$0 + 1 = 2x - 1 + 1$$
$$1 = 2x$$
$$\frac{1}{2} = x$$
The x-intercept is $\frac{1}{2}$.

Let $x = 0$:
$$y = 2x - 1$$
$$y = 2(0) - 1$$
$$y = 0 - 1$$
$$y = -1$$
The y-intercept is -1.

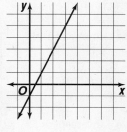

27. Let $y = 0$:
$$y = 3x + 4$$
$$0 = 3x + 4$$
$$0 - 4 = 3x + 4 - 4$$
$$-4 = 3x$$
$$-\frac{4}{3} = x$$
The x-intercept is $-\frac{4}{3}$.

Let $x = 0$:
$y = 3x + 4$
$y = 3(0) + 4$
$y = 0 + 4$
$y = 4$
The y-intercept is 4.

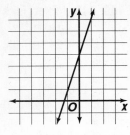

28. Let $y = 0$:
$y = -5x + 10$
$0 = -5x + 10$
$0 - 10 = -5x + 10 - 10$
$-10 = -5x$
$2 = x$
The x-intercept is 2.
Let $x = 0$:
$y = -5x + 10$
$y = -5(0) + 10$
$y = 0 + 10$
$y = 10$
The y-intercept is 10.

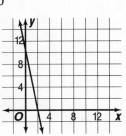

29. Let $y = 0$:
$y = \frac{1}{2}x - 5$
$0 = \frac{1}{2}x - 5$
$0 + 5 = \frac{1}{2}x - 5 + 5$
$5 = \frac{1}{2}x$
$10 = x$
The x-intercept is 10.
Let $x = 0$:
$y = \frac{1}{2}x - 5$
$y = \frac{1}{2}(0) - 5$
$y = 0 - 5$
$y = -5$
The y-intercept is -5.

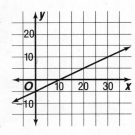

30. Let $y = 0$:
$y = 3 - 0.5x$
$0 = 3 - 0.5x$
$0 - 3 = 3 - 0.5x - 3$
$-3 = -0.5x$
$6 = x$
The x-intercept is 6.
Let $x = 0$:
$y = 3 - 0.5x$
$y = 3 - 0.5(0)$
$y = 3 - 0$
$y = 3$
The y-intercept is 3.

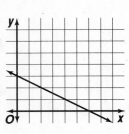

31. Let $y = 0$:
$y = \frac{1}{3}x + 2$
$0 = \frac{1}{3}x + 2$
$0 - 2 = \frac{1}{3}x + 2 - 2$
$-2 = \frac{1}{3}x$
$-6 = x$
The x-intercept is -6.
Let $x = 0$:
$y = \frac{1}{3}x + 2$
$y = \frac{1}{3}(0) + 2$
$y = 0 + 2$
$y = 2$
The y-intercept is 2.

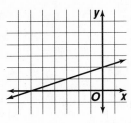

32. Let $y = 0$:
$y = \frac{2}{3}x + 4$
$0 = \frac{2}{3}x + 4$
$0 - 4 = \frac{2}{3}x + 4 - 4$
$-4 = \frac{2}{3}x$
$-6 = x$
The x-intercept is -6.
Let $x = 0$:
$y = \frac{2}{3}x + 4$
$y = \frac{2}{3}(0) + 4$
$y = 0 + 4$
$y = 4$
The y-intercept is 4.

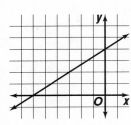

33. Let $y = 0$:
$y = 3x - 4$
$0 = 3x - 4$
$0 + 4 = 3x - 4 + 4$
$4 = 3x$
$\frac{4}{3} = x$
The x-intercept is $\frac{4}{3}$.
Let $x = 0$:
$y = 3x - 4$
$y = 3(0) - 4$
$y = 0 - 4$
$y = -4$
The y-intercept is -4.

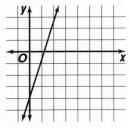

34. Let $y = 0$:
$y = -5x + 6$
$0 = -5x + 6$
$0 - 6 = -5x + 6 - 6$
$-6 = -5x$
$\frac{6}{5} = x$
The x-intercept is $\frac{6}{5}$.
Let $x = 0$:
$y = -5x + 6$
$y = -5(0) + 6$
$y = 0 + 6$
$y = 6$
The y-intercept is 6.

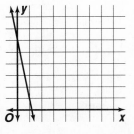

35. $y = \frac{2}{3}x + 3$

slope $= m = \frac{2}{3}$

Let $x = 0$:

$y = \frac{2}{3}x + 3$

$y = \frac{2}{3}(0) + 3$

$y = 3$

The y-intercept is $(0, 3)$.

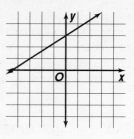

36. $y = \frac{3}{4}x + 4$

slope $= m = \frac{3}{4}$

Let $x = 0$:

$y = \frac{3}{4}x + 4$

$y = \frac{3}{4}(0) + 4$

$y = 4$

The y-intercept is $(0, 4)$.

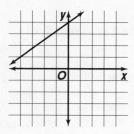

37. $y = -\frac{3}{4}x + 4$

slope $= m = -\frac{3}{4}$

Let $x = 0$:

$y = -\frac{3}{4}x + 4$

$y = -\frac{3}{4}(0) + 4$

$y = 4$

The y-intercept is $(0, 4)$.

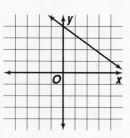

38. Rewrite $-4x + y = 6$
as $y = 4x + 6$.

slope $= m = 4$.

Let $x = 0$:

$y = 4x + 6$

$y = 4(0) + 6$

$y = 6$

The y-intercept is $(0, 6)$.

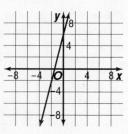

39. Rewrite $-2x + y = 3$
as $y = 2x + 3$.

slope $= m = 2$

Let $x = 0$:

$y = 2x + 3$

$y = 2(0) + 3$

$y = 3$

The y-intercept is $(0, 3)$.

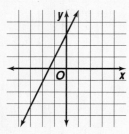

40. Rewrite $3y - 7 = 2x$
as $y = \frac{2}{3}x + \frac{7}{3}$.

slope $= m = \frac{2}{3}$

Let $x = 0$:

$y = \frac{2}{3}x + \frac{7}{3}$

$y = \frac{2}{3}(0) + \frac{7}{3}$

$y = \frac{7}{3}$ or $2\frac{1}{3}$

The y-intercept is $\left(0, 2\frac{1}{3}\right)$.

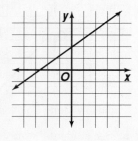

41.

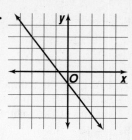

42.

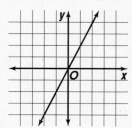

43. The x-intercept and y-intercept are both zero. The line, therefore, passes through the origin. Since two points are needed to graph a line, $y = 2x$ cannot be graphed using only the intercepts.

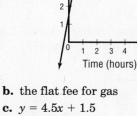

44. a.

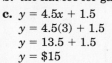

b. the flat fee for gas

c. $y = 4.5x + 1.5$

$y = 4.5(3) + 1.5$

$y = 13.5 + 1.5$

$y = \$15$

45. a.

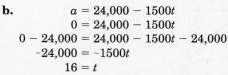

b. $a = 24{,}000 - 1500t$

$0 = 24{,}000 - 1500t$

$0 - 24{,}000 = 24{,}000 - 1500t - 24{,}000$

$-24{,}000 = -1500t$

$16 = t$

c. The x-intercept is the time when the plane lands.

46. slope $= \frac{-3 - (-5)}{-7 - (-4)}$

$\qquad = \frac{2}{-3}$

$\qquad = -\frac{2}{3}$

47. $2(624,168) + 100,000 = 1,348,336$
So, $2x + 100,000$ is an estimate of the number of visitors at Gettysburg.

48. $y = 15 - 8.7$

$\quad\ \ 15.0$
$\underline{-\ \ 8.7}$
$\quad\ \ \ 6.3$

$y = 6.3$

49. $39 = 3 \cdot \boxed{13}$
$65 = 5 \cdot \boxed{13}$
The GCF is 13.

50. $\qquad -41 > r - (-8)$
$\qquad -41 > r + 8$
$-41 - 8 > r + 8 - 8$
$\qquad -49 > r$

51. $-3a + 12a + (-14a) = [-3 + 12 + (-14)]a$
$\qquad\qquad\qquad\quad\ = [-3 + (-14) + 12]a$
$\qquad\qquad\qquad\quad\ = (-17 + 12)a$
$\qquad\qquad\qquad\quad\ = -5a$

52. $3 + x > 5$

53. associative property of addition

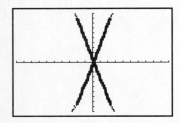

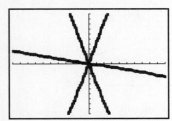

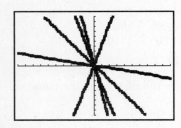

| 8-7B | **Math Lab: Families of Graphs** |

Pages 411

1. The family of graphs is lines having a slope of 1.5. All are parallel and have different x- and y-intercepts.

---

2. $y = 4x$ has a positive slope and $y = -4x$ has a negative slope.

3. Sample answer: $y = -5x$

4. The slopes are the same. The y-intercepts are different. The lines are parallel.

| 8-8 | **Systems of Equations** |

Page 412   Your Turn

a. The output for plan 1 shows $c = 10$ for $n = 1$, and each 1-unit increase in n results in an increase of 0.1 in c. The output for Plan 2 shows $c = 5$ for $n = 0$, and each 1-unit increase in n results in an increase of 0.2 in c.

b. $x = 50$; The cost is the same for both plans when 50 calls are made.

Pages 414–415   Checking Your Understanding

1. Sample answer: Two or more equations with the same variables form a system of equations. The coordinates of the point where the graphs of the two equations intersect is the solution.

2. Sample answer: Plan 1 costs more if less than 50 calls are made per month. Plan 2 costs more if more than 50 calls are made per month. Preferences will vary.

3. Sample answer: The graphs of the equations are parallel lines. Since they do not intersect, there is no solution.

4.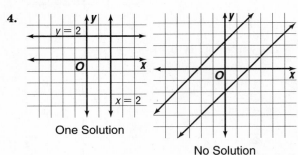

One Solution   No Solution

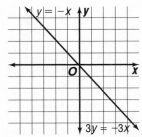

Infinitely Many Solutions

5. a. See students' work.

---

b.

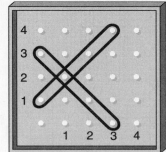

c. (1, 2)

d. (1, 2)

6. (3, -1) **7.** (1, 1) **8.** (150, 350)

9.

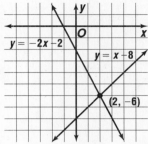

The solution is (2, -6).

10.

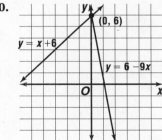

The solution is (0, 6).

11.

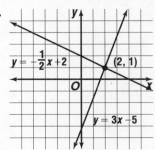

The solution is (2, 1).

12.

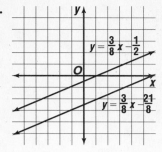

no solution.

13. a. $2\ell + 2w = 12$; $\ell = 2w$

b.

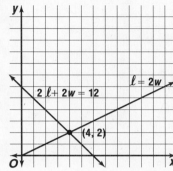

c. The length of the frame will be 4 feet and the width will be 2 feet.

Pages 415–416 Exercises

14. (-3, 3) **15.** (0, 0)

16. (5, -5) **17.** (2, 1)

18. (1, 3) **19.** no solution

20. (0, 0) **21.** no solution

22. (0, 0)

23.

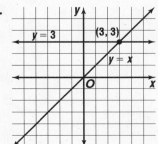

The solution is (5, 7).

24.

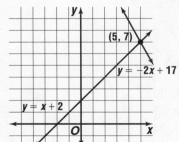

The solution is (3, 3).

25.

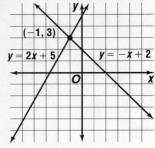

$y = 2x + 5$ $y = -x + 2$ $(-1, 3)$

The solution is $(-1, 3)$.

26.

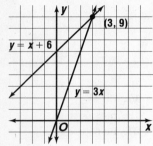

$y = -2x - 5$ $y = -2x - 8$

no solution

27.

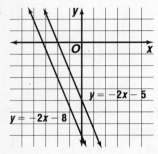

$y = x + 6$ $y = 3x$ $(3, 9)$

The solution is $(3, 9)$.

28.

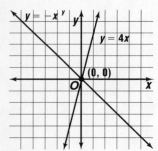

$y = -x$ $y = 4x$ $(0, 0)$

The solution is $(0, 0)$.

29.

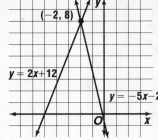

$(-2, 8)$ $y = 2x + 12$ $y = -5x - 2$

The solution is $(-2, 8)$.

30.

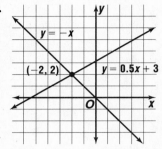

$y = -x$ $y = 0.5x + 3$ $(-2, 2)$

The solution is $(-2, 2)$.

31.

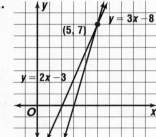

$y = 3x - 8$ $(5, 7)$ $y = 2x - 3$

The solution is $(5, 7)$.

32.

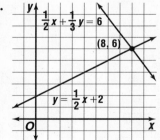

$\frac{1}{2}x + \frac{1}{3}y = 6$ $(8, 6)$ $y = \frac{1}{2}x + 2$

The solution is $(8, 6)$.

33.

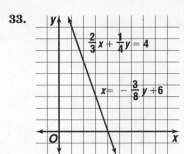

$$\frac{2}{3}x + \frac{1}{4}y = 4$$

$$x = -\frac{3}{8}y + 6$$

infinitely many solutions

34.

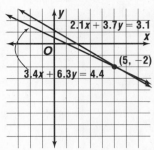

2.1x + 3.7y = 3.1

3.4x + 6.3y = 4.4

(5, -2)

The solution is (5, -2).

35.

$Ax + y = 6$	$Bx + y = 7$
$A(1) + 3 = 6$	$B(1) + 3 = 7$
$1A + 3 = 6$	$1B + 3 = 7$
$1A + 3 - 3 = 6 - 3$	$1B + 3 - 3 = 7 - 3$
$1A = 3$	$1B = 4$
$A = 3$	$B = 4$

36. a.

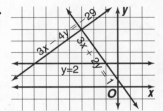

b. (-3, 5), (-1, 2), (-7, 2)

37. a.

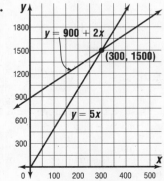

$y = 900 + 2x$

(300, 1500)

$y = 5x$

b. The break-even point would be at point (300, 1500) because that is the solution when cost equals the income, when 300 items are sold, resulting in an income of $1500.

38. a. Jordan: $w = 3 + 2a$, Paige: $w = 7 + a$

b.

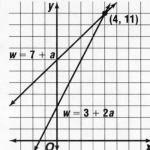

$w = 7 + a$

(4, 11)

$w = 3 + 2a$

c. Each baby weighs 11 pounds after 4 months.

39. a. $y = 15x$, $y = 5x + 60$

b.

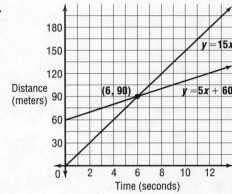

Distance (meters)

Time (seconds)

$y = 15x$

(6, 90)

$y = 5x + 60$

c. After 6 seconds, the dog will catch up to the prowler 90 meters from where the dog started.

40. Let $y = 0$:

$$y = -3x + 2$$
$$0 = -3x + 2$$
$$0 - 2 = -3x + 2 - 2$$
$$-2 = -3x$$
$$\frac{2}{3} = x$$

The x-intercept is $\frac{2}{3}$.

Let $x = 0$:

$$y = -3x + 2$$
$$y = -3(0) + 2$$
$$y = 0 + 2$$
$$y = 2$$

The y-intercept is 2.

(0, 2) $\left(\frac{2}{3}, 0\right)$

$y = -3x + 2$

41. Let x = integer

$$13 < 4.05x + 3.116 < 25$$
$$13 - 3.116 < 4.05x + 3.116 - 3.116 < 25 - 3.116$$
$$9.884 < 4.05x < 21.884$$
$$\frac{9.884}{4.05} < \frac{4.05x}{4.05} < \frac{21.884}{4.05}$$
$$2.44 < x < 5.4$$

The integer can be 3, 4, or 5.

42. $6\frac{3}{4} \div 3 = 6\frac{3}{4} \times \frac{1}{3}$

$$= \frac{27}{4} \times \frac{1}{3}$$
$$= \frac{27}{12}$$
$$= 2\frac{3}{12}$$
$$= 2\frac{1}{4} \text{ inches}$$

43. Checking Account: $575.29
Deposit Paycheck: +129.90
$701.19
Pay Bill: −397.28
303.91
Pay Bill: −225.40
$78.51

There is $78.51 in the checking account.

44. $-15 + t \le 12$
$-15 + t + 15 \le 12 + 15$
$t \le 27$

Check: Try 20, a number less than or equal to 27.
$-15 + t \le 12$
$-15 + 20 \overset{?}{\le} 12$
$5 \le 12$ ✔

45. $|-17| - |3| = 17 - 3$
$= 14$

46. $4(c + 3) = 4(c) + 4(3)$
$= 4c + 12$

8-9A | Math Lab: Graphing Inequalities

Page 417

1. Both graphs are shaded regions and the boundary is the same line.

2. The graph of $y < 2x + 5$ is the region below the line, whereas the graph of $y > 2x + 5$ is the region above the line.

3. The graph of $y = 2x + 5$ would not be shaded at all.

4. a. `2nd` `DRAW` 7 `(−)` 10 `,` `X,T,θ` `+` 4 `,` `ENTER`

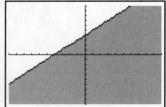

b. `2nd` `DRAW` 72 `X,T,θ` `(−)` 1 `,` 10 `,` `ENTER`

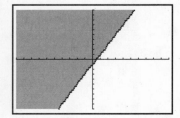

c. `2nd` `DRAW` 7 `(−)` `X,T,θ` `+` 3 `,` 10 `,` `ENTER`

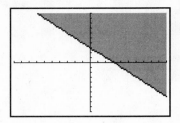

d. `2nd` `DRAW` 7 `(−)` 10 `,` `(−)` 2 `X,T,θ` `+` 2 `,` `ENTER`

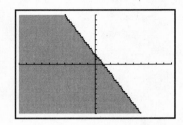

8-9 | Graphing Inequalities

Page 418 Your Turn

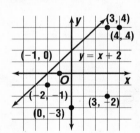

a. below the line
b. $y < x + 2$
c. $y > x + 2$
d. infinitely many

Pages 420–421 Exercises

1. $y > x - 3$

2. Sanura is correct. Dashed lines are for $<$ and $>$. Solid lines are for $\le$ or $\ge$.

3. $y < 9x + 4$

4. The solution would lie on the graph of the line $47.5x + 66.5y = 66,500$.

5. Sample answer: Choose a test point. Substitute its coordinates in the inequality. If the result is true, that side of the boundary is shaded.

6. yes   **7.** yes   **8.** no

9. (-2, 2)
$y < 2x + 1$
$2 \overset{?}{<} 2(-2) + 1$
$2 \overset{?}{<} -4 + 1$
$2 < -3$
Since $2 < -3$ is false,
(-2, 2) is not a solution.

(4, -1)
$y < 2x + 1$
$-1 \overset{?}{<} 2(4) + 1$
$-1 \overset{?}{<} 8 + 1$
$-1 < 9$ ✔
Since $-1 < 9$ is true,
(4, -1) is a solution.

(3, 1)
$y < 2x + 1$
$1 \overset{?}{<} 2(3) + 1$
$1 \overset{?}{<} 6 + 1$
$1 < 7$ ✔
Since $1 < 7$ is true,
(3, 1) is a solution.
b and c are solutions.

10. (-1, -1)
$4y > -3x - 2$
$4(-1) \overset{?}{>} -3(-1) - 2$
$-4 \overset{?}{>} 3 - 2$
$-4 > 1$
Since $-4 > 1$ is false,
(-1, -1) is not a solution.

(2, -2)
$4y > -3x - 2$
$4(-2) \overset{?}{>} -3(2) - 2$
$-8 \overset{?}{>} -6 - 2$
$-8 > -8$
Since $-8 > -8$ is
false (2, -2) is not a
solution.

(-2, 4)
$4y > -3x - 2$
$4(4) \overset{?}{>} -3(-2) - 2$
$16 \overset{?}{>} 6 - 2$
$16 > 4$ ✔
Since $16 > 4$ is true,
(-2, 4) is a solution.
c is a solution.

11. the region above the boundary

12. the region below the boundary

13. the region to the right of the boundary

14.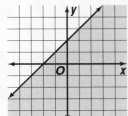

15.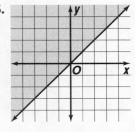

16.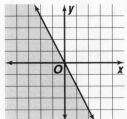

17.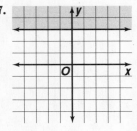

18. a.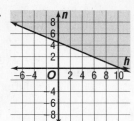

b. Silvina must spend at least 8 hours weeding the garden.

Pages 421–422   Exercises

19. (-2, 2)
$y < 3 - x$
$2 \overset{?}{<} 3 - (-2)$
$2 < 5$ ✔
Since $2 < 5$ is true,
(-2, 2) is a solution.

(4, -1)
$y < 3 - x$
$-1 \overset{?}{<} 3 - 4$
$-1 < -1$
Since $-1 < -1$ is false,
(4, -1) is not a solution.

(3, 1)
$y < 3 - x$
$1 \overset{?}{<} 3 - 3$
$1 < 0$
Since $1 < 0$ is false,
(3, 1) is not a solution.
a is a solution.

20. (2, 1)
$3y > -1 - 2x$
$3(1) \overset{?}{>} -1 - 2(2)$
$3 > -5$ ✔
Since $3 > -5$ is true,
(2, 1) is a solution.

(-5, 1)
$3y > -1 - 2x$
$3(1) \overset{?}{>} -1 - 2(-5)$
$3 > 9$
Since $3 > 9$ is false,
(-5, 1) is not a solution.

(1, 1)
$3y > -1 - 2x$
$3(1) \overset{?}{>} -1 - 2(1)$
$3 > -3$ ✔
Since $3 > -3$ is true,
(1, 1) is a solution.
a and c are solutions.

21. (0, 2)
$4y - 8 < 0$
$4(2) - 8 \overset{?}{<} 0$
$0 < 0$
Since $0 < 0$ is false,
(0, 2) is not a solution.

(2, 5)
$4y - 8 < 0$
$4(5) - 8 \overset{?}{<} 0$
$12 < 0$
Since $12 < 0$ is false,
(2, 5) is not a solution.

(-2, 0)
$4y - 8 < 0$
$4(0) - 8 \overset{?}{<} 0$
$-8 < 0$ ✔
Since $-8 < 0$ is true,
(-2, 0) is a solution.
c is a solution.

22. (1, 1)
$$3x + 4y \geq 17$$
$$3(1) + 4(1) \overset{?}{\geq} 17$$
$$7 \geq 17$$
Since 7 ≥ 17 is false,
(1, 1) is not a solution.

(4, 2)
$$3x + 4y \geq 17$$
$$3(4) + 4(2) \overset{?}{\geq} 17$$
$$20 \geq 17 \checkmark$$
Since 20 ≥ 17 is true,
(4, 2) is a solution.

(−3, 7)
$$3x + 4y \geq 17$$
$$3(-3) + 4(7) \overset{?}{\geq} 17$$
$$19 \geq 17 \checkmark$$
Since 19 ≥ 17 is true,
(−3, 7) is a solution.
b and c are solutions.

23. (5, 12)
$$2x \geq y - 8$$
$$2(5) \overset{?}{\geq} 12 - 8$$
$$10 \geq 4 \checkmark$$
Since 10 ≥ 4 is true,
(5, 12) is a solution.

(4, 8)
$$2x \geq y - 8$$
$$2(4) \overset{?}{\geq} 8 - 8$$
$$8 \geq 0 \checkmark$$
Since 8 ≥ 0 is true,
(4, 8) is a solution.

(−3, −1)
$$2x \geq y - 8$$
$$2(-3) \overset{?}{\geq} -1 - 8$$
$$-6 \geq -9 \checkmark$$
Since −6 ≥ −9 is true,
(−3, −1) is a solution.
a, b, and c are solutions.

24. (−2, 3)
$$5x + 1 \leq 3y$$
$$5(-2) + 1 \overset{?}{\leq} 3(3)$$
$$-9 \leq 9 \checkmark$$
Since −9 ≤ 9 is true,
(−2, 3) is a solution.

(4, 7)
$$5x + 1 \leq 3y$$
$$5(4) + 1 \overset{?}{\leq} 3(7)$$
$$21 \leq 21 \checkmark$$
Since 21 ≤ 21 is true,
(4, 7) is a solution.

(2, 3)
$$5x + 1 \leq 3y$$
$$5(2) + 1 \overset{?}{\leq} 3(3)$$
$$11 \leq 9$$
Since 11 ≤ 9 is false,
(2, 3) is not a solution.
a and b are solutions.

25. the region to the left of the boundary

26. the region to the right of the boundary

27. the region to the left of the boundary

28.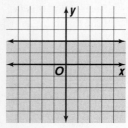

29.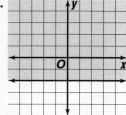

30.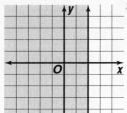

31.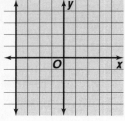

32.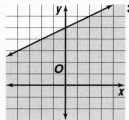

33.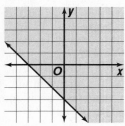

34.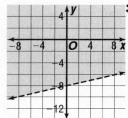

35.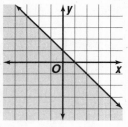

36.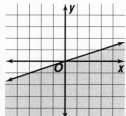

37.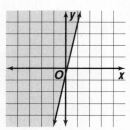

38.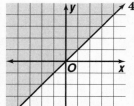

39.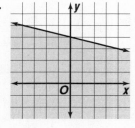

40.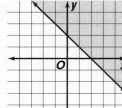

41.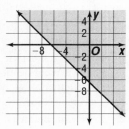

42. 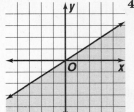 **43.**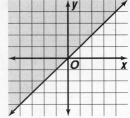

44. a. $y < -x - 1, y \geq 1.5x - 3.5$
   b. See students' work.

45. a. $0 < S - 3000$

   b.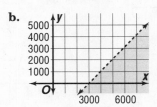

   c. below the line
   d. No; this would mean that your cost was greater than your sales, which doesn't happen in a successful business.
   e. Sample answer: (6600, 3600), (7000, 4000)

46. a. $L < 3.75Q$

   b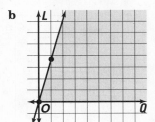

   c. Sample answer: (12, 4) would mean that the total length of the fish is 12 inches in a 4-quart tank. (20, 6) would mean the total length of the fish is 20 inches in a 6-quart tank.

47. a.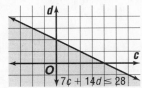

   b. Sample answer: (1, 1) means purchasing 1 cassette and 1 CD for a total cost of $21. (2, 1) means purchasing 2 cassettes and 1 CD for a total of $28.

48. See students' work.

49. (−1, −1)

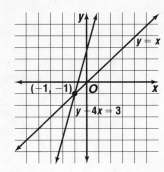

50. Let a = average
$$\frac{a}{2} - 7 = 53$$
$$\frac{a}{2} - 7 + 7 = 53 + 7$$
$$\frac{a}{2} = 60$$
$$2 \cdot \frac{a}{2} = 2 \cdot 60$$
$$a = 120$$

51. $\frac{3}{5}, 6.02 \times 10^{-1}, 0.63$ **52.** inductive

53. Since 8 is divisible by 2, 38 is divisible by 2. 3 + 8 = 11 and 11 is not divisible by 3, so 38 is not divisible by 3. 38 does not end in 0 or 5, so it is not divisible by 5. Since 38 is not divisible by 3, it is not divisible by 6. 38 does not end in 0, so it is not divisible by 10.

54. $6b > -31.2$ **55.** $\frac{96}{-8} = m$
   $\frac{6b}{6} > \frac{-31.2}{6}$ $-12 = m$
   $b > -5.2$

56. open

Chapter 8   Study Guide and Assessment

Page 423   Understanding and Using Vocabulary

1. function   2. domain
3. y-intercept   4. range
5. relation   6. Parallel
7. x-intercept   8. y-intercept

Pages 424–426   Skills and Concepts

9. {7, 9, 0, 6}; {17, 19, 18, 40}; yes
10. {4}; {5, 10, 22, 36}; no
11. {6, 8, 15}; {2}; yes
12. {1, 18, 35, 27}; {2, 4, 6}; no
13. {4, 5, −0.5, −2}; {3, 6, 1}; yes
14. positive, the points move up to the right
15. Sample answer: no
    See students' explanations.
16. Sample answer: negative
    See students' explanations.
17. Sample answer: negative
    See students' explanations.

18. Sample answer: positive
See students' explanations.

19. Sample answer: no
See students' explanations.

20.

x	$x - 1$	y
1	$1 - 1$	0
2	$2 - 1$	1
3	$3 - 1$	2
4	$4 - 1$	3

Answers will vary.
Sample answer:
$(1, 0)$, $(2, 1)$,
$(3, 2)$, $(4, 3)$

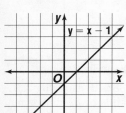

21.

x	$3x + 2$	y
0	$3(0) + 2$	2
1	$3(1) + 2$	5
-1	$3(-1) + 2$	-1
2	$3(2) + 2$	8

Answers will vary.
Sample answer:
$(0, 2)$, $(1, 5)$,
$(-1, -1)$, $(2, 8)$

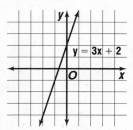

24. Rewrite $x - 2y = -1$
as $y = \frac{1}{2}x - \frac{1}{2}$.

x	$\frac{1}{2}x + \frac{1}{2}$	y
0	$\frac{1}{2}(0) + \frac{1}{2}$	0.5
1	$\frac{1}{2}(1) + \frac{1}{2}$	1
-1	$\frac{1}{2}(-1) + \frac{1}{2}$	0
3	$\frac{1}{2}(3) + \frac{1}{2}$	2

Answers will vary.
Sample answer:
$(0, 0.5)$, $(1, 1)$,
$(-1, 0)$, $(3, 2)$

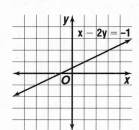

25.

x	y
7	0
7	2
7	4
7	6

Answers will vary.
Sample answer:
$(7, 0)$, $(7, 2)$,
$(7, 4)$, $(7, 6)$

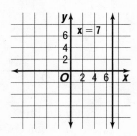

22. Rewrite $x + y = 5$
as $y = 5 - x$.

x	$5 - x$	y
0	$5 - 0$	5
1	$5 - 1$	4
-1	$5 - (-1)$	6
2	$5 - 2$	3

Answers will vary.
Sample answer:
$(0, 5)$, $(1, 4)$,
$(-1, 6)$, $(2, 3)$

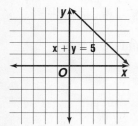

23. Rewrite $2x + y = 7$
as $y = 7 - 2x$.

x	$7 - 2x$	y
0	$7 - 2(0)$	7
1	$7 - 2(1)$	5
-1	$7 - 2(-1)$	9
2	$7 - 2(2)$	3

Answers will vary.
Sample answer:
$(0, 7)$, $(1, 5)$,
$(-1, 9)$, $(2, 3)$

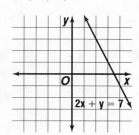

26.

x	y
0	1
1	1
-1	1
3	1

Answers will vary.
Sample answer:
$(0, 1)$, $(1, 1)$,
$(-1, 1)$, $(3, 1)$

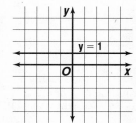

27.

x	$\frac{1}{2}x$	y
0	$\frac{1}{2}(0)$	0
2	$\frac{1}{2}(2)$	1
-2	$\frac{1}{2}(-2)$	-1
4	$\frac{1}{2}(4)$	2

Answers will vary.
Sample answer:
$(0, 0)$, $(2, 1)$,
$(-2, -1)$, $(4, 2)$

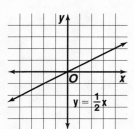

28. $f(x) = x + 5$
$f(2) = 2 + 5$
$\quad\ \ = 7$

29. $f(x) = x + 5$
$f(0) = 0 + 5$
$\quad\ \ = 5$

30. $\quad f(x) = x + 5$
$f(-6) = -6 + 5$
$\qquad\ \ = -1$

31. $g(x) = 3x^2 + 1$
$g(1) = 3(1)^2 + 1$
$\qquad = 3 \cdot 1 + 1$
$\qquad = 3 + 1$
$\qquad = 4$

32. $g(x) = 3x^2 + 1$
$g(5) = 3(5)^2 + 1$
$\quad\;\; = 3 \cdot 25 + 1$
$\quad\;\; = 75 + 1$
$\quad\;\; = 76$

33. slope $= \dfrac{5-7}{-3-2}$

$\quad = \dfrac{-2}{-5}$

$\quad = \dfrac{2}{5}$

34. slope $= \dfrac{1-6}{4-2}$

$\quad = \dfrac{-5}{2}$

$\quad = -2\dfrac{1}{2}$

35. slope $= \dfrac{0-(-3)}{4-7}$

$\quad = \dfrac{3}{-3}$

$\quad = -1$

36. slope $= \dfrac{18-40}{6-6}$

undefined

37. slope $= \dfrac{2-2}{0-3}$

$\quad = \dfrac{0}{-3}$

$\quad = 0$

38. slope $= \dfrac{8-5}{3-1}$

$\quad = \dfrac{3}{2}$

$\quad = 1\dfrac{1}{2}$

39. $y = 2x + 1$
slope $= m = 2$
Let $x = 0$:
$y = 2x + 1$
$y = 2(0) + 1$
$y = 1$
The y-intercept is $(0, 1)$.

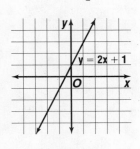

40. $y = \dfrac{2}{3}x - 3$
slope $= m = \dfrac{2}{3}$
Let $x = 0$:
$y = \dfrac{2}{3}x - 3$
$y = \dfrac{2}{3}(0) - 3$
$y = -3$
The y-intercept is $(0, -3)$.

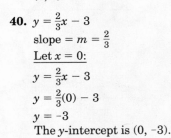

41. $y = -\dfrac{1}{2}x + 1$
slope $= m = -\dfrac{1}{2}$
Let $x = 0$:
$y = -\dfrac{1}{2}x + 1$
$y = -\dfrac{1}{2}(0) + 1$
$y = 1$
The y-intercept is $(0, 1)$.

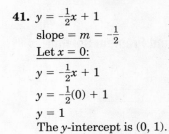

42. $y = 4$
slope $= 0$
The y-intercept is $(0, 4)$.

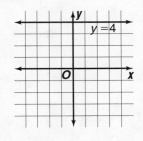

43. $x = 7$
slope $=$ undefined
There is no y-intercept.

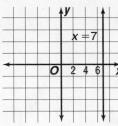

44. Rewrite $x + 2y = 6$
as $y = -\dfrac{1}{2}x + 3$.
slope $= m = -\dfrac{1}{2}$
Let $x = 0$:
$y = -\dfrac{1}{2}x + 3$
$y = -\dfrac{1}{2}(0) + 3$
$y = 3$
The y-intercept is $(0, 3)$.

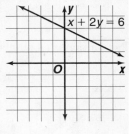

45. $y = 2 - \dfrac{1}{2}x$
slope $= m = -\dfrac{1}{2}$
Let $x = 0$:
$y = 2 - \dfrac{1}{2}x$
$y = 2 - \dfrac{1}{2}(0)$
$y = 2$
The y-intercept is $(0, 2)$.

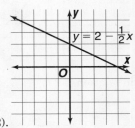

46. Rewrite $5x - y = 9$
as $y = 5x - 9$.
slope $= m = 5$
Let $x = 0$:
$y = 5x - 9$
$y = 5(0) - 9$
$y = -9$
The y-intercept is $(0, -9)$.

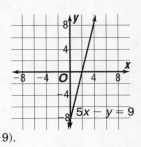

47.

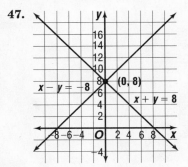

The solution is $(0, 8)$.

48.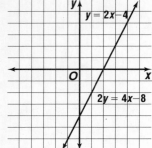

$y = 2x - 4$

$2y = 4x - 8$

The solution is all numbers.

49.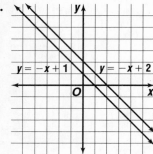

$y = -x + 1$ $y = -x + 2$

no solution

50.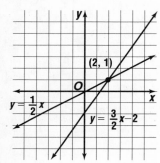

$(2, 1)$

$y = \frac{1}{2}x$ $y = \frac{3}{2}x - 2$

The solution is $(2, 1)$.

51.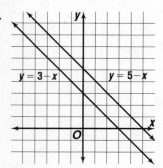

$y = 3 - x$ $y = 5 - x$

no solution

52.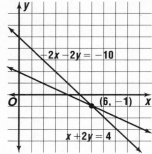

$2x - 2y = -10$

$(6, -1)$

$x + 2y = 4$

The solution is $(6, -1)$.

53.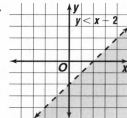

$y < x - 2$

54.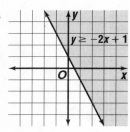

$y \geq -2x + 1$

55.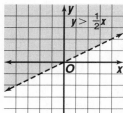

$y > \frac{1}{2}x$

56.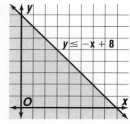

$y \leq -x + 8$

57.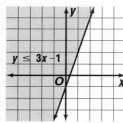

$y \leq 3x - 1$

58.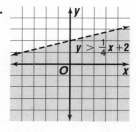

$y > \frac{1}{4}x + 2$

Page 426   Applications and Problem Solving

59. a.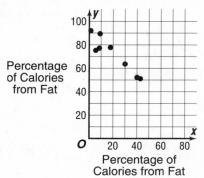

Percentage of Calories from Fat

Percentage of Calories from Fat

b. negative

60. Let the horizontal axis represent the year. Let the vertical axis represent the rent per month in dollars. Graph (1993, 495) for 1993 and $495 and (1995, 515) for 1995 and $515. Draw the line that contains these points. Thus, $565 corresponds to 2000. In the year 2000, the rent for a two-bedroom townhouse will be $565 per month.

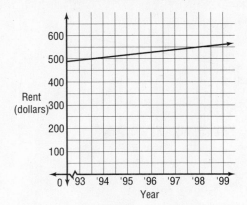

61. Let the horizontal axis represent the number of games played. Let the vertical axis represent the number of goals scored. Graph (82, 41) for 82 games and 41 goals and (66, 28) for 66 games and 28 goals. Draw the line that contains these points. Thus, about 36 corresponds to 76. In a 76-game season, there are approximately 36 goals scored.

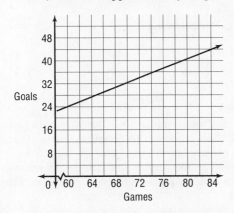

Page 427   Alternative Assessment

1.

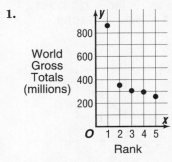

2. {1, 2, 3, 4, 5}   **3.** {868, 349, 303, 293, 258}

4. yes   **5.** Sample answer: no

6. a.

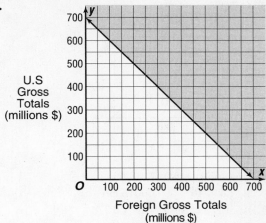

b. *Jurassic Park* would have made money, but the rest would not.

Page 427   Thinking Critically
See students' work.

Page 427   Portfolio
See students' work.

Page 427   Self Evaluation
See students' work.

Ongoing Assessment

Pages 428–429

1. B; $4x - 8 = 28$
$$4x - 8 + 8 = 28 + 8$$
$$4x = 36$$
$$\frac{4x}{4} = \frac{36}{4}$$
$$x = 9$$

2. A; Let x = cost per share of stock

bought	sold
$80x = \$2160$	$80x = \$1920$
$\frac{80x}{80} = \frac{2160}{80}$	$\frac{80x}{80} = \frac{1920}{80}$
$x = \$27.00$	$x = \$24.00$

This is a loss of $3.00 per share of stock. So, -3 represents the loss.

3. D; Let $x = 0$:
$y = x + 2$
$y = 0 + 2$
$y = 2$

4. D; $-20 + (-15) = -35m$

5. C; $5 \times 5 \times 5 = 5^3$

6. A; 50¢ for each card plus charge equals total charge
          $0.5n$ + 1.5 =   9

7. D;   0.5   2   3.5   5   6.5
              +1.5 +1.5 +1.5 +1.5

8. C;

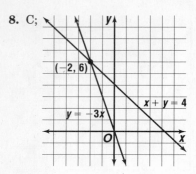

The solution is $(-2, 6)$.

9. B; $7.5 \times 10^{-4} = 0.00075$ cm

10. A; $3x + 4(x + 1) = 5x - 8$
$$3x + 4x + 4 = 5x - 8$$
$$7x + 4 = 5x - 8$$
$$7x - 5x + 4 = 5x - 5x - 8$$
$$2x + 4 = -8$$
$$2x + 4 - 4 = -8 - 4$$
$$2x = -12$$
$$x = -6$$

11. B; $65,000 = 6.5 \times 10^4$

12. John has $2.50. Before he bought the pop he had $2.50 + 50¢ or $3. He had $3 + $2 or $5 before he gave some to Lakesha. If John spent one third of the money on lunch, the $5 is two thirds of what he had.
$$\tfrac{2}{3}x = 5$$
$$\tfrac{3}{2} \times \tfrac{2}{3}x = \tfrac{3}{2} \cdot 5$$
$$x = 7.5$$

John started with $7.50.

13. $12 \times 8 = 96$
Lee must have 96 people to have 8 teams.

14. $4x + 26 \leq 50$
$$4x + 26 - 26 \leq 50 - 26$$
$$4x \leq 24$$
$$x \leq 6$$
Yolanda can spend no more than $6.00 for each gift.

15. $87\tfrac{7}{8} + \tfrac{7}{8} = 87 + \left(\tfrac{7}{8} + \tfrac{7}{8}\right)$
$$= 87 + \tfrac{14}{8}$$
$$= 87\tfrac{14}{8}$$
$$= 88\tfrac{6}{8}$$
$$= 88\tfrac{3}{4}$$
The closing price was $88\tfrac{3}{4}$.

16. Let x = number of miles
$$6x \geq 18$$
$$\tfrac{6x}{6} \geq \tfrac{18}{6}$$
$$x \geq 3$$
Jaime needs to run at least 3 miles each day.

17. Let the horizontal axis represent height in inches. Let the vertical axis represent weight in pounds. Graph (60, 118) for 60 inches and 118 pounds and (64, 134) for 64 inches and 134 pounds. Draw the line that contains these points. Mei's 5 foot 8 inches height equals 68 inches. Thus, 150 corresponds to 68. Mei's weight should be 150 pounds.

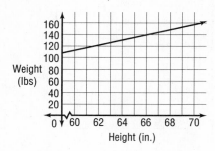

18. $21 \div 3\tfrac{1}{2} = 21 \div \tfrac{7}{2}$
$$= \tfrac{21}{1} \times \tfrac{2}{7}$$
$$= \tfrac{42}{7}$$
$$= 6$$
6 boards

19.

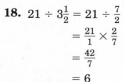

20. $4 \times 4 \times 4 \times 4 \times 4 \times 4 = 4^6$

21. The area of each wall is 8×12 or 96 square feet. Each of the 4 walls will be given two coats of paint. So, the contractor will need enough paint for $2 \times 4 \times 96$ or 768 square feet. Since each can will cover up to 400 square feet, the job will take 2 cans of paint.

22. $3542 - 1054 = 2488$
2488 runners finished the marathon.

23. The components cost $300 + 150 + 225$ or $675. The total bill was $675 + 71.50$ or $746.50.

24. See students' work.

25.

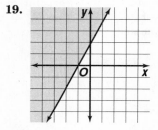

Chapter 9   Ratio, Proportion, and Percent

9-1   Ratios and Rates

Page 432   Your Turn

a. They are the same.

b. See students' work

Page 434   Checking Your Understanding

1. Ratios compare two like units. Rates compare two unlike units.

2. See students' work.

3. See students' work.

4. **a–b.** See students' work.

5. $\frac{100}{500} = \frac{1}{5}$ 6. $\frac{325}{25} = \frac{13}{1}$ 7. $\frac{150}{6} = \frac{25}{1}$

8. $\frac{98}{12} = \frac{49}{6}$ 9. $\frac{43}{46}$

10. $\frac{12 \text{ pounds}}{5 \text{ weeks}} = \frac{2.4 \text{ pounds}}{1 \text{ week}}$
    2.4 lb/week

11. $\frac{\$2.29}{6 \text{ pack}} = \frac{\$0.38}{1 \text{ can}}$
    $0.38/1 can

12. $\frac{99 \text{ cents}}{1 \text{ dozen}} = \frac{8.25 \text{ cents}}{1}$
    8.25¢/1

13. $\frac{6 \text{ inches}}{24 \text{ hours}} = \frac{0.25 \text{ inches}}{1 \text{ hour}}$
    0.25 in./1 hour

14. $\frac{4000 \text{ miles}}{190 \text{ gallons}} = \frac{21.1 \text{ miles}}{1 \text{ gallon}}$
    about 21.1 miles/1 gallon

Pages 435–436   Exercises

15. $\frac{13}{169} = \frac{1}{13}$ 16. $\frac{125}{50} = \frac{5}{2}$ 17. $\frac{64}{16} = \frac{4}{1}$

18. $\frac{351}{117} = \frac{3}{1}$ 19. $\frac{156}{84} = \frac{13}{7}$ 20. $\frac{35}{149}$

21. $\frac{2}{15}$ 22. $\frac{9}{7}$ 23. $\frac{5}{7}$

24. $\frac{11}{99} = \frac{1}{9}$ 25. $\frac{24}{56} = \frac{3}{7}$ 26. $\frac{15}{35} = \frac{3}{7}$

27. $\frac{399.3}{16.5 \text{ gallons}} = \frac{24.2 \text{ miles}}{1 \text{ gallon}}$
    24.2 miles/gallon

28. $\frac{\$9.60}{12 \text{ pounds}} = \frac{\$0.80}{1 \text{ pound}}$
    $0.80/lb

29. $\frac{100 \text{ meters}}{10.5 \text{ seconds}} = \frac{9.52 \text{ meters}}{1 \text{ second}}$
    9.52 m/s

30. $\frac{27 \text{ inches}}{9 \text{ hours}} = \frac{3 \text{ inches}}{1 \text{ hour}}$
    3 in./h

31. $\frac{\$210}{30 \text{ tickets}} = \frac{\$7}{1 \text{ ticket}}$
    $7/1 ticket

32. $\frac{\$3.50}{550 \text{ mL}} = \frac{0.6 \text{ cents}}{1 \text{ mL}}$
    0.6¢/mL

33. Sample answer: 2697: 13,485

34. **a–b.** Answers will vary.

35. **a.**

16-oz bag	32-oz bag
$\frac{\$2.49}{16 \text{ ounces}} = \frac{15.6 \text{ cents}}{1 \text{ ounce}}$	$\frac{\$3.69}{32 \text{ ounces}} = \frac{11.5 \text{ cents}}{1 \text{ ounce}}$
15.6¢/ounce	15.6¢/ounce

    The cost is about 15.6¢ per ounce for the 16-oz bag. The 32-oz bag is about 11.5¢ per ounce. So, the 32-oz bag at $3.69 is the better buy.

    b. Sample answer: When the quality of the less expensive product is not as good as that of the more expensive product, it may be better to buy the more expensive product.

36. See students' work.

37. **a.** 3   6   12   24   48
    $\frac{6}{3} = 2$ $\frac{12}{6} = 2$ $\frac{24}{12} = 2$ $\frac{48}{24} = 2$

    All ratios are 2.

    b. See students' work. The ratios approach the golden ratio.

38. $\frac{5 \text{ centimeters}}{10 \text{ miles}} = \frac{0.5 \text{ centimeters}}{1 \text{ mile}}$
    0.5 cm/mile

39. **a.** $\frac{4 \text{ miles}}{6.9 \text{ minutes}} \cdot \frac{60 \text{ minutes}}{1 \text{ hour}} = \frac{240 \text{ miles}}{6.9 \text{ hours}}$
    $= 34.8$ mph
    A pronghorn's speed is 34.8 mph.

    b. $\frac{300 \text{ feet}}{1 \text{ minute}} \cdot \frac{1 \text{ minute}}{60 \text{ seconds}} = \frac{300 \text{ feet}}{60 \text{ seconds}}$
    $= 5$ feet/s
    The tropical cockroach's speed is 5 feet/s.

40.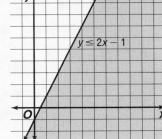

41.
$$7(a + 2) = 5a - 8$$
$$7(a) + 7(2) = 5a - 8$$
$$7a + 14 = 5a - 8$$
$$7a - 5a + 14 = 5a - 5a - 8$$
$$2a + 14 = -8$$
$$2a + 14 - 14 = -8 - 14$$
$$2a = -22$$
$$a = -11$$

42. The sum of the areas, in thousands of square miles, is 138,242.

    mean: $\frac{138,238,000}{21} = 6,582,761$

    median: 391,000

    mode: none

43. $456 = 2 \cdot 228$
$= 2 \cdot 2 \cdot 114$
$= 2 \cdot 2 \cdot 2 \cdot 57$
$= 2 \cdot 2 \cdot 2 \cdot 3 \cdot 19$

44. $x - 9 < 19$
$x - 9 + 9 < 19 + 9$
$x < 28$

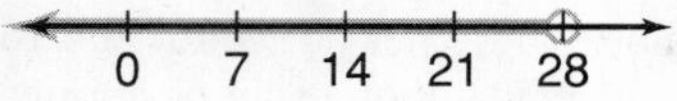

45. $-8 + (-5) = -13$

46. Let c = change in number of pets
$205 + c = 235$
$205 + c - 205 = 235 - 205$
$c = 30$ million

Page 436   Earth Watch

• density = $\frac{\text{mass}}{\text{volume}} = \frac{136}{191} \approx 0.712$

This sample has a density of about 0.712 grams per milliliter, so it must not be ethyl alcohol.

• Yes; The density of saltwater is about 1.04 grams per milliliter. So ethyl alcohol has a lower density and will float.

• See students' work.

9-2   ## Problem-Solving Strategy: Make a Table

Pages 437–438   Checking Your Understanding

1. Sample answer: A table helps you organize data.

2. Sample answer: Problems that involve data or counting.

3.

nickel	dime	quarter
10	0	0
8	1	0
6	2	0
5	0	1
4	3	0
3	1	1
2	4	0
1	2	1
0	5	0
0	0	2

There are 10 ways to make change for the 50-cent piece.

4.

Prime Numbers	2	3	5	7	11
7 + 5			1	1	
7 + 3 + 2	1	1		1	
5 + 5 + 2	1		2		
5 + 5 + 3 + 2	1	1	2		
3 + 3 + 3 + 3		4			
3 + 2 + 3 + 2 + 2	3	2			
2 + 2 + 2 + 2 + 2 + 2	6				

There are 7 ways to add prime numbers to make a sum of 12.

5.

	1	2	3	4	5	6	7	8
1	2	3	4	5	6	7	8	9
2	3	4	5	6	7	8	9	10
3	4	5	6	7	8	9	10	11
4	5	6	7	8	9	10	11	12
5	6	7	8	9	10	11	12	13
6	7	8	9	10	11	12	13	14
7	8	9	10	11	12	13	14	15
8	9	10	11	12	13	14	15	16

There are 21 ways to roll a sum less than 8.

Page 438   Exercises

6.

Name	Emily	Dani	Ted	Anita	Shawna
# of cards traded	40	40 − 7 + 5	38 − 3 + 4	39 − 2 + 1	38 − 11 + 8
Total # of Cards	40	38	39	38	35

Emily has 35 baseball cards.

7.

Penny	Nickel	Dime	Quarter	Amount
3	1			6 cents
1		1		11 cents
1			1	26 cents
	1	1		15 cents
	1		1	30 cents
		1	1	35 cents

A person can choose 6 cents, 11 cents, 26 cents, 15 cents, 30 cents, or 35 cents. Therefore, there are 6 amounts of money.

8.

Doorway	Amount after Doorway	Amount after Room
1	$1	$1 + $1 = $2
2	$2 + $1 = $3	$3 + $3 = $6
3	$6 + $1 = $7	$7 + $7 = $14
4	$14 + $1 = $15	$15 + $15 = $30
5	$30 + $1 = $31	$31 + $31 = $62
6	$62 + $1 = $63	$63 + $63 = $126
7	$126 + $1 = $127	$127 + $127 = $254
8	$254 + $1 = $255	———

Lisa will have $255 at the end.

9.

sold at $5975/share	bought $5970/share	sold $5973/share
100 · $5975 = $597,500	200 · $5970 = $1,194,000	100 · $5973 = $597,300

$597,500 − $1,194,000 + $597,300 = $800
Ms. Torres gained $800 in her transactions.

10.

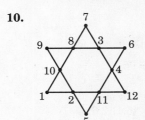

11. $-1 \quad -3 \quad -6 \quad -10 \quad -15 \quad -21$
$\qquad -2 \quad\; -3 \quad\; -4 \quad\; -5 \quad\; -6$

12. Try different combinations of 5 coins with a value of $1.05 to find a combination that does not include change for 5¢, 10¢, 25¢, 50¢, or $1.

nickels	dimes	quarters	half-dollars	total	meet requirements
1	0	4	0	$1.05	no
0	3	1	1	$1.05	yes

Tokala has one 50-cent piece, one quarter, and three dimes.

13.

w	ℓ
1	48
2	24
3	16
4	12
6	8

There are 5 different combinations in which $\ell \times w = 48$ in^2.

14. There are seven days (Sunday–Saturday) on which the first day of the month could fall and four possible numbers of days in a month (28, 29, 30, or 31 days). Therefore, 7×4 or 28 pages will need to be designed.

15. $\dfrac{23{,}452 \text{ miles}}{94 \text{ hours}} = \dfrac{249.5 \text{ miles}}{1 \text{ hour}}$
249.5 mph

16.
$3v + 7 < 19$
$3v + 7 - 7 < 19 - 7$
$3v < 12$
$\dfrac{3v}{3} < \dfrac{12}{3}$
$v < 4$

17. Sample answer:
$90.23 + 89.53 \rightarrow 90 + 90 = 180$
$90.23 + 89.53$ is about 180.

18. No; it involves subtraction.

19. $24 > 7$

9-3A Math Lab: Fair and Unfair Games

Page 439 Your Turn

1. Game A is fair because there are the same amount of odd and even sums. Game B is unfair because there are many more even products than odd products.

2. See students' work.

3. Yes; same amount of blue and red marbles.

4. No; there is a greater chance of getting two different numbers.

Integration: Probability
Simple Probability

Page 440   Your Turn

a–b. See students' work.

c. 7, 8; 0, 1, 2, 3, 4, 5, 6, 7, 8, 9

d. See students' work.

e. Sample answer: Yes; $\frac{2}{10}$ or 2 should qualify.

f. One bill would probably not qualify; Out of 100 bills, about 20 should qualify.

Page 442   Checking Your Understanding

1. Probability is the ratio of the number of ways that a certain outcome can happen to the number of possible outcomes that can happen. A sample space is the set of all possible ways an event can happen.

2. Sample answer: rolling a 5 on a die

3. An event with a probability of 0 cannot happen, an event with a probability of 1 will definitely happen. When the probability is 0 or 1, you know how the event will occur.

4. Manuel is correct because there are an equal number of ways each person can win.

5. a. Sample answer:

0 HEADS	T, T, T		
1 HEAD	T, T, H	T, H, T	H, T, T
2 HEADS	H, H, T	H, T, H	T, H, H
3 HEADS	H, H, H		

b. $P(\text{two heads}) = \frac{3}{8}$

c. $P(\text{at least 1 tail}) = \frac{7}{8}$

6. 0, there is no 30th of February.

7. $\frac{1}{12}$, June is one of 12 possible months.

8. $\frac{1}{6}$, 3 is one of the six possible outcomes.

9. $P(\text{a four}) = \frac{1}{8}$ 10. $P(\text{a one}) = \frac{1}{8}$

11. $P(\text{an even number}) = \frac{4}{8}$ or $\frac{1}{2}$

12. $P(\text{a two or a four}) = \frac{2}{8}$ or $\frac{1}{4}$

13. $P(\text{not a three}) = \frac{7}{8}$

14. $P(\text{less than a six}) = \frac{5}{8}$

15. 1529 of the 7424 state legislators were women. So, 7424 − 1529 or 5895 were men. Thus, the probability of choosing a man is $\frac{5895}{7424}$.

Pages 442–443   Exercises

16. $P(\text{red}) = \frac{5}{24}$ 17. $P(\text{orange}) = 0$

18. $P(\text{blue}) = \frac{8}{24}$ or $\frac{1}{3}$ 19. $P(\text{not green}) = \frac{17}{24}$

20. $P(\text{green or black}) = \frac{11}{24}$

21. $P(\text{not yellow}) = 1$

22. $P(\text{odd}) = \frac{3}{6}$ or $\frac{1}{2}$ 23. $P(\text{even}) = \frac{3}{6}$ or $\frac{1}{2}$

24. $P(\text{prime}) = \frac{3}{6}$ or $\frac{1}{2}$

25. $P(\text{greater than 6}) = 0$

26. $P(\text{both odd}) = \frac{9}{36}$ or $\frac{1}{4}$

27. $P(\text{both even}) = \frac{9}{36}$ or $\frac{1}{4}$

28. $P(\text{both prime}) = \frac{9}{36}$ or $\frac{1}{4}$

29. $P(\text{sum greater than 11}) = \frac{1}{36}$

30. $P(\text{sum of 7}) = \frac{6}{36}$ or $\frac{1}{6}$

31. $P(\text{sum of 1}) = 0$

32. $\frac{1}{100}$

33. If the batter hits 3 out of every 10 pitches, then she will not hit 10 − 3 or 7 pitches. So, the probability that she will not hit the next pitch is $\frac{7}{10}$.

34. a. U.S. Population: 248 million
There are 27 + 81 + 25 + 21 + 18 + 10 + 3 or 185 million people who are old enough to vote. So, the probability that a randomly chosen person is old enough to vote is $\frac{185}{248}$.

b. There are 18 + 10 + 3 or 31 million people who are 65 years old or older. So, the probability that a randomly chosen person is 65 years old or older is $\frac{31}{248}$.

35. 1—humans have been to the moon; 0—the Sun is too hot.

36. See students' work.

37. $2 \cdot 3 \cdot 5 = 30$
$2(2 \cdot 3 \cdot 5) = 60$
$3(2 \cdot 3 \cdot 5) = 90$
$4(2 \cdot 3 \cdot 5) = 120$
$5(2 \cdot 3 \cdot 5) = 150$
There are four whole numbers less than 124 that are divisible by 2, 3, and 5.

38. slope $= \frac{9 - (-3)}{3 - 1}$
$= \frac{12}{2}$
$= 6$

39. $6x + 3 = -9$
$6x + 3 - 3 = -9 - 3$
$6x = -12$
$x = -2$

40. $n - 9.06 = 2.31$
$n - 9.06 + 9.06 = 2.31 + 9.06$
$n = 11.37$

41. $P = 2(\ell + w)$ $A = \ell \times w$
$P = 2(5.1 + 2.6)$ $A = (5.1)(2.6)$
$P = 2(7.7)$ $A = 13.26$ sq m
$P = 15.4$ m

Using Proportions

Page 446   Checking Your Understanding

1. A proportion is made of two equal ratios.

2. Sample answer: Multiply cross products then solve the equations.

3. Sample answers: construction, travel, architecture

4. Sample answer:

$$\frac{1}{4} \stackrel{?}{=} \frac{2}{8}$$
$$1 \cdot 8 \stackrel{?}{=} 4 \cdot 2$$
$$8 = 8$$
So, $\frac{1}{4} = \frac{2}{8}$.

5. See students' work.

6.
$$\frac{2}{5} \stackrel{?}{=} \frac{4}{10}$$
$$2 \cdot 10 \stackrel{?}{=} 5 \cdot 4$$
$$20 = 20$$
So, $\frac{2}{5} = \frac{4}{10}$.

7.
$$\frac{6.25}{5} \stackrel{?}{=} \frac{2.5}{2}$$
$$6.25 \cdot 2 \stackrel{?}{=} 5 \cdot 2.5$$
$$12.5 = 12.5$$
So, $\frac{6.25}{5} = \frac{2.5}{2}$.

8.
$$\frac{2}{y} = \frac{10}{20}$$
$$2 \cdot 20 = y \cdot 10$$
$$40 = 10y$$
$$\frac{40}{10} = \frac{10y}{10}$$
$$4 = y$$

9.
$$\frac{5}{7} = \frac{n}{10.5}$$
$$5 \cdot 10.5 = 7 \cdot n$$
$$52.5 = 7n$$
$$\frac{52.5}{7} = \frac{7n}{7}$$
$$7.5 = n$$

10.
$$\frac{3}{a} = \frac{18}{24}$$
$$3 \cdot 24 = a \cdot 18$$
$$72 = 18a$$
$$\frac{72}{18} = \frac{18a}{18}$$
$$4 = a$$

11.
$$\frac{7}{16} = \frac{x}{4.8}$$
$$7 \cdot 4.8 = 16 \cdot x$$
$$33.6 = 16x$$
$$\frac{33.6}{16} = \frac{16x}{16}$$
$$2.1 = x$$

12.
$$\frac{3}{1.50} = \frac{x}{4.50}$$
$$3 \cdot 4.50 = 1.50 \cdot x$$
$$13.5 = 1.50x$$
$$\frac{13.5}{1.50} = \frac{1.50x}{1.50}$$
$$9 = x$$

13.
$$\frac{2.7}{m} = \frac{3}{7}$$
$$2.7 \cdot 7 = m \cdot 3$$
$$18.9 = 3m$$
$$\frac{18.9}{3} = \frac{3m}{3}$$
$$6.3 = m$$

14.
$$\frac{4\frac{1}{2} \text{ cups}}{72 \text{ cookies}} = \frac{x \text{ cups}}{48 \text{ cookies}}$$
$$4\frac{1}{2} \cdot 48 = 72 \cdot x$$
$$216 = 72x$$
$$\frac{216}{72} = \frac{72x}{72}$$
$$3 = x$$

3 cups of flour would be needed for 48 cookies.

Pages 446–447   Exercises

15.
$$\frac{16}{5} \stackrel{?}{=} \frac{4}{2}$$
$$16 \cdot 2 \stackrel{?}{=} 5 \cdot 4$$
$$32 \neq 20$$
So, $\frac{16}{5} \neq \frac{4}{2}$.

16.
$$\frac{15}{2} \stackrel{?}{=} \frac{18}{2.4}$$
$$15 \cdot 2.4 \stackrel{?}{=} 2 \cdot 18$$
$$36 = 36$$
So, $\frac{15}{2} = \frac{18}{2.4}$.

17.
$$\frac{1}{3} \stackrel{?}{=} \frac{8.6}{25.3}$$
$$1 \cdot 25.3 \stackrel{?}{=} 3 \cdot 8.6$$
$$25.3 \neq 25.8$$
So, $\frac{1}{3} \neq \frac{8.6}{25.3}$.

18.
$$\frac{2.1}{3.5} \stackrel{?}{=} \frac{3}{7}$$
$$2.1 \cdot 7 \stackrel{?}{=} 3.5 \cdot 3$$
$$14.7 \neq 10.5$$
So, $\frac{2.1}{3.5} \neq \frac{3}{7}$.

19.
$$\frac{2}{1} \stackrel{?}{=} \frac{15}{7.5}$$
$$2 \cdot 7.5 \stackrel{?}{=} 1 \cdot 15$$
$$15 = 15$$
So, $\frac{2}{1} = \frac{15}{7.5}$.

20.
$$\frac{3}{8} \stackrel{?}{=} \frac{2.4}{0.64}$$
$$3 \cdot 0.64 \stackrel{?}{=} 8 \cdot 2.4$$
$$1.92 \neq 19.2$$
So, $\frac{3}{8} \neq \frac{2.4}{0.64}$.

21.
$$\frac{5}{m} = \frac{25}{35}$$
$$5 \cdot 35 = m \cdot 25$$
$$175 = 25m$$
$$\frac{175}{25} = \frac{25m}{25}$$
$$7 = m$$

22.
$$\frac{r}{3.5} = \frac{7.2}{9}$$
$$r \cdot 9 = 3.5 \cdot 7.2$$
$$9r = 25.2$$
$$\frac{9r}{9} = \frac{25.2}{9}$$
$$r = 2.8$$

23.
$$\frac{9.6}{t} = \frac{1.6}{7}$$
$$9.6 \cdot 7 = t \cdot 1.6$$
$$67.2 = 1.6t$$
$$\frac{67.2}{1.6} = \frac{1.6t}{1.6}$$
$$42 = t$$

24.
$$\frac{6.4}{0.8} = \frac{8.1}{y}$$
$$6.4 \cdot y = 0.8 \cdot 8.1$$
$$6.4y = 6.48$$
$$\frac{6.4y}{6.4} = \frac{6.48}{6.4}$$
$$y = 1.0125$$

25.
$$\frac{5.1}{1.7} = \frac{7.5}{t}$$
$$5.1 \cdot t = 1.7 \cdot 7.5$$
$$5.1t = 12.75$$
$$\frac{5.1t}{5.1} = \frac{12.75}{5.1}$$
$$t = 2.5$$

26.
$$\frac{2.4}{1.6} = \frac{s}{3.4}$$
$$2.4 \cdot 3.4 = 1.6 \cdot s$$
$$8.16 = 1.6s$$
$$\frac{8.16}{1.6} = \frac{1.6s}{1.6}$$
$$5.1 = s$$

27.
$$\frac{18}{12} = \frac{24}{g}$$
$$18 \cdot g = 12 \cdot 24$$
$$18g = 288$$
$$\frac{18g}{18} = \frac{288}{18}$$
$$g = 16$$

28.
$$\frac{7}{45} = \frac{x}{9}$$
$$7 \cdot 9 = 45 \cdot x$$
$$63 = 45x$$
$$\frac{63}{45} = \frac{45x}{45}$$
$$1.4 = x$$

29.
$$\frac{7}{16} = \frac{x}{4.8}$$
$$7 \cdot 4.8 = 16 \cdot x$$
$$33.6 = 16x$$
$$\frac{33.6}{16} = \frac{16x}{16}$$
$$2.1 = x$$

30.
$$\frac{3.5}{6.2} = \frac{7.35}{b}$$
$$3.5 \cdot b = 6.2 \cdot 7.35$$
$$3.5b = 45.57$$
$$\frac{3.5b}{3.5} = \frac{45.57}{3.5}$$
$$b = 13.02$$

31.
$$\frac{3.2}{4.8} = \frac{6.8}{y}$$
$$3.2 \cdot y = 4.8 \cdot 6.8$$
$$3.2y = 32.64$$
$$\frac{3.2y}{3.2} = \frac{32.64}{3.2}$$
$$y = 10.2$$

32.
$$\frac{t}{0.2} = \frac{9.4}{2}$$
$$t \cdot 2 = 0.2 \cdot 9.4$$
$$2t = 1.88$$
$$\frac{2t}{2} = \frac{1.88}{2}$$
$$t = 0.94$$

33.
$$\frac{5}{6.15} = \frac{x}{8.00}$$
$$5 \cdot 8.00 = 6.15 \cdot x$$
$$40 = 6.15x$$
$$\frac{40}{6.15} = \frac{6.15x}{6.15}$$
$$6.5 = x$$

34.
$$\frac{625}{5} = \frac{250}{y}$$
$$625 \cdot y = 5 \cdot 250$$
$$625y = 1250$$
$$\frac{625y}{625} = \frac{1250}{625}$$
$$y = 2$$

35.
$$\frac{8}{2} = \frac{z}{5}$$
$$8 \cdot 5 = 2 \cdot z$$
$$40 = 2z$$
$$\frac{40}{2} = \frac{2z}{2}$$
$$20 = z$$

36.
$$\frac{100}{3} = \frac{300}{d}$$
$$100 \cdot d = 3 \cdot 300$$
$$100d = 900$$
$$\frac{100d}{100} = \frac{900}{100}$$
$$d = 9$$

37.
$$\frac{25}{5} = \frac{m}{25}$$
$$25 \cdot 25 = 5 \cdot m$$
$$625 = 5m$$
$$\frac{625}{5} = \frac{5m}{5}$$
$$125 = m$$

38.
$$\frac{12}{1} = \frac{30}{p}$$
$$12 \cdot p = 1 \cdot 30$$
$$12p = 30$$
$$\frac{12p}{12} = \frac{30}{12}$$
$$p = 2.5$$

39.
$$\frac{8}{28} = \frac{2x}{7}$$
$$8 \cdot 7 = 28 \cdot 2x$$
$$56 = 56x$$
$$\frac{56}{56} = \frac{56x}{56}$$
$$1 = x$$

40.
$$\frac{1.4}{4} = \frac{0.28}{m}$$
$$1.4 \cdot m = 4 \cdot 0.28$$
$$1.4m = 1.12$$
$$\frac{1.4m}{1.4} = \frac{1.12}{1.4}$$
$$m = 0.8$$

41.
$$\frac{5}{4} = \frac{x+5}{16}$$
$$5 \cdot 16 = 4 \cdot (x+5)$$
$$80 = 4(x+5)$$
$$80 = 4x + 20$$
$$80 - 20 = 4x + 20 - 20$$
$$60 = 4x$$
$$\frac{60}{4} = \frac{4x}{4}$$
$$15 = x$$

42.
$$\frac{15}{m-3} = \frac{3}{14}$$
$$15 \cdot 14 = (m-3) \cdot 3$$
$$210 = 3(m-3)$$
$$210 = 3m - 9$$
$$210 + 9 = 3m - 9 + 9$$
$$219 = 3m$$
$$\frac{219}{3} = \frac{3m}{3}$$
$$73 = m$$

43. Let x and y represent the integers. Then the difference is $x - y$, the sum is $x + y$ and the product is xy. Use guess and check to solve.

x	y	$x + y$	$x - y$	xy	$\dfrac{x-y}{x+y}$	$\dfrac{x+y}{xy}$
6	1	7	5	6	$\dfrac{5}{7}$	$\dfrac{7}{6}$
4	3	7	1	12	$\dfrac{1}{7}$	$\dfrac{7}{12}$
8	6	14	2	48	$\dfrac{2}{14} = \dfrac{1}{7}$	$\dfrac{14}{48} = \dfrac{7}{24}$

The numbers are 6 and 8.

44.
$$\frac{35 \text{ mm}}{185.5 \text{ cm}} = \frac{50 \text{ mm}}{x \text{ cm}}$$
$$35 \cdot x = 185.5 \cdot 50$$
$$35x = 9275$$
$$\frac{35x}{35} = \frac{9275}{35}$$
$$x = 265 \text{ cm}$$

45.
$$\frac{433 \text{ ft}}{54 \text{ ft}} = \frac{26 \text{ in.}}{x \text{ in.}}$$
$$433 \cdot x = 54 \cdot 26$$
$$433x = 1404$$
$$\frac{433x}{433} = \frac{1404}{433}$$
$$x = 3.24$$

The model should be 3.24 inches wide.

46. A standard deck of 52 playing cards contains 4 jacks, 4 queens, 4 kings and 4 aces. So, the probability of getting a jack or higher is $\frac{16}{52}$ or $\frac{4}{13}$.

47. slope $= \dfrac{6 - (-2)}{5 - 2}$
$$= \frac{8}{3}$$

48.
$$-8k - 21 = 75$$
$$-8k - 21 + 21 = 75 + 21$$
$$-8k = 96$$
$$\frac{-8k}{-8} = \frac{96}{-8}$$
$$k = -12$$

49. $9,412,000 = 9.412 \times 10^6$

50. Let $N = 0.777\ldots$ Then $10N = 7.777\ldots$
$$10N = 7.777\ldots$$
$$\underline{-\quad N = 0.777\ldots}$$
$$9N = 7$$
$$\frac{9N}{9} = \frac{7}{9}$$
$$N = \frac{7}{9}$$
So, $0.\overline{7} = \frac{7}{9}$.

51. $4^{-3} = \dfrac{1}{4^3}$

52. 1   2   4   5   7   8   10   11   13
   +1   +2   +1   +2   +1   +2   +1   +2

53. $b + 200$

9-4B Math Lab: Capture—Recapture

Page 448 Your Turn

1. Answers will vary. Sample answer: A larger sample will lead to a more reliable prediction and result.

2. Answers will vary. Sample answer: The estimate would become unreliable.

3. Answers will vary.

4. Researchers use the procedure described. They capture deer using tranquilizer guns. Then deer are tagged using ear tags. After the deer are released and allowed time to mix, a sample is recaptured. After several samples, a projected population is calculated.

9-5 Using the Percent Proportion

Pages 451–452 Checking Your Understanding

1. $\frac{r}{100}$ is the fractional representation of a percent, r.

2. Set up a proportion and solve.

3. Sample answer: percents are easier to compare than fractions because they always have the same base.

4. $\frac{p}{25} = \frac{r}{100}$; p is the number correct.

5. a. $\dfrac{52}{B} = \dfrac{80}{100}$ **b.** $\dfrac{p}{52} = \dfrac{80}{100}$ **c.** $\dfrac{52}{80} = \dfrac{r}{100}$

6.

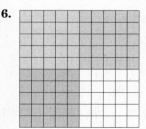

a. 100   **b.** 25   **c.** 25%
d. 4   **e.** $\dfrac{1}{4}$

7. $\dfrac{44}{100} = \dfrac{r}{100}$

$44 \cdot 100 = 100 \cdot r$

$4400 = 100r$

$\dfrac{4400}{100} = \dfrac{100r}{100}$

$44 = r$

So, $\dfrac{44}{100} = 44\%$.

8. $\dfrac{1}{20} = \dfrac{r}{100}$

$1 \cdot 100 = 20 \cdot r$

$100 = 20r$

$\dfrac{100}{20} = \dfrac{20r}{20}$

$5 = r$

So, $\dfrac{1}{20} = 5\%$.

19. $\dfrac{9}{4} = \dfrac{r}{100}$

$9 \cdot 100 = 4 \cdot r$

$900 = 4r$

$\dfrac{900}{4} = \dfrac{4r}{4}$

$225 = r$

So, $\dfrac{9}{4} = 225\%$.

20. $\dfrac{24}{25} = \dfrac{r}{100}$

$24 \cdot 100 = 25 \cdot r$

$2400 = 25r$

$\dfrac{2400}{25} = \dfrac{25r}{25}$

$96 = r$

So, $\dfrac{24}{25} = 96\%$.

9. $\dfrac{8}{250} = \dfrac{r}{100}$

$8 \cdot 100 = 250 \cdot r$

$800 = 250r$

$\dfrac{800}{250} = \dfrac{250r}{250}$

$3.2 = r$

So, $\dfrac{8}{250} = 3.2\%$.

10. $\dfrac{3}{2} = \dfrac{r}{100}$

$3 \cdot 100 = 2 \cdot r$

$300 = 2r$

$\dfrac{300}{2} = \dfrac{2r}{2}$

$150 = r$

So, $\dfrac{3}{2} = 150\%$

21. $\dfrac{45.3}{60} = \dfrac{r}{100}$

$45.3 \cdot 100 = 60 \cdot r$

$4530 = 60r$

$\dfrac{4530}{60} = \dfrac{60r}{60}$

$75.5 = r$

So, $\dfrac{45.3}{60} = 75.5\%$.

22. $\dfrac{24}{3} = \dfrac{r}{100}$

$24 \cdot 100 = 3 \cdot r$

$2400 = 3r$

$\dfrac{2400}{3} = \dfrac{3r}{3}$

$800 = r$

So, $\dfrac{24}{3} = 800\%$.

11. $\dfrac{P}{60} = \dfrac{15}{100}$

$P \cdot 100 = 60 \cdot 15$

$100P = 900$

$\dfrac{100P}{100} = \dfrac{900}{100}$

$P = 9$

15% of 60 is 9.

12. $\dfrac{52}{B} = \dfrac{40}{100}$

$52 \cdot 100 = B \cdot 40$

$5200 = 40B$

$\dfrac{5200}{40} = \dfrac{40B}{40}$

$130 = B$

52 is 40% of 130.

23. $\dfrac{P}{116} = \dfrac{92}{100}$

$P \cdot 100 = 116 \cdot 92$

$100P = 10{,}672$

$\dfrac{100P}{100} = \dfrac{10{,}672}{100}$

$P = 106.72$

92% of 116 is 106.72.

24. $\dfrac{16}{B} = \dfrac{40}{100}$

$16 \cdot 100 = B \cdot 40$

$1600 = 40B$

$\dfrac{1600}{40} = \dfrac{40B}{40}$

$40 = B$

16 is 40% of 40.

13. $\dfrac{37}{296} = \dfrac{r}{100}$

$37 \cdot 100 = 296 \cdot r$

$3700 = 296r$

$\dfrac{3700}{296} = \dfrac{296r}{296}$

$12.5 = r$

37 is 12.5% of 296.

25. $\dfrac{36}{80} = \dfrac{r}{100}$

$36 \cdot 100 = 80 \cdot r$

$3600 = 80r$

$\dfrac{3600}{80} = \dfrac{80r}{80}$

$45 = r$

36 is 45% of 80.

26. $\dfrac{21}{B} = \dfrac{35}{100}$

$B \cdot 35 = 21 \cdot 100$

$35B = 2100$

$\dfrac{35B}{35} = \dfrac{2100}{35}$

$B = 60$

21 is 35% of 60.

14. $\dfrac{18{,}735}{B} = \dfrac{27}{100}$

$18{,}735 \cdot 100 = B \cdot 27$

$1{,}873{,}500 = 27B$

$\dfrac{1{,}873{,}500}{27} = \dfrac{27B}{27}$

$69{,}388.\overline{8} = B$

In 1992, visitors spent about 69,389 hours in national parks.

27. $\dfrac{P}{50} = \dfrac{70}{100}$

$P \cdot 100 = 50 \cdot 70$

$100P = 3500$

$\dfrac{100P}{100} = \dfrac{3500}{100}$

$P = 35$

70% of 50 is 35.

28. $\dfrac{P}{48} = \dfrac{60}{100}$

$P \cdot 100 = 48 \cdot 60$

$100P = 2880$

$\dfrac{100P}{100} = \dfrac{2880}{100}$

$P = 28.8$

60% of 48 is 28.8.

Pages 452–453   Exercises

15. $\dfrac{1}{4} = \dfrac{r}{100}$

$1 \cdot 100 = 4 \cdot r$

$100 = 4r$

$\dfrac{100}{4} = \dfrac{4r}{4}$

$25 = r$

So, $\dfrac{1}{4} = 25\%$.

16. $\dfrac{7}{8} = \dfrac{r}{100}$

$7 \cdot 100 = 8 \cdot r$

$700 = 8r$

$\dfrac{700}{8} = \dfrac{8r}{8}$

$87.5 = r$

So, $\dfrac{7}{8} = 87.5\%$.

29. $\dfrac{P}{8} = \dfrac{200}{100}$

$P \cdot 100 = 8 \cdot 200$

$100P = 1600$

$\dfrac{100P}{100} = \dfrac{1600}{100}$

$P = 16$

200% of 8 is 16.

30. $\dfrac{P}{90} = \dfrac{78.5}{100}$

$P \cdot 100 = 90 \cdot 78.5$

$100P = 7065$

$\dfrac{100P}{100} = \dfrac{7065}{100}$

$P = 70.65$

78.5% of 90 is 70.65.

17. $\dfrac{3}{5} = \dfrac{r}{100}$

$3 \cdot 100 = 5 \cdot r$

$300 = 5r$

$\dfrac{300}{5} = \dfrac{5r}{5}$

$60 = r$

So, $\dfrac{3}{5} = 60\%$.

18. $\dfrac{1}{16} = \dfrac{r}{100}$

$1 \cdot 100 = 16 \cdot r$

$100 = 16r$

$\dfrac{100}{16} = \dfrac{16r}{16}$

$6.25 = r$

So, $\dfrac{1}{16} = 6.25\%$.

31. $\dfrac{36}{B} = \dfrac{45}{100}$

$36 \cdot 100 = B \cdot 45$

$3600 = 45B$

$\dfrac{3600}{45} = \dfrac{45B}{45}$

$80 = B$

36 is 45% of 80.

32. $\dfrac{28}{B} = \dfrac{20}{100}$

$28 \cdot 100 = B \cdot 20$

$2800 = 20B$

$\dfrac{2800}{20} = \dfrac{20B}{20}$

$140 = B$

28 is 20% of 140.

33. $\dfrac{126}{B} = \dfrac{10.5}{100}$

$126 \cdot 100 = B \cdot 10.5$

$12{,}600 = 10.5B$

$\dfrac{12{,}600}{10.5} = \dfrac{10.5B}{10.5}$

$1200 = B$

126 is 10.5% of 1200.

34. $\dfrac{P}{450} = \dfrac{0.1}{100}$

$P \cdot 100 = 450 \cdot 0.1$

$100P = 45$

$\dfrac{100P}{100} = \dfrac{45}{100}$

$P = 0.45$

0.1% of 450 is 0.45.

35. For all values of x, "x is $x\%$ of 100."

36.

$$\frac{1}{5} = \frac{20}{100}x$$

$$\frac{100}{20} \cdot \frac{1}{5} = \frac{100}{20} \cdot \frac{20}{100}x$$

$$1 = x$$

$\frac{1}{5} = 0.20$. If $\frac{1}{5}$ is 20% of 1, then $\frac{3}{5}$ of 1 is 0.60 or 60%.

37. a.

$$\frac{1.5}{B} = \frac{3}{100}$$

$$1.5 \cdot 100 = B \cdot 3$$

$$150 = 3B$$

$$\frac{150}{3} = \frac{3b}{3}$$

$$50 = B$$

50 grams of fat are recommended for a 2000-Calorie diet.

b.

$$\frac{760}{B} = \frac{32}{100}$$

$$760 \cdot 100 = B \cdot 32$$

$$76,000 = 32B$$

$$\frac{76,000}{32} = \frac{32B}{32}$$

$$2375 = B$$

The recommended daily value of sodium is about 2375 mg or 2.375 g.

38. a.

$$\frac{54.84}{B} = \frac{2}{100}$$

$$54.84 \cdot 100 = B \cdot 2$$

$$5484 = 2B$$

$$\frac{5484}{2} = \frac{2B}{2}$$

$$2742 = B$$

Louam's savings is $2742.

b.

$$\frac{P}{54.84} = \frac{2}{100}$$

$$P \cdot 100 = 54.84 \cdot 2$$

$$100P = 109.68$$

$$\frac{100P}{100} = \frac{109.68}{100}$$

$$P = 1.0968$$

The interest earned to the nearest cent is $1.10. Louam will earn 54.84 + 1.10 or $55.94.

39. Maine:

$$\frac{P}{35,387} = \frac{89.9}{100}$$

$$P \cdot 100 = 35,387 \cdot 89.9$$

$$100P = 3,181,291.3$$

$$\frac{100P}{100} = \frac{3,181,291.3}{100}$$

$$P = 31,812.913$$

Maine has 31,813 sq mi of forests.

New Hampshire:

$$\frac{P}{9351} = \frac{88.1}{100}$$

$$P \cdot 100 = 9351 \cdot 88.1$$

$$100P = 823,823.1$$

$$\frac{100P}{100} = \frac{823,823.1}{100}$$

$$P = 8238.231$$

New Hampshire has 8238 sq mi of forests.

West Virginia:

$$\frac{P}{24,231} = \frac{77.5}{100}$$

$$P \cdot 100 = 24,231 \cdot 77.5$$

$$100P = 1,877,902.5$$

$$\frac{100P}{100} = \frac{1,877,902.5}{100}$$

$$P = 18,779.025$$

West Virginia has 18,779 sq mi of forests.

Vermont:

$$\frac{P}{9615} = \frac{75.7}{100}$$

$$P \cdot 100 = 9615 \cdot 75.7$$

$$100P = 727,855.5$$

$$\frac{100P}{100} = \frac{727,855.5}{100}$$

$$P = 7278.555$$

Vermont has 7279 sq mi of forests.

Alabama:

$$\frac{P}{52,423} = \frac{66.9}{100}$$

$$P \cdot 100 = 52,423 \cdot 66.9$$

$$100P = 3,507,098.7$$

$$\frac{100P}{100} = \frac{3,507,098.7}{100}$$

$$P = 35,070.987$$

Alabama has 35,071 sq mi of forests.

40.

$$\frac{18}{24} = \frac{x}{15}$$

$$18 \cdot 15 = 24 \cdot x$$

$$270 = 24x$$

$$\frac{270}{24} = \frac{24x}{24}$$

$$11.25 = x$$

There are 11.25 grams of gold in a 15-gram piece of jewelry that is labeled as 18-karat gold.

41. $\frac{6}{8} = \frac{3}{4}$

42.

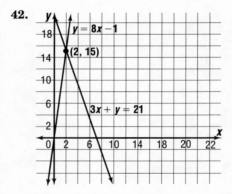

The solution is (2, 15).

43.

$$7.21 + 3.57 + x < 15$$

$$10.78 + x < 15$$

$$10.78 + x - 10.78 < 15 - 10.78$$

$$x < 4.22$$

Yolanda can spend no more than $4.22.

44.

$$4b = 4(3.2)$$

$$= 12.8$$

45.

$$65 = \boxed{5} \cdot 13$$

$$105 = 3 \cdot \boxed{5} \cdot 7$$

The GCF is 5.

46. Quadrant IV

Integration: Statistics
Using Statistics to Predict

Page 455   Checking Your Understanding

1. Write a proportion with the percentage of the sample and the percentage of the population.

2. large, random

3. Tamika; 152 is about 60% of 253.

4. $17 + 10 + 25 + 12 + 8 = 72$

5.
$$\frac{72}{3600} = \frac{x}{100}$$
$$72 \cdot 100 = 3600 \cdot x$$
$$7200 = 3600x$$
$$\frac{7200}{3600} = \frac{3600x}{3600}$$
$$2 = x$$

   The sample is 2%.

6. $\frac{12}{72}$ or $\frac{1}{6}$ chose fruit drink;
$$\frac{1}{6} = \frac{x}{100}$$
$$1 \cdot 100 = 6 \cdot x$$
$$100 = 6x$$
$$\frac{100}{6} = \frac{6x}{6}$$
$$16\frac{2}{3} = x$$

   $\frac{1}{6}$ is $16\frac{2}{3}\%$.

7. Sample answer: High school cafeteria because teen's tastes are not representative of all ages.

Pages 456–457   Exercises

8. Sample answer: This is a valid sample because a large number of customers were surveyed. This is not a valid sample because all the people were asked at the ice cream store, so they must prefer the type of ice cream served there.

9.
$$\frac{35}{100} = \frac{x}{100}$$
$$35 \cdot 100 = 100 \cdot x$$
$$3500 = 100x$$
$$35 = x$$

   35% of the people preferred peanut butter fudge.

10.
$$\frac{25}{100} = \frac{x}{800}$$
$$25 \cdot 800 = 100 \cdot x$$
$$20,000 = 100x$$
$$200 = x$$

   About 200 customers would prefer chocolate.

11.
$$\frac{x}{500} = \frac{25}{100}$$
$$x \cdot 100 = 500 \cdot 25$$
$$100x = 12,500$$
$$x = 125$$

   125 teens volunteer because they have free time.

12.
$$\frac{x}{250} = \frac{38}{100}$$
$$x \cdot 100 = 250 \cdot 38$$
$$100x = 9500$$
$$x = 95$$

   95 teens volunteer because they enjoy the work.

13. No; because the sample is too small and it is not random.

14. See students' work.

15. Sample answer: No; many of the common two-letter words like at, in, of and on do not contain the letter E.

16. a.
$$\frac{x}{445} = \frac{18.9}{100}$$
$$x \cdot 100 = 445 \cdot 18.9$$
$$100x = 8410.5$$
$$x = 84.105$$

   About 84 of the 445 cars have rock playing.

   b. See students' work.

17. a.
$$\frac{1872}{3600} = \frac{x}{100}$$
$$1872 \cdot 100 = 3600 \cdot x$$
$$187,200 = 3600x$$
$$52 = x$$

   52% of the population would feel the same.

   b.
$$\frac{2160}{3600} = \frac{x}{100}$$
$$2160 \cdot 100 = 3600 \cdot x$$
$$216,000 = 3600x$$
$$60 = x$$

   60% of the population would say they were slow to change with the fashions.

18. a. female
$$\frac{x}{346} = \frac{76}{100}$$
$$x \cdot 100 = 346 \cdot 76$$
$$100x = 26,296$$
$$x = 262.96$$

   b. male
$$\frac{x}{362} = \frac{46}{100}$$
$$x \cdot 100 = 362 \cdot 46$$
$$100x = 16,652$$
$$x = 166.52$$

   About 263 females and about 167 males made their beds.

   c. Sample answer: No, many adults are married. So if the woman made the bed, the man would not have to, and vice versa.

19.
$$\frac{10.28}{17.86} = \frac{x}{100}$$
$$10.28 \cdot 100 = 17.86 \cdot x$$
$$1028 = 17.86x$$
$$57.558 = x$$

   Approximately 58% of the candy is chocolate.

20. yes; 12.5, 14, 15.5

21. Let x = number
$$-2x + 15 > 12$$
$$-2x + 15 - 15 > 12 - 15$$
$$-2x > -3$$
$$\frac{-2x}{-2} < \frac{-3}{-2}$$
$$x < \frac{3}{2}$$
$$x < 1\frac{1}{2}$$

   The number must be less than $1\frac{1}{2}$. So, the correct choice is D.

22. $(-4, 2)$ is point B.

23.
$$14 \overset{?}{\geq} 2b + 4$$
$$14 \overset{?}{\geq} 2(3) + 4$$
$$14 \overset{?}{\geq} 6 + 4$$
$$14 \geq 10$$
   true

Page 457   Self Test

1. $\dfrac{300 \text{ feet}}{5 \text{ minutes}} = \dfrac{60 \text{ feet}}{1 \text{ minute}}$

   60 ft/min

2. $\dfrac{54 \text{ inches}}{4 \text{ months}} = \dfrac{13.5 \text{ inches}}{1 \text{ month}}$

   13.5 in/mo

3.

\$5	\$10	\$20
10	0	0
8	1	0
6	2	0
6	0	1
4	3	0
4	1	2
2	4	0
2	2	1
2	0	2
0	5	0
0	1	2
0	3	1

There are 12 ways to make change for the \$50-bill.

4. $P(\text{green}) = \dfrac{5}{16}$

5. $P(\text{blue or red}) = \dfrac{9}{16}$

6. $\dfrac{m}{7} = \dfrac{25}{35}$

   $m \cdot 35 = 7 \cdot 25$

   $35m = 175$

   $\dfrac{35m}{35} = \dfrac{175}{35}$

   $m = 5$

7. $\dfrac{1.5}{2} = \dfrac{s}{2.4}$

   $1.5 \cdot 2.4 = 2 \cdot s$

   $3.6 = 2s$

   $\dfrac{3.6}{2} = \dfrac{2s}{2}$

   $1.8 = s$

8. $\dfrac{P}{400} = \dfrac{75}{100}$

   $P \cdot 100 = 400 \cdot 75$

   $100P = 30,000$

   $\dfrac{100P}{100} = \dfrac{30,000}{100}$

   $P = 300$

   75% of 400 is 300.

9. $\dfrac{250}{B} = \dfrac{500}{100}$

   $250 \cdot 100 = B \cdot 500$

   $25,000 = 500B$

   $\dfrac{25,000}{500} = \dfrac{500B}{500}$

   $50 = B$

   250 is 500% of 50.

10. $\dfrac{x}{1500} = \dfrac{11}{100}$

    $x \cdot 100 = 1500 \cdot 11$

    $100x = 16,500$

    $x = 165$

    165 people chose New York as a destination.

11. $\dfrac{x}{300} = \dfrac{35}{100}$

    $x \cdot 100 = 300 \cdot 35$

    $100x = 10,500$

    $x = 105$

    They should expect 105 families.

Page 458   Your Turn

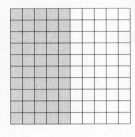

$\dfrac{1}{2}$

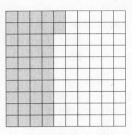

0.42

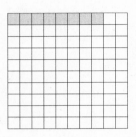

8%

a. 0.5, 50%

b. 42%; it moved 2 places right.

c. Sample answer: move decimal point to the right two places; rewrite fraction as a fraction with a denominator of 100, then the numerator is the percent.

Page 460   Checking Your Understanding

1. Sample answer: Move the decimal point two places to the left.

2. $\dfrac{16}{25}$, 0.64, 64%

3. Sample answer: a fraction is greater than 100% if it is greater than 1 and a fraction is less than 1% if it is less than $\dfrac{1}{100}$.

4. See students' work.

5. $0.37 \to \dfrac{0.37}{1} = \dfrac{37}{100}$ or 37%

6. $0.475 \to \dfrac{0.475}{1} = \dfrac{47.5}{100}$ or 47.5%

7. $1.03 \to \dfrac{1.03}{1} = \dfrac{103}{100}$ or 103%

8. $\dfrac{27}{100} = 27\%$

9. $\dfrac{36}{500} = 0.072 \to \dfrac{7.2}{100} = 7.2\%$

10. $\dfrac{6}{5} = 1.2 \to \dfrac{120}{100} = 120\%$

11. $25\% = \dfrac{25}{100}$

    $= \dfrac{1}{4}$

12. $33\frac{1}{3}\% = \dfrac{33\frac{1}{3}}{100}$

    $= 33\frac{1}{3} \div 100$

    $= \dfrac{100}{3} \times \dfrac{1}{100}$

    $= \dfrac{1}{3}$

---

13. $0.3\% = \frac{0.3}{100}$

$\qquad = \frac{3}{1000}$

14. $35\% = \frac{35}{100}$

$\qquad = 0.35$

15. $24\frac{1}{2}\% = \frac{24.5}{100}$

$\qquad = 0.245$

16. $0.4\% = \frac{0.4}{100}$

$\qquad = 0.004$

17. a. $\frac{48}{120} = \frac{2}{5}$

b. $\qquad \frac{48}{120} = \frac{r}{100}$

$\qquad 48 \cdot 100 = 120 \cdot r$

$\qquad\quad 4800 = 120r$

$\qquad\qquad 40 = r$

$\qquad$ 48 of 120 is 40%.

Pages 460–461 Exercises

18. $0.71 \to \frac{0.71}{1} = \frac{71}{100}$ or 71%

19. $0.03 \to \frac{0.03}{1} = \frac{3}{100}$ or 3%

20. $0.543 \to \frac{0.543}{1} = \frac{54.3}{100}$ or 54.3%

21. $2.37 \to \frac{2.37}{1} = \frac{237}{100}$ or 237%

22. $0.004 \to \frac{0.004}{1} = \frac{0.4}{100}$ or 0.4%

23. $1.32 \to \frac{1.32}{1} = \frac{132}{100}$ or 132%

24. $0.035 \to \frac{0.035}{1} = \frac{3.5}{100}$ or 3.5%

25. $0.0004 \to \frac{0.0004}{1} = \frac{0.04}{100}$ or 0.04%

26. $\frac{3}{16} = 0.1875 \to \frac{18.75}{100} = 18.75\%$

27. $\frac{7}{12} = 0.58\overline{3} \to \frac{58.\overline{3}}{100} = 58\frac{1}{3}\%$

28. $\frac{5}{4} = 1.25 \to \frac{125}{100} = 125\%$

29. $\frac{7}{3} = 2.33\overline{3} \to \frac{233.\overline{3}}{100} = 233\frac{1}{3}\%$

30. $\frac{4}{300} = 0.01\overline{3} \to \frac{1.\overline{3}}{100} = 1\frac{1}{3}\%$

31. $\frac{5}{9} = 0.55\overline{5} \to \frac{55.\overline{5}}{100} = 55\frac{5}{9}\%$

32. $1\frac{1}{4} = 1.25 \to \frac{125}{100} = 125\%$

33. $\frac{3}{40} = 0.075 \to \frac{7.5}{100} = 7.5\%$

34. $36\% = \frac{36}{100}$

$\qquad = \frac{9}{25}$

35. $125\% = \frac{125}{100}$

$\qquad = \frac{5}{4}$

36. $58\% = \frac{58}{100}$

$\qquad = \frac{29}{50}$

37. $34.5\% = \frac{34.5}{100}$

$\qquad = \frac{69}{200}$

38. $22\% = \frac{22}{100}$

$\qquad = \frac{11}{50}$

39. $37\frac{1}{2}\% = \frac{37\frac{1}{2}}{100}$

$\qquad = 37\frac{1}{2} \div 100$

$\qquad = \frac{75}{2} \times \frac{1}{100}$

$\qquad = \frac{3}{8}$

40. $66\frac{2}{3}\% = \frac{66\frac{2}{3}}{100}$

$\qquad = 66\frac{2}{3} \div 100$

$\qquad = \frac{200}{3} \times \frac{1}{100}$

$\qquad = \frac{2}{3}$

41. $16\frac{1}{3}\% = \frac{16\frac{1}{3}}{100}$

$\qquad = 16\frac{1}{3} \div 100$

$\qquad = \frac{49}{3} \times \frac{1}{100}$

$\qquad = \frac{49}{300}$

42. $35\% = \frac{35}{100}$

$\qquad = 0.35$

43. $75\% = \frac{75}{100}$

$\qquad = 0.75$

44. $93\% = \frac{93}{100}$

$\qquad = 0.93$

45. $39.8\% = \frac{39.8}{100}$

$\qquad = 0.398$

46. $42.7\% = \frac{42.7}{100}$

$\qquad = 0.427$

43. $0.4\% = \frac{0.4}{100}$

$\qquad = 0.004$

48. $127\% = \frac{127}{100}$

$\qquad = 1.27$

49. $235.4\% = \frac{235.4}{100}$

$\qquad = 2.354$

50. 80%

51. 22%

52. $0.05, 31\%, \frac{1}{2}$

53. $0.067, 16\%, \frac{1}{4}$

54. Suppose bottle C is 10 ounces and costs $1.00. Then bottle A costs $1.50 and Bottle B contains 15 ounces. Bottle A costs 15 + 0.20(15) = 15 + 3 or 18 ounces. Bottle B costs 1.50 + 0.25(1.50) = 1.50 + 0.375 or $1.86.

	A	B	C
size	1.8	15	10
price	1.50	1.86	1.00
price per ounce	$8\frac{1}{3}$¢	12.4¢	10¢

Bottle A is the best buy.

55. $33\frac{1}{3}\% = \frac{33\frac{1}{3}}{100}$

$\qquad = 33\frac{1}{3} \div 100$

$\qquad = \frac{100}{3} \times \frac{1}{100}$

$\qquad = \frac{1}{3}$

56. a. $\frac{3}{1000} = 0.003 \to \frac{0.3}{100} = 0.3\%$

$\qquad$ 3 out of 1000 is 0.3%.

b. $4\% = \frac{4}{100}$

$\qquad = \frac{1}{25}$

$\qquad \frac{1}{25}$ of babies are born on their due date.

57. $80\% = \frac{80}{100}$

$\qquad = \frac{4}{5}$

$\frac{4}{5}$ of a marshmallow is air.

58. $\qquad \frac{x}{50} = \frac{34}{100}$

$\qquad x \cdot 100 = 50 \cdot 34$

$\qquad\quad 100x = 1700$

$\qquad\qquad x = 17$

Expect 17 customers to choose a floral perfume.

59.

Let $y = 0$:	Let $x = 0$:

Let $y = 0$:
$$y = 8x - 12$$
$$0 = 8x - 12$$
$$0 + 12 = 8x - 12 + 12$$
$$12 = 8x$$
$$\frac{12}{8} = \frac{8x}{8}$$
$$1.5 = x$$

Let $x = 0$:
$$y = 8x - 12$$
$$y = 8(0) - 12$$
$$y = 0 - 12$$
$$y = -12$$

60.
$$\frac{b}{-2} - 12 \le 11$$
$$\frac{b}{-2} - 12 + 12 \le 11 + 12$$
$$\frac{b}{-2} \le 23$$
$$-2\left(\frac{b}{-2}\right) \ge -2(23)$$
$$b \ge -46$$

61. $\frac{4}{9} \cdot \frac{5}{12} = \frac{20}{108}$
$$= \frac{5}{27}$$

62.
$$x + 14.7 < 51.2$$
$$x + 14.7 - 14.7 < 51.2 - 14.9$$
$$x < 36.5$$

63. $n^4 \cdot n^{10} = n^{4+10}$
$$= n^{14}$$

64. $10^9 = 10 \cdot 10 \cdot 10 \cdot 10 \cdot 10 \cdot 10 \cdot 10 \cdot 10 \cdot 10$

65.
$$\frac{h}{0.7} = -2.8$$
$$0.7\left(\frac{h}{0.7}\right) = 0.7(-2.8)$$
$$h = -1.96$$
So, the correct choice is C.

66. $r = -9889 \div -319$
Both dividend and divisor are negative, so the quotient is positive.

$$\begin{array}{r} 31 \\ 319\overline{)9889} \\ -957 \\ \hline 319 \\ -319 \\ \hline 0 \end{array}$$

$r = 31$

67. $4 + x = 12$
$$x = 12 - 4$$
$$x = 8$$

9-8	**Percent and Estimation**

Page 464   Checking Your Understanding

1. Sample answer: 25% of 200 = 50.

2. Sample answer: Choose a fraction that is close to the percent like $\frac{1}{4}$ for 28%, and estimate the product.

3. 50%

4. Both; Angeni: $10\% + \frac{1}{2}(10\%) = 15\%$;
Darlene: $3(5\frac{1}{4}\%) \approx 15\%$

5. See students' work.

6. 3 of the 16 squares are shaded and $\frac{3}{16}$ is about $\frac{4}{16}$ or $\frac{1}{4}$. Since $\frac{1}{4} = 25\%$, the correct choice is b.

7. 2 of the 3 regions are shaded and $\frac{2}{3} = 66\frac{2}{3}\%$. So, the correct choice is c.

8. Sample answer:
24% is about 25%.
$25\% = \frac{1}{4}$

9. Sample answer:
79% is about 80%.
$80\% = \frac{4}{5}$

10. Sample answer:
145% is about 150%.
$150\% = 1\frac{1}{2}$

11. Sample answer:
45% is about 50% or $\frac{1}{2}$.
$\frac{1}{2}$ of 430 is 215.

12. Sample answer:
112% is about 110%.
$110\% = 100\% + 10\%$
$14.5(100\% + 10\%) = 14.5 + 1.45$ or 15.95
112% of 14.5 is about 16.

13. Sample answer:
0.6% is about 0.5% or $\frac{1}{200}$.
325 is about 300.
$\frac{1}{200}$ of 300 is 1.5.

14. Sample answer:
$\frac{8}{30}$ is about $\frac{10}{30}$ or $\frac{1}{3}$.
$\frac{1}{3} = 33\frac{1}{3}\%$

15. Sample answer:
$\frac{9}{19}$ is about $\frac{9}{18}$ or $\frac{1}{2}$.
$\frac{1}{2} = 50\%$

16. Sample answer:
$\frac{5}{7} \approx 0.7143$ or about 70%.

17. a. $\frac{29}{50}$ is about $\frac{30}{50}$ or $\frac{3}{5}$.
$\frac{3}{5} = 60\%$
Davon bought the pair of shoes for about 60% of the selling price.
b. The sale was about $100 - 60$ or 40% off.

Pages 464–466   Exercises

18. 39% is about 40% or $\frac{2}{5}$.
$\frac{2}{5}$ of 300 is 120.
So, the correct choice is c.

19. 47% is about 50% or $\frac{1}{2}$.
605 is about 600.
$\frac{1}{2}$ of 600 is 300.
So, the correct choice is c.

20. $\frac{1}{3}\% = \frac{\frac{1}{3}}{100} = \frac{1}{300}$
$\frac{1}{300}$ of 240 is 0.8.
So, the correct choice is a.

21. 129% is about 125% or $\frac{5}{4}$.
$\frac{5}{4}$ of 400 is 500.
So, the correct choice is b.

22. Sample answer:

67% is about 70% or $\frac{7}{10}$.

Also, 67% is about $66\frac{2}{3}\%$ or $\frac{2}{3}$.

23. Sample answer:
98% is about 100%.
100% = 1

24. Sample answer:
18% is about 20%.
20% = $\frac{1}{5}$

25. Sample answer:
$2\frac{1}{2}\%$ is about 3%.
3% = $\frac{3}{100}$

26. Sample answer:
148% is about 150%.
150% = $1\frac{1}{2}$

27. Sample answer:
$8\frac{5}{9}\%$ is about 10%.
10% = $\frac{1}{10}$

28. Sample answer:
0.8% is about 1%.
1% = $\frac{1}{100}$

29. Sample answer:
119% is about 120%.
120% = $1\frac{1}{5}$

30. Sample answer:
47% is about 50% or $\frac{1}{2}$.
$\frac{1}{2}$ of 84 is 42.

31. Sample answer:
28% is about 30% or $\frac{3}{10}$.
390 is about 400.
$\frac{3}{10}$ of 400 is 120.

32. Sample answer:
$8\frac{1}{5}\%$ is about 10% or $\frac{1}{10}$.
$\frac{1}{10}$ of 55 is 5.5.

33. Sample answer:
98% is about 100% or 1.
1 of 98 is 98.

34. Sample answer:
126% is about 125% or $\frac{5}{4}$.
198 is about 200.
$\frac{5}{4}$ of 200 is 250.

35. Sample answer:
0.9% is about 1% or $\frac{1}{100}$.
514 is about 515
$\frac{1}{100}$ of 515 is 5.15.

36. Sample answer:
15% = $\frac{15}{100}$ or $\frac{3}{20}$.
34 is about 30.
$\frac{3}{20}$ of 30 is 4.5.

37. Sample answer:
116% is about 100% or 1.
18 is about 20.
1 of 20 is 20.

38. Sample answer:
0.05% = $\frac{5}{10,000}$ or $\frac{1}{10,000}$.
$\frac{1}{10,000}$ of 1180 is 0.6.

39. Sample answer:
$\frac{12}{15} = \frac{4}{5}$
$\frac{4}{5}$ = 80%

40. Sample answer:
$\frac{8}{35}$ is about $\frac{7}{35}$ or $\frac{1}{5}$.
$\frac{1}{5}$ = 20%

41. Sample answer:
$\frac{39}{79}$ is about $\frac{40}{80}$ or $\frac{1}{2}$.
$\frac{1}{2}$ = 50%

42. Sample answer:
$\frac{57}{176}$ is about $\frac{60}{180}$ or $\frac{1}{3}$.
$\frac{1}{3}$ = 33%

43. Sample answer:
$\frac{9}{95}$ is about $\frac{9}{90}$ or $\frac{1}{10}$.
$\frac{1}{10}$ = 10%

44. Sample answer:
$\frac{13}{68}$ is about $\frac{15}{70}$ or $\frac{3}{14}$.
$\frac{3}{14}$ = 21%

45. Sample answer:
$\frac{1}{9}$ is about $\frac{1}{10}$.
$\frac{1}{10}$ = 10%

46. Sample answer:
$\frac{3}{200}$ = 1.5%

47. Sample answer:
$\frac{7}{2445}$ is about $\frac{8}{2400}$ or $\frac{1}{300}$.
$\frac{1}{300}$ = 0.3%

48. Let d represent the number of Democrats and r represent the number of Republicans. $0.4d$ is the number of Democrats who voted yes, and $0.925r$ the Republicans who voted yes.

$$\frac{0.4d + 0.925r}{r + d} = \frac{68}{100}$$
$$68(r + d) = 100(0.4d + 0.925r)$$
$$68r + 68d = 40d + 92.5r$$
$$68r + 68d - 68r = 40d + 92.5r - 68r$$
$$68d = 40d + 24.5r$$
$$68d - 40d = 40d + 24.5r - 40d$$
$$28d = 24.5r$$
$$\frac{28d}{r} = \frac{24.5r}{r}$$
$$28\frac{d}{r} = 24.5$$
$$\frac{d}{r} = \frac{24.5}{28}$$
$$\frac{d}{r} = \frac{7}{8}$$

The ratio of Democrats to Republicans is $\frac{7}{8}$.

49. shrimp:
$\frac{7}{90}$ is about $\frac{9}{90}$ or $\frac{1}{10}$.
$\frac{1}{10}$ = 10%

lobster:
$\frac{15}{90}$ is about $\frac{20}{100}$ or $\frac{1}{5}$.
$\frac{1}{5}$ = 20%.

chicken:
$\frac{171}{290}$ is about $\frac{180}{300}$ or $\frac{3}{5}$.
$\frac{3}{5}$ = 60%

ham:
$\frac{99}{220}$ is about $\frac{100}{222}$ or $\frac{10}{22}$.
$\frac{10}{22}$ = 45%

ground chuck:
$\frac{81}{222}$ is about $\frac{80}{200}$ or $\frac{2}{5}$.
$\frac{2}{5}$ = 40%

50. a. The size of Great Britain is 94,247 mi^2.
   b. Great Britain is about 90,000 mi^2. So Georgia is 60% or $\frac{2}{3}$ of 90,000. Georgia is about 54,000 mi^2.

The total population was 2780, in thousands.

51. Connecticut: $\frac{206.7}{2780}$ is about 10%.

Delaware: $\frac{45.4}{2780}$ is about $\frac{30}{3000}$ or $\frac{1}{100}$.

$\frac{1}{100} = 1\%$

Georgia: $\frac{56.1}{2780}$ is about $\frac{60}{3000}$ or $\frac{1}{50}$.

$\frac{1}{50} = 2\%$

Kentucky: $\frac{45.0}{2780}$ is about $\frac{30}{3000}$ or $\frac{1}{100}$.

$\frac{1}{100} = 1\%$

Maine: $\frac{49.1}{2780}$ is about $\frac{50}{2500}$ or $\frac{1}{50}$.

$\frac{1}{50} = 2\%$

Maryland: $\frac{245.5}{2780}$ is about $\frac{250}{2500}$ or $\frac{1}{10}$.

$\frac{1}{10} = 10\%$

New Hampshire: $\frac{87.8}{2780}$ is about $\frac{90}{3000}$ or $\frac{3}{100}$.

$\frac{3}{100} = 3\%$

New Jersey: $\frac{139.6}{2780}$ is about $\frac{140}{2800}$ or $\frac{1}{20}$.

$\frac{1}{20} = 5\%$

New York: $\frac{210.5}{2780}$ is about 10%.

North Carolina: $\frac{270.1}{2780}$ is about $\frac{270}{2700}$ or $\frac{1}{10}$.

$\frac{1}{10} = 10\%$

Pennsylvania: $\frac{327.3}{2780}$ is about $\frac{375}{2500}$ or $\frac{3}{20}$.

$\frac{3}{20} = 15\%$

Plymouth: $\frac{268.6}{2780}$ is about $\frac{270}{2700}$ or $\frac{1}{10}$.

$\frac{1}{10} = 10\%$

Rhode Island: $\frac{52.9}{2780}$ is about $\frac{50}{2500}$ or $\frac{1}{50}$.

$\frac{1}{50} = 2\%$

South Carolina: $\frac{180.0}{2780}$ is about 10%.

Tennessee: $\frac{10.0}{2780}$ is about 1%.

Vermont: $\frac{47.6}{2780}$ is about $\frac{50}{2500}$ or $\frac{1}{50}$.

$\frac{1}{50} = 2\%$

Virginia: $\frac{538.0}{2780}$ is about $\frac{540}{2700}$ or $\frac{1}{5}$.

$\frac{1}{5} = 20\%$

52. a. $\frac{288}{560}$ is about $\frac{280}{560}$ or $\frac{1}{2}$.

$\frac{1}{2} = 50\%$

About 50% of the calories are fat calories.

b. 2000 − 560 or 1440 Calories remain for the rest of the day. 30% of 2000 Calories is 600 fat Calories, so 600 − 288 or 312 fat Calories remain.

53. $64\% = \frac{64}{100} = \frac{16}{25}$

54. $\frac{130 \text{ km}}{1 \text{ hour}} \cdot \frac{1000 \text{ meters}}{1 \text{ km}} = 130{,}000$ m per h

55. geometric; 1.5; 60.75, 91.125, 136.6875

56. $\frac{9}{16} + \frac{11}{16} = y$

$\frac{20}{16} = y$

$1\frac{4}{16} = y$

$1\frac{1}{4} = y$

57. $5x = 105$

$\frac{5x}{5} = \frac{105}{5}$

$x = 21$

Check: $5x = 105$

$5(21) \stackrel{?}{=} 105$

$105 = 105$ ✔

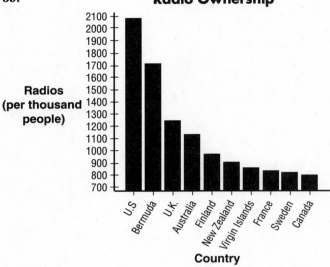

58. $|-21| = 21$

59.

Radio Ownership

60. $2(n + 7)$

Page 466 From the Funny Papers

1. See students' work.

2. The student answered 10 − 6 or 4 questions correctly.

3. $\frac{4}{10} = 0.4 \rightarrow \frac{40}{100} = 40\%$

4. See students' work.

9-9 Using Percent Equations

Page 467 Your Turn

a. Option 4 because it has a high interest rate, a long term, and a high initial investment.

b. $I = prt$

Page 469 Checking Your Understanding

1. $R = \frac{r}{100}$

2. Sample answer: Find 75% of $60 or find 25% of 60 and subtract from $60.

3. If the rate and the base are known, then you can just multiply.

4.
$$R = \frac{r}{100}$$
$$0.32 = \frac{r}{100}$$
$$0.32 \cdot 100 = r$$
$$32 = r$$

5. Jalisa; because 1.5% = 0.015 not 1.5.

6.
$$75 = 0.50 \cdot B$$
$$\frac{75}{0.50} = \frac{0.50B}{0.50}$$
$$150 = B$$
75 is 50% of 150.

7.
$$30 = 0.15 \cdot B$$
$$\frac{30}{0.15} = \frac{0.15B}{0.15}$$
$$200 = B$$
15% of 200 is 30.

8.
$$18 = R \cdot 60$$
$$\frac{18}{60} = \frac{60R}{60}$$
$$0.30 = R$$
18 is 30% of 60.

9.
$$P = 0.24 \cdot 72$$
$$P = 17.28$$
17.28 is 24% of 72.

10. 33% of $450 = d
$$(0.33)(450) = 148.50$$
The discount is $148.50.

11. 15% of $315 = d
$$(0.15)(315) = 47.25$$
The discount is $47.25.

12.
$$I = prt$$
$$I = (3500)(0.12)(2.5)$$
$$I = \$1050.00$$

13.
$$P = 0.28 \cdot 12{,}000{,}000$$
$$P = 3{,}360{,}000$$
About 3.36 million Japanese tourists visited the United States.

Pages 469–471 Exercises

14.
$$15 = R \cdot 100$$
$$\frac{15}{100} = \frac{100R}{100}$$
$$0.15 = R$$
15 is 15% of 100.

15.
$$P = 0.20 \cdot 135$$
$$P = 27$$
27 is 20% of 135.

16.
$$P = 0.43 \cdot 15$$
$$P = 6.45$$
6.45 is 43% of 15.

17.
$$28 = 0.40 \cdot B$$
$$\frac{28}{0.40} = \frac{0.40B}{0.40}$$
$$70 = B$$
28 is 40% of 70.

18.
$$39 = 0.15 \cdot B$$
$$\frac{39}{0.15} = \frac{0.15B}{0.15}$$
$$260 = B$$
15% of 260 is 39.

19.
$$P = 0.42 \cdot 75$$
$$P = 31.5$$
42% of 75 is 31.5.

20.
$$45 = R \cdot 150$$
$$\frac{45}{150} = \frac{150R}{150}$$
$$0.30 = R$$
45 is 30% of 150.

21.
$$42 = R \cdot 14$$
$$\frac{42}{14} = \frac{14R}{14}$$
$$3 = R$$
42 is 300% of 14.

22.
$$880 = 1.10 \cdot B$$
$$\frac{880}{1.10} = \frac{1.10B}{1.10}$$
$$800 = R$$
110% of 800 is 880.

23.
$$5 = R \cdot 300$$
$$\frac{5}{300} = \frac{300R}{300}$$
$$0.01\overline{6} = R$$
5 is 1.$\overline{6}$% of 300.

24.
$$P = 0.0204 \cdot 256$$
$$P = 5.2224$$
2.04% of 256 is 5.2224.

25.
$$18.6 = 0.155 \cdot B$$
$$\frac{18.6}{0.155} = \frac{0.155B}{0.155}$$
$$120 = B$$
18.6 is 15.5% of 120.

26.
$$P = 0.3\overline{3} \cdot 420$$
$$P = 140$$
$33\frac{1}{3}$% of 420 is 140.

27.
$$100 = 5 \cdot B$$
$$\frac{100}{5} = \frac{5B}{5}$$
$$20 = B$$
500% of 20 is 100.

28. 28% of $49.95 = d
$$(0.28)(49.95) = 13.986$$
The discount is $13.99.

29. 35% of $199.99 = d
$$(0.35)(199.99) = 69.9965$$
The discount is $70.

30. 40% of $299.99 = d
$$(0.40)(299.99) = 119.996$$
The discount is $120.00.

31. 15% of $1250 = d
$$(0.15)(1250) = 187.5$$
The discount is $187.50.

32.
$$I = prt$$
$$I = (500)(0.003)(15)$$
$$I = \$22.50$$

33.
$$I = prt$$
$$I = (250)(0.085)(2)$$
$$I = \$42.50$$

34.
$$I = prt$$
$$I = (1250)(0.015)(7)$$
$$I = \$131.25$$

35. $I = prt$: 15 months = $1\frac{1}{4}$ years
$$I = (945)(0.035)(1.25)$$
$$I = 41.34375$$
$$I = \$41.34$$

36. yes; x% of $y = \frac{x}{100} \cdot y$ or $\frac{xy}{100}$ and y% of $x = \frac{y}{100} \cdot x$ or $\frac{xy}{100}$

37.
$$P = 0.374 \cdot 249{,}000{,}000$$
$$P = 93{,}126{,}000$$
About 93 million Americans have O$^+$ blood.

38.
$$25.7 = R \cdot 43.3$$
$$\frac{25.7}{43.3} = \frac{43.3R}{43.3}$$
$$0.594 = R$$
59.4% of trips
car, not rented: 59.4%

$$12.0 = R \cdot 43.3$$
$$\frac{12.0}{43.3} = \frac{43.3R}{43.3}$$
$$0.277 = R$$
airplane: 27.7%

$$3.3 = R \cdot 43.3$$
$$\frac{3.3}{43.3} = \frac{43.3R}{43.3}$$
$$0.076 = R$$
car, rented: 7.6%

$$1.0 = R \cdot 43.3$$
$$\frac{1.0}{43.3} = \frac{43.3R}{43.3}$$
$$0.023 = R$$
motor home: 2.3%

$$0.7 = R \cdot 43.3$$
$$\frac{0.7}{43.3} = \frac{43.3R}{43.3}$$
$$0.0161 = R$$
bus: 1.6%

$$0.6 = R \cdot 43.3$$
$$\frac{0.6}{43.3} = \frac{43.3R}{43.3}$$
$$0.0138 = R$$
train: 1.4%

39. They would be paying the customers.

40. commission is 15% of $2300
$$(0.15)(2300) = 345$$
An associate would earn $345 from the sale of a $2300 computer.

41. a. $(0.10)(439) = 43.9$
With the 10% discount, the television would cost $439 - 43.9$ or \$395.10.
$(0.33)(395.10) = 130.383$
With the additional 33% discount, Jackee's price for the television is $395.10 - 130.383$ or \$264.72.

b. No; the price is the same either way.

c. You could not add the percents first. For example, if the price was \$100, $10\% + 33\% = 43\%$ off. Using this method, the price would be $100 - 43$ or \$57. Taking 33% off, then 10% would have the price as \$60.30.

42. $I = prt$
$I = (5500)(0.0024)(1)$
$I = \$13.20$

43. The statements are not equivalent. For example, suppose an item costs \$1.00 on day 1. According to the first statement, it would cost \$2.08, not $\$1.00 \times 2$ or \$2.00, on the fifth day.
Day 2 $1.2 \times 1.0 = \$1.20$
Day 3 $1.2 \times 1.20 = \$1.44$
Day 4 $1.2 \times 1.44 = \$1.728$ or \$1.73
Day 5 $1.2 \times 1.73 = \$2.076$ or \$2.08

44. Sample answer:
68% is about 70% or $\frac{7}{10}$.
210 is about 200.
$\frac{7}{10}$ of 200 is 140.

45. positive

46. yes

47. a. $3v - 298 = 1916$
b. $\quad 3v - 298 = 1916$
$3v - 298 + 298 = 1916 + 298$
$\quad\quad\quad 3v = 2214$
$\quad\quad\quad\quad v = 738$

48.
$$16)\overline{5.0000} \quad 0.3125$$
$\underline{-4\,8}$
$\quad 20$
$\quad \underline{-16}$
$\quad\quad 40$
$\quad\quad \underline{-32}$
$\quad\quad\quad 80$
$\quad\quad\quad \underline{-80}$
$\quad\quad\quad\quad 0$
$\frac{5}{16} = 0.3125$

49. $150 = 2 \cdot 3 \cdot 5 \cdot 5$
$345 = 3 \cdot 5 \cdot 23$
The GCF is $3 \cdot 5$ or 15.

50. a. $\quad r + 6 = 148$
b. $\quad r + 6 = 148$
$r + 6 - 6 = 148 - 6$
$\quad\quad\quad r = 142$

51. $12 + (-5) = +(|12| - |-5|)$
$\quad\quad\quad\quad = +(12 - 5)$
$\quad\quad\quad\quad = 7$

9-10   Percent of Change

Page 474   Checking Your Understanding

1. Sample answer: Find the change, then solve for the percent of the change to the original amount; or divide the new amount by the original amount, then subtract 1 and write the result as a percent.

2. $25 - 20 = 5$
$\quad\quad 5 = R \cdot 20$
$\quad\quad \frac{5}{20} = \frac{20R}{20}$
$\quad 0.25 = R$
an increase of 25%

3. the original amount

4. No;
$21 - 14 = 7$
$\quad\quad 7 = R \cdot 14$
$\quad\quad \frac{7}{14} = \frac{14R}{14}$
$\quad 0.50 = R$
The percent of change was 50%.

5. See students' work.

6. increase;
$16 - 10 = 6$
$\quad\quad 6 = R \cdot 10$
$\quad\quad \frac{6}{10} = \frac{10R}{10}$
$\quad 0.6 = R$
The percent of increase is 60%.

7. decrease;
$22 - 25 = -3$
$\quad\quad -3 = R \cdot 25$
$\quad\quad \frac{-3}{25} = \frac{25R}{25}$
$\quad -0.12 = R$
The percent of decrease is 12%.

8. increase;
$150 - 120 = 30$
$\quad\quad 30 = R \cdot 120$
$\quad\quad \frac{30}{120} = \frac{120R}{120}$
$\quad 0.25 = R$
The percent of increase is 25%.

9. decrease;
$55 - 59 = -4$
$\quad\quad -4 = R \cdot 59$
$\quad\quad \frac{-4}{59} = \frac{59R}{59}$
$\quad -0.067 = R$
The percent of decrease is about 7%.

10. At closing, the average was 1738.42 points. So, at the beginning of the day, the Dow was $1738.42 + 508.32$ or 2246.74 points.
$1738.42 - 2246.74 = -508.32$
$\quad\quad -508.32 = R \cdot 2246.74$
$\quad\quad \frac{-508.32}{2246.74} = \frac{2246.74R}{2246.74}$
$\quad\quad -0.226 = R$
The percent of decrease of the average was 22.6%.

Pages 474–475   Exercises

11. decrease;
$114 - 142 = -28$
$\quad\quad -28 = R \cdot 142$
$\quad\quad \frac{-28}{142} = \frac{142R}{142}$
$\quad -0.197 = R$
The percent of decrease is about 20%.

12. decrease;

$$0.30 - 0.59 = -0.29$$
$$-0.29 = R \cdot 0.59$$
$$\frac{-0.29}{0.59} = \frac{0.59R}{0.59}$$
$$-0.491 = R$$

The percent of decrease is about 49%.

13. increase;

$$480 - 425 = 55$$
$$55 = R \cdot 425$$
$$\frac{55}{425} = \frac{425R}{425}$$
$$0.129 = R$$

The percent of increase is about 13%.

14. decrease;

$$44 - 48 = -4$$
$$-4 = R \cdot 48$$
$$\frac{-4}{48} = \frac{48R}{48}$$
$$-0.83\overline{3} = R$$

The percent of decrease is about 8%.

15. increase;

$$108 - 96 = 12$$
$$12 = R \cdot 96$$
$$\frac{12}{96} = \frac{96R}{96}$$
$$0.125 = R$$

The percent of increase is about 13%.

16. decrease;

$$12.5 - 14.5 = -2$$
$$-2 = R \cdot 14.5$$
$$\frac{-2}{14.5} = \frac{14.5R}{14.5}$$
$$-0.137 = R$$

The percent of decrease is about 14%.

17. increase;

$$251 - 228 = 23$$
$$23 = R \cdot 228$$
$$\frac{23}{228} = \frac{228R}{228}$$
$$0.101 = R$$

The percent of increase is about 10%.

18. decrease;

$$26.5 - 29.5 = -3$$
$$-3 = R \cdot 29.5$$
$$\frac{-3}{29.5} = \frac{29.5R}{29.5}$$
$$-0.101 = R$$

The percent of decrease is about 10%.

19. increase;

$$42.59 - 39.99 = 2.6$$
$$2.6 = R \cdot 39.99$$
$$\frac{2.6}{39.99} = \frac{39.99R}{39.99}$$
$$0.065 = R$$

The percent of increase is about 7%.

20. increase;

$$137 - 124 = 13$$
$$13 = R \cdot 124$$
$$\frac{13}{124} = \frac{124R}{124}$$
$$0.104 = R$$

The percent of increase is about 10%.

21. increase;

$$250 - 106 = 144$$
$$144 = R \cdot 106$$
$$\frac{144}{106} = \frac{106R}{106}$$
$$1.358 = R$$

The percent of increase is about 136%.

22. increase;

$$4351.50 - 4329.80 = 21.7$$
$$21.7 = R \cdot 4329.80$$
$$\frac{21.7}{4329.80} = \frac{4329.80R}{4329.80}$$
$$0.005 = R$$

The percent of increase is about 1%.

23 a. No; Suppose the price of the outfit is $100. The price would be $50 after the first reduction. After the second reduction, the price would be $50 - 0.3(50) = 50 - 15$ or $35. A final price of $35 is $\frac{100 - 35}{100}$ or 65% off, not 80% off.

b. 65%

24. Let x represent the original amount. After the increase it is still $1.1x$. After the decrease it is $0.9(1.1x)$ or $0.99x$. Since when x is positive, $0.99x < x$, the final amount is less than the original.

25.
$$6225 - 7800 = -1575$$
$$-1575 = R \cdot 7800$$
$$\frac{-1575}{7800} = \frac{7800R}{7800}$$
$$-0.201 = R$$

The percent of decrease of the value of the car is about 20%.

26. a. The percent of profit at a sale price of $110 is $\frac{115 - 85}{85} = \frac{25}{85}$ or 29%.

b. The original selling price was $85 + 0.65(85) = 85 + 55.25$ or 140.25. The percent of discount from the original selling price is $\frac{140.25 - 110}{140.25} = \frac{30.25}{140.25}$ or 22%.

27.
$$\frac{0.32}{0.29} = \frac{x}{2.90}$$
$$0.32 \cdot 2.90 = 0.29 \cdot x$$
$$0.928 = 0.29x$$
$$3.2 = x$$

Priority mail would cost $3.20.

28. a.
$$5.5 - 6 = -0.5$$
$$-0.5 = R \cdot 6$$
$$\frac{-0.5}{6} = \frac{6R}{6}$$
$$-0.833 = R$$

The percent of decrease is 8.3%.

b.

6 ounce cans
$$\frac{\$1.59}{6 \text{ ounce}} = \frac{26.5 \text{ cents}}{1 \text{ ounce}}$$
26.5 cents/ounce

5.5 ounce cans
$$\frac{\$1.59}{5.5 \text{ ounce}} = \frac{28.9 \text{ cents}}{1 \text{ ounce}}$$
28.9 cents/ounce

$$28.9 - 26.5 = 2.4$$
$$2.4 = R \cdot 26.5$$
$$\frac{2.4}{26.5} = \frac{26.5R}{26.5}$$
$$0.091 = R$$

The percent of increase in price per ounce is 9.1%.

29. $P = R \cdot B$
$P = 2.5 \cdot 50$
$P = 125$
A breeder should expect to sell 125 hedgehogs.

30. $(0.35)(15.50) = 5.425$
With the 35% discount, the sale price of the earrings is $15.50 - 5.425$ or \$10.08.

31. Yes; it passes the vertical line test.

32. $\frac{1}{2}(4{,}921{,}000{,}000) = 2{,}460{,}500{,}000$
About 2,500,000,000 barrels of oil are produced each year.

33. **Shirt** **Pants**

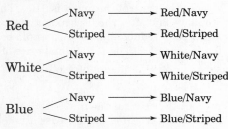

Without the blazer, there are 6 possible outfits. Adding the blazer to each outfit, there will be 6 more outfits. So, there is a total of 12 outfits.

34. $n = 14 - (-3)$
$n = 14 + 3$
$n = 17$

Chapter 9   Study Guide and Assessment

Page 477   Understanding and Using Vocabulary

1. true

2. false; A percentage is a ratio that compares a number to 100.

3. false; In this proportion, 16 is the percentage.

4. false; A sample space is the set of all possible outcomes of an event.

5. true

6. false; A ratio is a comparison of two numbers by divisions.

7. false; The property of proportions allows you to compare two ratios.

Pages 478–480   Skills and Concepts

8. $\frac{10}{18} = \frac{5}{9}$

9. $\frac{287}{315} = \frac{41}{15}$

10. $\frac{15}{90} = \frac{1}{6}$

11. $\frac{600}{1000} = \frac{3}{5}$

12. $\frac{339.2 \text{ miles}}{10.6 \text{ gallons}} = \frac{32 \text{ miles}}{1 \text{ gallon}}$

13. $\frac{\$1.78}{2 \text{ pounds}} = \$0.89$ per pound

14. $\frac{\$425}{17 \text{ tickets}} = \frac{\$25}{1 \text{ ticket}}$

15. $\frac{142.5 \text{ miles}}{2.5 \text{ hours}} = \frac{57 \text{ miles}}{1 \text{ hour}}$

16. $P(\text{cola}) = \frac{6}{21}$ or $\frac{2}{7}$

17. $P(\text{fruit punch or iced tea}) = \frac{13}{21}$

18. $P(\text{not carbonated}) = \frac{15}{21}$ or $\frac{5}{7}$

19. $P(\text{cola or lemonade}) = \frac{8}{21}$

20. $P(\text{iced tea}) = \frac{9}{21}$ or $\frac{3}{7}$

21. $P(\text{neither cola nor fruit punch}) = \frac{11}{21}$

22. $\frac{8}{6} = \frac{z}{14}$
$8 \cdot 14 = 6 \cdot z$
$112 = 6z$
$\frac{112}{6} = \frac{6z}{6}$
$18\frac{2}{3} = z$

23. $\frac{5.1}{1.7} = \frac{7.5}{a}$
$5.1 \cdot a = 1.7 \cdot 7.5$
$5.1a = 12.75$
$\frac{5.1a}{5.1} = \frac{12.75}{5.1}$
$a = 2.5$

24. $\frac{5.60}{20} = \frac{9.80}{x}$
$5.60 \cdot x = 20 \cdot 9.80$
$5.60x = 196$
$\frac{5.60x}{5.60} = \frac{196}{5.60}$
$x = 35$

25. $\frac{88.4}{3.4} = \frac{161.2}{g}$
$88.4 \cdot g = 3.4 \cdot 161.2$
$88.4g = 548.08$
$\frac{88.4g}{88.4} = \frac{548.08}{88.4}$
$g = 6.2$

26. $\frac{P}{5} = \frac{40}{100}$
$P \cdot 100 = 5 \cdot 40$
$100P = 200$
$\frac{100P}{100} = \frac{200}{100}$
$P = 2$
40% of 5 is 2.

27. $\frac{19}{25} = \frac{r}{100}$
$19 \cdot 100 = 25 \cdot r$
$1900 = 25r$
$\frac{1900}{25} = \frac{25r}{25}$
$76 = r$
19 is 76% of 25.

28. $\frac{P}{50} = \frac{120}{100}$
$P \cdot 100 = 50 \cdot 120$
$100P = 6000$
$\frac{100P}{100} = \frac{6000}{100}$
$P = 60$
60 is 120% of 50.

29. $\frac{P}{4000} = \frac{0.1}{100}$
$P \cdot 100 = 4000 \cdot 0.1$
$100P = 400$
$\frac{100P}{100} = \frac{400}{100}$
$P = 4$
4 is 0.1% of 4000.

30. $\frac{x}{459} = \frac{37}{110}$
$x \cdot 110 = 459 \cdot 37$
$110x = 16{,}983$
$x = 154.39$
About 154 customers would choose apple pie.

31. $\frac{x}{500} = \frac{7}{110}$
$x \cdot 110 = 500 \cdot 7$
$110x = 3500$
$x = 31.818$
About 32 customers would choose cheesecake.

32. $0.92 \rightarrow \frac{0.92}{1} = \frac{92}{100}$ or 92%

33. $0.0056 \rightarrow \frac{0.0056}{1} = \frac{0.56}{100}$ or 0.56%

34. $\frac{63}{100} = 63\%$

35. $\frac{113}{200} = 0.565 \rightarrow \frac{56.5}{100} = 56.5\%$

36. $90\% = \frac{90}{100}$ **37.** $65\% = \frac{65}{100}$

     $= \frac{45}{50}$ $= \frac{13}{20}$

38. $45\% = \frac{45}{100}$ **39.** $235\% = \frac{235}{100}$

     $= 0.45$ $= 2.35$

40. $2\% = \frac{2}{100} = \frac{1}{50}$

$\frac{1}{50}$ of 180 is 3.6.

So, the correct choice is b.

41. 198% is about 200% or 2.

2 of 5 is 10.

So, the correct choice is a.

42. 8% is about 10% or $\frac{1}{10}$

$\frac{1}{10}$ of 420 is 42.

So, the correct choice is a.

43. 73% is about 75% or $\frac{3}{4}$.

$\frac{3}{4}$ of 80 is 60.

So, the correct choice is a.

44. 352% is about 350% or $3\frac{1}{2}$.

$3\frac{1}{2}$ of 20 is 70.

So, the correct choice is c.

45. 0.6% is about 1% or $\frac{1}{100}$.

620 is about 600.

$\frac{1}{100}$ of 600 is 6.

So, the correct choice is b.

46. $54 = 1.50 \cdot B$ **47.** $3.2 = 0.16 \cdot B$

$\frac{54}{1.50} = \frac{1.50B}{1.50}$ $\frac{3.2}{0.16} = \frac{0.16B}{0.16}$

$36 = B$ $20 = B$

54 is 150% of 36.   16% of 20 is 3.2.

48. $63 = R \cdot 105$ **49.** $2600 = 0.65 \cdot B$

$\frac{63}{105} = \frac{105R}{105}$ $\frac{2600}{0.65} = \frac{0.65B}{0.65}$

$0.6 = R$ $4000 = B$

63 is 60% of 105.   2600 is 65% of 4000.

50. $16 = R \cdot 2$ **51.** $5 = R \cdot 16$

$\frac{16}{2} = \frac{2R}{2}$ $\frac{5}{16} = \frac{16R}{16}$

$8 = R$ $0.3125 = R$

16 is 800% of 2.   31.25% of 16 is 5.

52. increase;

$0.75 - 0.60 = 0.15$

$0.15 = R \cdot 0.60$

$\frac{0.15}{0.60} = \frac{0.60R}{0.60}$

$0.25 = R$

The percent of increase is 25%.

53. decrease;

$15.8 - 16 = -0.2$

$-0.2 = R \cdot 16$

$\frac{-0.2}{16} = \frac{16R}{16}$

$-0.0125 = R$

The percent of decrease is about 1%.

54. decrease;

$17.5 - 18.4 = -0.9$

$-0.9 = R \cdot 18.4$

$\frac{-0.9}{18.4} = \frac{18.4R}{18.4}$

$-0.048 = R$

The percent of decrease is about 5%.

55. decrease;

$11.75 - 15.00 = -3.25$

$-3.25 = R \cdot 15.00$

$\frac{-3.25}{15.00} = \frac{15.00R}{15.00}$

$-0.21\overline{6} = R$

The percent of decrease is about 22%.

56. increase;

$118 - 84 = 34$

$34 = R \cdot 84$

$\frac{34}{84} = \frac{84R}{84}$

$0.404 = R$

The percent of increase is about 40%.

57. decrease;

$185 - 210 = -25$

$-25 = R \cdot 210$

$\frac{-25}{210} = \frac{210R}{210}$

$-0.119 = R$

The percent of decrease is about 12%.

Page 480   Applications and Problem Solving

58. $\frac{0.001 \text{ m}}{1 \text{ m}} = \frac{1}{1000}$

59.

Blank	1	2	3	4	5	6
Blank	1	2	3	4	5	6
1	2	3	4	5	6	
2	3	4	5	6		
3	4	5	6			
4	5	6				
5	6					
6						

There are 28 dominoes in a set.

60. 58% of 185 million

$(0.58)(185) = 107.3$

About 107 million American adults wear their seat belts all the time.

Page 481   Alternative Assessment

1–7. See students' work.

Page 481   Thinking Critically

- Move the decimal point two places to the right.
- Sample answer: no; the chance would have to be 100% both days for it to be 100% for the whole weekend.

Page 481   Portfolio

- See students' work.

Page 481   Self–Evaluation

- See students' work.

Chapter 10 More Statistics and Probability

10-1	Stem-and-Leaf Plots

Pages 487–488 Checking Your Understanding

1. A stem-and-leaf plot is used to summarize numerical data.

2. The stems are 3, 4, 5, and 6.

3. It is similar to a horizontal bar graph because the more leaves a stem has the longer the line of leaves is. It is different because there are no bars drawn and the individual data can be read.

4. Sample answer: Olajuwon's highest and lowest scores.

5. **a–b.** See students' work.

6. Stems: 6, 7, 8, 9

$$
\begin{array}{c|l}
6 & 5\ 9 \\
7 & 3\ 8 \\
8 & 0\ 2\ 6\ 8 \\
9 & 1\ 5
\end{array}
$$
$$6\,|\,5 = 65$$

7. Stems: 5, 6, 7, 8

$$
\begin{array}{c|l}
5 & 4\ 7 \\
6 & 3\ 7\ 8\ 9 \\
7 & 1\ 5\ 7 \\
8 & 5
\end{array}
$$
$$5\,|\,4 = 5.4$$

8. **a.** The highest score was 70 and the lowest score was 23.

   b. The highest score was 72 and the lowest score was 36.

   c. Knox: 23, 31, 33, 36, 42, 44, 44, 45, 46, 48, 49, 52, 56, 56, 58, 58, 59, 60, 65, 70
   median: $\frac{48 + 49}{2} = 48.5$

   Opponents: 36, 37, 40, 43, 44, 45, 45, 46, 51, 51, 53, 55, 56, 56, 57, 61, 63, 65, 66, 72
   median: $\frac{51 + 53}{2} = 52$

Pages 488–489 Exercises

9.
$$
\begin{array}{c|l}
6 & 0\ 1\ 4\ 5\ 7\ 8 \\
7 & 0\ 0\ 2\ 3 \\
8 & 0\ 0
\end{array}
$$
$$6\,|\,0 = 60$$

10.
$$
\begin{array}{c|l}
1 & 4\ 9 \\
2 & 1\ 3\ 5\ 8 \\
3 & 2\ 4\ 6\ 9\ 9 \\
4 & 5\ 5\ 8\ 8\ 8 \\
5 & 1
\end{array}
$$
$$1\,|\,4 = 14$$

11.
$$
\begin{array}{c|l}
0 & 5\ 6\ 7\ 9\ 9 \\
1 & 1\ 2 \\
2 & 1\ 3 \\
3 & \\
4 & 0\ 2\ 5
\end{array}
$$
$$4\,|\,0 = 40$$

12.
$$
\begin{array}{c|l}
5 & 4\ 4 \\
6 & 8 \\
7 & 5 \\
8 & 3\ 5\ 9 \\
9 & 2\ 4\ 6\ 9 \\
10 & \\
11 & 6\ 7
\end{array}
$$
$$5\,|\,4 = 54$$

13.
$$
\begin{array}{c|l}
9 & 2 \\
10 & 4\ 8 \\
11 & 1\ 2\ 2\ 7 \\
12 & 3\ 6\ 8\ 9 \\
13 & 3\ 8 \\
14 & 7
\end{array}
$$
$$9\,|\,2 = 9.2$$

14. **a.**
$$
\begin{array}{c|l}
2 & 3\ 5\ 8\ 8 \\
3 & 1\ 2\ 3\ 3\ 6\ 9 \\
4 & 2\ 5\ 7 \\
5 & 1\ 3
\end{array}
$$
$$4\,|\,2 = 42$$

   b. The greatest number of floors is 53.

   c. The least number of floors is 23.

   d. 8 buildings had 34 or less floors.

   e. 6 buildings were in the 30–39 floor range.

15. **a.**

women's		men's
5	4	5
5 5	5	
7 5 0	6	
5 2 0 0 0	7	0 0 0 0 0 5
5 0	8	2 2 3
0	9	
	10	0
	11	0
4	12	0 5
	13	3

$$5\,|\,4 = 45 \qquad\qquad 4\,|\,5 = 45$$

   b. Sample answer: Men's running shoes are more expensive than women's. The typical running shoe costs $70.

16. You must have data that are in a relatively small range.

17. Sample answer: Yes; since all the data can be read from a stem-and-leaf plot, you can estimate their sum and divide by the number of leaves to estimate the mean.

18. **a.**
$$
\begin{array}{c|l}
3 & 7\ 7\ 8 \\
4 & 0\ 0\ 0\ 2\ 2\ 6\ 9\ 9 \\
5 & 1\ 2\ 3 \\
6 & 0\ 7
\end{array}
$$
$$3\,|\,7 = 37°$$

   b. Sample answer: Somewhere in the 40s.

19. **a.**

Distress		No Distress
8 7 3	5	
3	6	6 7 7 7 8 9
5 0 0	7	0 0 2 3 5 6 6 8 9
	8	1

$$3\,|\,5 = 53 \qquad\qquad 7\,|\,0 = 70$$

   b. Answers will vary. Sample answer: The O-rings appear more reliable at higher temperatures.

   c. Answers will vary. Sample answer: Yes; There were more cases of distress at the lower temperatures.

20. $236.4 - 233.2 = 3.2$
$$3.2 = R \cdot 233.2$$
$$\frac{3.2}{233.2} = \frac{233.2R}{233.2}$$
$$0.013 = R$$
The percent of increase is about 1%.

21. $45\% = \frac{45}{100}$
$$= \frac{9}{20}$$

22.
$$x - 3.4 = 9.2$$
$$x - 3.4 + 3.4 = 9.2 + 3.4$$
$$x = 12.6$$
Check: $x - 3.4 = 9.2$
$$12.6 - 3.4 \stackrel{?}{=} 9.2$$
$$9.2 = 9.2 \checkmark$$

23. Let $n =$ number
$$-2n + 5 > 10$$
$$-2n + 5 - 5 > 10 - 5$$
$$-2n > 5$$
$$\frac{-2n}{-2} < \frac{5}{-2}$$
$$n < -2\frac{1}{2}$$

The number must be less than $-2\frac{1}{2}$. Since $-4 < -2\frac{1}{2}$, the correct choice is d.

24. $|-9| + 14 = 9 + 14$
$$= 23$$

10-2   Measures of Variation

Page 490   Your Turn

a. The difference of adult prices is slightly greater.

b. The median of the lower half of the youth prices is higher than the lower half of the adult prices. The median of the upper halves are the same.

Page 492   Checking Your Understanding

1. Sample answer: Measures of variation describe the spread of data. Measures of central tendency describe the set as a whole.

2. Sample answer: 10, 12, 16, 18, 18, 20, 22, 24, 26, 26, 28, 40, 60

10 12 16 18 18 20 22 24 26 26 28 40 60

$LQ = \frac{16 + 18}{2} = 17$ Median $UQ = \frac{26 + 28}{2} = 27$

The range is $60 - 10$ or 50.
The interquartile range is $27 - 17$ or 10.

3. The data is clustered about the median.

4. 63 65 71 78 80 82 86 89 92 95
The range is $95 - 63$ or 32.

5. The range is $24 - 11$ or 13.

6. 29.8 29.9 30.1 30.2 30.5 30.7 30.8 33.2
The range is $33.2 - 29.8$ or 3.4.

7. The range is $94 - 42$ or 52.

8. a. 42 43 49 54 55 67 73 78 82 91 93 94

Median

The median is $\frac{67 + 73}{2}$ or 70.

b. 42 43 49 54 55 67 73 78 82 91 93 94

LQ   Median   UQ

The upper quartile is $\frac{82 + 91}{2}$ or 86.5 and the

lower quartile is $\frac{49 + 54}{2}$ or 51.5.

c. The interquartile range is $86.5 - 51.5$ or 35.

---

9. a. Sample answer:

3	8 9
4	0 2 6
5	8
6	1 2 3 3
7	0
8	0 4
9	4

$3|8 = 38$

b. 38 39 40 42 46 58 61 62 63 63 70 80 84 94

Median

The median is $\frac{61 + 62}{2}$ or 61.5.

c. 38 39 40 42 46 58 61 62 63 63 70 80 84 94

LQ   UQ

The upper quartile is 70 and the lower quartile is 42.

d. The interquartile range is $70 - 42$ or 28.

Pages 493–494   Exercises

10. 10 29 34 37 43 45 56

LQ Median UQ

The range is $56 - 10$ or 46.
The median is 37.
The upper quartile is 45 and the lower quartile is 29.
The interquartile range is $45 - 29$ or 16.

11. 30 40 50 60 70 80 90 100

LQ   Median   UQ

The range is $100 - 30$ or 70.
The median is $\frac{60 + 70}{2}$ or 65.

The upper quartile is $\frac{80 + 90}{2}$ or 85 and the lower

quartile is $\frac{40 + 50}{2}$ or 45.
The interquartile range is $85 - 45$ or 40.

12. 17 18 18 19 21 22 36

LQ Median UQ

The range is $36 - 17$ or 19.
The median is 19.
The upper quartile is 22 and the lower quartile is 18.
The interquartile range is $22 - 18$ or 4.

13. 2 2 4 4 7 8 11 16 23

LQ   Median   UQ

The range is $23 - 2$ or 21.
The median is 7.
The upper quartile is $\frac{11 + 16}{2}$ or 13.5 and the lower

quartile is $\frac{2 + 4}{2}$ or 3.
The interquartile range is $13.5 - 3$ or 10.5.

14. 125 135 136 145 156 170 174 180 188

LQ   Median   UQ

The range is $188 - 125$ or 63.
The median is 156.

The upper quartile is $\frac{174 + 180}{2}$ or 177 and the lower quartile is $\frac{135 + 136}{2}$ or 135.5.

The interquartile range is $177 - 135.5$ or 41.5.

15. 180 199 200 205 207 208 210 211 213 225 229

        ↑   ↑   ↑

        LQ   Median   UQ

The range is $229 - 180$ or 49.

The median is 208.

The upper quartile is 213 and the lower quartile is 200.

The interquartile range is $213 - 200$ or 13.

16. 59 60 60 61 62 62 63 65 71 72

      ↑   ↑   ↑

     LQ Median UQ

The range is $72 - 59$ or 13.

The median is $\frac{62 + 62}{2}$ or 62.

The upper quartile is 65 and the lower quartile is 60.

The interquartile range is $65 - 60$ or 5.

17. 7.3 7.5 8.3 8.8 8.9 9.0 9.0 9.1 9.2

          ↑   ↑

         LQ   Median

9.4 9.4 9.7 9.7 9.8 10.3 10.6 11.4

       ↑

      UQ

The range is $11.4 - 7.3$ or 4.1.

The median is 9.2.

The upper quartile is $\frac{9.7 + 9.8}{2}$ or 9.75 and the lower quartile is $\frac{8.8 + 8.9}{2}$ or 8.85.

The interquartile range is $9.75 - 8.85$ or 0.9.

18. 250 253 257 259 261 263 264 265

               ↑

              LQ

265 266 271 275 276 276 279 281

        ↑

     Median

282 283 285 288 292 295 296 299

   ↑

  UQ

The range is $299 - 250$ or 49.

The median is $\frac{275 + 276}{2}$ or 275.5.

The upper quartile is $\frac{283 + 285}{2}$ or 284 and the lower quartile is $\frac{263 + 264}{2}$ or 263.5.

The interquartile range is $284 - 263.5$ or 20.5.

19. 28,800,000
30,200,000
33,100,000 ← LQ
34,600,000
35,100,000
51,100,000 ← Median
51,700,000
52,600,000 ← UQ
54,100,000
66,400,000

The range is $66,400,000 - 28,800,000$ or 37,600,000.

The median is $\frac{35,100,000 + 51,100,000}{2}$ or 43,100,000.

The upper quartile is 52,600,000 and the lower quartile is 33,100,000.

The interquartile range is $52,600,000 - 33,100,000$ or 19,500,000.

20. 20,848
23,845
28,330 ← LQ
28,396
31,457
55,795 ← Median
64,200
79,440 ← UQ
140,985
159,973

The range is $159,973 - 20,848$ or 139,125.

The median is $\frac{31,457 + 55,795}{2}$ or 43,626.

The upper quartile is 79,440 and the lower quartile is 28,330.

The interquartile range is $79,440 - 28,330$ or 51,110.

21. American League
22 32 32 32 32 33 36 36 37 39

                   ↑

                 LQ

39 39 40 40 40 40 41 42 43 43

               ↑

           Median

44 44 44 44 45 45 46 46 48 49

             ↑

          UQ

49 49 49 50 51 61

The range is $61 - 22$ or 39.

The median is $\frac{42 + 43}{2}$ or 42.5.

The upper quartile is $\frac{46 + 46}{2}$ or 46 and the lower quartile is $\frac{37 + 39}{2}$ or 38.

The interquartile range is $46 - 38$ or 8.

National League
31 35 36 36 36 37 37 37 38 38

                   ↑

                 LQ

38 39 39 40 40 40 40 40 41 43

               ↑

           Median

44 44 44 45 45 46 46 47 47 48

             ↑

          UQ

48 48 49 49 52 52

The range is $52 - 31$ or 21.

The median is $\frac{40 + 41}{2}$ or 40.5.

The upper quartile is $\frac{46 + 47}{2}$ or 46.5 and the lower quartile is $\frac{38 + 38}{2}$ or 38.

The interquartile range is $46.5 - 38$ or 8.5.

22. See students' work.

23. a. See students' work.

   b. See students' work.

   c. Sample answer: The first set of data has a smaller interquartile range, thus the data in the first set are more tightly clustered around the mean and the data in the second set are spread out over the range.

24. a.

```
January │   │ July
      1 │ 0 │ 0 0 1 4
  9 7 7 5 │ 1 │
8 7 7 1 1 │ 2 │ 0 1 8 9
    5 3 │ 3 │ 0 1 9
    9 5 │ 4 │ 3 6 7
  3 0 0 │ 5 │
        │ 6 │ 0 7 7 7
        │ 7 │
        │ 8 │
      9 │ 9 │
```

$1\,|\,0 = 0.1 \qquad 0\,|\,1 = 0.1$

b. January:

0.1 1.5 1.7 1.7 1.9 2.1 2.1 2.7 2.7 2.8
               ↑   ↑
               LQ   Median

3.3 3.5 4.5 4.9 5.0 5.0 5.3 9.9
          ↑
          UQ

The total amount of precipitation is 60.7 in.

Therefore, the mean is $\frac{60.7}{18}$ or about 3.4 in.

The median is $\frac{2.7 + 2.8}{2} = 2.75$

July:

0.0 0.0 0.1 0.4 2.0 2.1 2.8 2.9 3.0 3.1
               ↑   ↑
               LQ   Median

3.9 4.3 4.6 4.7 6.0 6.7 6.7 6.7
          ↑
          UQ

The total amount of precipitation is 60 in.

Therefore, the mean is $\frac{60}{18}$ or about 3.3 in.

The median is $\frac{3.0 + 3.1}{2}$ or 3.05.

c. The January mean is about 0.1 higher.

d. The July median is 0.3 higher.

e. January: The interquartile range is $4.9 - 1.9$ or 3.
July: The interquartile range is $4.7 - 2.0$ or 2.7. The January IQ is 0.3 higher.

f. Sample answer: July; The data are more tightly clustered around the median.

25. participants

12 13 13 14 18 20 23 25
        ↑   ↑
        LQ   Median

35 43 56 65 67 68 72
        ↑
        UQ

observers:

9 15 16 18 23 25 39 41 42
                ↑
                LQ

43 43 50 51 54 55 55 60 63
↑   ↑
Median   UQ

70 75 75 80

a. participants: The range is $72 - 12$ or 60.
observers: The range is $80 - 9$ or 71.

b. participants: The interquartile range is $65 - 14$ or 51.
observers: The interquartile range is $60 - 25$ or 35.

c. Sample answer: The participants ages are between 12 and 72. Their ages are spread out over the range of the data. The median age of the participants is 25 years.

d. Sample answer: The observers are both younger and older than the participants. The median age of the observers is 46.5 while the median age of the participants is 25.

26.
```
0 │ 8 8 9
1 │ 1 2 4 5 7
2 │ 5 7 8 9 9 9
3 │ 0 1 6 9
4 │ 0 1
```
$4\,|\,0 = 40$

27. $\frac{2}{3} > \frac{5}{8}$

28.
$$x + 19.95 \le 50$$
$$x + 19.95 - 19.95 \le 50 - 19.95$$
$$x \le \$30.05$$

29. $\frac{c^2 d^5}{cd} = c^{2-1}d^{5-1}$
$\phantom{\frac{c^2 d^5}{cd}} = cd^4$

30. False, a point with one positive and one negative coordinate would be in quadrant II or IV.

| 10-3 | **Displaying Data** |

Pages 498–499   Checking Your Understanding

1. Sample answer: The median is the point inside the box with the vertical line through it.

2. The data between the upper and lower quartiles.

3. Lower extreme, lower quartile, median, upper quartile, upper extreme

4. Sample answer: An outlier is an item of data that is more than 1.5 times the interquartile range from the quartiles.

5. Sample answer: It summarizes the data. A stem-and-leaf plot lists all data.

6. a–d. See students' work.

7. a. 40   **b.** 50
   c. 30   **d.** $50 - 30$ or 20
   e. 25, 55
   f. $1.5\,(20) = 30$, so $30 - 30$ or 0 and $50 + 30$ or 80 are the limits for the outliers. There are no outliers.

8. a. 134 145 165 173 185 194 198 201 204 205
                ↑   ↑   ↑
              LQ   Median   UQ

The range is $205 - 134$ or 71.

The median is $\frac{185 + 194}{2}$ or 189.5.

The upper quartile is 201 and the lower quartile is 165.

The interquartile range is $201 - 165$ or 36.

---

b. 1.5(36) = 54, so 165 − 54 or 111 and 201 + 54 or 255 are the limits for the outliers.

c.
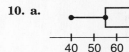
130 140 150 160 170 180 190 200 210

Pages 499–501 Exercises

9. a. 74 − 59 or 15 **b.** 68
 c. 71 **d.** 65
 e. 71 − 65 or 6
 f. 1.5(6) = 9, so 65 − 9 or 56 and 71 + 9 or 80 are the limits for the outliers. There are no outliers.

10. a.
40 50 60 70 80 90

 b. 67 **c.** 77
 d. 55 **e.** 77 − 55 or 22
 f. 40, 81
 g. 1.5(22) = 33, so 55 − 33 or 22 and 77 + 33 or 110 are the limits for the outliers.
 h. none

11. a. 50% **b.** 50%
 c. 25% **d.** 25%
 e. Scores were closer together between 80–83.
 f. The scores were spread further apart.

12. Sample answer: bar graph or pictograph
 See students' explanations.

13. Sample answer: box-and-whisker plot
 See students' explanations.

14. Sample answer: pictograph or bar graph
 See students' explanations.

15. Sample answer: box-and-whisker plot
 See students' explanations.

16. Sample answer: comparative graph
 See students' explanations.

17. Sample answer: line graph or comparative graph
 See students' explanations.

18. a.
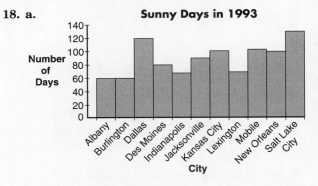

b.
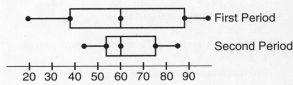

Sunny Days in 1993	(○ = 20 days)
Albany, NY	○ ○ ○
Burlington, VT	○ ○ ○
Dallas, TX	○ ○ ○ ○ ○ ○
Des Moines, IA	○ ○ ○ ○
Indianapolis, IN	○ ○ ○ ◖
Jacksonville, FL	○ ○ ○ ○ ◖
Kansas City, MO	○ ○ ○ ○ ○
Lexington, KY	○ ○ ○ ◖
Mobile, AL	○ ○ ○ ○ ○
New Orleans, LA	○ ○ ○ ○ ○
Salt Lake City, UT	○ ○ ○ ○ ○ ○ ◖

c. Bar graph is easier and more exact.

d. Pictograph is easy to read at a glance, but not as detailed.

19. The box did not change. The weight 200 is an outlier.

20. Yes; if an extreme value is the same as the upper or lower quartile.

21. a.
First Period
Second Period
20 30 40 50 60 70 80 90

b. The medians are the same.

c. The range and interquartile range are greater for the first period class.

d. Answers will vary.

22. a.
0.90 0.95 1.00 1.05 1.10 1.15 1.20

b. $1.12

c. The interquartile range is 1.16 − 0.95 or 0.21. 1.5(0.21) = 0.32, so 0.95 − 0.32 or 0.63 and 1.16 + 0.32 or 1.48 are the limits for the outliers. There are no outliers.

d.
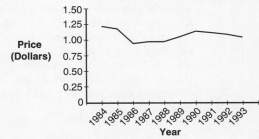

e. Yes; Sample answer: You can see the changes over a period of time.

23. a.

Holding Down Two Jobs

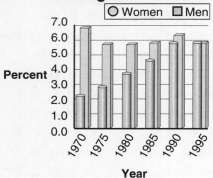

b. Men's employment decreased from 1970 to 1975, but since 1975, men's employment has been relatively consistent.

c. Women's employment increase steadily from 1970 to 1990 and has remained steady from 1990–95.

d. Sample answer: Women are as likely as men to have two jobs.

24. 40 42 51 55 59 63 65 67 68 72 73 77 78 80 81

        LQ   Median   UQ

The range is 81 − 40 or 41.
The median is 67.
The upper quartile is 77 and the lower quartile is 55.
The interquartile range is 77 − 55 or 22.

25. {5, -1, 4.5}; {-3, 4, 0}

26. 0.046 × 1000 = 46
0.046 kg = 46 g

27. Sample answer:
0.25 × 27.98 → 0.25 × 28 = 7
0.25 + 27.98 is about 7.

28. a. estimation, an exact answer is not needed

b. Explore—We know that one cup of skim milk has 80 Calories and one cup of whole milk has 150 Calories. We need to determine the number of Calories that would be saved each year by switching from whole milk to skim milk.

Plan—Multiply the number of Calories in each milk by the number of days in one year to find the amount of Calories that would be consumed each year. Then use subtraction to determine the number of Calories that would be saved by switching from whole milk to skim.

Solve—80 × 365 → 80 × 370 = 29,600
About 30,000 Calories would be consumed each year by drinking skim milk.
150 × 365 → 150 × 370 = 55,500
About 56,000 Calories would be consumed each year by drinking whole milk.

Therefore, about 56,000 − 30,000 or 26,000 Calories would be saved by switching from whole milk to skim.
Examine—80 × 365 = 29,200
150 × 365 = 54,750
54,750 − 29,200 = 25,550
The actual answer is 25,550 Calories. Therefore, the estimate of 26,000 Calories is reasonable.

10-3B

Math Lab: Making Statistical Graphs

Page 502   Your Turn

1.

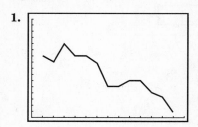

2. Answers will vary. Sample answer: The unemployment rate will probably go down because the rate declines from August to November.

3.

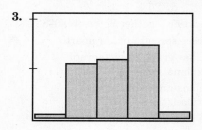

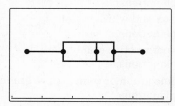

4. 5; 35 ÷ 7 = 5

10-4

Misleading Statistics

Pages 505–506   Checking Your Understanding

1. Sample answer: The units on the axes may not be uniformly marked or there may not be a title or axis labels.

2. Sample answer: What were the ages of those surveyed, who was surveyed, and how many people were surveyed?

3. Khandi; the scale is not consistent.

4. See students' work.

5. a. $\frac{9702}{8811} = 1.101$

The ratio of the number of cars produced in 1992 to the number of cars produced in 1991 is about 1.1.

b. The second car is shorter in length and width.

c. Yes; the actual number of cars sold in 1992 is 1.1 times greater than the number sold in 1991. However, the graph appears to be longer and wider, but both dimensions of the car should not have changed.

6. a. Sample answer: different scales

b. Graph A because it looks like there is a dramatic rise in social studies grades.

Pages 506–508   Exercises

7. a. Sample answer: Median; there are large and small values.

b. Mean; the high values will raise the center of the data.

8. $\frac{40 + 24 + 33 + 28 + 41}{5} = 33.2$

The average age is 33; mean

9. $\frac{185 + 163 + 165 + 157 + 193}{5} = 172.6$; mean

10. $30,500; median

11. sports; mode

12. Sample answer: 33 years old, favorite entertainment: sports; 172.6 cm tall, $30,500 salary.

13.

	Company A	Company B
mean	$22,413.79	$21,935.48
median	$15,000.00	$20,000.00
mode	$15,000.00	$20,000.00
range	$85,000.00	$30,000.00

You would probably prefer to work for Company B because the salary is higher for more workers.

14. See students' work.

15. a. Answers will vary. Sample answer: no; it only shows the population increases for 6 years.

b.

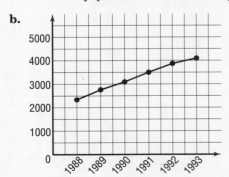

16. a. The mode or median because it makes the current salaries look low.

b. Answers will vary. Sample answer: Both sides should agree to use the same measure of central tendency.

17. a. $70 - 12$ or $58   **b.** $25

c. $35   **d.** $15

e. $35 - 15$ or $20   **f.** $12, $70

g. $1.5(20) = 30$, so a limit for outliers is $35 + 30$ or $65. Since $15 - 30 = -15$ and you cannot have a negative amount of money, the other limit for outliers is $0.

h. $70

18. $(4, 0)$ $(0, 4)$

$3x + 2y = 12$ $3x + 2y = 12$

$3(4) + 2(0) \overset{?}{=} 12$ $3(0) + 2(4) \overset{?}{=} 12$

$12 + 0 \overset{?}{=} 12$ $0 + 8 \overset{?}{=} 12$

$12 = 12$ ✔ $8 \neq 12$

$(5, -1.5)$ $(-5, 1.5)$

$3x + 2y = 12$ $3x + 2y = 12$

$3(5) + 2(-1.5) \overset{?}{=} 12$ $3(-5) + 2(1.5) \overset{?}{=} 12$

$15 + (-3) \overset{?}{=} 12$ $-15 + 3 \overset{?}{=} 12$

$12 = 12$ ✔ $-12 \neq 12$

$(4, 0)$ and $(5, -1.5)$ are solutions to the equation. Therefore, a and c are the correct choices.

19. a. $\frac{400,000}{550,000} = \frac{8}{11}$

The ratio of the 1980 population to the 1990 population is $\frac{8}{11}$.

b.

1980	1990	2000
400,000	550,000	756,250
2010	**2020**	**2030**
1,039,844	1,429,785	1,965,955

In 2030, the population of Alaska would be 1,965,955.

20. $\frac{1000 \text{ meters}}{10^{-3} \text{ meters}} = \frac{10^3}{10^{-3}}$

$= 10^{3-(-3)}$

$= 10^6$

$= 1,000,000$

There are 1,000,000 millimeters in a kilometer.

21. $0 \ \ -2 \ \ 2 \ \ -4 \ \ 4 \ \ -6 \ \ 6$

    $-2 \ \ +4 \ \ -6 \ \ +8 \ \ -10 \ \ +12$

10-5   Counting

Page 511   Checking Your Understanding

1. a. Sample answer: What are the outcomes from two tosses of a three-colored dice? What are the outcomes from spinning a three-choice spinner?

b. (green, green), (green, blue), (green, yellow), (blue, green), (blue, blue), (blue, yellow), (yellow, green), (yellow, blue), (yellow, yellow)

2. Sample answer: The Fundamental Counting Principal is faster and takes less space.

3. a.

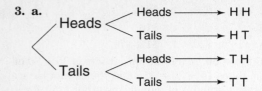

4 outcomes

b. P(two heads) $= \frac{1}{4}$ or 0.25

c. See students' work.

d. Answers will vary.

e. Answers will vary.

f. Answers will vary.

4. a.

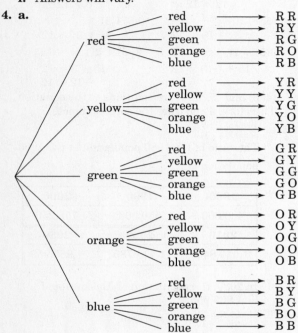

b. 25 outcomes

c. 2 outcomes show red and blue

d. P(two oranges) $= \frac{1}{25}$

5. a. $2 \times 6 = 12$

12 outcomes

b. P(heads and a 4) $= \frac{1}{12}$

6. $2 \times 2 \times 2 = 8$

8 outcomes

7. $3 \times 3 \times 2 = 18$

18 outcomes

Pages 511–513 Exercises

8.

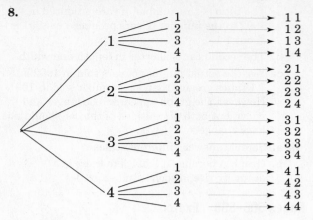

16 outcomes

9.

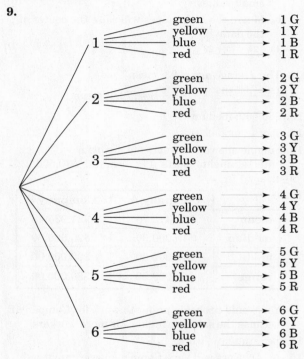

24 outcomes

10.

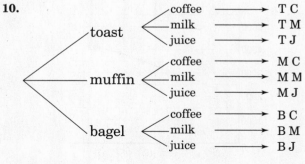

9 outcomes

11.

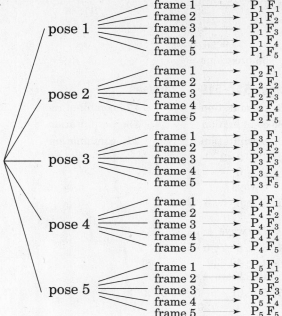

25 ways

12. $2 \times 2 \times 2 \times 2 = 16$
16 outcomes

13. $6 \times 6 = 36$
36 outcomes

14. $2 \times 2 \times 6 = 24$
24 outcomes

15. a. $2 \times 4 = 8$
8 outcomes

b. $P(\text{large grey}) = \frac{1}{8}$

16. $2 \times 2 \times 6 = 24$
24 autos

17. $2 \times 2 \times 2 \times 2 \times 2 = 32$
32 outcomes

18. a. $8 \times 8 \times 8 \times 8 = 4096$
4096 outcomes

b. $P(\text{four 7s}) = \frac{1}{4096}$

19. a. $\underbrace{2 \times 2 \times \ldots \times 2}_{30 \text{ times}} = 2^{30}$

2^{30} outcomes

b. $P(\text{heads every time}) = 2^{\frac{1}{30}}$

20. 2^x

21. a. $10 \times 10 \times 10 \times 10 = 10{,}000$
10,000 extensions

b. $486 \times 10{,}000$ or $4{,}860{,}000$

c. By extending the three-digit exchange, it appears that there are $8 \cdot 10 \cdot 10$ or 800 exchanges. Since 26 exchanges are not available, there are $800 - 26$ or 774 exchanges. Thus, there are $774 \times 10{,}000$ or 7,740,000 numbers in each area code. So, by allowing 0 and 1 in the second and third digits, $7{,}740{,}000 - 4{,}860{,}000$ or 2,880,000 new numbers became available.

22. $6 \cdot 6 \cdot x = 1512$
$36x = 1512$
$\frac{36x}{36} = \frac{1512}{36}$
$x = 42$
42 toppings

23. Sample answer: The median, because it is close to three of four actual prices.

24. $I = prt$; 6 months = 0.5 year
$I = (500)(0.0425)(0.5)$
$I = \$10.63$

25. $f(x) = 2x + 4$
$f(-5) = 2(-5) + 4$
$= -10 + 4$
$= -6$

26. $2(k - 3) \leq 8$
$2k - 6 \leq 8$
$2k - 6 + 6 \leq 8 + 6$
$2k \leq 14$
$\frac{2k}{2} \leq \frac{14}{2}$
$k \leq 7$

Check: Try 5, a number less than or equal to 7.
$2(k - 3) \leq 8$
$2(5 - 3) \overset{?}{\leq} 8$
$2(2) \overset{?}{\leq} 8$
$4 \leq 8$ ✔

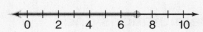

27. Let h = hours
$3.5h < 20$
$\frac{3.5h}{3.5} < \frac{20}{3.5}$
$h < 5.7$

Page 513   Self Test

1.
```
2 | 8
3 | 6 7 9
4 | 3 7 9
5 | 0 1 1 3
6 | 2
```
$6 \mid 2 = 6.2$

2. 1.0 1.2 1.3 1.5 2.1 2.4 2.7 2.9 3.0 3.4 3.9 5.5

            ↑   ↑   ↑

        LQ   Median   UQ

The range is $5.5 - 1.0$ or 4.5.

The upper quartile range is $\frac{3.0 + 3.4}{2}$ or 3.2 and the lower quartile is $\frac{1.3 + 1.5}{2}$ or 1.4.

Therefore, the interquartile range is $3.2 - 1.4$ or 1.8.

3. 2.7, 4.7

4.

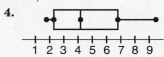

5. Answers will vary. A comparative graph is the best way.

6. Sample answer: They do not have the same scale on the y-axis.

7. Brian would use the bottom graph because it makes the increases he has received appear smaller.

8.

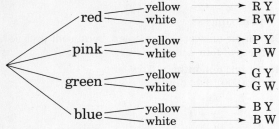

red — yellow → R Y
red — white → R W

pink — yellow → P Y
pink — white → P W

green — yellow → G Y
green — white → G W

blue — yellow → B Y
blue — white → B W

9. $3 \times 4 \times 2 = 24$
24 outcomes

10. There are $2 \times 2 \times 2$ or 8 possible outcomes. The probability that all 3 coins land heads up is $\frac{1}{8}$.

10-6A | **Math Lab: Permutations and Combinations**

Page 514   Your Turn

1. 120 words

2. In a permutation, order is important.

10-6 | **Permutations and Combinations**

Page 517   Checking Your Understanding

1. Sample answer: The number of ways 4 things can be selected 3 at a time.

2. Sample answer: 6! means $6 \cdot 5 \cdot 4 \cdot 3 \cdot 2 \cdot 1$

3. Sample answer: $C(25, 5)$

4. See students' work.

5. combination   **6.** permutation

7. $2! = 2 \cdot 1$
$= 2$

8. $5! = 5 \cdot 4 \cdot 3 \cdot 2 \cdot 1$
$= 120$

9. $4! = 4 \cdot 3 \cdot 2 \cdot 1$
$= 24$

10. $P(6, 3) = 6 \cdot 5 \cdot 4$
$= 120$

11. $5! = 5 \cdot 4 \cdot 3 \cdot 2 \cdot 1$
$= 120$

12. $C(5, 4) = \frac{P(5, 4)}{4!}$
$= \frac{5 \cdot 4 \cdot 3 \cdot 2}{4 \cdot 3 \cdot 2 \cdot 1}$
$= 5$

13. $\frac{7!3!}{5!0!} = \frac{7 \cdot 6 \cdot 3 \cdot 2 \cdot 1}{1}$
$= 252$

14. $C(12, 6) = \frac{P(12, 6)}{6!}$
$= \frac{12 \cdot 11 \cdot 10 \cdot 9 \cdot 8 \cdot 7}{6 \cdot 5 \cdot 4 \cdot 3 \cdot 2 \cdot 1}$
$= 924$
924 combinations

15. $C(8, 3) = \frac{P(8, 3)}{3!}$
$= \frac{8 \cdot 7 \cdot 6}{3 \cdot 2 \cdot 1}$
$= 56$
56 programs

Pages 517–519   Exercises

16. permutation   **17.** combination

18. combination   **19.** permutation

20. permutation   **21.** combination

22. $3! = 3 \cdot 2 \cdot 1$
$= 6$
6 ways

23. $6! = 6 \cdot 5 \cdot 4 \cdot 3 \cdot 2 \cdot 1$
$= 720$
720 ways

24. $8! = 8 \cdot 7 \cdot 6 \cdot 5 \cdot 4 \cdot 3 \cdot 2 \cdot 1$
$= 40,320$
40,320 ways

25. $P(6, 6) = 6 \cdot 5 \cdot 4 \cdot 3 \cdot 2 \cdot 1$
$= 720$

26. $7! = 7 \cdot 6 \cdot 5 \cdot 4 \cdot 3 \cdot 2 \cdot 1$
$= 5040$

27. $9! = 9 \cdot 8 \cdot 7 \cdot 6 \cdot 5 \cdot 4 \cdot 3 \cdot 2 \cdot 1$
$= 362,880$

28. $C(6, 6) = \frac{P(6, 6)}{6!}$
$= \frac{6 \cdot 5 \cdot 4 \cdot 3 \cdot 2 \cdot 1}{6 \cdot 5 \cdot 4 \cdot 3 \cdot 2 \cdot 1}$
$= 1$

29. $11! = 11 \cdot 10 \cdot 9 \cdot 8 \cdot 7 \cdot 6 \cdot 5 \cdot 4 \cdot 3 \cdot 2 \cdot 1$
$= 39,916,800$

30. $P(5, 1) = 5$

31. $C(7, 3) = \frac{P(7, 3)}{3!}$
$= \frac{7 \cdot 6 \cdot 5}{3 \cdot 2 \cdot 1}$
$= 35$

32. $P(8, 4) = 8 \cdot 7 \cdot 6 \cdot 5$
$= 1680$

33. $0! = 1$

34. $C(8, 4) = \frac{P(8,4)}{4!}$
$= \frac{8 \cdot 7 \cdot 6 \cdot 5}{4 \cdot 3 \cdot 2 \cdot 1}$
$= 70$

35. $C(10, 2) = \frac{P(10, 2)}{2!}$
$= \frac{10 \cdot 9}{2 \cdot 1}$
$= 45$

36. $P(12, 12) = 12 \cdot 11 \cdot 10 \cdot 9 \cdot 8 \cdot 7 \cdot 6 \cdot 5 \cdot 4 \cdot 3 \cdot 2 \cdot 1$
$= 479,001,600$

37. $\frac{7!3!}{5!1!} = \frac{7 \cdot 6 \cdot 3 \cdot 2 \cdot 1}{1}$
$= 252$

38. $10!0! = \frac{10 \cdot 9 \cdot 8 \cdot 7 \cdot 1}{2 \cdot 1}$
$= 2520$

39. $\frac{5!2!}{4!3!} = \frac{5}{3}$
$= 1\frac{2}{3}$

40. $\frac{9!5!0!}{11!} = \frac{5 \cdot 4 \cdot 3 \cdot 2 \cdot 1}{11 \cdot 10}$
$= 1\frac{1}{11}$

41. $C(15, 6) = \frac{P(15, 6)}{6!}$

$= \frac{15 \cdot 14 \cdot 13 \cdot 12 \cdot 11 \cdot 10}{6 \cdot 5 \cdot 4 \cdot 3 \cdot 2 \cdot 1}$

$= 5005$

5005 squads

42. $3! = 3 \cdot 2 \cdot 1$

$= 6$

6 numbers

43. $3! = 3 \cdot 2 \cdot 1$

$= 6$

6 ways

44. $C(52, 5) = \frac{P(52, 5)}{5!}$

$= \frac{52 \cdot 51 \cdot 50 \cdot 49 \cdot 48}{5 \cdot 4 \cdot 3 \cdot 2 \cdot 1}$

$= 2{,}598{,}960$

2,598,960 hands

45. If x students are competing, there are $P(x, 3)$ ways to choose first, second and third. Use guess and check to find x. When $x = 10$, $P(x, 3) = 720$. There were 10 students competing.

46. $P(10, 2) \cdot C(8, 3) = 10 \cdot 9 \cdot \frac{P(8, 3)}{3!}$

$= 90 \cdot \frac{8 \cdot 7 \cdot 6}{3 \cdot 2 \cdot 1}$

$= 90 \cdot 56$

$= 5040$

5040 ways

47. $C(15, 9) = \frac{P(15, 9)}{9!}$

$= \frac{15 \cdot 14 \cdot 13 \cdot 12 \cdot 11 \cdot 10 \cdot 9 \cdot 8 \cdot 7}{9 \cdot 8 \cdot 7 \cdot 6 \cdot 5 \cdot 4 \cdot 3 \cdot 2 \cdot 1}$

$= 5005$

5005 combinations

48. $C(12, 2) = \frac{P(12, 2)}{2!}$

$= \frac{12 \cdot 11}{2 \cdot 1}$

$= 66$

66 line segments

49. $26 \cdot 25 \cdot 24 \cdot 9 \cdot 10 \cdot 10 \cdot 10$

$= 140{,}400{,}000$

140,400,000 license plates

50.

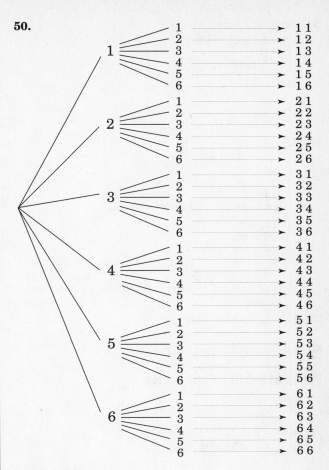

36 outcomes

51. Let the horizontal axis represent temperature in Celsius. Let the vertical axis represent temperature in Fahrenheit. Graph (0, 32) for 0° Celsius and 32° Fahrenheit and (100, 212) for 100° Celsius and 212° Fahrenheit. Draw the line that contains these points. Thus, about –15° Celsius corresponds to 0° Fahrenheit. At 0° Fahrenheit, the temperature is about –15° Celsius.

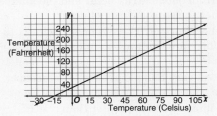

52. Let w = width, then length = $2w - 5$

$P = 2(\ell + w)$

$38 = 2(2w - 5 + w)$

$38 = 2(3w - 5)$

$38 = 6w - 10$

$38 + 10 = 6w - 10 + 10$

$48 = 6w$

$8 = w$

The width is 8 m and the length is $2(8) - 5$ or 11 m.

53. $5.4c = -13.5$

$\frac{5.4c}{5.4} = \frac{-13.5}{5.4}$

$c = -2.5$

54. Sample answer:

$1\frac{3}{5} - \frac{5}{12} \rightarrow 1\frac{1}{2} - \frac{1}{2} = 1$

$1\frac{3}{5} - \frac{5}{12}$ is about 1.

55. $5x^{-2} = 5(2)^{-2}$

$= \frac{5}{(2)^2}$

$= \frac{5}{4}$

56. a. $d = rt$

$120 = 50t$

$\frac{120}{50} = \frac{50t}{50}$

$2.4 = t$

2.4 hours or 2 hours 24 minutes

b. $d = rt$

$120 = 40t$

$\frac{120}{40} = \frac{40t}{40}$

$3 = t$

It will take $3 - 2.4$ or 0.6 hours or 36 minutes longer.

57. $3x - 12x = (3 - 12)x$

$= -9x$

58. Associative Property of Addition

Pages 518–519   Earth Watch

See students' work.

10-7	Odds

Page 520   Your Turn

a. White. There are more white squares.

b. 9 ways

c. 27 ways

Pages 521–522   Checking Your Understanding

1. Sample answer: Write a ratio of the number of ways a certain outcome can occur and the number of ways that the outcome cannot occur.

2. They are both correct. There is one way in six to roll a 2. There are five ways to roll something besides a 2.

3. Answers will vary. Sample answer: A newspaper listing the odds of winning some sporting event.

4. odds of rolling a number greater than 5 = 1:5
The odds of rolling a number greater than 5 are 1:5.

5. odds of rolling a multiple of 2
= 3:3
= 1:1
The odds of rolling a multiple of 2 are 1:1.

6. odds of rolling a number less than 4
= 3:3
= 1:1
The odds of rolling a number less than 4 are 1:1.

7. odds of rolling a number that is not a 3
= 5:1
The odds of rolling a number that is not a 3 are 5:1.

8. **a.** odds that an unmarried adult was never married
= 58:42
= 29:21
The odds that an unmarried adult was never married are 29:21.

b. $\frac{x}{200} = \frac{58}{100}$

$x \cdot 100 = 200 \cdot 58$

$100x = 11{,}600$

$\frac{100x}{100} = \frac{11{,}600}{100}$

$x = 116$

About 116 adults had never been married.

Pages 522–523   Exercises

9. odds of landing on blue = 1:4
The odds of stopping on blue are 1:4.

10. The odds of stopping on purple are 0.

11. odds of stopping on a color that is not green = 4:1
The odds of stopping on a color that is not green are 4:1.

12. odds of stopping on red or orange = 2:3
The odds of stopping on red or orange are 2:3.

13. odds of rolling an even sum
= 18:18
= 1:1
The odds of rolling an even sum are 1:1.

14. odds of rolling an odd sum
= 18:18
= 1:1
The odds of rolling an odd sum are 1:1.

15. odds of rolling a sum that is a multiple of 3
= 12:24
= 1:2
The odds of rolling a sum that is a multiple of 3 are 1:2.

16. It is impossible to roll a sum less than 2.

17. odds of rolling a composite number
= 21:15
= 7:5
The odds of rolling a composite number are 7:5.

18. odds of rolling a prime number greater than 9
= 2:34
= 1:17
The odds of rolling a prime number greater than 9 are 1:17.

19. odds of *not* rolling a sum of 7
= 30:6
= 5:1
The odds of *not* rolling a sum of 7 are 5:1.

20. odds of *not* rolling a sum of 11 or 12

= 33:3

= 11:1

The odds of *not* rolling a sum of 11 or 12 are 11:1.

21. odds of rolling a sum of 8 with a 6 on one side

= 2:34

= 1:17

The odds of rolling a sum of 8 with a 6 on one side are 1:17.

22. odds of rolling an even sum or a sum less than 6

= 24:12

= 2:1

23. odds of rolling *neither* an odd sum *nor* a sum greater than 8

= 14:22

= 7:11

The odds of rolling *neither* an odd sum *nor* a sum greater than 8 are 7:11.

24. odds of selecting a black king

= 2:50

= 1:25

The odds of selecting a black king are 1:25.

25. odds of *not* selecting a heart or a seven

= 36:16

= 9:4

The odds of *not* selecting a heart or a seven are 9:4.

26. Draw a tree diagram that shows the 36 possible outcomes. The odds that the number showing on the red die is less than the number showing on the blue die are 15:21 or 5:7.

27. There are $10 \times 10 \times 10 \times 10$ or 10,000 possible outcomes. Therefore, the odds that the four digits called out are the last four digits of your telephone number are 1:9999.

28. Write the odds 1:3 as an equivalent ratio so that the total number of events is 32.

$\frac{1}{3} = \frac{x}{32 - x}$

$3x = 32 - x$

$4x = 32$

$x = 8$

8:24 is equivalent to 1:3. Thus, about 8 students will appear on television.

29. a. Sample answer: less than 1 or none

b. $\frac{8}{90} = \frac{x}{1000}$

$8 \cdot 1000 = 90 \cdot x$

$8000 = 90x$

$\frac{8000}{90} = \frac{90x}{90}$

$88.\overline{8} = x$

About 89 people would develop this cancer.

30. See student's work.

31. $8! = 8 \cdot 7 \cdot 6 \cdot 5 \cdot 4 \cdot 3 \cdot 2 \cdot 1$

= 40,320

32. a.

```
6 | 0 1 4 5 7 8
7 | 0 0 2 3
8 | 0 0
      6 | 0 = 60 inches
```

b. 50%; Sample answer: average height for age group < 70 in.

33.

penny	nickel	dime	quarter	total
1	1	1	0	$0.16
1	1	0	1	$0.31
1	0	1	1	$0.36
0	1	1	1	$0.40
1	0	0	2	$0.51
0	1	0	2	$0.55
0	0	1	2	$0.60

Andie could have chosen $0.16, $0.31, $0.36, $0.40, $0.51, $0.55, or $0.60.

34. $C = \pi d$

$C = \pi \cdot 5$

$C \approx 15.71$ ft

35. $\frac{1}{6} > 0.16$

36. open

Page 523   From the Funny Papers

1. 1×10^{100}

2. No; the smaller number (1) should be stated first.

3. Googol is short for googolplex. It was invented in 1938 by Milton Sirotta. He was 9 years old at the time.

10-8   Problem-Solving Strategy Use a Simulation

Page 524   Your Turn

a. Yes, because you are actually going through the process.

b. Sample answer: You may be able to find an approximation for a complicated probability.

Page 526   Checking Your Understanding

1. Sample answer: A simulation is an imitation of a given problem.

2. Sample answer: The results of a simulation will not be exactly the same as the actual problem because the simulation is just a way of acting out the problem to predict what might happen.

3. Modify to three sections

4. See students' work.

5. a. Sample answer: Select a marble out of a bag that has three marbles of the same color and one marble of a different color. Then repeat three more times.

b. See students' work.

c. See students' work.

Pages 526–528   Exercises

6. a. See students' work.

b. Sample answer: at least 6

7. **a.** Roll a die.
   b. See students' work.
   c. See students' work.

8. There are $241 - 125$ or 116 pages in the unit.

9.

Antonio had \$15 left	→	15.00
Undo the $\frac{1}{6}$ he lost	→	$\times \quad \frac{6}{5}$
(15 is $\frac{5}{6}$ of the remaining money)		18.00
Undo the \$6 earned	→	$- \quad 6.00$
		12.00
Undo the $\frac{1}{2}$ he spent	→	$\times \quad 2$
		24.00
Undo the \$1 he loaned	→	$+ \quad 1.00$
to his brother		25.00

   Antonio's grandmother sent him \$25.00.

10. Answers will vary. Sample answer: The probability will depend on the results of the simulation. If the simulation is repeated 10 times and one of them results in 3 green lights, the probability is 0.1.

11. **a.** Each of the teams, except the champion, will lose exactly once, so there are 15 games in the tournament.
    b. $16 \cdot 15 = 240$
    240 ways

12. Answers will vary. The probability should be about $\frac{5}{8}$.

13. **a.** See students' work.
    b. Change the second line to "For (N, 1, 50)"

14.

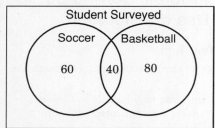

   A Venn diagram shows that $60 + 40 + 80$ or 180 students play one or both sports. Thus, $240 - 180$ or 60 students play neither.

15. odds of stopping on 2
    $= 1:5$
    The odds of stopping on a 2 are 1:5.

16. Slope $= \frac{5-3}{1-3}$
    $= \frac{2}{-2}$
    $= -1$

17. **a.** $110 = \frac{1}{2}x + 20$
    b. $110 = \frac{1}{2}x + 20$
    $110 - 20 = \frac{1}{2}x + 20 - 20$
    $90 = \frac{1}{2}x$
    $2 \cdot 90 = 2 \cdot \frac{1}{2}x$
    $\$180 = x$

18. $r^4 = r \cdot r \cdot r \cdot r$

19. $20 - (-15) = 20 + 15$
    $= 35°F$

Page 529

1. Answers will vary. Sample answer: The most frequently drawn color is probably the one with the greatest number of marbles in the bag.

2. See students' work.

3. Yes; It's more likely to happen with fewer draws and could possibly happen after more draws if you draw from the same side of the bag each time and don't mix the marbles.

4. Sample answer: As the number of draws increased, the experimental probability was closer to the theoretical probability.

5. See students' work.

6. See students' work.

Page 530   Your Turn

a. Sample answer: Kiona
b. The probability is 20%.

Pages 532–533   Checking Your Understanding

1. Events are independent when neither affects the other and dependent when the first event does affect the following event.

2. See students' work.

3. Sample answer: Place the number of occurrences of the event in the numerator and reduce the possible occurrences by one.

4. independent; the outcome of rolling a die does not affect the outcome of spinning a spinner.

5. dependent; the outcome of drawing a marble and not replacing it will affect the outcome of drawing a second marble.

6. P(Diet Coke and regular Mountain Dew)
   $= \frac{4}{20} \cdot \frac{7}{19}$
   $= \frac{28}{380}$ or $\frac{7}{95}$

7. P(regular Coke and regular Mountain Dew)
   $= \frac{3}{20} \cdot \frac{7}{19}$
   $= \frac{21}{380}$

8. P(diet Mountain Dew and regular Mountain Dew)
   $= \frac{6}{20} \cdot \frac{7}{19}$
   $= \frac{42}{380}$ or $\frac{21}{190}$

9. P(regular Coke and diet Mountain Dew)
   $= \frac{3}{20} \cdot \frac{6}{19}$
   $= \frac{9}{190}$

---

10. Dependent; one outcome affects the other.

11. $\frac{44}{100} \cdot \frac{4}{100} = \frac{176}{10,000}$

$= \frac{11}{625}$ or 1.76%

The probability that a full-time hourly wage earner is a woman who is paid the minimum wage is $\frac{11}{625}$ or 1.76%.

Pages 533–534   Exercises

12. dependent; the outcome of choosing a card and not replacing it will affect the outcome of choosing a second card.

13. independent; the outcome of the first roll of a die does not affect the outcome of the second roll.

14. independent; the outcome of selecting a name from the Raleigh telephone book does not affect the outcome of selecting a name from the Miami telephone book.

15. independent; the outcome of tossing a coin does not affect the outcome of spinning a spinner.

16. dependent; the outcome of selecting a first player will affect the outcome of selecting the second player.

17. $P(1 \text{ and } D) = \frac{1}{6} \cdot \frac{1}{5}$

$= \frac{1}{30}$

18. $P(\text{an odd number and } C) = \frac{3}{6} \cdot \frac{1}{5}$

$= \frac{3}{30}$ or $\frac{1}{10}$

19. $P(\text{a composite number and a vowel})$

$= \frac{2}{6} \cdot \frac{2}{5}$

$= \frac{4}{30}$ or $\frac{2}{15}$

20. $P(\text{an even number and a consonant})$

$= \frac{3}{6} \cdot \frac{3}{5}$

$= \frac{9}{30}$ or $\frac{3}{10}$

21. $P(\text{a 6 and } F) = \frac{1}{6} \cdot 0$

$= 0$

22. $P(\text{two green marbles in a row})$

$= \frac{2}{14} \cdot \frac{1}{13}$

$= \frac{2}{182}$ or $\frac{1}{91}$

23. $P(\text{a red and then a yellow marble})$

$= \frac{5}{14} \cdot \frac{4}{13}$

$= \frac{20}{182}$ or $\frac{10}{91}$

24. $P(\text{two red marbles in a row})$

$= \frac{5}{14} \cdot \frac{4}{13}$

$= \frac{20}{182}$ or $\frac{10}{91}$

25. $P(\text{a green and then a blue marble})$

$= \frac{2}{14} \cdot \frac{3}{13}$

$= \frac{6}{182}$ or $\frac{3}{91}$

26. $P(\text{a red marble, a green marble, and then a blue marble})$

$= \frac{5}{14} \cdot \frac{2}{13} \cdot \frac{3}{12}$

$= \frac{30}{2184}$ or $\frac{5}{364}$

27. $P(\text{three yellow marbles in a row})$

$= \frac{4}{14} \cdot \frac{3}{13} \cdot \frac{2}{12}$

$= \frac{24}{2184}$ or $\frac{1}{91}$

28. a. Sample answer: 3 red, 2 white, and 4 blue.

b. Sample answer: The numerator must be 24. Any combination of 3, 2, and 4 will have a probability of $\frac{1}{21}$.

29. a. $P(\text{first draw is a strike}) = \frac{3}{8}$

b. $P(\text{next two draws will be strikes})$

$= \frac{3}{5} \cdot \frac{2}{4}$

$= \frac{6}{20}$ or $\frac{3}{10}$

30. a. $P(\text{both ambulances will be available})$

$= \frac{80}{100} \cdot \frac{80}{100}$

$= \frac{6400}{10,000}$ or $\frac{16}{25}$

b. $P(\text{neither will be available})$

$= \frac{20}{100} \cdot \frac{20}{100}$

$= \frac{400}{10,000}$ or $\frac{1}{25}$

c. Sample answer: Some of the time one ambulance is available when the other is not.

31. If the probability of failure for each motion sensor and the signal conditioner is 0.0001, then the probability of success is $1 - 0.0001$ or 0.9999. If the probability of failure for the transmitter is 0.001, then the probability of success is $1 - 0.001$ or 0.999.

$P(\text{success for the telemetry system})$

$= \frac{9999}{10,000} \times \frac{9999}{10,000} \times \frac{9999}{10,000} \times \frac{999}{1000}$

$= \frac{998,700,330,000,000}{1,000,000,000,000,000}$

$= \frac{4993}{5000}$ or 99.86%

32. Sample answer: Use a spinner with four equal sections and let one section represent a miss.

33. Sample answer:

20% or $49.99

20% $= \frac{1}{5}$

49.99 is about 50.

$\frac{1}{5}$ of 50 is 10.

Keandre will save about 10.

The sale price will be about $50 - 10$ or $40.

34. $c - a = \frac{5}{9} - \frac{2}{9}$

$= \frac{3}{9}$

$= \frac{1}{3}$

35. $14 = b - (-12)$

$14 = b + 12$

$14 - 12 = b + 12 - 12$

$2 = b$

Check: $14 = b - (-12)$

$14 \stackrel{?}{=} 2 - (-12)$

$14 \stackrel{?}{=} 2 + 12$

$14 = 14$ ✓

36. positive;
$-3(5)(-2) = -15(-2)$
$\qquad\qquad = 30$

37. $2(n + 3)$

10-10 Probability of Compound Events

Page 535 Your Turn

+	1	2	3	4	5	6
1	2	3	4	5	⑥	7
2	3	4	5	⑥	7	8
3	4	5	⑥	7	8	9
4	5	⑥	7	8	9	⑩
5	⑥	7	8	9	⑩	11
6	7	8	9	⑩	11	12

a. $P(\text{sum of the dice will be 6}) = \frac{5}{36}$

b. $P(\text{sum of the dice will be 10}) = \frac{3}{36}$ or $\frac{1}{12}$

c. $P(\text{sum of the dice will be 6 or 10}) = \frac{8}{36}$ or $\frac{2}{9}$

d. The sum of the probabilities of pairs a and b equals the probability in part c.

Page 537 Checking Your Understanding

1. Answers will vary. Sample answer: walking the dog and practicing the piano.

2. Sample answer: Mutually exclusive events cannot occur at the same time while inclusive events can occur at the same time.

3. Sample answer: The occurrences have already been counted in the probability of the separate events.

4. a. inclusive, a student can be both male and a ninth grader

   b. exclusive, a student cannot be both male and female

   c. inclusive, a student can be both female and an eighth grader

   d. exclusive, a student cannot be both a seventh and an eighth grader

5. a. $P(C \text{ or } D) = \frac{1}{6} + \frac{1}{6}$
$\qquad\qquad\quad = \frac{2}{6}$ or $\frac{1}{3}$

   b. $P(E \text{ or vowel}) = \frac{1}{6} + \frac{2}{6} - \frac{1}{6}$
$\qquad\qquad\qquad = \frac{2}{6}$ or $\frac{1}{3}$

   c. $P(B \text{ or consonant}) = \frac{1}{6} + \frac{4}{6} - \frac{1}{6}$
$\qquad\qquad\qquad\quad = \frac{4}{6}$ or $\frac{2}{3}$

6. a. $P(\text{not effective or somewhat effective})$
$= \frac{44}{100} + \frac{44}{100}$
$= \frac{88}{100}$ or 88%

b. $P(\text{somewhat or very effective})$
$= \frac{44}{100} + \frac{11}{100}$
$= \frac{55}{100}$ or 55%

Pages 537–538 Exercises

7. a. inclusive;
$P(\text{even or less than 5}) = \frac{4}{8} + \frac{4}{8} - \frac{2}{8}$
$\qquad\qquad\qquad\qquad = \frac{6}{8}$ or $\frac{3}{4}$

   b. exclusive;
$P(\text{6 or odd}) = \frac{1}{8} + \frac{4}{8}$
$\qquad\qquad\quad = \frac{5}{8}$

   c. exclusive;
$P(\text{4 or prime}) = \frac{1}{8} + \frac{4}{8}$ *Recall that 1 is not*
$\qquad\qquad\quad = \frac{5}{8}$ *prime.*

   d. inclusive;
$P(\text{greater than 4 or an 8}) = \frac{4}{8} + \frac{1}{8} - \frac{1}{8}$
$\qquad\qquad\qquad\qquad\qquad = \frac{4}{8}$ or $\frac{1}{2}$

8. a. inclusive;
$P(\text{6 or even}) = \frac{1}{7} + \frac{2}{7} - \frac{1}{7}$
$\qquad\qquad\quad = \frac{2}{7}$

   b. exclusive;
$P(\text{9 or even}) = \frac{1}{7} + \frac{2}{7}$
$\qquad\qquad\quad = \frac{3}{7}$

   c. exclusive;
$P(\text{odd or even}) = \frac{5}{7} + \frac{2}{7}$
$\qquad\qquad\qquad = \frac{7}{7}$ or 1

   d. exclusive;
$P(\text{5 or less than 3}) = \frac{1}{7} + \frac{1}{7}$
$\qquad\qquad\qquad\quad = \frac{2}{7}$

   e. inclusive;
$P(\text{4 or greater than 3}) = \frac{1}{7} + \frac{5}{7} - \frac{1}{7}$
$\qquad\qquad\qquad\qquad\quad = \frac{5}{7}$

9. $P(A \text{ and } B) = 0$

10. $P(A \text{ or } B) = \frac{1}{5} + \frac{2}{3}$
$\qquad\qquad\qquad = \frac{3}{15} + \frac{10}{15}$
$\qquad\qquad\qquad = \frac{13}{15}$

11. $P(A \text{ and } B) = \frac{1}{5} \cdot \frac{2}{3}$
$\qquad\qquad\qquad\quad = \frac{2}{15}$

12. $P(A \text{ or } B) = \frac{1}{5} + \frac{2}{3} - \frac{2}{15}$
$\qquad\qquad\qquad = \frac{3}{15} + \frac{10}{15} - \frac{2}{15}$
$\qquad\qquad\qquad = \frac{11}{15}$

13. $P(\text{both aces}) = \frac{4}{52} \cdot \frac{3}{51}$
$\qquad\qquad\qquad\quad = \frac{12}{2652}$ or $\frac{1}{221}$

$P(\text{both jacks}) = \frac{4}{52} \cdot \frac{3}{51}$
$\qquad\qquad\qquad\quad = \frac{12}{2652}$ or $\frac{1}{221}$

So, $P(\text{both aces or both jacks}) = \frac{1}{221} + \frac{1}{221}$
$\qquad\qquad\qquad\qquad\qquad\qquad = \frac{2}{221}$

14. $P(\text{both red}) = \frac{26}{52} \cdot \frac{25}{51}$
$= \frac{650}{2652} \text{ or } \frac{325}{1326}$

$P(\text{both face cards}) = \frac{12}{52} \cdot \frac{11}{51}$
$= \frac{132}{2652} \text{ or } \frac{66}{1326}$

$P(\text{both red and face cards}) = \frac{6}{52} \cdot \frac{5}{51}$
$= \frac{30}{2652} \text{ or } \frac{15}{1326}$

So, $P(\text{both red or both face cards})$
$= \frac{325}{1326} + \frac{66}{1326} - \frac{15}{1326}$
$= \frac{376}{1326} \text{ or } \frac{188}{663}$

15. $P(\text{red/blue}) = \frac{3}{9} \cdot \frac{6}{9}$ $\quad$ $P(\text{blue/red}) = \frac{6}{9} \cdot \frac{3}{9}$
$= \frac{18}{81} \text{ or } \frac{2}{9}$ $\qquad\qquad$ $= \frac{18}{81} \text{ or } \frac{2}{9}$

So, $P(\text{red marble and blue marble in either order})$
$= \frac{2}{9} + \frac{2}{9}$
$= \frac{4}{9}$

16. $P(\text{a 5 or a 7}) = \frac{1}{8} + \frac{1}{8}$
$= \frac{2}{8} \text{ or } \frac{1}{4}$

So, if the die is tossed 40 times, expect a 5 or a 7 about $\frac{1}{4} \cdot 40$ or 10 times.

17. $P(\text{a 6 or a 3}) = \frac{1}{8} + \frac{1}{8}$
$= \frac{2}{8} \text{ or } \frac{1}{4}$

So, if the die is tossed 40 times, expect a 6 or a 3 about $\frac{1}{4} \cdot 40$ or 10 times.

18. $P(\text{an even number or a 5}) = \frac{4}{8} + \frac{1}{8}$
$= \frac{5}{8}$

So, if the die is tossed 40 times, expect an even number or a 5 about $\frac{5}{8} \cdot 40$ or 25 times.

19. $P(\text{a prime number or an even number}) = \frac{4}{8} + \frac{4}{8} - \frac{1}{8}$
$= \frac{7}{8}$

So, if the die is tossed 40 times, expect a prime number or an even number about $\frac{7}{8} \cdot 40$ or 35 times.

20. $P(\text{a multiple of 3 or a multiple of 2})$
$= \frac{2}{8} + \frac{4}{8} - \frac{1}{8}$
$= \frac{5}{8}$

So, if the die is tossed 40 times, expect a multiple of 3 or a multiple of 2 about $\frac{5}{8} \cdot 40$ or 25 times.

21. $P(\text{a multiple of 2 or a multiple of 4})$
$= \frac{4}{8} + \frac{2}{8} - \frac{2}{8}$
$= \frac{4}{8} \text{ or } \frac{1}{2}$

So, if the die is tossed 40 times, expect a multiple of 2 or a multiple of 4 about $\frac{1}{2} \cdot 40$ or 20 times.

22.

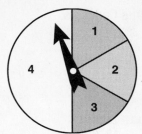

23. $P(\text{between 16 and 24 years old})$
$= \frac{31}{100} + \frac{22}{100}$
$= \frac{53}{100} \text{ or } 53\%$

24. There are $23 - 17$ or 6 female representatives. There are 8 Democrats, and $8 - 4$ or 4 female Democrats.
$P(\text{female or Democrat}) = P(\text{female}) + P(\text{Democrat})$
$\qquad\qquad\qquad - P(\text{female Democrat})$
$= \frac{6}{23} + \frac{8}{23} - \frac{4}{23}$
$= \frac{10}{23}$

The probability of choosing a woman or a Democrat is $\frac{10}{23}$.

25. independent; the outcome of choosing a card and replacing it does not affect the outcome of choosing a second card.

26. $\frac{\$3.69}{13 \text{ ounce}} = \frac{28.4 \text{ cents}}{1 \text{ ounce}}$
28.4 cents per ounce
$0.95¢$ is not the current unit price. The unit price is 28.4 cents per ounce.

27.

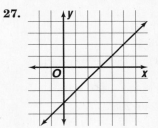

28. $n < 28$;

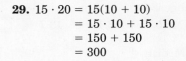

29. $15 \cdot 20 = 15(10 + 10)$
$= 15 \cdot 10 + 15 \cdot 10$
$= 150 + 150$
$= 300$

Chapter 10 Study Guide and Assessment

Page 539 Understanding and Using Vocabulary

1. C; inclusive $\qquad$ **2.** F; range

3. I; permutation $\qquad$ **4.** D; upper quartile

5. A; mutually exclusive $\quad$ **6.** E; interquartile range

7. G; combination

8.
```
0 | 3 4 6 7 8
1 | 7 9
2 | 1
3 |
4 | 0 3
```
$0|3 = 3$

9.
```
 9 | 5 8
10 | 7 7 8
11 | 0 5 9
```
$9|5 = 9.5$

10.
```
1 | 5 6 8 8
2 | 0 1 3 5 9
3 | 0 0
```
$1|5 = 15$

11.
```
11 | 1 2 7
12 | 0 1
13 | 3
14 | 6 8
```
$11|1 = 111$

12. 16   23   45   47   51

LQ   Median   UQ

The range is $51 - 16$ or 35.

The median is 45.

The lower quartile is $\frac{16 + 23}{2}$ or 19.5 and the upper

quartile is $\frac{47 + 51}{2}$ or 49.

The interquartile range is $49 - 19.5$ or 29.5.

13. 6   10   15   21   28   36

LQ   Median   UQ

The range is $36 - 6$ or 30.

The median is $\frac{15 + 21}{2}$ or 18.

The lower quartile is 10 and the upper quartile is 28.

The interquartile range is $28 - 10$ or 18.

14. 95 97 99 101 103 106 112 113 118 119

LQ   Median   UQ

The range is $119 - 95$ or 14.

The median is $\frac{103 + 106}{2}$ or 104.5.

The lower quartile is 99 and the upper quartile is 113.

The interquartile range is $113 - 99$ or 14.

15. 200 205 214 217 236 240 298

LQ   Median   UQ

The range is $298 - 200$ or 98.

The median is 217.

The lower quartile is 205 and the upper quartile is 240.

The interquartile range is $240 - 205$ or 35.

16. 11.0 11.0 11.6 12.5 12.5 12.8 13.1 13.3 13.7

LQ   Median   UQ

The range is $13.7 - 11.0$ or 2.7.

The median is 12.5.

The lower quartile is $\frac{11.0 + 11.6}{2}$ or 11.3 and the

upper quartile is $\frac{13.1 + 13.3}{2}$ or 13.2.

The interquartile range is $13.2 - 11.3$ or 1.9.

17. Median = $\frac{34 + 36}{2}$ or 35

Lower Quartile = $\frac{27 + 29}{2}$ or 28

Upper Quartile = $\frac{41 + 43}{2}$ or 42

Interquartile range = $42 - 28$ or 14

Outliers must be less than $28 - 1.5(14)$ or 7 or greater than $42 + 1.5(14)$ or 63. There are no outliers.

a.

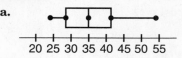
```
20 25 30 35 40 45 50 55
```

b. 35

c. none

18. soccer; mode

19. $\frac{9 + 10 + 5 + 3}{4} = 6.75$; mean

20. $\frac{3 + 5 + 12 + 6}{4} = 6.5$; median

21. favorite sport: soccer; 6.75 classes in school; 6.5 members in family

22. $8 \times 8 = 64$

64 outcomes

23. $4 \times 4 \times 4 \times 4 \times 4 = 1024$

1024 outcomes

24. $6 \times 2 = 12$

12 outcomes

25. $52 \times 2 = 104$

104 outcomes

26. permutation   **27.** combination

28. $P(7, 4) = 7 \cdot 6 \cdot 5 \cdot 4$

$= 840$

29. $5! = 5 \cdot 4 \cdot 3 \cdot 2 \cdot 1$

$= 120$

30. $C(8, 2) = \frac{P(8, 2)}{2!}$

$= \frac{8 \cdot 7}{2 \cdot 1}$

$= \frac{56}{2}$

$= 28$

31. $\frac{6! \, 3!}{4! \, 2!} = 6 \cdot 5 \cdot 3$

$= 90$

32. odds of selecting a queen

$= 4:48$

$= 1:12$

The odds of a selecting a queen are 1:12.

33. odds of not selecting a face card

$= 40:12$

$= 10:3$

The odds of not selecting a face card are 10:3.

34. odds of selecting an ace or six

$= 8:44$

$= 2:11$

The odds of selecting an ace or six are 2:11.

35. odds of selecting a red card

$= 26:26$

$= 1:1$

The odds of selecting a red card are 1:1.

36. dependent; the outcome of choosing a recipe and not replacing it will affect the outcome of choosing another recipe.

37. dependent; the outcome of buying property on the first turn will affect the outcome of buying property on the second turn.

38. $P(\text{two green marbles}) = 0$

39. $P(\text{a red and a yellow}) = \frac{5}{11} \cdot \frac{3}{10}$
$$= \frac{15}{110}$$
$$= \frac{3}{22}$$

40. $P(\text{two yellow}) = \frac{3}{11} \cdot \frac{2}{10}$
$$= \frac{6}{110}$$
$$= \frac{3}{55}$$

41. $P(\text{a purple and a red}) = \frac{3}{11} \cdot \frac{5}{10}$
$$= \frac{15}{110}$$
$$= \frac{3}{22}$$

42. inclusive;
$P(\text{rolling a six or sum greater than ten})$
$$= \frac{11}{36} + \frac{3}{36} - \frac{3}{36}$$
$$= \frac{11}{36}$$

43. inclusive;
$P(\text{rolling an even number or sum is odd})$
$$= \frac{27}{36} + \frac{18}{36} - \frac{18}{36}$$
$$= \frac{27}{36}$$

44. $P(\text{3 or 4}) = \frac{1}{6} + \frac{1}{6}$
$$= \frac{2}{6} \text{ or } \frac{1}{3}$$

45. $P(\text{4 or even}) = \frac{1}{6} + \frac{3}{6} - \frac{1}{6}$
$$= \frac{3}{6} \text{ or } \frac{1}{2}$$

Page 542　Applications and Problem Solving

46.

```
0 |
0 | 72  97
1 | 00  12  13  24  31  41  44  48  (49)
1 | 85  86
2 | 21  48
2 | 54  66  81  88
3 |
3 | 90  98            1 | 00 = 100
```

Median = 149

Lower Quartile $= \frac{113 + 124}{2}$ or 118.5

Upper Quartile $= \frac{254 + 266}{2}$ or 260

Interquartile range $= 260 - 118.5$ or 141.5
Outliers must be less than $118.5 - 1.5(141.5)$
or −93.75 or greater than $260 + 1.5(141.5)$
or 472.25. There are no outliers.

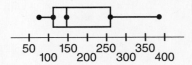

47. $8 \times 8 = 64$
64 ways

48. Sample answer: Use a spinner with 4 equal
sections. Three of the four spaces means a win.
Tally 25 groups of 3 spins as either 3 wins or not.

Page 543　Alternative Assessment

See students' work.

Page 543　Thinking Critically

See students' work.

Page 543　Portfolio

See students' work.

Page 543　Self-Evaluation

See students' work.

Pages 544–545　Ongoing Assessment

1. D; $-2(8) = -16$ pounds

2. B; 6° 10° 15° 18° 18° 25° 25° 25° 30° 38°
　　　　　↑　　　↑　　　↑
　　　　LQ　Median　UQ

The lower quartile is $15°$ and the upper quartile
is 25°.

3. D; $\frac{2}{6} = \frac{4}{12}$
Since $\frac{4}{12} < \frac{5}{12}, \frac{2}{6} < \frac{5}{12}$.

4. A;　$m + 2.1 = 8$
　　　$m + 2.1 - 2.1 = 8 - 2.1$
　　　　　　　$m = 5.9$

5. B; $P(\text{blue}) = \frac{2}{10}$ or $\frac{1}{5}$

6. D; $3 \times 3 \times 4 = 36$
36 different combinations

7. D;　　$5y - 4 = 3y + 12$
　　　$5y - 4 + 4 = 3y + 12 + 4$
　　　　　$5y = 3y + 16$
　　　$5y - 3y = 3y - 3y + 16$
　　　　　$2y = 16$
　　　　$\frac{2y}{2} = \frac{16}{2}$
　　　　　$y = 8$

8. C; $24 - 15 = 9$
　　　$9 = R \cdot 15$
　　$\frac{9}{15} = \frac{15R}{15}$
　　$0.6 = R$
The percent of increase is 60%.

9. A; $P(\text{tossing tails and rolling a 5})$
$$= \frac{1}{2} \cdot \frac{1}{6}$$
$$= \frac{1}{12}$$

10. A; $(-3, -9)$　　　　$(2, 1)$
　　$y = 2x - 3$　　　　$y = 2x - 3$
　　$-9 \overset{?}{=} 2(-3) - 3$　　$1 \overset{?}{=} 2(2) - 3$
　　$-9 \overset{?}{=} -6 - 3$　　　$1 \overset{?}{=} 4 - 3$
　　$-9 = -9$ ✔　　　　$1 = 1$ ✔
$(-3, -9)$ is a solution. $(2, 1)$ is a solution.
$(4, 5)$
$y = 2x - 3$
$5 \overset{?}{=} 2(4) - 3$
$5 \overset{?}{=} 8 - 3$
$5 = 5$ ✔
$(4, 5)$ is a solution.
$(-3, -9)$, $(2, 1)$ and $(4, 5)$ are solutions for
$y = 2x - 3$. So, the correct choice is A.

11. $7\frac{1}{8} - 4\frac{3}{4} = 7\frac{1}{8} - 4\frac{6}{8}$

$\qquad\qquad = 6\frac{9}{8} - 4\frac{6}{8}$

$\qquad\qquad = 2\frac{3}{8}$

She needs $2\frac{3}{8}$ pounds.

12. $\frac{350\ \text{miles}}{14\ \text{gallons}} = \frac{25\ \text{miles}}{1\ \text{gallon}}$

25 miles per gallon

13. $\quad C = \pi \cdot d$

$17.27 = \pi \cdot d$

$\frac{17.27}{\pi} = \frac{\pi d}{\pi}$

$\quad 5.5 \approx d$

The diameter of the circle is about 5.5 feet.

14. slope $= \frac{-4-2}{3-(-2)}$

$\qquad\ = \frac{-6}{5}$

$\qquad\ = -1.2$

15. $\frac{24}{40} = 0.6 \rightarrow \frac{60}{100} = 60\%$

16. total price $\leq 1500 + (3 \cdot 12)(200)$

$\qquad\qquad \leq 1500 + 7200$

$\qquad\qquad \leq 8700$

The car must be less or equal to $8700.

17. odds of rolling a number divisible by 3

$= 2{:}4$

$= 1{:}2$

The odds of rolling a number that is divisible by 3 are 1:2.

18. $4! = 4 \cdot 3 \cdot 2 \cdot 1$

$\quad\ = 24$

24 ways

19. See students' work.

20. See students' work.

11-1 The Language of Geometry

Pages 551–552 Checking Your Understanding

1. a. none **b.** two **c.** one

2. Parallel lines never intersect and are in the same plane. Skew lines never intersect but are in different planes.

3. See students' work.

4.

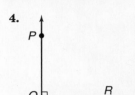

5. Acute angles measure less than 90°. Obtuse angles measure more than 90°, but less than 180°.

6. a.

 **b.**

c.  **d.**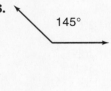

7. Sample answer: plane
See students' explanations.

8. Sample answer: point
See students' explanations.

9. Sample answer: A **10.** Sample answer: $\overrightarrow{AC}$

11. Sample answer: $\overleftrightarrow{CD}$ **12.** Sample answer: $\overrightarrow{AE}$

13. 63°; acute   **14.** 90°; right

15.

78°

16.

145°

17. The three "pods" determine a plane.

Pages 552–553 Exercises

18. Sample answer: segment
See students' explanations.

19. Sample answer: plane
See students' explanations.

20. Sample answer: line
See students' explanations.

21. Sample answer: ray
See students' explanations.

22. •
T

23.

Q

24. ℓ

25. X   Y

26.

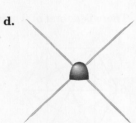
R   S   T

27. E   F

28.

B
O   Y

29.

B
A

30.

ℓ
m

31.

A   B
C   D

32.

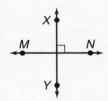
X
M   N
Y

33.

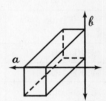
b
a

34. 90°; right   **35.** 155°; obtuse

36. 130°; obtuse   **37.** 65°; acute

38. 90°; right   **39.** 15°; acute

40. obtuse   **41.** acute

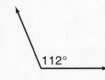
112°

47°

42. obtuse   **43.** acute

95°

16°

44. obtuse

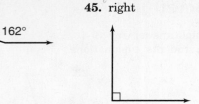

45. right

46. a. False; a segment is part of a line.

    b. False; all or part of the rays may coincide, forming a single ray or a line segment.

47. Let x = angle that a commercial jet makes its approach.

$$6x = 18$$
$$\frac{6x}{6} = \frac{18}{6}$$
$$x = 3$$

A commercial jet approaches the runway at an angle of 3°. See students' work.

48.

49. Use an analog clock to determine the number of times that the hands of a clock form a right angle for each hour of a twelve-hour period. Choose 3:00 P.M. as a starting point.

Time	Number of Right Angles
3:00–3:59 P.M.	2
4:00–4:59	2
5:00–5:59	2
6:00–6:59	2
7:00–7:59	2
8:00–8:59	1
9:00–9:59	2
10:00–10:59	2
11:00–11:59	2
12:00–12:59 A.M.	2
1:00–1:59	2
2:00–2:59	1

Notice the pattern:
2, 2, 2, 2, 2, 1, 2, 2, 2, 2, 2, 1, . . .
In twelve hours, the hands of a clock form a right angle $2 + 2 + 2 + 2 + 2 + 1 + 2 + 2 + 2 + 2 + 2 + 1$ or 22 times.
In twelve hours, the hands of a clock form a right angle 22 times.

50. inclusive:

$$P(\text{even or prime}) = \frac{3}{6} + \frac{3}{6} - \frac{1}{6}$$
$$= \frac{5}{6}$$

51.
$$\frac{1.5}{2} \overset{?}{=} \frac{1.8}{2.4}$$
$$1.5 \cdot 2.4 \overset{?}{=} 2 \cdot 1.8$$
$$3.6 = 3.6$$
So, $\frac{1.5}{2} = \frac{1.8}{2.4}$.

52. positive; See students' explanations.

53. Let x = even integer, then $x + 2$ = next greater even integer.

$$x + x + 2 > 98$$
$$2x + 2 > 98$$
$$2x + 2 - 2 > 98 - 2$$
$$2x > 96$$
$$\frac{2x}{2} > \frac{96}{2}$$
$$x > 48$$

If x must be greater than 48, then the even integer is 50 and the next greater even integer is $50 + 2$ or 52.

54.
$$n - 6.2 \le 5.8$$
$$n - 6.2 + 6.2 \le 5.8 + 6.2$$
$$n \le 12$$

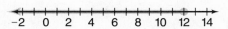

55. There is a total of 6 members.

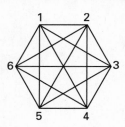

member #1 = 5 handshakes   Since #1 shook
member #2 = 4 handshakes   hands with #2, #2
member #3 = 3 handshakes   does not need to
member #4 = 2 handshakes   shake hands with
member #5 = 1 handshake   #1. #1 and #2
member #6 = <u>0 handshakes</u>   have already
          15 handshakes   shaken hands
                            with #3.

56. $P = 2(\ell \cdot w)$ $A = \ell \cdot w$
     $P = 2(15 + 12)$ $A = 15 \cdot 12$
     $P = 2(27)$ $A = 180 \text{ ft}^2$
     $P = 54$ ft

57. $\frac{d}{8} = \frac{-96}{8}$
     $= -12$

58. $3d = 24$ What number
     $3(8) = 24$ times 3 is 24?
       $d = 8$

Pages 554–555

1. See students' work.
2. See students' work.
3. Cut into two equal pieces.
4. right angles
5. They are the same.
6. It separates the angle into two equal angles.

11-2   Integration: Statistics
        Making Circle Graphs

Page 558   Checking Your Understanding

1. A circle graph shows how each piece of data compares to the whole while a bar graph compares data pieces to each other. A line graph shows how data change over time. A circle graph is appropriate when you want to compare parts of a whole.

2. Multiply the percent by 360 to find the number of degrees for each section. Draw the angles. Label each section and give the graph a title.

3. Find the total of the data. Write ratios comparing each part to the whole. Multiply each ratio by 360 to find the number of degrees for each angle.

4. See students' work.

5. $\frac{1}{4} = 25\%$. So, the element that makes up approximately $\frac{1}{4}$ or 25% of Earth's crust is silicon.

6. 47 + 28 = 75. So, 75% of Earth's crust is composed of oxygen and silicon.

7. **a.** 100%   **b.** 360°
   c. The total amount is 640 + 400 + 450 + 140 + 90 + 360 or $2080.
   Housing: 640 ÷ 2080 = 0.31 → 31%
   Food: 400 ÷ 2080 = 0.19 → 19%
   Trans.: 450 ÷ 2080 = 0.22 → 22%
   Insurance: 140 ÷ 2080 = 0.07 → 7%
   Savings: 90 ÷ 2080 = 0.04 → 4%
   Misc.: 360 ÷ 2080 = 0.17 → 17%
   Housing: 0.31 × 360 = 111.6 → 111.6°
   Food: 0.19 × 360 = 68.4 → 68.4°
   Trans.: 0.22 × 360 = 79.2 → 79.2°
   Insurance: 0.07 × 360 = 25.2 → 25.2°
   Savings: 0.04 × 360 = 14.4 → 14.4°
   Misc.: 0.17 × 360 = 61.2 → 61.2°

Monthly Budget			
Category	Amount ($)	Percent	Angle(°)
Housing	640	31	111.6
Food	400	19	68.4
Transportation	450	22	79.2
Insurance	140	7	25.2
Savings	90	4	14.4
Misc.	360	17	61.2
Totals	2080	100	360.0

d.   **Monthly Budget**

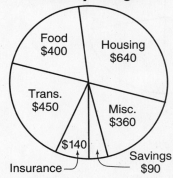

8. P(tossing a head) = $\frac{1}{2}$; half for heads and half for tails.

Pages 558–560   Exercises

9. 28 or 29 days: 1 month
   30 days: 4 months
   31 days: 7 months
   There are 1 + 4 + 7 or 12 months.
   28 or 29 days: 1 ÷ 12 = 0.08$\overline{3}$
   30 days: 4 ÷ 12 = 0.33$\overline{3}$
   31 days: 7 ÷ 12 = 0.58$\overline{3}$
   28 or 29 days: 0.08$\overline{3}$ × 360 = 30.0 → 30°
   30 days: 0.33$\overline{3}$ × 360 = 120.0 → 120°
   31 days: 0.58$\overline{3}$ × 360 = 210.0 → 210°

Days in the Month

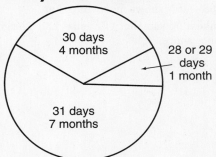

10. Summer: 27% = 0.27
Autumn: 22% = 0.22
Winter: 18% = 0.18
Spring: 33% = 0.33
Summer: 0.27 × 360 = 97.2 → 97°
Autumn: 0.22 × 360 = 79.2 → 79°
Winter: 0.18 × 360 = 64.8 → 65°
Spring: 0.33 × 360 = 118.8 → 119°

Season Preference

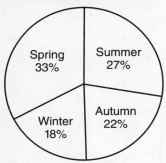

11. a. $P(\text{win}) = \frac{3}{8}$

b. $P(\text{win})$: $\frac{3}{8}$ = 0.375

$P(\text{lose})$: $\frac{5}{8}$ = 0.625
$P(\text{win})$: 0.375 × 360 = 135.0 → 135°
$P(\text{lose})$: 0.625 × 360 = 225.0 → 225°

**Probability
of
Winning or Losing**

12. a. No, the section for NBC should only have 68°—this shows more than that.

b. To make it appear that "Friends" had a larger audience share.

13. The total area, in square miles, is 64,186,300 + 33,420,000 + 28,350,500 + 5,105,700 or 131,062,500.

Pacific: 64,186,300 ÷ 131,062,500 = 0.489738
Atlantic: 33,420,000 ÷ 131,062,500 = 0.254993
Indian: 28,350,500 ÷ 131,062,500 = 0.216313
Arctic: 5,105,700 ÷ 131,062,500 = 0.038956

Pacific: 0.489738 × 360 = 176.30568 → 176°
Atlantic: 0.254993 × 360 = 91.79748 → 92°
Indian: 0.216313 × 360 = 77.87268 → 78°
Arctic: 0.038956 × 360 = 14.02416 → 14°

**Areas of Oceans
of the World**

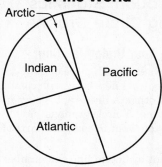

14. Oxygen: 65% = 0.65
Carbon: 18% = 0.18
Hydrogen: 10% = 0.10
Nitrogen: 3% = 0.03
Other: 4% = 0.04

Oxygen: 0.65 × 360 = 234.0 → 234°
Carbon: 0.18 × 360 = 64.8 → 65°
Hydrogen: 0.10 × 360 = 36.0 → 36°
Nitrogen: 0.03 × 360 = 10.8 → 11°
Other: 0.04 × 360 = 14.4 → 14°

**Chemical Composition
of the Human Body**

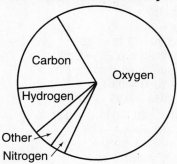

15. a. VNS Kent. Blue: 30% = 0.30
Regar Brome: 10% = 0.10
Lincoln Smooth: 10% = 0.10
Med. Red Clover: 5% = 0.05
VNS Timothy: 25% = 0.25
Alsike Clover: 10% = 0.10
VNS Tall Fescue: 10% = 0.10

VNS Kent. Blue: $0.30 \times 360 = 108.0 \rightarrow 108°$
Regar Brome: $0.10 \times 360 = 36.0 \rightarrow 36°$
Lincoln Smooth: $0.10 \times 360 = 36.0 \rightarrow 36°$
Med. Red Clover: $0.05 \times 360 = 18.0 \rightarrow 18°$
VNS Timothy: $0.25 \times 360 = 90.0 \rightarrow 90°$
Alsike Clover: $0.10 \times 360 = 36.0 \rightarrow 36°$
VNS Tall Fescue: $0.10 \times 360 = 36.0 \rightarrow 36°$

**Black Hills'
Reclamation Mix**

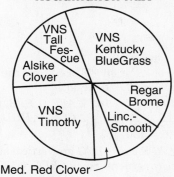

Med. Red Clover

b. $0.30 \times 250 = 75$
75 lb VNS Kentucky Bluegrass
$0.10 \times 250 = 25$
25 lb each of Regar Bromegrass, Lincoln Smooth Brome, Alsike Clover and VNS Tall Fescue
$0.05 \times 250 = 12.5$
12.5 lb Medium Red Clover
$0.25 \times 250 = 62.5$
62.5 lb VNS Timothy

16. a–b. See students' work.

17.

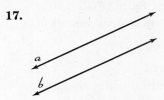

18. $10 \times 10 \times 10 \times 10 = 10,000$
10,000 combinations

19. slope $= m = \frac{1}{2}$
Let $x = 0$:
$y = \frac{1}{2}x - 4$
$y = \frac{1}{2}(0) - 4$
$y = -4$
The y-intercept is (0, 4)

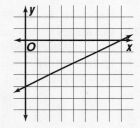

20. 1 mile = 5280 feet
$\frac{1800}{5280}$ is close to $\frac{1800}{5400}$.
$\frac{1800}{5400} = \frac{1}{3}$
So, 1800 feet is about $\frac{1}{3}$ of a mile.

21. Sample answer: Joe earned 3 times as much as Sue. If Joe earned $25, how much did Sue earn?

Page 560   The Shape of Things to Come

- Virtual reality systems use tracking computers. A tracking computer detects head movements and tells the main computer the direction in which a person is looking.

- The first, second, and third dimensions are the three dimensions of a virtual reality system. In the first dimension, the images along the vertical axis are scanned by moving your head up and down. In the second dimension, the images along the horizontal axis are scanned by moving your head left to right. In the third dimension, distant objects are scanned by special lenses that cover the screen.

- A virtual reality screen is similar to a living, moving graph in that both have a vertical axis and a horizontal axis.

- Look straight ahead. Have your partners move to your right and left. Hold your arms out to show the angle formed by pointing at them when they are just within your field of vision. Measure the angle. Find the vertical field of view by having your partners move one stick up and one down until the sticks are just visible to you as you look straight ahead. Form the angle with your arms and measure.

- The reality of virtual reality headsets is referred to as "virtual" because the images and sounds appear to be real.

| 11-3 | **Angle Relationships and Parallel Lines** |

Page 561   Your Turn

a. 8

b. There are just two different measures.

c. Sample answers: the angles across from each other; the angles in the same position on each of the parallel lines; the angles on opposite sides inside the parallel lines; the angles on opposite sides above and below the parallel lines.

d. Their sum is 180°.

Pages 564–565   Checking Your Understanding

1. Vertical angles are formed by two intersecting lines. They share only a common vertex. Adjacent angles share a vertex and a common side.

2. Sample answers:

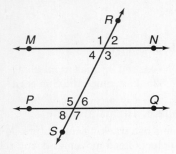

   a. ∠1 and ∠5
   b. ∠4 and ∠6
   c. ∠1 and ∠7
   d. ∠1 and ∠2
   e. ∠1 and ∠4

3.

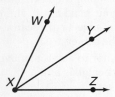

∠WXY and ∠YXZ share a common vertex and side.

4.

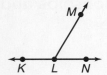

∠GHI and ∠IHJ share a common vertex and side and together they form a right angle.

5.

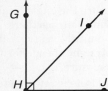

∠KLM and ∠MLN share a common vertex and side and together they form a straight angle.

6. In the last figure, ∠1 and ∠2 form a line. Therefore, ∠1 and ∠2 are supplementary. So, the correct choice is d.

7. Since the angles are vertical angles, they are congruent. So, $x = 40$.

8. The angles form a straight line so they are supplementary. Therefore, $x = 180 - 25$ or 155.

9. $m\angle C + m\angle D = 90$
    $m\angle C + 75 = 90$
 $m\angle C + 75 - 75 = 90 - 75$
      $m\angle C = 15$
The measure of ∠C is 15°.

10. $m\angle P + m\angle Q = 180$
      $m\angle P + 90 = 180$
 $m\angle P + 90 - 90 = 180 - 90$
        $m\angle P = 90$
The measure of ∠P is 90°.

11. $m\angle X + m\angle Y = 180$
    $2x + 4x = 180$
        $6x = 180$
       $\dfrac{6x}{6} = \dfrac{180}{6}$
         $x = 30$
The measure of ∠X is 2(30) or 60° and the measure of ∠Y is 4(30) or 120°.

12. $m\angle F + m\angle G = 90$
   $(x + 8) + (x - 10) = 90$
    $x + 8 + x - 10 = 90$
        $2x - 2 = 90$
  $2x - 2 + 2 = 90 + 2$
        $2x = 92$
       $\dfrac{2x}{2} = \dfrac{92}{2}$
        $x = 46$
The measure of ∠F is 46 + 8 or 54° and the measure of ∠G is 46 − 10 or 36°.

13. ∠AFG, ∠GFB,   **14.** ∠AFE, ∠EFB,
    ∠CGF, ∠FGD   ∠CGH, ∠HGD

15. a–b. $m\angle AFE = 130°$
    Since ∠AFE and ∠BFG are vertical angles, they are congruent. So, $m\angle BFG = 130°$.
    Since ∠BFG and ∠CGF are alternate interior angles, they are congruent. So, $m\angle CGF = 130°$.
    ∠BFG and ∠DGH are corresponding so they are congruent. Therefore, $m\angle DGH = 130°$.
    ∠EFB and ∠AFG are supplementary to ∠AFE. 180 − 130 = 50. So, $m\angle EFB = 50°$ and $m\angle AFG = 50°$.
    ∠EFB and ∠CGH are alternate exterior angles so they are congruent. So, $m\angle CGH = 50°$.
    Since ∠CGH and ∠FGD are vertical angles, they are congruent. So, $m\angle FGD = 50°$.

16. No, the corresponding angle has a measure of only 55°.

Pages 565–566   Exercises

17. Since the angles are vertical angles, they are congruent. So, $x = 105$.

18. The angles form a straight line so they are supplementary. 180 − 45 = 135. So, $x = 135$.

19. Since the angles are vertical angles, they are congruent. So, $x = 66$.

20. The angles form a straight line so they are supplementary. 180 − 52 = 128. So, $x = 128$.

21. The angles are complementary. 90 − 35 = 55. So, $x = 55$.

22. The angles form a right angle so they are complementary.

$$y + 4y = 90$$
$$5y = 90$$
$$\frac{5y}{5} = \frac{90}{5}$$
$$y = 18$$

So, $y = 18$.

23. The angles form a straight line so they are supplementary.

$$x + 2x = 180$$
$$3x = 180$$
$$\frac{3x}{3} = \frac{180}{3}$$
$$x = 60$$

$x = 60$ and $2x = 120$.
The measures of the angles are 60° and 120°.

24. The angles form a straight line so they are supplementary.

$$x + (x + 10) = 180$$
$$x + x + 10 = 180$$
$$2x + 10 = 180$$
$$2x + 10 - 10 = 180 - 10$$
$$2x = 170$$
$$\frac{2x}{2} = \frac{170}{2}$$
$$x = 85$$

$x = 85$ and $x + 10 = 95$.
The measures of the angles are 95° and 85°.

25. The angles form a right angle so they are complementary.

$$y + 4y = 90$$
$$5y = 90$$
$$\frac{5y}{5} = \frac{90}{5}$$
$$y = 18$$

$y = 18$ and $4y = 72$.
The measures of the angles are 18° and 72°.

26. $\angle 1$ and $\angle 2$ are supplementary. $180 - 47 = 133$. So, $m\angle 2 = 133°$.

27. Since $\angle 3$ and $\angle 1$ are vertical angles, they are congruent. So, $m\angle 3 = 47°$.

28. $\angle 1$ and $\angle 5$ are corresponding angles so they are congruent. Thus, $m\angle 5 = 47°$.

29. $\angle 1$ and $\angle 4$ are supplementary. $180 - 47 = 133$. So, $m\angle 4 = 133°$.

30. Since $\angle 7$ and $\angle 1$ are alternate exterior angles, they are congruent. So, $m\angle 7 = 47°$.

31. $\angle 7$ and $\angle 8$ are supplementary. $180 - 47 = 133$. So, $m\angle 8 = 133°$.

32.
$$m\angle A + m\angle B = 90$$
$$(2x + 15) + (x - 3) = 90$$
$$2x + 15 + x - 3 = 90$$
$$3x + 12 = 90$$
$$3x + 12 - 12 = 90 - 12$$
$$3x = 78$$
$$\frac{3x}{3} = \frac{78}{3}$$
$$x = 26$$

$2x + 15 = 67$ and $x - 3 = 23$.
The measure of $\angle A$ is 67° and the measure of $\angle B$ is 23°.

33.
$$m\angle R + m\angle S = 90$$
$$(x - 9) + (x + 17) = 90$$
$$x - 9 + x + 17 = 90$$
$$2x + 8 = 90$$
$$2x + 8 - 8 = 90 - 8$$
$$2x = 82$$
$$\frac{2x}{2} = \frac{82}{2}$$
$$x = 41$$

$x - 9 = 32$ and $x + 17 = 58$.
The measure of $\angle R$ is 32° and the measure of $\angle S$ is 58°.

34.
$$m\angle T + m\angle S = 180$$
$$(2x + 17) + (5x - 40) = 180$$
$$2x + 17 + 5x - 40 = 180$$
$$7x - 23 = 180$$
$$7x - 23 + 23 = 180 + 23$$
$$7x = 203$$
$$\frac{7x}{7} = \frac{203}{7}$$
$$x = 29$$

$2x + 17 = 75$ and $5x - 40 = 105$.
The measure of $\angle T$ is 75° and the measure of $\angle S$ is 105°.

35.
$$m\angle F + m\angle G = 180$$
$$(3x + 40) + (2x + 10) = 180$$
$$3x + 40 + 2x + 10 = 180$$
$$5x + 50 = 180$$
$$5x + 50 - 50 = 180 - 50$$
$$5x = 130$$
$$\frac{5x}{5} = \frac{130}{5}$$
$$x = 26$$

$3x + 40 = 118$ and $2x + 10 = 62$.
The measure of $\angle F$ is 118° and the measure of $\angle G$ is 62°.

36. $\angle 1$ is supplementary to $\angle 2$.

$$m\angle 1 + m\angle 2 = 180$$
$$(6x - 20) + (x - 40) = 180$$
$$6x - 20 + x - 40 = 180$$
$$7x + 20 = 180$$
$$7x + 20 - 20 = 180 - 20$$
$$7x = 160$$
$$\frac{7x}{7} = \frac{160}{7}$$
$$x = 22.9$$

37. $\angle 4$ and $\angle 5$ are supplementary.

$$m\angle 4 + m\angle 5 = 180$$
$$(3x + 17) + (2x + 13) = 180$$
$$3x + 17 + 2x + 13 = 180$$
$$5x + 30 = 180$$
$$5x + 30 - 30 = 180 - 30$$
$$5x = 150$$
$$\frac{5x}{5} = \frac{150}{5}$$
$$x = 30$$

38. ∠6 is supplementary to ∠7.

$$m\angle 6 + m\angle 7 = 180$$
$$(9x - 10) + (5x + 36) = 180$$
$$9x - 10 + 5x + 36 = 180$$
$$14x + 26 = 180$$
$$14x + 26 - 26 = 180 - 26$$
$$14x = 154$$
$$\frac{14x}{14} = \frac{154}{14}$$
$$x = 11$$

39. Let x represent the angle. Then the angle's supplement is $180 - x$ and the angle's complement is $90 - x$.

$$180 - x = 4(90 - x) - 15$$
$$180 - x = 360 - 4x - 15$$
$$180 - x = 345 - 4x$$
$$180 - x + 4x = 345 - 4x + 4x$$
$$180 + 3x = 345$$
$$180 + 3x - 180 = 345 - 180$$
$$3x = 165$$
$$\frac{3x}{3} = \frac{165}{3}$$
$$x = 55$$

The measure of the angle is 55°.

40.
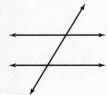

They are supplementary.

41.
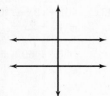

Yes; all the angles formed are right angles.

42. The angle of incidence and the angle of reflection have the same measure. Therefore, the measure of the angle between the incident ray and the reflected ray is $180 - 52 - 52$ or 76°.

43. The first vertical post is a transversal to the parallel rails. Therefore, the two interior angles are supplementary. $180 - 45 = 135$. So, $x = 135°$.

44. $17\% \times 360 = 61.2$
The measure of the angle to represent produce is 61.2°.

45. $P(\text{sum} > 8) = \frac{10}{36}$
$$= \frac{5}{18}$$

46. There are 1600 bacteria ⟶ 1600
Undo the third day ⟶ $\div \ 4$
400
Undo the second day ⟶ $\div \ 4$
100
Undo the first day ⟶ $\div \ 4$
25

There were 25 bacteria at the beginning of the first day.

47. $56{,}780 = 5.678 \times 10^4$

48. $\frac{12}{54} = \dfrac{\overset{1}{\cancel{2}} \cdot 2 \cdot \overset{1}{\cancel{3}}}{\underset{1}{\cancel{2}} \cdot \underset{1}{\cancel{3}} \cdot 3 \cdot 3} = \frac{2}{9}$

49. $9b + (-16)b = [9 + (-16)]b$
$$= -7b$$

50. $|5| - |2| = 5 - 2$
$$= 3$$

51. $8 + n = 13$ What number
$8 + 5 = 13$ plus 8 is 13?
$n = 5$

11-3B | **Math Lab: Slopes of Parallel Lines**

Page 567   Your Turn
See students' work.

1. It divides the difference of the y-coordinates by the difference of the x-coordinates.

2. They are the same.

3. yes

4. See students' work.

5. Draw two lines with the same slope.

11-4 | **Triangles**

Page 570   Checking Your Understanding

1. Subtract the sum of the known angles from 180°.

2. Sample answer: wire hanger

3. Sample answer: pattern block triangle

4. Sample answer: triangle formed by stairs, wall, and floor

5. See students' work.

6. $x + 84 + 27 = 180$
$x + 111 = 180$
$x + 111 - 111 = 180 - 111$
$x = 69$
The triangle is acute.

7. $x + 18 + 45 = 180$
$x + 63 = 180$
$x + 63 - 63 = 180 - 63$
$x = 117$
The triangle is obtuse.

8. Let x represent the measure of one angle, $3x$ the measure of a second angle, and $5x$ the measure of the third angle.
$$x + 3x + 5x = 180$$
$$9x = 180$$
$$\frac{9x}{9} = \frac{180}{9}$$
$$x = 20$$
$x = 20$, $3x = 60$, and $5x = 100$.
The measures of the angles are 20°, 60°, and 100°.

9.
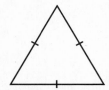

There are three congruent sides. So, the triangle is an equilateral triangle.

10.

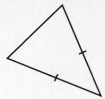

There are two congruent sides. So, the triangle is an isosceles triangle.

11. $x + 27 + 34 = 180$
$x + 61 = 180$
$x + 61 - 61 = 180 - 61$
$x = 119$
The measure of the angle is 119°.

Pages 570–572 Exercises

12. $x + 36 + 32 = 180$
$x + 68 = 180$
$x + 68 - 68 = 180 - 68$
$x = 112$
The triangle is obtuse.

13. $x + 90 + 40 = 180$
$x + 130 = 180$
$x + 130 - 130 = 180 - 130$
$x = 50$
The triangle is a right triangle.

14. $x + 70 + 55 = 180$
$x + 125 = 180$
$x + 125 - 125 = 180 - 125$
$x = 55$
The triangle is acute.

15. Let $2x$ represent the measure of one angle, $3x$ the measure of a second angle, and $5x$ the measure of the third angle.
$2x + 3x + 5x = 180$
$10x = 180$
$\frac{10x}{10} = \frac{180}{10}$
$x = 18$
$2x = 36$, $3x = 54$, and $5x = 90$.
The measures of the angles are 36°, 54°, and 90°.

16. Let x represent the measure of one angle, $4x$ the measure of a second angle, and $7x$ the measure of the third angle.
$x + 4x + 7x = 180$
$12x = 180$
$\frac{12x}{12} = \frac{180}{12}$
$x = 15$
$x = 15$, $4x = 60$, and $7x = 105$.
The measures of the angles are 15°, 60°, and 105°.

17.

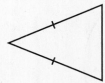

There are two congruent sides. So, the triangle is an isosceles triangle.

18.

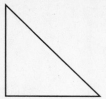

There are no congruent sides. So, the triangle is a scalene triangle.

19.

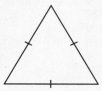

There are three congruent sides. So, the triangle is an equilateral triangle.

20. 40°, 50°, 90°
The triangle is a right triangle.

21. 105°, 40°, 35°
The triangle is obtuse.

22. 70°, 60°, 50°
The triangle is acute.

23. $m\angle 1 + m\angle 2 + m\angle 3 = 180$
$m\angle 1 + 40 + 55 = 180$
$m\angle 1 + 95 = 180$
$m\angle 1 + 95 - 95 = 180 - 95$
$m\angle 1 = 85$
The measure of $\angle 1$ is 85°.

24. $m\angle 1 + m\angle 2 + m\angle 3 = 180$
$m\angle 1 + 60 + 60 = 180$
$m\angle 1 + 120 = 180$
$m\angle 1 + 120 - 120 = 180 - 120$
$m\angle 1 = 60$
The measure of $\angle 1$ is 60°.

25. $m\angle 1 + m\angle 2 + m\angle 3 = 180$
$m\angle 1 + 81 + 74 = 180$
$m\angle 1 + 155 = 180$
$m\angle 1 + 155 - 155 = 180 - 155$
$m\angle 1 = 25$
The measure of $\angle 1$ is 25°.

26. $m\angle 1 + m\angle 2 + m\angle 3 = 180$
$45 + m\angle 2 + 75 = 180$
$m\angle 2 + 120 = 180$
$m\angle 2 + 120 - 120 = 180 - 120$
$m\angle 2 = 60$
The measure of $\angle 2$ is 60°.

27. $m\angle 1 + m\angle 2 + m\angle 3 = 180$
$47 + m\angle 2 + 48 = 180$
$m\angle 2 + 95 = 180$
$m\angle 2 + 95 - 95 = 180 - 95$
$m\angle 2 = 85$
The measure of $\angle 2$ is 85°.

28. $2x + 3x + x = 180$
$6x = 180$
$\frac{6x}{6} = \frac{180}{6}$
$x = 30$
$2x = 60$, $3x = 90$, and $x = 30$.
The measures of the angles are 60°, 90°, and 30°.

29. $x + 80 + (x + 10) = 180$

$\qquad x + 80 + x + 10 = 180$

$\qquad\qquad\quad 2x + 90 = 180$

$\qquad 2x + 90 - 90 = 180 - 90$

$\qquad\qquad\qquad 2x = 90$

$\qquad\qquad\quad \dfrac{2x}{2} = \dfrac{90}{2}$

$\qquad\qquad\qquad\ x = 45$

$x = 45$ and $x + 10 = 55$.

The measures of the angles are 45°, 80°, and 55°.

30. $(x + 35) + 5x + (2x - 15) = 180$

$\qquad x + 35 + 5x + 2x - 15 = 180$

$\qquad\qquad\qquad\quad 8x + 20 = 180$

$\qquad\qquad 8x + 20 - 20 = 180 - 20$

$\qquad\qquad\qquad\qquad 8x = 160$

$\qquad\qquad\qquad\ \dfrac{8x}{8} = \dfrac{160}{8}$

$\qquad\qquad\qquad\qquad\ x = 20$

$x + 35 = 55$, $5x = 100$, and $2x - 15 = 25$.

The measures of the angles are 55°, 100°, and 25°.

31. a–c. See students' work.

32. Yes, their sum must be 90° to have the three angles add to 180°.

33. $x + x + x = 180$

$\qquad\quad 3x = 180$

$\qquad\ \dfrac{3x}{3} = \dfrac{180}{3}$

$\qquad\qquad x = 60$

The measure of each angle is 60°.

34.

10   15

21   28

35. Let x represent the measure of the angle formed by the guy wire and the pole.

$\qquad x + 65 + 90 = 180$

$\qquad\qquad x + 155 = 180$

$x + 155 - 155 = 180 - 155$

$\qquad\qquad\qquad x = 25$

The measure of the angle formed by the guy wire and the pole is 25°.

36. $\qquad m\angle X + m\angle Y = 180$

$\qquad\qquad 35 + m\angle Y = 180$

$35 + m\angle Y - 35 = 180 - 35$

$\qquad\qquad\qquad m\angle Y = 145$

The measure of $\angle Y$ is 145°.

37. Odds of rolling a sum less than $6 = 10{:}26$ or $\frac{5}{13}$.

38.

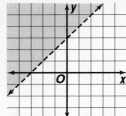

39. Let x = length of the fabric

$x = 42\frac{3}{4} + 4 + 4 + 2\frac{1}{2} + 6$

$x = 42\frac{3}{4} + 16\frac{1}{2}$

$x = 42\frac{3}{4} + 16\frac{2}{4}$

$x = 58\frac{5}{4}$ or $59\frac{1}{4}$

The fabric should be $59\frac{1}{4}$ inches.

40. a. $-8 > -14$

b. $-|20| = -20$

c. $0 < |2|$

41. $4(x + 3) = 4(x) + 4(3)$

$\qquad\qquad\ = 4x + 12$

Page 572   Self Test

1.

60°

The angle is acute.

2.

115°

The angle is obtuse.

3.

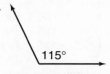

20°

The angle is acute.

4. CDs: 42% = 0.42

tapes: 28% = 0.28

equipment: 18% = 0.18

other: 12% = 0.12

CDs: $0.42 \times 360 = 151.2 \rightarrow 151°$

tapes: $0.28 \times 360 = 100.8 \rightarrow 101°$

equipment: $0.18 \times 360 = 64.8 \rightarrow 65°$

other: $0.12 \times 360 = 43.2 \rightarrow 43°$

Sales at Recordtown

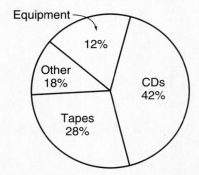

5. Since $\angle 1$ and $\angle 3$ are vertical angles, they are congruent. So, $m\angle 1 = 34°$.

6. $\angle 4$ and $\angle 3$ are supplementary. $180 - 34 = 146$. So, $m\angle 4 = 146°$.

7. Since $\angle 5$ and $\angle 3$ are alternate interior angles, they are congruent. So, $m\angle 5 = 34°$.

8.
$$m\angle A + m\angle B = 90$$
$$(x + 25) + (2x - 10) = 90$$
$$x + 25 + 2x - 10 = 90$$
$$3x + 15 = 90$$
$$3x + 15 - 15 = 90 - 15$$
$$3x = 75$$
$$\frac{3x}{3} = \frac{75}{3}$$
$$x = 25$$
$x + 25 = 50$ and $2x - 10 = 40$.
The measure of $\angle A$ is 50° and the measure of $\angle B$ is 40°.

9.
$$m\angle F + m\angle G = 180$$
$$(3x - 50) + (2x - 20) = 180$$
$$3x - 50 + 2x - 20 = 180$$
$$5x - 70 = 180$$
$$5x - 70 + 70 = 180 + 70$$
$$5x = 250$$
$$\frac{5x}{5} = \frac{250}{5}$$
$$x = 50$$
$3x - 50 = 100$ and $2x - 20 = 80$.
The measure of $\angle F$ is 100° and the measure of $\angle G$ is 80°.

10.
$$x + 30 + 90 = 180$$
$$x + 120 = 180$$
$$x + 120 - 120 = 180 - 120$$
$$x = 60$$
The triangle is a right triangle.

11.
$$x + 42 + 38 = 180$$
$$x + 80 = 180$$
$$x + 80 - 80 = 180 - 80$$
$$x = 100$$
The triangle is obtuse.

12.
$$x + 65 + 52 = 180$$
$$x + 117 = 180$$
$$x + 117 - 117 = 180 - 117$$
$$x = 63$$
The triangle is acute.

11-5   Congruent Triangles

Page 573   Your Turn

a. same

b. $\angle X$ to $\angle X'$, $\angle Y$ to $\angle Y'$, $\angle Z$ to $\angle Z'$

c. $\overline{XY}$ to $\overline{X'Y'}$, $\overline{YZ}$ to $\overline{Y'Z'}$, $\overline{XZ}$ to $\overline{X'Z'}$

Pages 575–576   Checking Your Understanding

1. All corresponding parts are congruent.

2. $\overline{XY}$ corresponds to $\overline{ST}$ and $\angle Y$ corresponds to $\angle T$.

3. Since figure c appears to have the same size and shape, it appears to be congruent.

---

4. a. $\triangle ABC \cong \triangle FED$

   b. $\angle A \cong \angle F$,
$\angle B \cong \angle E$,
$\angle C \cong \angle D$,
$\overline{AB} \cong \overline{FE}$,
$\overline{BC} \cong \overline{ED}$,
$\overline{AC} \cong \overline{FD}$

5. a. $\triangle ABC \cong \triangle ZYX$

   b. $\overline{AB} \cong \overline{ZY}$

   c. $\angle Y \cong \angle B$

   d. $\angle C \cong \angle X$

   e. $\overline{BC} \cong \overline{YX}$

   f. $\overline{XZ} \cong \overline{CA}$

   g. $\angle Z \cong \angle A$

6. $\angle A \cong \angle F$ $\overline{AB} \cong \overline{FE}$
$\angle B \cong \angle E$ $\overline{BC} \cong \overline{ED}$
$\angle C \cong \angle D$ $\overline{AC} \cong \overline{FD}$
So, $\triangle ABC \cong \triangle FED$.

7. $\overline{EH} \cong \overline{ED}$. The measure of $\overline{ED}$ is 10 units. So, $\overline{EH}$ also has a measure of 10 units. The correct choice is c.

8. Since the two gardens are congruent, their sides have the same measure. Therefore, the second garden will also need 12 meters of fence.

Pages 576–577   Exercises

9. $\triangle ABC \cong \triangle FED$;
$\angle A \cong \angle F$,
$\angle B \cong \angle E$,
$\angle C \cong \angle D$,
$\overline{AB} \cong \overline{FE}$,
$\overline{BC} \cong \overline{ED}$,
$\overline{AC} \cong \overline{FD}$

10. $\triangle CBA \cong \triangle DEF$;
$\angle C \cong \angle D$,
$\angle B \cong \angle E$,
$\angle A \cong \angle F$,
$\overline{CB} \cong \overline{DE}$,
$\overline{BA} \cong \overline{EF}$,
$\overline{CA} \cong \overline{DF}$

11. $\triangle BAD \cong \triangle ABC$;
$\angle BAD \cong \angle ABC$,
$\angle D \cong \angle C$,
$\angle ABD \cong \angle BAC$,
$\overline{BA} \cong \overline{AB}$,
$\overline{AD} \cong \overline{BC}$,
$\overline{BD} \cong \overline{AC}$

12. $\triangle BCD \cong \triangle BAE$;
$\angle C \cong \angle A$,
$\angle D \cong \angle E$,
$\angle CBD \cong \angle ABE$,
$\overline{BC} \cong \overline{BA}$,
$\overline{CD} \cong \overline{AE}$,
$\overline{BD} \cong \overline{BE}$

13. $\angle D \cong \angle H$ $\overline{DE} \cong \overline{HG}$
       $\angle E \cong \angle G$ $\overline{EF} \cong \overline{GF}$
       $\angle DFE \cong \angle HGF$ $\overline{DF} \cong \overline{HF}$
       So, $\triangle DEF \cong \triangle HGF$.

14. $\angle QPR \cong \angle SPR$ $\overline{PQ} \cong \overline{PS}$
       $\angle Q \cong \angle S$ $\overline{QR} \cong \overline{SR}$
       $\angle QRP \cong \angle SRP$ $\overline{PR} \cong \overline{RP}$
       So, $\triangle PQR \cong \triangle PSR$.

15. $\overline{RS} \cong \overline{MA}$

16. $\angle P \cong \angle T$

17. $\overline{MP} \cong \overline{RT}$

18. $\overline{ST} \cong \overline{AP}$

19. $\angle R \cong \angle M$

20. $\angle A \cong \angle S$

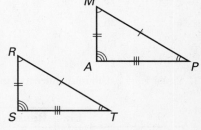

21. $x = 3$ **22.** $x = 6$ **23.** $x = 8$

---

24. Not necessarily: similar triangles, like △ABC and △DEF, have congruent corresponding angles but are not congruent triangles.

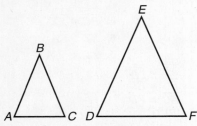

25. $\angle BAH \cong \angle JIG$ $\overline{AB} \cong \overline{IJ}$
$\angle ABH \cong \angle IJG$ $\overline{BH} \cong \overline{JG}$
$\angle AHB \cong \angle IGJ$ $\overline{AH} \cong \overline{IG}$
So, $\triangle ABH \cong \triangle IJG$.
$\angle CAG \cong \angle EIF$ $\overline{AC} \cong \overline{IE}$
$\angle ACG \cong \angle IEF$ $\overline{CG} \cong \overline{EF}$
$\angle AGC \cong \angle IFE$ $\overline{AG} \cong \overline{IF}$
So, $\triangle ACG \cong \triangle IEF$.

26. a. $\triangle ABC \cong \triangle GFE$
   b. $\triangle BDC \cong \triangle FDE$
   c. $\triangle ADC \cong \triangle GDE$

27. Since the two triangles are congruent, their sides have the same measure. Therefore, the second triangle also has a perimeter of 5 ft.

28. See students' work.

29. $m\angle P + m\angle Q + m\angle R = 180$
$\qquad 45 + 40 + m\angle R = 180$
$\qquad\qquad 85 + m\angle R = 180$
$\qquad 85 + m\angle R - 85 = 180 - 85$
$\qquad\qquad\qquad m\angle R = 95$
The measure of $\angle R$ is 95°. The triangle is obtuse.

30. $\dfrac{x}{45} = \dfrac{15}{100}$
$x \cdot 100 = 45 \cdot 15$
$\quad 100x = 675$
$\quad \dfrac{100x}{100} = \dfrac{675}{100}$
$\qquad\quad x = 6.75$
The amount of savings is $6.75.

31. $\dfrac{a}{5} - 6 = 19$
$\dfrac{a}{5} - 6 + 6 = 19 + 6$
$\qquad \dfrac{a}{5} = 25$
$\qquad 5 \cdot \dfrac{a}{5} = 5 \cdot 25$
$\qquad\qquad a = 125$

32. Since $1\frac{3}{5} = \frac{8}{5}$, the multiplicative inverse is $\frac{5}{8}$.

33.

	Liz	Renee	Pablo
Sack Lunch	○	✕	✕
Plate Lunch	✕	✕	○
Snack Bar	✕	○	✕

Page 578   Your Turn

a. Corresponding angles have the same measure.

b. The ratios are the same.

c. yes

Page 581–582   Checking Your Understanding

1. Corresponding angles are congruent and corresponding sides are proportional.

2. Marta; the corresponding angles are not congruent.

3. See students' work.

4. Measure the shadow cast by the object you can measure, like a meterstick. Write and solve a proportion to find the height of the object.

5. See students' work.

6. See students' work; yes.

7. a. $\dfrac{m\overline{AB}}{m\overline{AC}} = \dfrac{m\overline{BE}}{m\overline{CD}} = \dfrac{m\overline{AE}}{m\overline{AD}}$
   b. $\angle CAD$ corresponds to $\angle BAE$.
   c. $\overline{CD}$ corresponds to $\overline{BE}$.
   d. $\dfrac{m\overline{BE}}{m\overline{CD}} = \dfrac{m\overline{AE}}{m\overline{AD}}$
$\qquad \dfrac{4}{x} = \dfrac{6}{15}$
$\qquad 4 \cdot 15 = x \cdot 6$
$\qquad\quad 60 = 6x$
$\qquad\quad \dfrac{60}{6} = \dfrac{6x}{6}$
$\qquad\quad 10 = x$
The measure of $\overline{CD}$ is 10 ft.

8. $\dfrac{4}{8} = \dfrac{x}{10}$
$4 \cdot 10 = 8 \cdot x$
$\quad 40 = 8x$
$\quad \dfrac{40}{8} = \dfrac{8x}{8}$
$\quad 5 = x$

9. $\dfrac{1}{x} = \dfrac{2}{6}$
$1 \cdot 6 = x \cdot 2$
$\quad 6 = 2x$
$\quad \dfrac{6}{2} = \dfrac{2x}{2}$
$\quad 3 = x$

10. a; the measures of the sides are proportional.

11. $\dfrac{m\overline{DA}}{m\overline{BA}} = \dfrac{m\overline{DE}}{m\overline{BC}}$
$\quad \dfrac{220}{100} = \dfrac{x}{55}$
$220 \cdot 55 = 100 \cdot x$
$\quad 12{,}100 = 100x$
$\quad \dfrac{12{,}100}{100} = \dfrac{100x}{100}$
$\qquad 121 = x$
The distance across Brandon Lake is 121 m.

Pages 582–583   Exercises

12. $\dfrac{4}{10} = \dfrac{6}{x}$
$4 \cdot x = 10 \cdot 6$
$\quad 4x = 60$
$\quad \dfrac{4x}{4} = \dfrac{60}{4}$
$\quad x = 15$

13. $\dfrac{3}{2} = \dfrac{x}{3}$
$3 \cdot 3 = 2 \cdot x$
$\quad 9 = 2x$
$\quad \dfrac{9}{2} = \dfrac{2x}{2}$
$\quad 4.5 = x$

14. $\frac{3}{2} = \frac{5.5}{x}$

$3 \cdot x = 2 \cdot 5.5$

$3x = 11$

$\frac{3x}{3} = \frac{11}{3}$

$x = 3\frac{2}{3}$

15. $\frac{4}{5} = \frac{8}{x}$

$4 \cdot x = 5 \cdot 8$

$4x = 40$

$\frac{4x}{4} = \frac{40}{4}$

$x = 10$

16. $\frac{24}{56} = \frac{21}{x}$

$24 \cdot x = 56 \cdot 21$

$24x = 1176$

$\frac{24x}{24} = \frac{1176}{24}$

$x = 49$

17. $\frac{3}{5} = \frac{4.5}{x}$

$3 \cdot x = 5 \cdot 4.5$

$3x = 22.5$

$\frac{3x}{3} = \frac{22.5}{3}$

$x = 7.5$

18.

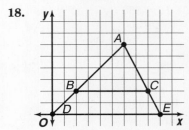

a. Yes. The corresponding angles are congruent.

b. yes

c. Yes, because the corresponding angles are congruent.

19. a. Yes; the ratio of the corresponding sides is 1:1.

b. No; only those where the ratio of the corresponding sides is 1:1.

20. 15.24 cm = 152.4 mm

$\frac{52.5}{35} = \frac{152.4}{x}$

$52.5 \cdot x = 35 \cdot 152.4$

$52.5x = 5334$

$\frac{52.5x}{52.5} = \frac{5334}{52.5}$

$x = 101.6$

Area of the negative = 52.5×35
$= 1837.5$ sq mm

Area of the print = 152.4×101.6
$= 15,483.84$ sq mm

$\frac{15,483.84}{1837.5} = 8.427$

The area of the print is about 8.4 times greater than the area of the negative.

21. $\frac{6}{x} = \frac{9}{4}$

$6 \cdot 4 = 9 \cdot x$

$24 = 9x$

$\frac{24}{9} = \frac{9x}{9}$

$2.7 = x$

The length of the brace is 2.7 ft.

22.

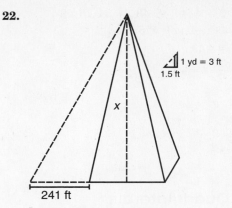

$\frac{\text{yardstick shadow}}{\text{pyramid shadow}} = \frac{\text{yardstick}}{\text{pyramid}}$

$\frac{1.5}{241} = \frac{3}{h}$

$1.5 \cdot h = 241 \cdot 3$

$1.5h = 723$

$\frac{1.5h}{1.5} = \frac{723}{1.5}$

$h = 482$

The height of the pyramid is 482 ft.

23. Sample answer: Stand on the shore (at point Q) and sight straight across the river to a point on the other shore, perhaps a tree (a point V). Walk along the shore 26 m (to point T); then walk perpendicular to the shore 20 m (to point S). Sight from S across the river to point V. Have a second person stand along the shore so that he or she is in the line of sight from S to V. Measure the distance from that person to Q and T (16 m and 10 m).

$\frac{10}{16} = \frac{20}{x}$

$10 \cdot x = 16 \cdot 20$

$10x = 320$

$\frac{10x}{10} = \frac{320}{10}$

$x = 32$

The distance across the river is 32 m.

24. Since the two triangles are congruent, their sides have the same measure. Therefore, the second triangle also has an area of 15 ft^2.

25. $2 \cdot 2 \cdot 2 \cdot 2 \cdot 2 = 2^5$

2^5 outcomes

26.

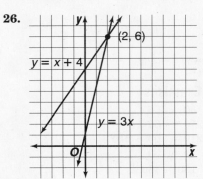

The solution is (2.6).

27. 26 32 34 36 39 40 45 48 54 54 78 89

The sum of the data is 575.

mean: $\frac{575}{12} = 47.9$

median: $\frac{40 + 45}{2} = 42.5$

mode: 54

28. $14n^2 = \boxed{2} \cdot 7 \cdot n \cdot n$

$22p^2 = \boxed{2} \cdot 11 \cdot p \cdot p$

$36n^2p = \boxed{2} \cdot 2 \cdot 3 \cdot 3 \cdot n \cdot n \cdot p$

The GCF is 2.

11-7   Quadrilaterals

Page 586   Checking Your Understanding

1. See students' work.

2. Susan. Angles are congruent and sides are proportional.

3. c; the measures of the sides are proportional.

4. **a.** See students' work.

   b. See students' work.

   c. 2

   d. 180°, 360°

   e. Since the two triangles have an angle sum of 180°, the sum of the measures of the quadrilateral is 2(180) or 360°.

5. $x + 115 + 65 + 65 = 360$

        $x + 245 = 360$

  $x + 245 - 245 = 360 - 245$

            $x = 115$

6. $x + 90 + 120 + (x + 10) = 360$

  $x + 90 + 120 + x + 10 = 360$

          $2x + 220 = 360$

  $2x + 220 - 220 = 360 - 220$

              $2x = 140$

            $\frac{2x}{2} = \frac{140}{2}$

               $x = 70$

So, $x = 70°$ and $x + 10 = 80°$.

7. quadrilateral, trapezoid; trapezoid

8. quadrilateral, parallelogram, rectangle; rectangle

9. $\frac{1 \text{ cm}}{0.5 \text{ m}} = \frac{12 \text{ cm}}{x}$

    $1x = 0.5(12)$

      $x = 6$

The actual room is 6 m long.

Pages 586–588   Exercises

10. $150 + 30 + x + 30 = 360$

          $x + 210 = 360$

  $x + 210 - 210 = 360 - 210$

             $x = 150$

11. $110 + x + 90 + 130 = 360$

          $x + 330 = 360$

  $x + 330 - 330 = 360 - 330$

             $x = 30$

12. $x + 125 + x + 35 = 360$

      $2x + 160 = 360$

 $2x + 160 - 160 = 360 - 160$

          $2x = 200$

         $\frac{2x}{2} = \frac{200}{2}$

           $x = 100$

13. $2x + x + 2x + x = 360$

        $6x = 360$

       $\frac{6x}{6} = \frac{360}{6}$

        $x = 60$

So, $x = 60°$ and $2x = 120°$.

14. $x + 120 + 50 + (x + 10) = 360$

  $x + 120 + 50 + x + 10 = 360$

          $2x + 180 = 360$

 $2x + 180 - 180 = 360 - 180$

             $2x = 180$

           $\frac{2x}{2} = \frac{180}{2}$

             $x = 90$

So, $x = 90°$ and $x + 10 = 100°$.

15. $x + x + 2x + 2x = 360$

        $6x = 360$

       $\frac{6x}{6} = \frac{360}{6}$

        $x = 60$

So, $x = 60°$ and $2x = 120°$.

16. rhombus   **17.** square

18. parallelogram

19. See students' drawings. rectangle

20. See students' drawings. parallelogram

21. See students' drawings. quadrilateral

22. always   **23.** sometimes

24. sometimes   **25.** never

26. always   **27.** always

28. **a.** 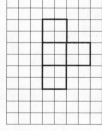 Area of original = 4 units

Area of enlargement = 16 units

   b.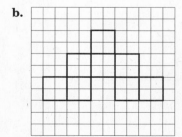

Area of original = 8 units

Area of enlargement = 32 units

            Pre-Algebra   Chapter 11

c.

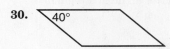

Area of original = 9 units
Area of enlargement = 36 units
$16 \div 4 = 4$, $32 \div 8 = 4$, and $36 \div 9 = 4$. So, the area of each enlargement is 4 times greater.

29. a. Yes; a rhombus is equilateral but may not be equiangular.

b. Yes; a rectangle is equiangular but may not be equilateral.

30.

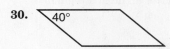

Since the opposite sides are parallel, adjacent angles of the parallelogram are supplementary. Thus, the other angles are 40°, 140°, and 140°.

31. See students' work.

32. $\dfrac{8 \text{ feet}}{2 \text{ inches}} = \dfrac{60 \text{ feet}}{x}$

$\quad 8 \cdot x = 2 \cdot 60$

$\quad\quad 8x = 120$

$\quad\quad \dfrac{8x}{8} = \dfrac{120}{8}$

$\quad\quad\quad x = 15$

In the blueprint, the length of the house is 15 inches long.

33. See students' work.

34. $\quad \dfrac{3\frac{1}{2}}{5} = \dfrac{3}{x}$

$\quad 3\frac{1}{2} \cdot x = 5 \cdot 3$

$\quad\quad 3\frac{1}{2}x = 15$

$\quad\quad \dfrac{3\frac{1}{2}x}{3\frac{1}{2}} = \dfrac{15}{3\frac{1}{2}}$

$\quad\quad\quad x = 4.29$

The reduced photograph will be about 4.3 inches.

35. $\dfrac{m\overline{AB}}{m\overline{DE}} = \dfrac{m\overline{BC}}{m\overline{EC}}$

$\quad \dfrac{10}{6} = \dfrac{5}{x}$

$\quad 10 \cdot x = 6 \cdot 5$

$\quad\quad 10x = 30$

$\quad\quad \dfrac{10x}{10} = \dfrac{30}{10}$

$\quad\quad\quad x = 3$

36. $m\angle A + m\angle B + m\angle C = 180$

$\quad\quad\quad x + 30 + 90 = 180$

$\quad\quad\quad\quad\quad x + 120 = 180$

$\quad\quad x + 120 - 120 = 180 - 120$

$\quad\quad\quad\quad\quad\quad\quad x = 60$

The measure of $\angle A$ is 60°.

37. $\dfrac{450 \text{ miles}}{20 \text{ gallons}} = \dfrac{22.5 \text{ miles}}{1 \text{ gallon}}$

22.5 miles per gallon

38. $\quad\quad C = \pi d$

$\quad 25{,}000 = \pi d$

$\quad \dfrac{25{,}000}{\pi} = \dfrac{\pi d}{\pi}$

$\quad 7957.7 \approx d$

The diameter is approximately 7957.7 miles.

39. inductive

40. Sample answer: 1001

11-8 **Polygons**

Page 589   Your Turn

For both figures, you must turn a 90° angle to return the turtle to its starting position.

a. They always add to 180.

b. To draw a particular angle, make a turn equal to the supplement of the angle.

c. $60 + 90 + 120 + 90 = 360$
$60 + 60 + 60 + 90 + 90 = 360$
The sum for both figures is 360°.

Page 592   Checking Your Understanding

1. All sides and angles are congruent.

2. The number of triangles is equal to the number of sides minus two.

3. Equiangular means all angles are congruent, while equilateral means all sides are congruent. A rectangle is equiangular but may not be equilateral.

4.

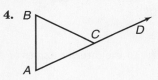

5. See students' work.

6. pentagon; regular

7. hexagon; not regular

8. An octagon has 8 sides. Therefore, $n = 8$.
$(n - 2)180 = (8 - 2)180$
$\quad\quad\quad\quad\quad = 6(180)$
$\quad\quad\quad\quad\quad = 1080$
The sum of the measures of the interior angles of an octagon is 1080°.

9. $360 \div 9 = 40$
So, the measure of each exterior angle is 40°.
$180 - 40 = 140$
So, the measure of each interior angle is 140°.

10.
$$\frac{1 \text{ in.}}{50 \text{ ft}} = \frac{x}{5280 \text{ ft}}$$
$$1 \cdot 5280 = 50 \cdot x$$
$$5280 = 50x$$
$$\frac{5280}{50} = \frac{50x}{50}$$
$$105.6 = x$$
Each side of the scale model should be
105.6 inches.

Pages 592–593 Exercises

11. A heptagon has 7 sides. Therefore, $n = 7$.
$$(n - 2)180 = (7 - 2)180$$
$$= 5(180)$$
$$= 900$$
The sum of the measures of the interior angles of a heptagon is 900°.

12. A decagon has 10 sides. Therefore, $n = 10$.
$$(n - 2)180 = (10 - 2)180$$
$$= 8(180)$$
$$= 1440$$
The sum of the measures of the interior angles of a decagon is 1440°.

13. A dodecagon has 12 sides. Therefore, $n = 12$.
$$(n - 2)180 = (12 - 2)180$$
$$= 10(180)$$
$$= 1800$$
The sum of the measures of the interior angles of a dodecagon is 1800°.

14. A nonagon has 9 sides. Therefore, $n = 9$.
$$(n - 2)180 = (9 - 2)180$$
$$= 7(180)$$
$$= 1260$$
The sum of the measures of the interior angles of a nonagon is 1260°.

15. A 15-gon has 15 sides. Therefore, $n = 15$.
$$(n - 2)180 = (15 - 2)180$$
$$= 13(180)$$
$$= 2340$$
The sum of the measures of the interior angles of a 15-gon is 2340°.

16. A 25-gon has 25 sides. Therefore, $n = 25$.
$$(n - 2)180 = (25 - 2)180$$
$$= 23(180)$$
$$= 4140$$
The sum of the measures of the interior angles of a 25-gon is 4140°.

17. $360 \div 6 = 60$
So, the measure of each exterior angle is 60°.
$180 - 60 = 120$
So, the measure of each interior angle is 120°.

18. $360 \div 10 = 36$
So, the measure of each exterior angle is 36°.
$180 - 36 = 144$
So, the measure of each interior angle is 144°.

19. $360 \div 12 = 30$
So, the measure of each exterior angle is 30°.
$180 - 30 = 150$
So, the measure of each interior angle is 150°.

20. $360 \div 20 = 18$
So, the measure of each exterior angle is 18°.
$180 - 18 = 162$
So, the measure of each interior angle is 162°.

21. A regular triangle has 3 sides. Therefore, $n = 3$.
$$\frac{180(n - 2)}{n} = \frac{180(3 - 2)}{3}$$
$$= \frac{180 \cdot 1}{3}$$
$$= \frac{180}{3}$$
$$= 60$$
The measure of an interior angle in a regular triangle is 60°.

22. $27 \cdot 3 = 81$
The perimeter is 81 feet.

23. $18 \cdot 4 = 72$
The perimeter is 72 cm.

24. $3 \cdot 5 = 15$
The perimeter is 15 m.

25. $4.5 \times 6 = 27$
The perimeter is 27 in.

26. $5\frac{3}{4} \times 8 = 46$
The perimeter is 46 yd.

27.

28. Square, narrow bridge ahead;
square, curve in the road ahead;
triangle, yield to oncoming traffic;
square, stop sign or light ahead;
octagon, stop;
rectangle, speed limit 50 miles per hour;
rectangle, one way street;
rectangle, no passing allowed

29. a. trapezoid

b.

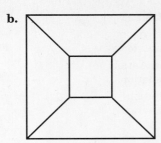

The angle formed by the tops of two trays will be 360 − 90 or 270°. Thus, the angle between the top and side of each tray should be $\frac{270}{2}$ or 135°. The angles between the bottom of the tray and the two sides are congruent. So they each measure $\frac{360 - 270}{2}$ or 45°.

c. square

30. $x + 90 + 90 + 80 = 360$
$x + 260 = 360$
$x + 260 - 260 = 360 - 260$
$x = 100$
The measure of the fourth angle is 100°.

31. $P(\text{an even number and a vowel}) = \frac{3}{6} \cdot \frac{4}{10}$
$= \frac{12}{60}$
$= \frac{1}{5}$

32. $3.5x + 2.8x + 1.5x = (3.5 + 2.8 + 1.5)x$
$= 7.8x$

33. $1604 = (1 \times 10^3) + (6 \times 10^2) + (4 \times 10^0)$

34. $-6 - 8 = c$
$-6 + (-8) = c$
$-14 = c$

11-8B   Math Lab: Tessellations

Page 594   Your Turn

Triangle: $(n - 2)180 = (3 - 2)180$
$= 1(180)$
$= 180$
The sum of the measures of the interior angles is 180°.

$180 \div 3 = 60$
So, the measure of one angle is 60°.

Square: $(n - 2)180 = (4 - 2)180$
$= 2(180)$
$= 360$
The sum of the measures of the interior angles is 360°.

$360 \div 4 = 90$
So, the measure of one angle is 90°.

Pentagon: $(n - 2)180 = (5 - 2)180$
$= 3(180)$
$= 540$
The sum of the measures of the interior angles is 540°.

$540 \div 5 = 108$
So, the measure of one angle is 108°.

Hexagon: $(n - 2)180 = (6 - 2)180$
$= 4(180)$
$= 720$
The sum of the measure of the interior angles is 720°.

$720 \div 6 = 120$
So, the measure of one angle is 120°.

Octagon: $(n - 2)180 = (8 - 2)180$
$= 6(180)$
$= 1080$
The sum of the measures of the interior angles is 1080°.

$1080 \div 8 = 135$
So, the measure of one angle is 135°.

Dodecagon: $(n - 2)180 = (12 - 2)180$
$= 10(180)$
$= 1800$
The sum of the measures of the interior angles is 1800°.

$1800 \div 12 = 150$
So, the measure of one angle is 150°.

Number of Sides	Sum of Angle Measures	Measure of One Angle
3	180°	60°
4	360°	90°
5	540°	108°
6	720°	120°
8	1080°	135°
12	1800°	150°

1. If 360 is a multiple of the angle's measure it will tessellate.

a.

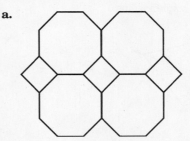

b.

c.

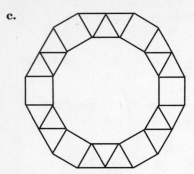

d. See students' work.

2. If the sum of the angle measures at each meeting point of the vertices is 360° it will tessellate.

11-9 | **Transformations**

Page 595   Your Turn

Each *x*-coordinate is 4 units less; each *y*-coordinate is 3 units less.

Page 597   Checking Your Understanding

1. In a translation, the figure changes position but its orientation remains the same; in a reflection, each part of the figure is reversed; in a rotation, the orientation of the figure changes.

2.

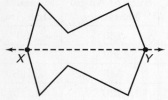

3. a–d. See students' work.
  e. midpoint

4. Sample answer: rotation
See students' explanations.

5. Sample answer: translation
See students' explanations.

6.

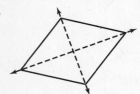

7.

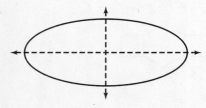

8. Answers may vary.
See students' work.

Pages 598–599   Exercises

9. Sample answer: reflection
See students' explanations.

10. Sample answer: translation
See students' explanations.

11. Sample answer: rotation
See students' explanations.

12.

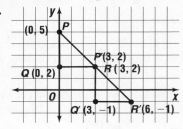

$P'(3, 2)$, $Q'(3, -1)$, $R'(6, -1)$

13. Choice a is a reflection, choice c is a translation, and choice b is a rotation. So, the correct choice is b.

14. 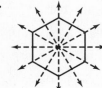   **15.**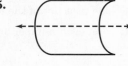

16.

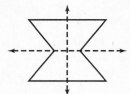

17. 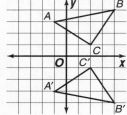   **18.**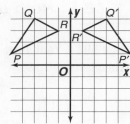

19.

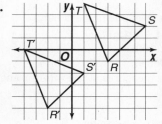

20.

Triangle
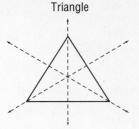

Quadrilateral
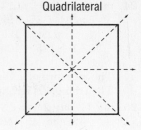

Pentagon
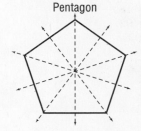

Hexagon
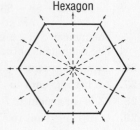

Octagon
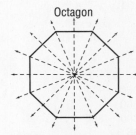

Decagon
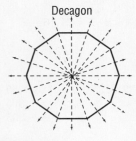

Polygon	Diagonals
Triangle	3
Quadrilateral	4
Pentagon	5
Hexagon	6
Octagon	8
Decagon	10

There are *n* lines of symmetry in a regular *n*-gon.

21. top to bottom: all except NOUYZ
side to side: CDEFIJMPQRSVWX
diagonal: FILMNPQRSUVWXY

22. a.

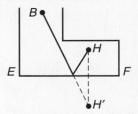

b.

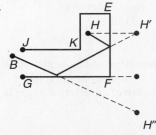

23. See students' work.

24. A 15-gon has 15 sides. Therefore, $n = 15$.
$$(n - 2)180 = (15 - 2)180$$
$$= 13(180)$$
$$= 2340$$
The sum of the measures of the angles is 2340°.

25. $21 - 7 = 14$
$$14 = R \cdot 7$$
$$\frac{14}{7} = \frac{7R}{7}$$
$$2 = R$$
There is a 200% increase in weight in the first year.

26. $\frac{2}{5}x \leq 0.16$
$$\frac{5}{2}\left(\frac{2}{5}\right)x \leq \frac{5}{2}(-0.16)$$
$$x \leq -0.4$$

27. $-84 > 4t$
$$\frac{-84}{4} > \frac{4t}{4}$$
$$-21 > t$$

28. Sample answer: (4, 0)

Page 599   From the Funny Papers

1. See students' work.

2. The ball is bouncing off the walls at various angles.

3. He had to calculate the angles of all the bounces.

Chapter 11 Study Guide and Assessments

Page 601   Understanding and Using Vocabulary

1. b; An acute angle measures between 0° and 90°.

2. h; Two angles are complementary if the sum of their measures is 90°.

3. g; When a transversal intersects two parallel lines, the corresponding angles are congruent.

4. f; When a line is perpendicular to another line, the angles formed are right angles.

5. a; An obtuse angle measures between 90° and 180°.

6. e; A parallelogram with four congruent sides is a rhombus.

7. i; Two angles are supplementary if the sum of their measures is 180°.

Pages 602–604   Skills and Concepts

8. •
R

9. S
T

10.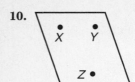

11.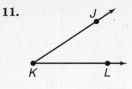

12.

13.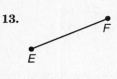

14.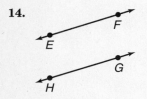

15.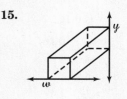

16. The total number of entries is
266 + 266 + 176 + 165 + 131 + 592 or 1596.

Strawberry: 266 ÷ 1596 = 0.167
Raspberry: 266 ÷ 1596 = 0.167
Blackberry: 176 ÷ 1596 = 0.110
Grape: 165 ÷ 1596 = 0.103
Plum: 131 ÷ 1596 = 0.082
Other: 592 ÷ 1596 = 0.371

Strawberry: 0.167 × 360 = 60.1 → 60°
Raspberry: 0.167 × 360 = 60.1 → 60°
Blackberry: 0.110 × 360 = 39.6 → 40°
Grape: 0.103 × 360 = 37.1 → 37°
Plum: 0.082 × 360 = 29.5 → 30°
Other: 0.371 × 360 = 133.6 → 134°

1994 Jams and Jellies

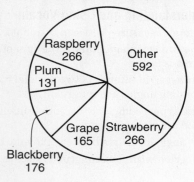

17. See students' work.

18. ∠1 and the 48° angle are complementary.
90 − 48 = 42. So, $m\angle 1 = 42°$.

19. ∠2 and the 48° angle are corresponding angles so
they are congruent. So, $m\angle 2 = 48°$.

20. ∠3 and ∠2 are supplementary.
180 − 48 = 132. So, $m\angle 3 = 132°$.

21. Since ∠4 and ∠2 are vertical angles, they are
congruent. So, $m\angle 4 = 48°$.

22. ∠5 and ∠2 are supplementary.
180 − 48 = 132. So, $m\angle 5 = 132°$.

23. Since ∠6 and the right angle are vertical angles,
they are congruent. So, $m\angle 6 = 90°$.

24. $m\angle 1 + m\angle 2 + m\angle 3 = 180$
$m\angle 1 + 35 + 90 = 180$
$m\angle 1 + 125 = 180$
$m\angle 1 + 125 - 125 = 180 - 125$
$m\angle 1 = 55$
The measure of ∠1 is 55°.
The triangle is a right triangle.

25. $m\angle 1 + m\angle 2 + m\angle 3 = 180$
$42 + m\angle 2 + 46 = 180$
$m\angle 2 + 88 = 180$
$m\angle 2 + 88 - 88 = 180 - 88$
$m\angle 2 = 92$
The measure of ∠2 is 92°.
The triangle is obtuse.

26. ∠x is congruent to ∠A.

27. ∠B is congruent to ∠Y.

28. $\overline{YZ}$ is congruent to $\overline{BC}$.

29. $\overline{AC}$ is congruent to $\overline{XZ}$.

30. $\frac{x}{21} = \frac{6}{7}$
$x \cdot 7 = 21 \cdot 6$
$7x = 126$
$\frac{7x}{7} = \frac{126}{7}$
$x = 18$

31. $\frac{5}{2} = \frac{5}{x}$
$5 \cdot x = 2 \cdot 5$
$5x = 10$
$\frac{5x}{5} = \frac{10}{5}$
$x = 2$

32. $125 + x + 125 + 55 = 360$
$x + 305 = 360$
$x + 305 - 305 = 360 - 305$
$x = 55$
The measure of the angle is 55°.

33. $90 + (x + 30) + (x - 10) + 90 = 360$
$90 + x + 30 + x - 10 + 90 = 360$
$2x + 200 = 360$
$2x + 200 - 200 = 360 - 200$
$2x = 160$
$\frac{2x}{2} = \frac{160}{2}$
$x = 80$
$x + 30 = 110$ and $x - 10 = 70$.
The measures of the angles are 70° and 110°.

34. A hexagon has 6 sides. Therefore, $n = 6$.
$(n - 2)180 = (6 - 2)180$
$= 4(180)$
$= 720$
The sum of the measures of the angles is 720°.

35. A decagon has 10 sides. Therefore, $n = 10$.
$(n - 2)180 = (10 - 2)180$
$= 8(180)$
$= 1440$
The sum of the measures of the interior angles is
1440°.
$1440 ÷ 10 = 144$
So, the measure of one interior angle is 144°.

36. A pentagon has 5 sides. Therefore, $n = 5$.
$(n - 2)180 = (5 - 2)180$
$= 3(180)$
$= 540$
The sum of the measures of the angles is 540°.
The measure of one interior angle is 540 ÷ 5 or
108°. So, the measure of an exterior angle is
180 − 108 or 72°.

37.

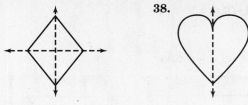

38.

39. Sample answer: reflection
See students' explanations.

40. Sample answer: rotation
See students' explanations.

Page 604   Applications and Problem Solving

41. Agriculture: 36% = 0.36
Public Water: 8% = 0.08
Utilities: 33% = 0.33
Industry: 23% = 0.23

Agriculture: $0.36 \times 360 = 129.6°$
Public Water: $0.08 \times 360 = 28.8°$
Utilities: $0.33 \times 360 = 118.8°$
Industry: $0.23 \times 360 = 82.8°$

Water Use in U.S.

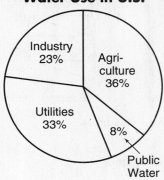

42.

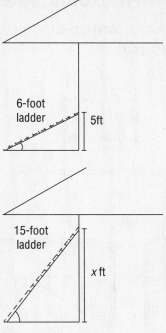

$$\frac{6}{5} = \frac{15}{x}$$
$$6 \cdot x = 5 \cdot 15$$
$$6x = 75$$
$$\frac{6x}{6} = \frac{7.5}{6}$$
$$x = 12.5$$

Yes, a 15-foot ladder can be used to reach a point 12 feet above the ground; a 15-foot ladder will reach 12.5 feet above the ground.

Page 605   Alternative Assessment

1–6. See students' work.

Page 605   Critically Thinking

• square, rhombus, rectangle, or parallelogram.

• $x + 2x + 3x = 180$
$6x = 180$
$\frac{6x}{6} = \frac{180}{6}$
$x = 30$

$x = 30, 2x = 60,$ and $3x = 90$.
The measures of the angles are 30°, 60°, and 90°.
The triangle is a right triangle.

• See students' work.

Page 605   Portfolio

See students' work.

Page 605   Self Evaluation

See students' work.

Chapter 12   Measuring Area and Volume

12-1A   Math Lab: Areas and Geoboards

Pages 610–611

a. 5 sq units

b. 6 sq units

c. $3\frac{1}{2}$ sq units

d. 11 sq units

e. 4 sq units

f. 5 sq units

g. Answers will vary.

1. Sample answer: count whole-squares and half-squares.

2. See students' work.

h.

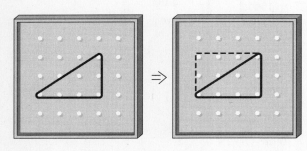

The area of the rectangle is 6 square units. So, the area of each triangle is 6 ÷ 2 or 3 square units.

i.

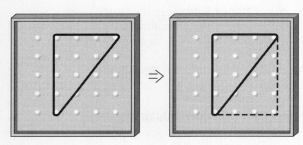

The area of the rectangle is 12 square units. So, the area of each triangle is 12 ÷ 2 or 6 square units.

j.

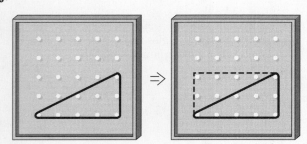

The area of the rectangle is 8 square units. So, the area of each triangle is 8 ÷ 2 or 4 square units.

k. See students' work.

3. Sample answer: Find the area of the rectangle and divide by 2.

l.

Step 1   Step 2

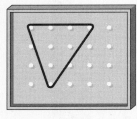

area of large rectangle: 9 sq units

area of triangle a: $1\frac{1}{2}$ sq units

area of triangle b: 3 sq units

The area of the original polygon is $9 - 1\frac{1}{2} - 3$ or $4\frac{1}{2}$ square units.

m.

Step 1   Step 2

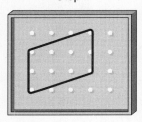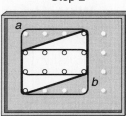

area of large rectangle: 9 sq units

area of triangle a: $1\frac{1}{2}$ sq units

area of triangle b: $1\frac{1}{2}$ sq units

The area of the original polygon is $9 - 1\frac{1}{2} - 1\frac{1}{2}$ or 6 square units.

n.

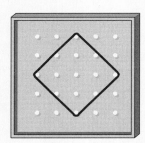

The polygon is made up of 4 whole-squares and 8 half-squares. Therefore, the area of the polygon is 8 square units.

240

o.

Step 1	Step 2

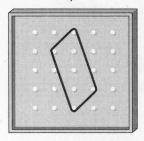 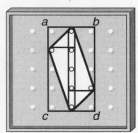

area of large rectangle: 8 sq units

area of triangle a: $\frac{1}{2}$ sq unit

area of triangle b: $1\frac{1}{2}$ sq units

area of triangle c: $1\frac{1}{2}$ sq units

area of triangle d: $\frac{1}{2}$ sq unit

The area of the original polygon is

$8 - \frac{1}{2} - 1\frac{1}{2} - \frac{1}{2}$ or 4 square units.

p.

Step 1	Step 2

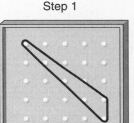 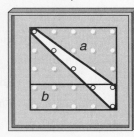

area of large rectangle: 16 sq units
area of triangle a: 6 sq units
area of triangle b: 8 sq units
The area of the original polygon is $16 - 6 - 8$ or 2 square units.

q.

Step 1	Step 2

 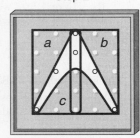

area of large rectangle: 16 sq units
area of triangle a: 4 sq units
area of triangle b: 4 sq units

area of triangle c: $\frac{1}{4}$ of 16 or 4 sq units

The area of the original polygon is
$16 - 4 - 4 - 4$ or 4 square units.

r. See students' work.

4. Find the area of a rectangle around the polygon and subtract the areas not included in the polygon.

12-1	**Area: Parallelograms, Triangles, and Trapezoids**

Page 612 Your Turn

See students' work.

a. They are the same.

b. The length of the rectangle is the same as the base of the parallelogram; the height of the rectangle is the same as the distance from the top to the bottom of the parallelogram.

c. multiply length by width

d. $10 \cdot 2$ or 20 cm^2

e. It has a base of 10 cm and a height of 2 cm.

Pages 615–616 Checking Your Understanding

1. In a triangle, an altitude is drawn from a vertex and is perpendicular to the opposite side. In a parallelogram or trapezoid, an altitude is any segment perpendicular to the bases.

2. In triangle ABC below, the altitudes are $\overline{AB}$, $\overline{BC}$, and $\overline{BD}$.

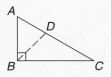

3. Sample answer: Multiply the sum of the bases by half the height.

4. See students' work.

5. base = 3 cm
height = 4 cm
$A = \frac{1}{2}bh$
$A = \frac{1}{2}(3)(4)$
$A = \frac{1}{2}(12)$
$A = 6$
The area is 6 cm^2.

6. base = 6 cm
height = 4 cm
$A = bh$
$A = 6 \cdot 4$
$A = 24$
The area is 24 cm^2.

7. bases = 15 m and 5 m
height = 6 m
$A = \frac{1}{2}h(a + b)$
$A = \frac{1}{2} \cdot 6(15 + 5)$
$A = \frac{1}{2} \cdot 6 \cdot 20$
$A = 60$
The area is 60 m^2.

8. $A = \frac{1}{2}bh$
$A = \frac{1}{2}(10)(4.5)$
$A = \frac{1}{2}(45)$
$A = 22.5$
The area is 22.5 cm^2.

9. $A = bh$
$A = 12 \cdot 18$
$A = 216$
The area is 216 cm^2.

---

10. $A = \frac{1}{2}h(a + b)$

$A = \frac{1}{2} \cdot 5\left(6\frac{1}{2} + 11\right)$

$A = \frac{1}{2} \cdot 5 \cdot 17\frac{1}{2}$

$A = 43\frac{3}{4}$

The area is $43\frac{3}{4}$ ft^2.

11. a. $A = \frac{1}{2}h(a + b)$

$A = \frac{1}{2} \cdot 140(200 + 280)$

$A = \frac{1}{2} \cdot 140 \cdot 480$

$A = 33,600$

The area is about 33,600 mi^2.

b. The actual area is 35,936 mi^2.

Pages 616–617   Exercises

12. $A = bh$

$A = 3 \cdot 2$

$A = 6$

The area is 6 in^2.

13. $A = \frac{1}{2}bh$

$A = \frac{1}{2}(3)(4)$

$A = \frac{1}{2}(12)$

$A = 6$

The area is 6 cm^2.

14. $A = \frac{1}{2}h(a + b)$

$A = \frac{1}{2} \cdot 3(4 + 1)$

$A = \frac{1}{2} \cdot 3 \cdot 5$

$A = 7\frac{1}{2}$

The area is $7\frac{1}{2}$ ft^2.

15. $A = \frac{1}{2}bh$

$A = \frac{1}{2}(15)(12)$

$A = \frac{1}{2}(180)$

$A = 90$

The area is 90 cm^2.

16. $A = \frac{1}{2}h(a + b)$

$A = \frac{1}{2} \cdot 9.2(14 + 20)$

$A = \frac{1}{2} \cdot 9.2 \cdot 34$

$A = 156.4$

The area is 156.4 in^2.

17. $A = \frac{1}{2}bh$

$A = \frac{1}{2}(6)(7.2)$

$A = \frac{1}{2}(43.2)$

$A = 21.6$

The area is 21.6 in^2.

18. $A = \frac{1}{2}h(a + b)$

$A = \frac{1}{2} \cdot 5.3(6.7 + 9.9)$

$A = \frac{1}{2} \cdot 5.3 \cdot 16.6$

$A = 43.99$

The area is 43.99 cm^2.

19. Area of figure = (area of parallelogram)
                + (area of triangle)

area of parallelogram: $A = bh$

$A = 8 \cdot 6$

$A = 48$ ft^2

area of triangle: $A = \frac{1}{2}bh$

$A = \frac{1}{2}(6)(3)$

$A = \frac{1}{2}(18)$

$A = 9$ ft^2

The area of the figure is 48 + 9 or 57 ft^2.

20. The area is 8 sq units.

21. $A = \frac{1}{2}h(a + b)$

$A = \frac{1}{2} \cdot 2(3 + 6)$

$A = \frac{1}{2} \cdot 2 \cdot 9$

$A = 9$

The area is 9 in^2.

22. $A = \frac{1}{2}bh$

$A = \frac{1}{2}(10)(7)$

$A = \frac{1}{2}(70)$

$A = 35$

The area is 35 in^2.

23. $A = bh$

$A = 3\frac{1}{4} \cdot 2$

$A = 6\frac{1}{2}$

The area is $6\frac{1}{2}$ ft^2.

24. $A = \frac{1}{2}bh$

$A = \frac{1}{2}(0.8)(2)$

$A = \frac{1}{2}(1.6)$

$A = 0.8$

The area is 0.8 km^2.

25. $A = \frac{1}{2}h(a + b)$

$A = \frac{1}{2} \cdot 3.5(10 + 11)$

$A = \frac{1}{2} \cdot 3.5 \cdot 21$

$A = 36.75$

The area is 36.75 m^2.

26. $A = bh$

$A = 25 \cdot 11$

$A = 275$

The area is 275 yd^2.

27. $A_1 = \frac{1}{2}h_1 d$; $A_2 = \frac{1}{2}h_2 d$

$A_1 + A_2 = \frac{1}{2}d(h_1 + h_2)$

$= \frac{1}{2}d(d)$

$= \frac{1}{2}d^2$

28. $A = \frac{1}{2}h(a + b)$; In a triangle, one "base" = 0, so

$A = \frac{1}{2}h(0 + b)$, then

$A = \frac{1}{2}hb$ or $A = \frac{1}{2}bh$. In a parallelogram, the bases

are congruent, so $a = b$. Thus, $A = \frac{1}{2}h(b + b)$ or $A =$

$\frac{1}{2}h(2b)$, then $A = bh$.

29. a. $A = bh$

$A = 14 \cdot 22$

$A = 308$

The area of the room is 308 ft^2.

b. Since the width of the room is 14 feet, the
12-foot width of carpet would need to be
doubled. Therefore, there would be $2(12) - 14$
or 10 ft of waste. The 15-foot width would leave
$15 - 14$ or 1 ft of waste. So, the 15-foot width
will result in less waste.

30. $A = bh$

$A = 447 \cdot 116$

$A = 51,852$

The area is about 51,852 mi^2.

31. A shape as close as possible to a square gives the
greatest area; see students' explanations.

32. $A_1 = \frac{1}{2}(9^2) = 40.5$ in^2

$A_2 = \frac{1}{2}(10^2) = 50$ in^2

percent of increase

$\frac{50 - 40.5}{40.5} \approx 23\%$;

The advertisement is close to correct.

33.

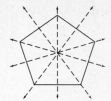

A regular pentagon has 5 lines of symmetry.

34. 26% is close to 25%.

$25\% = \frac{1}{4}$.

$\frac{1}{4}$ of 120 is 30.

So, 26% of 120 is about 30.

35. $n = -9.45 \div -4.5$ **36.** $(-4)^3$

$$4.5\overline{)9.45}$$

$$\begin{array}{r} 2.1 \\ 45\overline{)94.5} \\ -90 \\ \hline 45 \\ -45 \\ \hline 0 \end{array}$$

$n = 2.1$

37. associative: $3 + (x + 4) = (3 + x) + 4$

commutative: $3 + (x + 4) = (x + 4) + 3$

$$\begin{aligned} 3 + (x + 4) &= (x + 4) + 3 \\ &= x + (4 + 3) \\ &= x + 7 \end{aligned}$$

12-1B   Math Lab: Fractals

Page 618   Your Turn

a–f. See students' work.

Length of stage 0 curve	Length of stage 1 curve	Length of stage 2 curve	Length of stage 3 curve
1 unit	$\frac{4}{3}$ unit	$\frac{16}{9}$ unit	$\frac{64}{27}$ unit

1. Each section is a replica of the whole curve.

2. increases by a factor of $\frac{4}{3}$

3. infinite

4. See students' work.

5. See students' work. The area of the snowflake increases with every stage, but it does approach a limit.

12-2   Area: Circles

Page 619   Your Turn

See students' work.

a. half the circumference

b. radius

---

c. 30 cm, 10 cm

d. $A = bh$

$A \approx 30 \cdot 10$

$A \approx 300$

The area is about 300 cm².

e. They should be about the same.

Page 621   Checking Your Understanding

1. Multiply π by the square of the radius.

2. The area is about 50 square units;

$A = \pi r^2$

$A = \pi \cdot 4^2$

$A = \pi \cdot 16$

$A \approx 50.27$

The area is 50.27 square units.

$\frac{50.27 - 50}{50.27} \approx 0.0054$

The percent of error is about 0.54%.

3. Joyce; you use the radius of 5 cm to calculate the area.

4. $A = \pi r^2$ **5.** $A = \pi r^2$

$A = \pi \cdot 9^2$ $A = \pi \cdot 12^2$

$A = \pi \cdot 81$ $A = \pi \cdot 144$

$A \approx 254.5$ cm² $A \approx 452.4$ in²

6. $A = \frac{1}{2}(\pi r^2)$

$A = \frac{1}{2}(\pi \cdot 21^2)$

$A = \frac{1}{2} \cdot \pi \cdot 441$

$A \approx 692.7$ m²

7. $A = \pi r^2$

$A = \pi \cdot 125^2$

$A = \pi \cdot 15{,}625$

$A \approx 49{,}087.4$

The grass and sidewalk cover an area of about 49,087.4 ft².

Pages 621–622   Exercises

8. $A = \pi r^2$ **9.** $A = \pi r^2$

$A = \pi \cdot 2^2$ $A = \pi \cdot 4^2$

$A = \pi \cdot 4$ $A = \pi \cdot 16$

$A \approx 12.6$ in² $A \approx 50.3$ cm²

10. $A = \pi r^2$ **11.** $A = \pi r^2$

$A = \pi\left(35\frac{1}{4}\right)^2$ $A = \pi \cdot (6.2)^2$

$A = \pi(1242.6)$ $A = \pi \cdot 38.4$

$A \approx 3903.6$ ft² $A \approx 120.8$ m²

12. $A = \pi r^2$ **13.** $A = \pi r^2$

$A = \pi\left(21\frac{1}{4}\right)^2$ $A = \pi \cdot (12 \cdot 3)^2$

$A = \pi(451.6)$ $A = \pi \cdot 151.3$

$A \approx 1418.6$ in² $A \approx 475.3$ cm²

14. $A = \pi r^2$ **15.** $A = \pi r^2$

$A = \pi \cdot 23^2$ $A = \pi \cdot (7.3)^2$

$A = \pi \cdot 529$ $A = \pi \cdot 53.3$

$A \approx 1661.9$ cm² $A \approx 167.4$ in²

16. $A = \pi r^2$ **17.** $A = \frac{1}{2}(\pi r^2)$

$A = \pi \cdot (24.6)^2$ $A = \frac{1}{2}(\pi \cdot 5^2)$

$A = \pi \cdot 605.2$ $A = \frac{1}{2} \cdot \pi \cdot 25$

$A \approx 1901.2$ m² $A \approx 39.3$ ft²

18. Area of figure = (area of parallelogram) $+ \left(\frac{1}{2} \text{ of area of circle}\right)$

area of parallelogram: $A = bh$
$$A = (2.5)(2.5)$$
$$A = 6.25 \text{ m}^2$$

area of circle: $A = \frac{1}{2}(\pi r^2)$
$$A = \frac{1}{2}[\pi \cdot (1.25)^2]$$
$$A = \frac{1}{2} \cdot \pi \cdot 1.56$$
$$A \approx 2.45 \text{ m}^2$$

The area of the figure is about $6.25 + 2.45$ or 8.7 m^2.

19. $A = \frac{1}{4}(\pi r^2)$
$$A = \frac{1}{4}(\pi \cdot 100^2)$$
$$A = \frac{1}{4} \cdot \pi \cdot 10{,}000$$
$$A \approx 7854.0 \text{ ft}^2$$

20. a. If $A = C$ and $A = \pi r^2$ and $C = 2\pi r$, then $\pi r^2 = 2\pi r$.
$$\pi r^2 = 2\pi r$$
$$\frac{\pi r^2}{\pi} = \frac{2\pi r}{\pi}$$
$$r^2 = 2r$$
$$\frac{r^2}{r} = \frac{2r}{r}$$
$$r = 2$$
The radius of the circle is 2 units.

b. When $r = 2$, r^2 and $2(r)$ have the same value.

21. $A = \pi r^2$
$$A = \pi \cdot 15^2$$
$$A = \pi \cdot 225$$
$$A \approx 706.9$$
The area is about 707 m^2.

22. $C = \pi d$
$$6.25 = \pi d$$
$$\frac{6.25}{\pi} = \frac{\pi d}{\pi}$$
$$2 \approx d$$
The diameter is about 2 inches.

23. <u>Pantheon</u>

$A = \pi r^2$
$A = \pi \cdot (21.35)^2$
$A = \pi \cdot 455.8$
$A \approx 1431.9 \text{ m}^2$

<u>Astrodome</u>

$A = \pi r^2$
$A = \pi \cdot (108.2)^2$
$A = \pi \cdot 11{,}707.2$
$A \approx 36{,}779.3 \text{ m}^2$

$\frac{36{,}779.3}{1431.9} \approx 25.7$

The Astrodome covers about 26 times more area than the Pantheon.

24. The area is a 50 by 100 yard rectangle and a circle with a radius of 25 yards.

area of infield = (area of rectangle) $+$ (area of circle)

area of rectangle: $A = bh$
$$A = 50 \cdot 100$$
$$A = 5000 \text{ yd}^2$$

area of circle: $A = \pi r^2$
$$A = \pi \cdot 25^2$$
$$A = \pi \cdot 625$$
$$A = 1963.5 \text{ yd}^2$$

The area of the infield is about $5000 + 1963.5$ or 6963.5 yd^2. Therefore, they must raise $50(6963.5)$ or \$348,175.

25. $A = \pi r^2$
$$A = \pi \cdot 2^2$$
$$A = \pi \cdot 4$$
$$A \approx 12.6$$
The area that will benefit from the system is about 13 mi^2.

26. $A = \frac{1}{2}h(a + b)$
$$A = \frac{1}{2} \cdot 1320(220 + 176)$$
$$A = \frac{1}{2} \cdot 1320 \cdot 396$$
$$A = 261{,}360$$
The farmer has $261{,}360 \text{ yd}^2$ of land.

27. $\frac{15}{c} = \frac{8}{9.6}$
$$15 \cdot 9.6 = c \cdot 8$$
$$144 = 8c$$
$$\frac{144}{8} = \frac{8c}{8}$$
$$18 = c$$

28. $3x - 5 > 3x + 4$
$$3x - 3x - 5 > 3x - 3x + 4$$
$$-5 > 4$$
This sentence is never true.
The solution is $\varnothing$.

29. Let $N = 0.444 \ldots$ Then $10N = 4.444 \ldots$
$$\begin{array}{r} 10N = 4.444 \ldots \\ -\ 1N = 0.444 \ldots \\ \hline 9N = 4 \end{array}$$
$$N = \frac{4}{9}$$
Therefore, $0.\overline{4} = \frac{4}{9}$.

30. $9c = -54$
$$\frac{9c}{9} = \frac{-54}{9}$$
$$c = -6$$

$\xleftarrow{\hspace{1em}}$ $\underset{-12}{|}$ $\underset{-10}{|}$ $\underset{-8}{|}$ $\underset{-6}{\blacklozenge}$ $\underset{-4}{|}$ $\underset{-2}{|}$ $\underset{0}{|}$ $\xrightarrow{\hspace{1em}}$

Page 622   From the Funny Papers

1. $A = \pi r^2$

2. the area of a circle

3. See students' work.

12-3	Integration: Probability Geometric Probability

Page 625   Checking Your Understanding

1. Find the area of the circle for winning a soft drink and stuffed animal combined. Then divide this area by the area of the square.

A(soft drink and stuffed animal)
$\quad = \pi(9)^2$ or 254.5 in^2

A(square) $= (36)^2$ or 1296 in^2

P(soft drink or stuffed animal) $= \frac{254.5}{1296}$ or 19.6%

2. See students' work.

3. See students' work.

4. $P(\text{shaded}) = \frac{\text{shaded area}}{\text{area of target}}$

$= \frac{2}{6}$

$= \frac{1}{3}$

5. $P(\text{shaded}) = \frac{\text{shaded area}}{\text{area of target}}$

$= \frac{18}{100}$

$= \frac{9}{50}$

6. Let n represent the darts landing in the shaded region.

$\frac{n}{50} = \frac{1}{3}$

$n \cdot 3 = 50 \cdot 1$

$3n = 50$

$\frac{3n}{3} = \frac{50}{3}$

$n = 16.7$

About 17 darts should land in the shaded region.

7. Let n represent the darts landing in the shaded region.

$\frac{n}{50} = \frac{9}{50}$

$n \cdot 50 = 50 \cdot 9$

$50n = 450$

$\frac{50n}{50} = \frac{450}{50}$

$n = 9$

About 9 darts should land in the shaded region.

8. The field is a 100-yard by 100-yard square.

$A = s^2$

$A = 100^2$

$A = 10,000$

The field has an area of 10,000 yd^2.

Each corner of the field is $\frac{1}{4}$ of a circle. So, the area of the four corners combined will equal the area of a circle with a radius of 6 yd.

$A = \pi r^2$

$A = \pi \cdot 6^2$

$A = \pi \cdot 36$

$A \approx 113.1$

The corners have a total area of about 113.1 yd^2. Therefore, the area of a clear landing is $10,000 - 113.1$ or 9886.9 yd^2.

So,

$P(\text{clear landing}) = \frac{\text{area of clear landing}}{\text{area of field}}$

$\approx \frac{9886.9}{10,000}$

≈ 0.989

The probability of a clear landing is about 98.9%.

Pages 626–627 Exercises

9. $P(\text{shaded}) = \frac{\text{shaded area}}{\text{area of target}}$

$= \frac{3}{8}$

10. $P(\text{shaded}) = \frac{\text{shaded area}}{\text{area of target}}$

$= \frac{1}{4}$

11. $P(\text{shaded}) = \frac{\text{shaded area}}{\text{area of target}}$

$= \frac{6}{36}$

$= \frac{1}{6}$

12. $P(\text{shaded}) = \frac{\text{shaded area}}{\text{area of target}}$

$= \frac{6}{35}$

13. Area of shaded region = (area of large circle) $-$ (area of small circle)

area of large circle: $A = \pi r^2$

$A = \pi \cdot 1^2$

$A \approx 3.14$ m^2

area of small circle: $A = \pi r^2$

$A = \pi \cdot (0.5)^2$

$A = \pi \cdot 0.25$

$A \approx 0.79$ m^2

The area of the shaded region is about $3.14 - 0.79$ or 2.35 m^2.

So,

$P(\text{shaded}) = \frac{\text{shaded area}}{\text{area of target}}$

$\approx \frac{2.35}{3.14}$

≈ 0.75 or $\frac{3}{4}$

14. Area of shaded region

= (area of 5-inch square) $-$ (area of 3-inch square)

area of 5-inch square: $A = s^2$

$A = 5^2$

$A = 25$ in^2

area of 3-inch square: $A = s^2$

$A = 3^2$

$A = 9$ in^2

The area of the shaded region is $25 - 9$ or 16 in^2.

So,

$P(\text{shaded}) = \frac{\text{shaded area}}{\text{area of target}}$

$= \frac{16}{64}$

$= \frac{1}{4}$

15. Let n represent the darts landing in the shaded region.

$\frac{n}{100} = \frac{3}{8}$

$n \cdot 8 = 100 \cdot 3$

$8n = 300$

$\frac{8n}{8} = \frac{300}{8}$

$n = 37.5$

About 38 darts should land in the shaded region.

16. Let n represent the darts landing in the shaded region.

$\frac{n}{75} = \frac{6}{35}$

$n \cdot 35 = 75 \cdot 6$

$35n = 450$

$\frac{35n}{35} = \frac{450}{35}$

$n = 12.9$

About 13 darts should land in the shaded region.

17.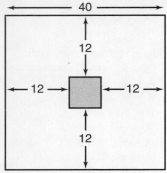

The center of the quarter must land more than 12 mm from the edge of the square. That is the shaded area. It is a square with sides $40 - 12 - 12$ or 16 mm long.

So,

$$P(\text{winning}) = \frac{\text{shaded area}}{\text{area of target}}$$
$$= \frac{16^2}{40^2}$$
$$= \frac{256}{1600}$$
$$= 0.16$$

18. The area for winning a stuffed animal is a circle with a radius of 3 in.

$A = \pi r^2$
$A = \pi \cdot 3^2$
$A = \pi \cdot 9$
$A \approx 28.3 \text{ in}^2$

So, $P(\text{winning a stuffed animal}) = \dfrac{\text{winning area}}{\text{total area}}$
$$\approx \frac{28.3}{1296}$$
$$\approx \frac{9}{400}$$

The probability of winning a stuffed animal is about $\frac{9}{400}$.

19. $P(\text{oil}) = \frac{500}{17,500}$
$= \frac{1}{35}$

20. a. $P(\text{less than 2}) = \frac{1}{2}$

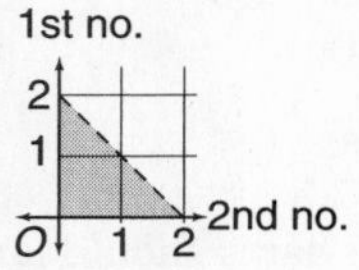

b. $P(\text{greater than 1}) = \frac{7}{8}$

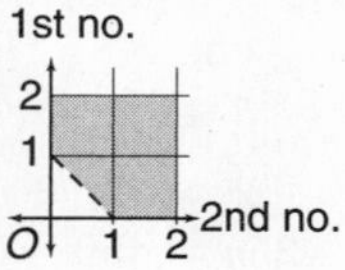

c. $P(\text{between 1 and 2}) = \frac{3}{8}$

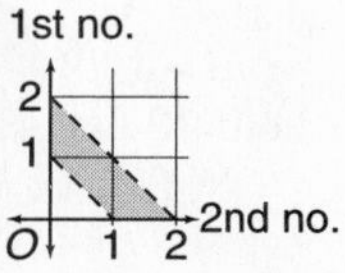

21. $A = \pi r^2$
$A = \pi \cdot 12^2$
$A \approx 3 \cdot 150$
$A \approx 450$
The area is about 450 cm².

22. Let x represent the measure of one angle, $3x$ the measure of a second angle, and $5x$ the measure of the third angle.

$1x + 3x + 5x = 180$
$9x = 180$
$\frac{9x}{9} = \frac{180}{9}$
$x = 20$

$x = 20$, $3x = 60$, and $5x = 100$. The measures of the angles are 20°, 60°, and 100°.

23. slope $= \frac{\text{rise}}{\text{run}}$
$= \frac{0.3}{3}$
$= 0.1$

24. $xy = \frac{1}{5} \cdot \frac{3}{5}$
$= \frac{1 \cdot 3}{5 \cdot 5}$
$= \frac{3}{25}$

25. $32 < w < 212$

Page 627   The Shape of Things to Come
See students' work.

12-3B   Math Lab: Geometric Probability

Page 628   Your Turn
See students' work.

1. The ratios should be similar.

2. See students' work.

3. More data makes the ratios closer.

4. See students' work.

12-4   Problem-Solving Strategy: Make a Model or a Drawing

Page 630   Checking Your Understanding
1. The grazing areas overlap.

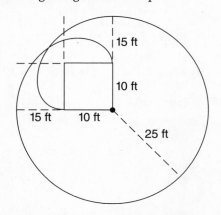

2. It can make the problem easier to visualize.

3. See students' work.

4. Area of large section: $A = \pi r^2 \times \frac{3}{4}$

$$A = \pi \times 15^2 \times \frac{3}{4}$$
$$A = \pi \times 225 \times \frac{3}{4}$$
$$A \approx 530.1 \text{ ft}^2$$

Area of each small section: $A = \pi r^2 \times \frac{1}{4}$

$$A = \pi \times 5^2 \times \frac{1}{4}$$
$$A = \pi \times 25 \times \frac{1}{4}$$
$$A \approx 19.6 \text{ ft}^2$$

The grazing area is about $530.1 + 2(19.6)$ or about 569 ft^2.

5.

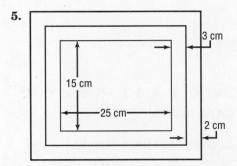

The length is $25 + 2(3) + 2(2)$ or 35 cm.
The width is $15 + 2(3) + 2(2)$ or 25 cm.
So, the area is $35 \cdot 25$ or 875 cm^2.

Pages 630–631   Exercises

6.

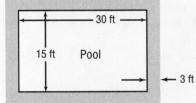

Area of walkway = (total area) − (area of pool)
The total length is $30 + 2(3)$ or 36 ft.
The total width is $15 + 2(3)$ or 21 ft.
Therefore,
total area: $A = bh$
$$A = 36 \cdot 21$$
$$A = 756 \text{ ft}^2$$
area of pool: $A = bh$
$$A = 15 \cdot 30$$
$$A = 450 \text{ ft}^2$$
So, the area of the walkway is $745 - 450$ or 306 ft^2.

7. a.

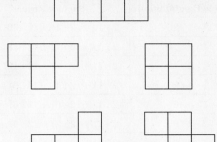

b. 10 units; 10 units; 8 units; 10 units; 10 units

c. Shapes where two squares share one side with another square and the rest of the squares share two sides with other squares are the greatest in perimeter.

d. Square shapes have the least perimeter.

e. 12; yes

8. Sum of first 100 even positive numbers:

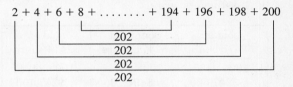

$2 + 4 + 6 + 8 + \ldots\ldots + 194 + 196 + 198 + 200$

50 sums of $202 = 10,100$

9.

$\ell \cdot w = 48$		Is $2(\ell + w) = 32$?	
1	48	$2(1 + 48) = 2(49) = 98$	
2	24	$2(2 + 24) = 2(26) = 52$	
3	16	$2(3 + 16) = 2(19) = 38$	
4	12	$2(4 + 12) = 2(16) = 32$	✔

The rectangle is 4 m by 12 m.

10. Let x represent the number of minutes since Antonio started running. After x minutes, Les will have traveled $600x + 600$ feet. After x minutes, Antonio will have traveled $700x$ feet.

$$600x + 600 = 700x$$
$$600x - 600x + 600 = 700x - 600x$$
$$600 = 100x$$
$$\frac{600}{100} = \frac{100x}{100}$$
$$6 = x$$

After Antonio runs 6 minutes, he and Les will have traveled the same distance. They will be $700(6)$ or 4200 feet from the starting point. The track has a circumference of $\pi(400)$ or about 1257 feet. Thus, they will have made $\frac{4200}{1257}$ or about 3.3 laps. Since $3.25 < 3.3 < 3.5$, Antonio will pass Les in the second quarter of the track.

11.

Possible Combinations	Surface Area
1 · 1 · 36	(2 · 1) + (2 · 1) + (2 · 36) = 76
1 · 2 · 18	(2 · 1) + (2 · 2) + (2 · 18) = 42
1 · 3 · 12	(2 · 1) + (2 · 3) + (2 · 12) = 32
1 · 4 · 9	(2 · 1) + (2 · 4) + (2 · 9) = 28
1 · 6 · 6	(2 · 1) + (2 · 6) + (2 · 6) = 26
2 · 2 · 9	(2 · 2) + (2 · 2) + (2 · 9) = 26
2 · 3 · 6	(2 · 2) + (2 · 3) + (2 · 6) = 22
3 · 3 · 4	(2 · 3) + (2 · 3) + (2 · 4) = 20

Sandy can arrange the cubes in a pattern of $3 \times 3 \times 4$ for the smallest surface area.

12. a.

b. See students' work.

13.

sold at $2475/share	bought at $2471/share	sold at $2474/share
100 · 2475 = $247,500	200 · 2471 = $494,200	100 · 2474 = $247,400

$247,500 − $494,200 + 247,400 = $700
Ms. Warren gains $700 in her transactions.

14. Fill the 5-quart pail from the 8-quart pail. Fill the 3-quart pail from the 5-quart pail, leaving 2 quarts in the 5-quart pail. Empty the 3-quart pail into the 8-quart pail. Pour 2 quarts from the 5-quart pail into the 3-quart pail. Fill the 5-quart pail from the 8-quart pail. Pour from the 5-quart pail into the 3-quart pail until full, leaving 4 quarts in the 5-quart pail. Empty the 3-quart pail into the 8-quart pail, making 4 quarts in the 8-quart pail.

15. A

16.
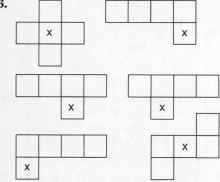

17. $P(\text{shaded}) = \frac{8}{20}$
$= \frac{2}{5}$

18. $P(5, 4) = 5 \cdot 4 \cdot 3 \cdot 2$
$= 120$

19. Let h = hour
$8h + 12 \geq 100$
$8h + 12 - 12 \geq 100 - 12$
$8h \geq 88$
$\frac{8h}{8} \geq \frac{88}{8}$
$h \geq 11$
11 hours

20. $2^{-3} = \frac{1}{2^3}$

21. a. Nevada
b. $47 - 30 = 17$
17 million acres

12-5   **Surface Area: Prisms and Cylinders**

Page 635   Checking Your Understanding

1. You are covering all the surfaces with paper, so the area of the paper must be at least as large as the surface area of the package.
2. Sample answer: The amount of material needed to cover a solid figure.
3. Use πr^2 to find the area of each base; use $2\pi rh$ to find the area of the rectangular region. Then add.
4. See students' work.
5. $8 \times 8 \times 8$; all sides have the same length.
6. **a.** rectangle
   b. See students' work.
7. triangular prism;
   Two Bases: $2\left(\frac{1}{2} \cdot 6 \cdot 4\right) = 24$
   Front: $5 \cdot 10 = 50$
   Bottom: $6 \cdot 10 = 60$
   Back: $5 \cdot 10 = 50$
   The surface area of the triangular prism is $24 + 50 + 60 + 50$ or 184 ft².
8. rectangular prism;
   Front and Back: $2(12 \cdot 3.5) = 84$
   Top and Bottom: $2(12 \cdot 3.5) = 84$
   Two sides: $2(3.5 \cdot 3.5) = 24.5$
   The surface area of the rectangular prism is $84 + 84 + 24.5$ or 192.5 m².
9. cylinder;
   $2(\pi r^2) + 2\pi rh = 2(\pi \cdot 14^2) + 2 \cdot \pi \cdot 14 \cdot 22$
   $= 2(\pi \cdot 196) + 2 \cdot \pi \cdot 14 \cdot 22$
   $\approx 1231.5 + 1935.2$
   ≈ 3166.7
   The surface area of the cylinder is about 3166.7 m².
10. $2(\pi r^2) + 2\pi rh = 2(\pi \cdot 50^2) + 2 \cdot \pi \cdot 50 \cdot 40$
    $= 2(\pi \cdot 2500) + 2 \cdot \pi \cdot 50 \cdot 40$
    $\approx 15,708 + 12,566$
    $\approx 28,274$
    The area that needs to be painted is about 28,274 ft².
    $28,274 \div 500 = 56.5$. So, 57 gallons of paint are needed.

11. Front and Back: $2(12 \cdot 3) = 72$
Top and Bottom: $2(12 \cdot 7) = 168$
Two sides: $2(7 \cdot 3) = 42$
The surface area of the rectangular prism is
$72 + 168 + 42$ or 282 in^2.

12. $2(\pi r^2) + 2\pi rh = 2(\pi \cdot 10^2) + 2 \cdot \pi \cdot 10 \cdot 20$
$= 2(\pi \cdot 100) + 2 \cdot \pi \cdot 10 \cdot 20$
$\approx 628.3 + 1256.6$
≈ 1884.9
The surface area of the cylinder is about 1884.9 ft^2.

13. Two Bases: $2\left(\frac{1}{2} \cdot 4 \cdot 3\right) = 12$
Front: $10 \cdot 4 = 40$
Bottom: $10 \cdot 5 = 50$
Back: $10 \cdot 3 = 30$
The surface area of the triangular prism is $12 + 40 + 50 + 30$ or 132 cm^2.

14. $2(\pi r^2) + 2\pi rh = 2(\pi \cdot 2^2) + 2 \cdot \pi \cdot 2 \cdot 20$
$= 2(\pi \cdot 4) + 2 \cdot \pi \cdot 2 \cdot 20$
$\approx 25.1 + 251.3$
≈ 276.4 m^2
The surface area of the cylinder is about 276.4 m^2.

15. Two Bases: $2\left(\frac{1}{2} \cdot 6 \cdot 5.2\right) = 31.2$
Front: $6 \cdot 10 = 60$
Bottom: $6 \cdot 10 = 60$
Back: $6 \cdot 10 = 60$
The surface area of the triangular prism is $31.2 + 60 + 60 + 60$ or 211.2 cm^2.

16. $2(\pi r^2) + 2\pi rh = 2[\pi \cdot (7.5)^2] + 2 \cdot \pi \cdot 7.5 \cdot 2$
$= 2(\pi \cdot 56.25) + 2 \cdot \pi \cdot 7.5 \cdot 2$
$\approx 353.4 + 94.2$
≈ 447.6
The surface area of the cylinder is about 447.6 m^2.

17. $2(\pi r^2) + 2\pi rh = 2(\pi \cdot 5)^2 + 2 \cdot \pi \cdot 5 \cdot 15\frac{1}{4}$
$= 2(\pi \cdot 25) + 2 \cdot \pi \cdot 5 \cdot 15\frac{1}{4}$
$\approx 157.1 + 479.1$
≈ 636.2
The surface area of the cylinder is about 636.2 in^2.

18. Front and Back: $2(7 \cdot 7) = 98$
Top and Bottom: $2(7 \cdot 7) = 98$
Two sides: $2(7 \cdot 7) = 98$
The surface area of the rectangular prism is $98 + 98 + 98$ or 294 ft^2.

19. Find the area of the rectangular prism.
Front and Back: $2(12 \cdot 4) = 96$
Bottom: $12 \cdot 4 = 48$
Two sides: $2(4 \cdot 4) = 32$
Find the area of half of the cylinder.
$\frac{1}{2}[2(\pi r^2) + 2\pi rh] = \frac{1}{2}[2(\pi \cdot 2^2) + 2 \cdot \pi \cdot 2 \cdot 12]$
$= \frac{1}{2}[2(\pi \cdot 4) + 2 \cdot \pi \cdot 2 \cdot 12]$
$= \frac{1}{2}[25.1 + 150.8]$
$\approx \frac{1}{2}[175.9]$
≈ 88
The surface area is about $96 + 48 + 32 + 88$ or 264 in^2.

20. Front and Back: $2(a \cdot a) = 2a^2$
Top and Bottom: $2(a \cdot a) = 2a^2$
Two sides: $2(a \cdot a) = 2a^2$
The surface area is $2a^2 + 2a^2 + 2a^2$ or $6a^2$.
Therefore, a formula for the surface area of the cube in terms of a is $S = 6a^2$.

21. d; need more information

22. Front and Back: $2(2a \cdot 2a) = 8a^2$
Top and Bottom: $2(2a \cdot 2a) = 8a^2$
Two sides: $2(2a \cdot 2a) = 8a^2$
When the sides of a cube are doubled, the surface area is $8a^2 + 8a^2 + 8a^2$ or $24a^2$. $24a^2 \div 6a^2 = 4$. So, the surface area is 4 times greater than the original cube that has sides measuring a units.

23. a. 15-inch cube
Each face: $15 \cdot 15 = 225$
12-inch cube
Each face: $12 \cdot 12 = 144$
9-inch cube
Each face: $9 \cdot 9 = 81$
Only 5 faces of the 9- and 12-inch cubes are included in the surface area of the tower. Also, the bottom of the 12-inch cube covers 144 in^2 on the top of the 15-inch cube and the bottom of the 9-inch cube covers 81 in^2 on the top of the 12-inch cube. So the surface area of the tower is $6(225) - 144 + 5(144) - 81 + 5(81)$ or 2250 in^2.

b. No, as long as the entire surface of the face of the smaller cube is touching a face of the larger cube, the surface area of the tower will be the same.

24. Front and Back: $2\left(\frac{1}{2} \cdot 4 \cdot 4\right) = 16$
Two sides: $2(6 \cdot 4.5) = 54$
Bottom: $4 \cdot 6 = 24$
$16 + 54 + 24 = 94$. So, 94 ft^2 of canvas is needed to make the tent.

25. $24(2\pi rh) = 24(2 \cdot \pi \cdot 3.8 \cdot 10.8)$
≈ 6188.6
About 6189 cm^2 of paper is needed to make the labels for the 24 cans.

26. Two sides: $2\left(20 \cdot 12\frac{1}{2}\right) = 500$
Front and Back: $2\left(24 \cdot 12\frac{1}{2}\right) = 600$
Ceiling: $24 \cdot 20 = 480$
The garage walls and ceiling have a combined area of $500 + 600 + 480$ or 1580 ft^2. A sheet of drywall will cover an area $4 \cdot 12$ or 48 ft^2. $1580 \div 48 = 32.9$. So, he will need to purchase 33 sheets of drywall.

27. 8 in. $\times$ 8 in. $\times$ 8 in. box
Front and Back: $2(8 \cdot 8) = 128$
Top and Bottom: $2(8 \cdot 8) = 128$
Two sides: $2(8 \cdot 8) = 128$
Overlapping Pieces: $2(8 \cdot 8) = 128$
$128 + 128 + 128 + 128$ or 512 in^2 of cardboard is needed.

15 in. × 10 in. × 12 in. box

Front and Back: $2(15 \cdot 12) = 360$
Top and Bottom: $2(15 \cdot 10) = 300$
Two sides: $2(10 \cdot 12) = 240$
Overlapping Pieces: $2(15 \cdot 10) = 300$
$360 + 300 + 240 + 300$ or 1200 in^2 of cardboard is needed.

20 in. × 14 in. × 10 in. box

Front and Back: $2(20 \cdot 10) = 400$
Top and Bottom: $2(20 \cdot 14) = 560$
Two sides: $2(14 \cdot 10) = 280$
Overlapping Pieces: $2(20 \cdot 14) = 560$
$400 + 560 + 280 + 560$ or 1800 in^2 of cardboard is needed.

$\frac{\$1.25}{512} = 0.0024$ $\frac{\$2.00}{1600} = 0.0013$

$\frac{\$2.50}{1800} = 0.0014$

The ratio of price to material is not about the same.

28. Semi-circular arch
$\frac{1}{2}(2\pi rh) = \frac{1}{2}(2 \cdot \pi \cdot 3 \cdot 20)$
≈ 188.5 ft^2

Walls
$2(20 \cdot 8) = 320$ ft^2
The hallway has a surface area of about $188.5 + 320$ or 508.5 ft^2. Two coats of paint will be applied. Therefore, there needs to be enough paint to cover an area of $2(508.5)$ or 1017 ft^2.
$1017 \div 400 = 2.5$. So, 3 gallons of paint will be needed.

29. **a–b.** See students' work.

30. Grazing area = area of large section +
       area of left section +
       area of top section
$= \frac{3}{4}(\pi \cdot 25^2) + \frac{1}{4}(\pi \cdot 15^2) + \frac{1}{4}(\pi \cdot 10^2)$
$= 468.75\pi + 56.25\pi + 25\pi$
$= 550\pi$
≈ 1727.9

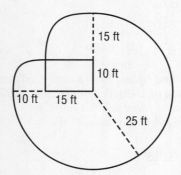

The goat has a grazing area of about 1727.9 ft^2.

31.

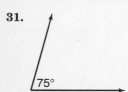

32. $C(12.6) = \frac{P(12, 6)}{6!}$
$= \frac{12 \cdot 11 \cdot 10 \cdot 9 \cdot 8 \cdot 7}{6 \cdot 5 \cdot 4 \cdot 3 \cdot 2 \cdot 1}$
$= 924$

33. $3.605 \times 10^3 = 3.605 \times 1000$
$= 3605$

34. Let v = amount sold
$v > 3(32,000)$
$v > \$96,000$

12-6 Surface Area: Pyramids and Cones

Page 640 Checking Your Understanding

1. It is the altitude of a triangular face of a pyramid; it is the length from the vertex of a cone to the edges of its base.

2. The base of a circular cone is a circle; the perimeter of a circle is $2\pi r$.

3. Use $A = \frac{1}{2}bh$ to find the area of each side. Add the areas of the sides.

4. See students' work.

5. pyramid;
Base: $A = s^2$
$A = 6^2$
$A = 36$ m^2

Side: $A = \frac{1}{2}bh$
$A = \frac{1}{2}(6)(8.2)$
$A = \frac{1}{2}(49.2)$
$A = 24.6$ m^2
The surface area is $36 + 4(24.6)$ or 134.4 m^2.

6. cone;
Base: $A = \pi r^2$
$A = \pi \cdot 5^2$
$A = \pi \cdot 25$
$A \approx 78.5$ cm^2

Surface: $A = \pi rs$
$A = \pi \cdot 5 \cdot 12$
$A \approx 188.5$ cm^2
The surface area is about $78.5 + 188.5$ or 267 cm^2.

7. triangular pyramid;
Base: $A = \frac{1}{2}bh$
$A = \frac{1}{2}(6)(4)$
$A = \frac{1}{2}(24)$
$A \approx 12$ in^2

Side: $A = \frac{1}{2}bh$
$A = \frac{1}{2}(6)(5)$
$A = \frac{1}{2}(30)$
$A = 15$ in^2
The surface area is $12 + 3(15)$ or 57 in^2.

8. Side: $A = \frac{1}{2}bh$

$$A = \frac{1}{2}(8)(75.3)$$
$$A = \frac{1}{2}(602.4)$$
$$A = 301.2 \text{ ft}^2$$

8(301.2) or about 2410 ft² of roofing will be needed.

Pages 641–642   Exercises

9. Base: $A = s^2$

$$A = 4^2$$
$$A = 16 \text{ ft}^2$$

Side: $A = \frac{1}{2}bh$

$$A = \frac{1}{2}(4)(6.3)$$
$$A = \frac{1}{2}(25.2)$$
$$A = 12.6 \text{ ft}^2$$

The surface area is 16 + 4(12.6) or 66.4 ft².

10. Base: $A = \pi r^2$

$$A = \pi \cdot 5^2$$
$$A = \pi \cdot 25$$
$$A \approx 78.5 \text{ in}^2$$

Surface: $A = \pi r s$

$$A = \pi \cdot 5 \cdot 16.6$$
$$A \approx 260.8 \text{ in}^2$$

The surface area is about 78.5 + 260.8 or 339.3 in².

11. Base: $A = \pi r^2$

$$A = \pi \cdot 7^2$$
$$A = \pi \cdot 49$$
$$A \approx 153.9 \text{ m}^2$$

Surface: $A = \pi r s$

$$A = \pi \cdot 7 \cdot 11.4$$
$$A \approx 250.7 \text{ m}^2$$

The surface area is about 153.9 + 250.7 or 404.6 m².

12. Side: $A = \frac{1}{2}bh$

$$A = \frac{1}{2}(8)(10.3)$$
$$A = \frac{1}{2}(82.4)$$
$$A = 41.2$$

The surface area is 4(41.2) or 164.8 ft².

13. Base: $A = \pi r^2$

$$A = \pi \cdot 5^2$$
$$A = \pi \cdot 25$$
$$A \approx 78.5 \text{ in}^2$$

Surface: $A = \pi r s$

$$A = \pi \cdot 5 \cdot 13$$
$$A \approx 204.2 \text{ in}^2$$

The surface area is about 78.5 + 204.2 or 282.7 in².

14. Base: $A = \pi r^2$

$$A = \pi \cdot 15^2$$
$$A = \pi \cdot 225$$
$$A \approx 706.9 \text{ m}^2$$

Surface: $A = \pi r s$

$$A = \pi \cdot 15 \cdot 10.6$$
$$A \approx 499.5 \text{ m}^2$$

The surface area is about 706.9 + 499.5 or 1206.4 m².

15. Surface: $A = \pi r s$

$$A = \pi \cdot 5 \cdot 15$$
$$A \approx 235.6$$

The surface area is about 2(235.6) or 471.2 cm².

16. Base: $A = 48 \text{ m}^2$

Side: $A = \frac{1}{2}bh$

$$A = \frac{1}{2}(8.3)(10.6)$$
$$A = \frac{1}{2}(87.98)$$
$$A = 43.99 \text{ m}^2$$

The surface area is 48 + 6(43.99) or 311.9 m².

17. Side (Top): $A = \frac{1}{2}bh$

$$A = \frac{1}{2}(5)(12.3)$$
$$A = \frac{1}{2}(61.5)$$
$$A = 30.75 \text{ in}^2$$

Side (Bottom): $A = \frac{1}{2}bh$

$$A = \frac{1}{2}(5)(15.2)$$
$$A = \frac{1}{2}(76)$$
$$A = 38 \text{ in}^2$$

The surface area is 4(30.75) + 4(38) or 275 in².

18. Original Lead Bar

Back and Front: 2(13 · 1) = 26
Top and Bottom: 2(13 · 2) = 52
Two sides: 2(2 · 1) = 4
The surface area of the original lead bar is
26 + 52 + 4 or 82 in².

Sinkers

Base: $A = \pi r^2$

$$A = \pi \cdot (0.5)^2$$
$$A = \pi \cdot 0.25$$
$$A \approx 0.785 \text{ in}^2$$

Surface: $A = \pi r s$

$$A = \pi \cdot 0.5 \cdot 1.1$$
$$A \approx 1.728 \text{ in}^2$$

The total surface area of all the sinkers is about
100(0.785 + 1.728) or about 251 in².

$$\frac{251}{82} \approx 3.06$$

So, the surface area is about tripled.

19. Face: $A = \frac{1}{2}bh$

$$A = \frac{1}{2}(98.4)(131)$$
$$A = \frac{1}{2}(12{,}890.4)$$
$$A = 6445.2$$

The lateral surface area is 4(6445.2) or about 25,780.8 ft².

20. Face: $A = \frac{1}{2}bh$

$$A = \frac{1}{2}(26)(20.6)$$
$$A = \frac{1}{2}(535.6)$$
$$A = 267.8$$

It took 4(267.8) or about 1071.2 ft² of glass to cover one of these pyramids.

21. Surface: $A = \pi r s$
$\qquad A = \pi \cdot 21 \cdot 47.9$
$\qquad A \approx 3160.1$
About 3160.1 sq. ft of canvas was used to make the cover of the tepee.

22.

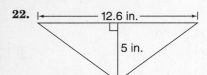

23. Front and Back: $2(15 \cdot 12) = 360$
Top and Bottom: $2(15 \cdot 10) = 300$
Two sides: $\qquad 2(10 \cdot 12) = 240$
The surface area is $360 + 300 + 240$ or 900 cm^2.

24. $P(\text{heads and tails}) = \frac{2}{4}$
$\qquad\qquad\qquad\qquad = \frac{1}{2}$

25. Let $x =$ number
$\qquad 4x + 8 = 20$
$4x + 8 - 8 = 20 - 8$
$\qquad\quad 4x = 12$
$\qquad\quad \frac{4x}{4} = \frac{12}{4}$
$\qquad\qquad x = 3$

26. $\qquad\qquad w + \frac{1}{6} = 3\frac{2}{3}$
$w + \frac{1}{6} - \frac{1}{6} = 3\frac{2}{3} - \frac{1}{6}$
$\qquad\qquad\quad w = \frac{11}{3} - \frac{1}{6}$
$\qquad\qquad\quad w = \frac{22}{6} - \frac{1}{6}$
$\qquad\qquad\quad w = \frac{21}{6}$
$\qquad\qquad\quad w = 3\frac{1}{2}$

27. $(5x)(-3y) = -15xy$

Page 642　Self Test

1. $A = \frac{1}{2}h(a + b)$
$A = \frac{1}{2} \cdot 3(4 + 6)$
$A = \frac{1}{2} \cdot 3 \cdot 10$
$A = 15$ m^2

2. $A = \frac{1}{2}bh$
$A = \frac{1}{2}(8)(6)$
$A = \frac{1}{2}(48)$
$A = 24$ ft^2

3. $A = \pi r^2$
$A = \pi \cdot 6^2$
$A = \pi \cdot 36$
$A \approx 113.1$ in^2

4. rectangular prism;
Front and Back: $\quad 2(7 \cdot 5) = 70$
Top and Bottom: $\quad 2(7 \cdot 4) = 56$
Two sides: $\qquad\quad 2(4 \cdot 5) = 40$
The surface area is $70 + 56 + 40$ or 166 mm^2.

5. cylinder;
$2(\pi r^2) + 2\pi r h = 2(\pi \cdot 4^2) + 2 \cdot \pi \cdot 4 \cdot 12$
$\qquad\qquad\qquad = 2(\pi \cdot 16) + 2 \cdot \pi \cdot 4 \cdot 12$
$\qquad\qquad\qquad \approx 100.5 + 301.6$
$\qquad\qquad\qquad \approx 402.1$
The surface area is about 402.1 in^2.

6. Square pyramid;
Base: $A = s^2$
$\qquad A = 8^2$
$\qquad A = 64$ m^2
Side: $A = \frac{1}{2}bh$
$\qquad A = \frac{1}{2}(8)(9)$
$\qquad A = \frac{1}{2}(72)$
$\qquad A = 36$ m^2
The surface area is $64 + 4(36)$ or 208 m^2.

7. area of target: $A = \pi r^2$
$\qquad\qquad\qquad A = \pi \cdot 12^2$
$\qquad\qquad\qquad A = \pi \cdot 144$
$\qquad\qquad\qquad A \approx 452.4$ in^2

area of 8-point region: $A = \frac{1}{4}(\pi r^2)$
$\qquad\qquad\qquad\qquad A = \frac{1}{4}(\pi \cdot 4^2)$
$\qquad\qquad\qquad\qquad A = \frac{1}{4}(\pi \cdot 16)$
$\qquad\qquad\qquad\qquad A \approx 12.6$ in^2

So, $P(\text{8-point region}) = \frac{\text{8-point area}}{\text{area of target}}$
$\qquad\qquad\qquad\qquad\quad = \frac{12.6}{452.4}$
$\qquad\qquad\qquad\qquad\quad = 0.0278$
The probability that the dart lands in the 8-point region is 0.028 or about $\frac{3}{100}$.

8.

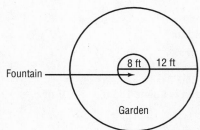

Area of garden =
(Total area) − (Area of fountain)
Area of fountain: $A = \pi r^2$
$\qquad\qquad\qquad A = \pi \cdot 4^2$
$\qquad\qquad\qquad A = \pi \cdot 16$
$\qquad\qquad\qquad A \approx 50.3$ ft^2

Total area: $A = \pi r^2$
$\qquad\qquad\quad A = \pi \cdot 16^2$
$\qquad\qquad\quad A = \pi \cdot 256$
$\qquad\qquad\quad A \approx 804.3$ ft^2

The area of the garden is about $804.3 - 50.3$ or 754.0 ft^2. $754.0 \div 300 = 2.5$. So, 3 lbs. of fertilizer is needed for the garden.

9. $A = \pi r s$
$A = \pi \cdot 2\frac{1}{2} \cdot 6$
$A \approx 47.1$
About 47.1 in^2 of paper would be used to make the open paper cone.

12-7A	Math Lab: Volume

Page 643   Your Turn

See students' work.

1. triangular prism; cylinder
2. same height; 5 in.
3. same; 8 in.
4. circular: ≈ 5 in^2; triangular: ≈ 3 in^2; square: 4 in^2
5. cylinder
6. Yes; the greater the base area, the greater the volume.

12-7	Volume: Prisms and Cylinders

Page 644   Your Turn

a. length, width, height
b. The volume is the product of the dimensions.
c. The area of the base times the height equals the volume.

Pages 646–647   Checking Your Understanding

1. Their volumes both depend on the area of the base and the height.
2. V = volume; B = area of the base; h = height
3. Both are measures of three-dimensional objects; surface area covers the outside of a solid while volume fills the inside.
4. Carlos is correct; a cube has three dimensions and when you multiply each dimension by 2, you multiply the volume by $2 \times 2 \times 2$ or 8.
5. See students' work.

6. $V = Bh$
   $V = 4 \cdot 5 \cdot 8$
   $V = 160$ cm^3

7. $V = Bh$
   $V = \left(\frac{1}{2} \cdot 10 \cdot 8\right) \cdot 15$
   $V = 40 \cdot 15$
   $V = 600$ in^3

8. $V = \pi r^2 h$
   $V = \pi \cdot 5^2 \cdot 15$
   $V = \pi \cdot 25 \cdot 15$
   $V \approx 1178.1$ cm^3

9. $V = Bh$
   $V = 3 \cdot 5 \cdot 15$
   $V = 225$ in^2

10. $V = Bh$
    $V = 25 \cdot 1.5$
    $V = 37.5$ m^3

11. $V = \pi r^2 h$
    $V = \pi \cdot 2^2 \cdot 2\frac{1}{4}$
    $V = \pi \cdot 4 \cdot 2\frac{1}{4}$
    $V \approx 28.3$ ft^3

12. $V = Bh$
    $V = (\pi \cdot 1^2) \cdot 6$
    $V = \pi \cdot 1 \cdot 6$
    $V \approx 19$
    The fish tank holds about 19 ft^3 of water.

13. $V = Bh$
    $V = 5 \cdot 5 \cdot 5$
    $V = 125$ ft^3

14. $V = Bh$
    $V = \left(\frac{1}{2} \cdot 7 \cdot 8\right) \cdot 15$
    $V = 28 \cdot 15$
    $V = 420$ in^3

15. $V = Bh$
    $V = 16 \cdot 4 \cdot 8$
    $V = 512$ cm^3

16. $V = Bh$
    $V = 4.5 \cdot 10$
    $V = 45$ m^3

17. $V = \pi r^2 h$
    $V = \pi \cdot 8^2 \cdot 8$
    $V = \pi \cdot 64 \cdot 8$
    $V \approx 1608.5$ ft^3

18. $V = \pi r^2 h$
    $V = \pi \cdot 7^2 \cdot 6$
    $V = \pi \cdot 49 \cdot 6$
    $V \approx 923.6$ in^3

19. $V = \pi r^2 h$
    $V = \pi \cdot 3^2 \cdot 20$
    $V = \pi \cdot 9 \cdot 20$
    $V \approx 565.5$ cm^3

20. $V = \pi r^2 h$
    $V = \pi \cdot 1.35^2 \cdot 30$
    $V = \pi \cdot 1.8225 \cdot 30$
    $V \approx 171.8$ m^3

21. $V = \frac{1}{2}(\pi r^2 h)$
    $V = \frac{1}{2}(\pi \cdot 1.25^2 \cdot 10)$
    $V = \frac{1}{2}(\pi \cdot 1.5625 \cdot 10)$
    $V \approx 24.5$ ft^3

22. $V = Bh$
    $V = 6 \cdot 6 \cdot 6$
    $V = 216$ in^3

23. $V = Bh$
    $V = 4.2 \cdot 3.2 \cdot 6.2$
    $V = 83.3$ cm^3

24. $V = Bh$
    $V = 45.2 \cdot 47.8$
    $V = 2160.6$ cm^3

25. $V = \pi r^2 h$
    $V = \pi \cdot 10^2 \cdot 15$
    $V = \pi \cdot 100 \cdot 15$
    $V \approx 4712.4$ yd^3

26. $V = Bh$
    $V = \left(\frac{1}{2} \cdot 8 \cdot 15\right) \cdot 6.5$
    $V = 60 \cdot 6.5$
    $V = 390$ in^3

27. $V = \pi r^2 h$
    $V = \pi \cdot 1.3^2 \cdot 3.5$
    $V = \pi \cdot 1.69 \cdot 3.5$
    $V \approx 18.6$ m^3

28. a. Change lines 1–2 to Input "Radius =", R
       Change line 4 to $\pi * R^2 \to A$
       Change line 5 to $A * H \to V$
    b. See students' work.
    c. See students' work.

29. The volume is greater with the $8\frac{1}{2}$-inch side as the height.

30. $V = Bh$
    $V = a \cdot a \cdot a$
    $V = a^3$

31. $V = Bh$
    $4.64 = 1.41 \cdot h$
    $\frac{4.64}{1.41} = \frac{1.41h}{1.41}$
    $3.29 = h$
    The height is 3.29 cm.

32.

Rectangle	Round
$V = Bh$	$V = 2(\pi r^2 h)$
$V = 30 \cdot 21 \cdot 5$	$V = 2(\pi \cdot 10.5^2 \cdot 4)$
$V = 3150 \text{ cm}^3$	$V = 2(\pi \cdot 110.25 \cdot 4)$
	$V \approx 2770.9 \text{ cm}^2$

A rectangular pan will hold more batter.

33. a. $V = 20 \cdot 50 \cdot 6$
$V = 6000 \text{ ft}^3$
The swimming pool requires $6000 \cdot 7.481$ or 44,886 gallons of water.

b. $V = 15 \cdot 12 \cdot 12$
$V = 2160 \text{ ft}^3$
The swimming pool requires $2160 \cdot 7.481$ or 16,158.96 gallons of water.

c. $V = 45 \cdot 80 \cdot 12$
$V = 43{,}200 \text{ ft}^3$
The swimming pool requires $43{,}200 \cdot 7.481$ or 206,539.2 gallons of water.

The first swimming pool requires about 45,000 gallons of water. So the correct choice is a.

34. a.

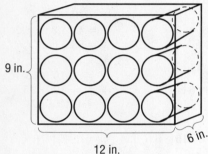

9 in.

12 in.

6 in.

This box is 12 by 9 by 6 inches.

b. Volume of box $= Bh$
$= 12 \cdot 6 \cdot 9$
$= 648 \text{ in}^3$
Volume of can $= \pi r^2 h$
$= \pi \cdot 1.5^2 \cdot 6$
$= \pi \cdot 2.25 \cdot 6$
$\approx 42.4 \text{ in}^3$
The amount of space wasted is about $648 - 12(42.4)$ or about 140 in^3.

35. a. $V = 8 \cdot 4 \cdot 4$
$V = 128$
The volume of a full cord is 128 ft^3.

b. $V = 8 \cdot 4 \cdot 2\frac{1}{2}$
$V = 80$
The volume of a "short cord" is 80 ft^3. Thus, a "short cord" is $\frac{80}{128}$ or $\frac{5}{8}$ of a full cord.

36. Base: $A = s^2$
$A = 14 \cdot 14$
$A = 196 \text{ yd}^2$
Side: $A = \frac{1}{2}bh$
$A = \frac{1}{2} \cdot 14 \cdot 3$
$A = 21 \text{ yd}^2$
The surface area is $196 + 4(21)$ or 280 yd^2.

37. $\frac{x}{2.5} = \frac{8}{5}$
$x \cdot 5 = 2.5 \cdot 8$
$5x = 20$
$\frac{5x}{5} = \frac{20}{5}$
$x = 4 \text{ mi}$

38. $m\angle X + m\angle Y = 180$
$58 + m\angle Y = 180$
$58 + m\angle Y - 58 = 180 - 58$
$m\angle Y = 122$
The measure of $\angle Y$ is $122°$.

39. $f(x) = 5x - 3$
$f(2) = 5(2) - 3$
$= 10 - 3$
$= 7$

40. Drew has $2.25 ⟶ 2.25
Undo the amount that ⟶ + 2.00
he loaned to Cassie. 4.25
Undo the half that was ⟶ × 2
spent on lunch. 8.50
Drew started with $8.50.

41. $4 \times 4 \times 4 = 64$
64 combinations

42. Sample answer: Candy is on sale for 3 pieces for 25 cents. How much is one piece?

12-8 Volume: Pyramids and Cones

Page 649 Your Turn

See students' work.

a. about 3

b. They are the same.

c. They appear to be the same.

d. The volume of the pyramid is $\frac{1}{3}$ the volume of the cube.

Page 651 Checking Your Understanding

1. The base is a circle.

2. $V = \frac{1}{3}Bh$; V represents volume, B represents the area of the base, h represents the height of the pyramid.

3. $V = \frac{1}{3}\pi r^2 h$; V represents volume, r represents the radius of the base, h represents the height of the cone.

4. See students' work.

5. See students' explanations.
$V = \frac{1}{3}Bh$
$V = \frac{1}{3} \cdot 4 \cdot 4 \cdot 6$
$V = 32 \text{ ft}^3$

6. See students' explanations.

$V = \frac{1}{3}\pi r^2 h$

$V = \frac{1}{3} \cdot \pi \cdot 5^2 \cdot 12$

$V = \frac{1}{3} \cdot \pi \cdot 25 \cdot 12$

$V \approx 314.2 \text{ cm}^3$

7. See students' explanations.

$V = \frac{1}{3}Bh$

$V = \frac{1}{3} \cdot \left(\frac{1}{2} \cdot 6 \cdot 8\right) \cdot 20$

$V = \frac{1}{3} \cdot 24 \cdot 20$

$V = 160 \text{ ft}^3$

8. $V = \frac{1}{3}\pi r^2 h$

$V = \frac{1}{3} \cdot \pi \cdot 6^2 \cdot 15$

$V = \frac{1}{3} \cdot \pi \cdot 36 \cdot 15$

$V = 565.5 \text{ m}^3$

9. $V = \frac{1}{3}Bh$

$V = \frac{1}{3} \cdot 125 \cdot 6\frac{1}{2}$

$V = 270.8 \text{ in}^3$

10. $V = \frac{1}{3}Bh$

$V = \frac{1}{3} \cdot 34^2 \cdot 54$

$V = \frac{1}{3} \cdot 1156 \cdot 54$

$V = 20{,}808 \text{ ft}^3$

Pages 652–653   Exercises

11. $V = \frac{1}{3}Bh$

$V = \frac{1}{3} \cdot 5 \cdot 6 \cdot 7$

$V = 70 \text{ ft}^3$

12. $V = \frac{1}{3}\pi r^2 h$

$V = \frac{1}{3} \cdot \pi \cdot 5^2 \cdot 15$

$V = \frac{1}{3} \cdot \pi \cdot 25 \cdot 15$

$V = 392.7 \text{ in}^3$

13. $V = \frac{1}{3}Bh$

$V = \frac{1}{3} \cdot 48 \cdot 10$

$V = 160 \text{ m}^3$

14. $V = \frac{1}{3}\pi r^2 h$

$V = \frac{1}{3} \cdot \pi \cdot 7^2 \cdot 9$

$V = \frac{1}{3} \cdot \pi \cdot 49 \cdot 9$

$V = 461.8 \text{ mm}^3$

15. $V = \frac{1}{3}Bh$

$V = \frac{1}{3} \cdot \left(\frac{1}{2} \cdot 5 \cdot 12\right) \cdot 15$

$V = \frac{1}{3} \cdot 30 \cdot 15$

$V = 150 \text{ in}^3$

16. $V = \frac{1}{3}\pi r^2 h$

$V = \frac{1}{3} \cdot \pi \cdot 2.5^2 \cdot 12$

$V = \frac{1}{3} \cdot \pi \cdot 6.25 \cdot 12$

$V = 78.5 \text{ in}^3$

17. $V = \frac{1}{3}\pi r^2 h$

$V = \frac{1}{3} \cdot \pi \cdot 15^2 \cdot 39$

$V = \frac{1}{3} \cdot \pi \cdot 225 \cdot 39$

$V = 9189.2 \text{ m}^3$

18. $V = \frac{1}{3}Bh$

$V = \frac{1}{3} \cdot 120 \cdot 80 \cdot 90$

$V = 288{,}000 \text{ ft}^3$

19. $V = \left(\frac{1}{3}\pi r^2 h\right) + \left(\frac{1}{3}\pi r^2 h\right)$

$V = \left(\frac{1}{3} \cdot \pi \cdot 5^2 \cdot 20\right) + \left(\frac{1}{3} \cdot \pi \cdot 5^2 \cdot 8\right)$

$V = \left(\frac{1}{3} \cdot \pi \cdot 25 \cdot 20\right) + \left(\frac{1}{3} \cdot \pi \cdot 25 \cdot 8\right)$

$V = 523.6 + 209.4$

$V = 733 \text{ cm}^3$

20. $V = \frac{1}{3}Bh$

$V = \frac{1}{3} \cdot 9 \cdot 7 \cdot 18$

$V = 378 \text{ in}^3$

21. $V = \frac{1}{3}Bh$

$V = \frac{1}{3} \cdot 5 \cdot 5 \cdot 6$

$V = 50 \text{ cm}^3$

22. $V = \frac{1}{3}\pi r^2 h$

$V = \frac{1}{3} \cdot \pi \cdot 3^2 \cdot 14$

$V = \frac{1}{3} \cdot \pi \cdot 9 \cdot 14$

$V = 131.9 \text{ ft}^3$

23. $V = \frac{1}{3}\pi r^2 h$

$V = \frac{1}{3} \cdot \pi \cdot 10^2 \cdot 18$

$V = \frac{1}{3} \cdot \pi \cdot 100 \cdot 18$

$V = 1885.0 \text{ m}^3$

24. $V = Bh + \left(\frac{1}{3}Bh\right)$

$V = (20 \cdot 20 \cdot 20) + \left(\frac{1}{3} \cdot 20 \cdot 20 \cdot 15\right)$

$V = 8000 + 2000$

$V = 10{,}000 \text{ ft}^3$

25. $V = (\pi r^2 h) + \left(\frac{1}{3}\pi r^2 h\right)$

$V = (\pi \cdot 2^2 \cdot 3) + \left(\frac{1}{3} \cdot \pi \cdot 2^2 \cdot 1.5\right)$

$V = (\pi \cdot 4 \cdot 3) + \left(\frac{1}{3} \cdot \pi \cdot 4 \cdot 1.5\right)$

$V = 37.7 + 6.3$

$V = 44 \text{ m}^3$

26. $V = 2\left(\frac{1}{3}\pi r^2 h\right) + (\pi r^2 h)$

$V = 2\left(\frac{1}{3} \cdot \pi \cdot 21.5^2 \cdot 42\right) + (\pi \cdot 21.5^2 \cdot 57)$

$V = 2\left(\frac{1}{3} \cdot \pi \cdot 462.25 \cdot 42\right) + (\pi \cdot 462.25 \cdot 57)$

$V = 40{,}661.6 + 82{,}775.5$

$V = 123{,}437.1 \text{ cm}^3$

27. No; the customer gets only $\frac{1}{3}$ as much popcorn for $\frac{1}{2}$ the price.

28. a. The volume doubles.

   b. The volume quadruples.

29. $V = \frac{1}{3}Bh$

$V = \frac{1}{3} \cdot 756 \cdot 756 \cdot 481$

$V = 91{,}636{,}272 \text{ ft}^3$

30. a. $V = \frac{1}{3}\pi r^2 h$

$V = \frac{1}{3} \cdot \pi \cdot 0.75^2 \cdot 4$

$V = \frac{1}{3} \cdot \pi \cdot 0.5625 \cdot 4$

$V = 2.4 \text{ ft}^3$

   b. $2.4 \times 131 = 314.4$

   The stalactite weighs 314.4 lb.

31.

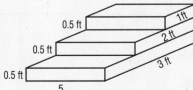

$V = (5 \cdot 3 \cdot 0.5) + (5 \cdot 2 \cdot 0.5) + (5 \cdot 1 \cdot 0.5)$

$V = 7.5 + 5 + 2.5$

$V = 15$

15 ft^3 of concrete will be needed.

32. The probability of rolling a 1 or a 6 is $\frac{2}{6}$ or $\frac{1}{3}$. Therefore, if a die is tossed 30 times, expect a 1 or a 6 $\frac{1}{3}(30)$ or 10 times.

33. $\frac{18}{90} = \frac{x}{100}$

$18 \cdot 100 = 90 \cdot x$

$1800 = 90x$

$\frac{1800}{90} = \frac{90x}{90}$

$20 = x$

18 is 20% of 90.

34. $x = 3\frac{3}{5} - 1\frac{3}{10}$

$x = \frac{18}{5} - \frac{13}{10}$

$x = \frac{36}{10} - \frac{13}{10}$

$x = \frac{23}{10}$

$x = 2\frac{3}{10}$

35. $P = 2(\ell + w)$ $A = \ell \cdot w$

$P = 2(16 + 11.5)$ $A = 16 \cdot 11.5$

$P = 2(27.5)$ $A = 184 \text{ cm}^2$

$P = 55 \text{ cm}$

36. $\frac{-144}{6} = k$

$-24 = k$

12-8B   Math Lab: Similar Solid Figures

Page 654

In the first activity, 8 cubes are used to make a larger cube that has sides twice as long as the original cube.

1. 1 unit^2

2. 4 units^2

3. 1 unit^3

4. 8 units^3

In the second activity, 27 cubes are used to make a larger cube that has sides three times as long as the original cube.

5. 9 units^2

6. 27 units^2

7.

Scale Factor	Length of a Side	Area of a Face	Volume
1	1	1	1
2	2	4	8
3	3	9	27

8. $\times 4; \times 9$

9. x^2

10. $\times 8; \times 27$

11. x^3

12. $16 \text{ units}^2; 64 \text{ units}^3$

Chapter 12   Study Guide and Assessment

Page 655   Understanding and Using Vocabulary

1. G; The square centimeter is a common unit of measure for area.

---

2. B; The cubic centimeter is a common unit of measure for volume.

3. H; The surface area of a solid is the sum of the areas of its faces.

4. I; Volume is the amount of space that a solid contains.

5. A; The altitude of a parallelogram is a segment perpendicular to the bases with endpoints on the bases.

6. F; The slant height of a pyramid is the length of an altitude of one of its lateral faces.

7. C; The height of a pyramid is the length of a segment from the vertex perpendicular to the base of the pyramid.

8. D, E; A prism or a pyramid is named by the shape of its base.

Pages 656–658   Skills and Concepts

9. $A = bh$

$A = 2\frac{1}{4} \cdot 1\frac{3}{4}$

$A = 3\frac{15}{16} \text{ in}^2$

10. $A = \frac{1}{2}bh$

$A = \frac{1}{2}(15)(11)$

$A = \frac{1}{2}(165)$

$A = 82.5 \text{ ft}^2$

11. $A = \frac{1}{2}h(a + b)$

$A = \frac{1}{2} \cdot 16(39.5 + 20)$

$A = \frac{1}{2} \cdot 16 \cdot 59.5$

$A = 476 \text{ mm}^2$

12. $A = \pi r^2$

$A = \pi \cdot 9^2$

$A = \pi \cdot 81$

$A \approx 254.5 \text{ mi}^2$

13. $A = \pi r^2$

$A = \pi \cdot (2.1)^2$

$A = \pi \cdot 4.41$

$A \approx 13.9 \text{ m}^2$

14. $P(\text{shaded}) = \frac{\text{shaded area}}{\text{area of target}}$

$= \frac{10}{25}$

$= \frac{2}{5}$

15. Area of border = (Total area) − (Area of garden)

Area of garden: $A = \pi r^2$

$A = \pi \cdot (2.3)^2$

$= \pi \cdot (5.29)$

$\approx 16.6 \text{ m}^2$

Total area: $A = \pi r^2$

$A = \pi \cdot (2.8)^2$

$= \pi \cdot 7.84$

$\approx 24.6 \text{ m}^2$

The area of the border is about 24.6 − 16.6 or 8.0 m².

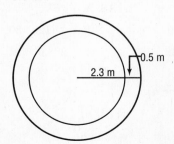

---

16. Top and Bottom: $2(1 \cdot 1) = 2$
Front and Back: $2(1 \cdot 1) = 2$
Two sides: $\quad 2(1 \cdot 1) = 2$
The surface area is $2 + 2 + 2$ or 6 cm^2.

17. Two Bases: $2\left(\frac{1}{2} \cdot \frac{3}{4} \cdot \frac{1}{2}\right) = \frac{3}{8}$
Front: $\quad\quad 1\frac{1}{2} \cdot \frac{5}{8} = \frac{15}{16}$
Bottom: $\quad\quad 1\frac{1}{2} \cdot \frac{3}{4} = 1\frac{1}{8}$
Back: $\quad\quad 1\frac{1}{2} \cdot \frac{5}{8} = \frac{15}{16}$
The surface area is $\frac{3}{8} + \frac{15}{16} + 1\frac{1}{8} + \frac{15}{16}$ or $3\frac{3}{8}$ ft^2.

18. $2(\pi r^2) + 2\pi rh = 2(\pi \cdot 1^2) + 2 \cdot \pi \cdot 1 \cdot 2.3$
$\quad\quad\quad\quad\quad = 2(\pi \cdot 1) + 2 \cdot \pi \cdot 1 \cdot 2.3$
$\quad\quad\quad\quad\quad \approx 6 + 15$
$\quad\quad\quad\quad\quad \approx 21$
The surface area is about 21 m^2.

19. $2(\pi r^2) + 2\pi rh = 2(\pi \cdot 20^2) + 2 \cdot \pi \cdot 20 \cdot 41$
$\quad\quad\quad\quad\quad = 2(\pi \cdot 400) + 2 \cdot \pi \cdot 20 \cdot 41$
$\quad\quad\quad\quad\quad \approx 2513 + 5152$
$\quad\quad\quad\quad\quad \approx 7665$ ft^2
The surface area is about 7665 ft^2.

20. Base: $A = s^2$
$\quad\quad\quad A = 10^2$
$\quad\quad\quad A = 100$ in^2

Side: $A = \frac{1}{2}bh$
$\quad\quad A = \frac{1}{2} \cdot 10 \cdot 8\frac{1}{4}$
$\quad\quad A = 41.25$ in^2

The surface area is $100 + 4(41.25)$ or 265 in^2.

21. Base: $A = \pi r^2$
$\quad\quad\quad A = \pi \cdot 1^2$
$\quad\quad\quad A = \pi \cdot 1$
$\quad\quad\quad A \approx 3.1$ m^2

Surface: $A = \pi rs$
$\quad\quad\quad\quad A = \pi \cdot 1 \cdot 2$
$\quad\quad\quad\quad A \approx 6.3$ m^2

The surface area is about $3.1 + 6.3$ or 9.4 m^2.

22. $V = Bh$
$\quad V = \left(\frac{1}{2} \cdot 5 \cdot 3.4\right) \cdot 12$
$\quad V = 8.5 \cdot 12$
$\quad V = 102$ cm^3

23. $V = Bh$
$\quad V = 166.25 \cdot 20$
$\quad V = 3325$ in^3

24. $V = Bh$
$\quad V = 4 \cdot 4 \cdot 16$
$\quad V = 256$ m^3

25. $V = \pi r^2 h$
$\quad V = \pi \cdot 7^2 \cdot 18$
$\quad V = \pi \cdot 49 \cdot 18$
$\quad V \approx 2770.9$ ft^3

26. $V = \pi r^2 h$
$\quad V = \pi \cdot 5^2 \cdot 22$
$\quad V = \pi \cdot 25 \cdot 22$
$\quad V \approx 1727.9$ m^3

27. $V = \frac{1}{3}Bh$
$\quad V = \frac{1}{3} \cdot 8 \cdot 9 \cdot 21$
$\quad V \approx 504$ m^3

28. $V = \frac{1}{3}\pi r^2 h$
$\quad V = \frac{1}{3} \cdot \pi \cdot 6^2 \cdot 11$
$\quad V = \frac{1}{3} \pi \cdot 36 \cdot 11$
$\quad V \approx 414.7$ in^3

Page 658 Applications and Problem Solving

29. $A = \frac{1}{2}bh$
$\quad A = \frac{1}{2}(36)(48)$
$\quad A = \frac{1}{2}(1728)$
$\quad A = 844$
The area of one of these flags is 864 in^2.

30. a. $2\pi rh = 2 \cdot \pi \cdot 20 \cdot 60$
$\quad\quad\quad\quad \approx 7540$
The area of the curved surface is about 7540 ft^2.

b. $2(\pi r^2) + 2\pi rh = 2(\pi \cdot 20^2) + 2 \cdot \pi \cdot 20 \cdot 60$
$\quad\quad\quad\quad\quad\quad = 2(\pi \cdot 400) + 2 \cdot \pi \cdot 20 \cdot 60$
$\quad\quad\quad\quad\quad\quad \approx 2513 + 7540$
$\quad\quad\quad\quad\quad\quad \approx 10{,}053$
The area to be painted is $10{,}053$ ft^2.
$10{,}053 \div 450 = 22.34$. So, 23 gallons of paint would be needed.

c. It would cost $23(10)$ or $\$230$ to paint the silo.

d. It would cost $2(230)$ or $\$460$ to apply two coats of paint.

31. $V = 6 \cdot 11 \cdot 3$
$\quad V = 198$
There are 198 sugar cubes in the box.

32. 225 mL ≈ 225 cm^3
$\quad\quad V = \pi r^2 h$
$\quad 225 = \pi \cdot 6^2 \cdot h$
$\quad 225 = \pi \cdot 36 \cdot h$
$\quad \frac{225}{\pi \cdot 36} = \frac{\pi \cdot 36 \cdot h}{\pi \cdot 36}$
$\quad\quad 2 \approx h$
She should fill the container to about 2 cm.

33. 6 feet $= 72$ inches; 3 feet $= 36$ inches
$\quad V = \frac{1}{2}(\pi r^2 h)$
$\quad V = \frac{1}{2}(\pi \cdot 72^2 \cdot 36)$
$\quad V = \frac{1}{2}(\pi \cdot 5184 \cdot 36)$
$\quad V \approx 293{,}148$
The volume of the water trough is $293{,}148$ in^3.
$293{,}148 \div 230 \approx 1275$
So, the water trough will hold about 1275 gallons of water.

34. $V = \frac{1}{3}(\pi r^2 h)$
$\quad V = \frac{1}{3} \cdot \pi \cdot 210^2 \cdot 250$
$\quad V = \frac{1}{3} \cdot \pi \cdot 44{,}100 \cdot 250$
$\quad V = 11{,}545{,}353$
About $11{,}545{,}353$ ft^3 of material was removed.

Page 659 Alternative Assessment
1–5. See students' work.

Page 659 Thinking Critically
- cylinder; cylinder
- circle; circle
- See students' work.

Page 659 Portfolio
See students' work.

See students' work.

Ongoing Assessment

Pages 660–661

1. D; $A = \frac{1}{2}h(a + b)$

$A = \frac{1}{2} \cdot 8(12 + 16)$

$A = \frac{1}{2} \cdot 8 \cdot 28$

$A = 112 \text{ ft}^2$

2. B; $s = g + c$

$186 = g + 15$

$186 - 15 = g + 15 - 15$

$171 = g$

3. A; Area of label $= 2\pi rh$

$= 2 \times \pi \times 5 \times 12$

$= \pi \times 10 \times 12$

4. D; $a^5 \cdot a^2 = a^{5+2}$

$= a^7$

5. D; $V = Bh$

$V = \left(\frac{1}{2} \cdot 30 \cdot 40\right) \cdot 60$

$V = 600 \cdot 60$

$V = 36{,}000 \text{ cm}^3$

6. B; $\frac{3}{5}$, 0.7, $\frac{9}{12}$

7. A; $2500 \times 5 \times 2 = 25{,}000$ m

$25{,}000 \div 1000 = 25$

$25{,}000$ m $= 25$ km

8. B

9. C; $4 \times 3 \times 2 \times 1 = 24$

24 ways

10. B; $\frac{12}{x} = \frac{16}{24}$

$12 \cdot 24 = x \cdot 16$

$288 = 16x$

$\frac{288}{16} = \frac{16x}{16}$

$18 = x$

11. C; $C = \pi d$

$C = \pi \cdot 1.2$

$C \approx 3.8$

12. $28 + x + 18 = 180$

$x + 46 = 180$

$x + 46 - 46 = 180 - 46$

$x = 134$

The triangle is obtuse.

13. $\frac{16}{x} = \frac{80}{100}$

$16 \cdot 100 = x \cdot 80$

$1600 = 80x$

$\frac{1600}{80} = \frac{80x}{80}$

$20 = x$

The regular price is $20.

14. The length of the walkway is $14 + 14 + 6 + 6$ or 40 meters long.

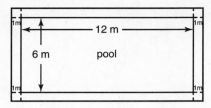

$V = 40 \cdot 1 \cdot 0.2$

$V = 8$

The volume of the concrete is 8 m³.

15. $\frac{104 \text{ miles}}{2 \text{ hours}} = \frac{550 \text{ miles}}{x \text{ hours}}$

$104 \cdot x = 2 \cdot 550$

$104x = 1100$

$\frac{104x}{104} = \frac{1100}{104}$

$x = 10.5$

The trip will take about 10.5 hours.

16. $P(\text{both Kings}) = \frac{4}{52} \cdot \frac{3}{51}$

$= \frac{12}{2652}$

$= \frac{1}{221}$

17. Since $\angle 1$ and $\angle 3$ are vertical angles, they are congruent. So, $m\angle 3 = 108°$;

$\angle 1$ and $\angle 2$ are supplementary. $180 - 108 = 72$. So, $m\angle 2 = 72°$;

Since $\angle 2$ and $\angle 4$ are vertical angles, they are congruent. So, $m\angle 4 = 72°$;

$\angle 1$ and $\angle 5$ are corresponding angles so they are congruent. Thus, $m\angle 5 = 108°$;

$\angle 4$ and $\angle 6$ are alternate interior angles so they are congruent. Thus, $m\angle 6 = 72°$;

$\angle 6$ and $\angle 7$ are supplementary. $180 - 72 = 108$. So, $m\angle 7 = 108°$;

Since $\angle 6$ and $\angle 8$ are vertical angles, they are congruent. So, $m\angle 8 = 72°$.

18. $40 + 140 + 40 + x = 360$

$220 + x = 360$

$220 + x - 220 = 360 - 220$

$x = 140$

19. $p + 52 \geq 106$

$p + 52 - 52 \geq 106 - 52$

$p \geq 54$

20. See students' work.

21. See students' work.

Chapter 13   Applying Algebra to Right Triangles

| 13-1 | Squares and Square Roots |

Pages 666–667   Checking Your Understanding

1. Sample answer: Each positive number has a positive square root and a negative square root.

2.

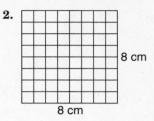

8 cm

8 cm

3. It is the square of 7.

4. Sample answer: Squaring "undoes" taking a square root.

5. **a.** The square has 36 tiles, with 4 left over.
   b. 9 tiles
   c. 6 and 7

6. Since $3 \cdot 3 = 9$, $-\sqrt{9} = -3$.

7. Since $4 \cdot 4 = 16$, $\sqrt{16} = 4$.

8. Since $2 \cdot 2 = 4$, $-\sqrt{4} = -2$.

9. Since $9 \cdot 9 = 18$, $\sqrt{81} = 9$.

10. $\sqrt{64} < \sqrt{79} < \sqrt{81}$
    $\sqrt{8^2} < \sqrt{79} < \sqrt{9^2}$
    $8 < \sqrt{79} < 9$
    $\quad\quad 9$
    Check: $\sqrt{79} \approx 8.9$

11. $-\sqrt{49} < -\sqrt{53} < -\sqrt{64}$
    $-\sqrt{7^2} < -\sqrt{53} < -\sqrt{8^2}$
    $-7 < -\sqrt{53} < -8$
    $\quad\quad -7$
    Check $-\sqrt{53} \approx 7.3$

12. $\sqrt{25} < \sqrt{29} < \sqrt{36}$
    $\sqrt{5^2} < \sqrt{29} < \sqrt{6^2}$
    $5 < \sqrt{29} < 6$
    $\quad\quad 5$
    Check: $\sqrt{29} \approx 5.4$

13. $\sqrt{100} < \sqrt{120} < \sqrt{121}$
    $\sqrt{10^2} < \sqrt{120} < \sqrt{11^2}$
    $10 < \sqrt{120} < 11$
    $\quad\quad 11$
    Check: $\sqrt{120} \approx 11.0$

14. $V = 1.22 \times \sqrt{A}$
    $V = 1.22 \times \sqrt{60,000}$
    $V \approx 298.8$
    The pilot can see about 298.8 miles.

Pages 667–668   Exercises

15. Since $2 \cdot 2 = 4$, $\sqrt{4} = 2$.

16. Since $8 \cdot 8 = 64$, $\sqrt{64} = 8$.

17. Since $3 \cdot 3 = 9$, $\sqrt{9} = 3$

18. Since $5 \cdot 5 = 25$, $-\sqrt{25} = -5$

19. Since $4 \cdot 4 = 16$, $-\sqrt{16} = -4$.

20. Since $9 \cdot 9 = 81$, $-\sqrt{81} = -9$.

21. Since $10 \cdot 10 = 100$, $\sqrt{100} = 10$.

22. Since $1 \cdot 1 = 1$, $\sqrt{1} = 1$.

23. Since $12 \cdot 12 = 144$, $-\sqrt{144} = -12$.

24. Since $13 \cdot 13 = 169$, $\sqrt{169} = 13$.

25. Since $20 \cdot 20 = 400$, $\sqrt{400} = 20$.

26. Since $(1.5)(1.5) = 2.25$, $\sqrt{2.25} = 1.5$.

27. $\sqrt{81} < \sqrt{89} < \sqrt{100}$
    $\sqrt{9^2} < \sqrt{89} < \sqrt{10^2}$
    $9 < \sqrt{89} < 10$
    $\quad\quad 9$
    Check: $\sqrt{89} \approx 9.4$

28. $-\sqrt{36} < -\sqrt{44} < -\sqrt{49}$
    $-\sqrt{6^2} < -\sqrt{44} < -\sqrt{7^2}$
    $-6 < -\sqrt{44} < -7$
    $\quad\quad -7$
    Check: $-\sqrt{44} \approx -6.6$

29. $\sqrt{196} < \sqrt{200} < \sqrt{225}$
    $\sqrt{14^2} < \sqrt{200} < \sqrt{15^2}$
    $14 < \sqrt{200} < 15$
    $\quad\quad 14$
    Check: $\sqrt{200} \approx 14.1$

30. $-\sqrt{169} < -\sqrt{170} < -\sqrt{196}$
    $-\sqrt{13^2} < -\sqrt{170} < -\sqrt{14^2}$
    $-13 < -\sqrt{170} < -14$
    $\quad\quad -13$
    Check: $-\sqrt{170} \approx -13.0$

31. $-\sqrt{81} < -\sqrt{97} < -\sqrt{100}$
    $-\sqrt{9^2} < -\sqrt{97} < -\sqrt{10^2}$
    $-9 < -\sqrt{97} < -10$
    $\quad\quad -10$
    Check: $-\sqrt{97} \approx -9.8$

32. $-\sqrt{4} < -\sqrt{6.76} < -\sqrt{9}$
    $-\sqrt{2^2} < -\sqrt{6.76} < -\sqrt{3^2}$
    $-2 < -\sqrt{6.76} < -3$
    $\quad\quad -3$
    Check: $-\sqrt{6.76} \approx -2.6$

33. $\sqrt{2500} < \sqrt{2600} < \sqrt{2601}$
    $\sqrt{50^2} < \sqrt{2600} < \sqrt{51^2}$
    $50 < \sqrt{2600} < 51$
    $\quad\quad 51$
    Check: $\sqrt{2600} \approx 51.0$

34. Since $25 \cdot 25 = 625$, $\sqrt{625} = 25$.

35. $\sqrt{100} < \sqrt{118} < \sqrt{121}$
    $\sqrt{10^2} < \sqrt{118} < \sqrt{11^2}$
    $10 < \sqrt{118} < 11$
    $\quad\quad 11$
    Check: $\sqrt{118} \approx 10.9$

36. $\sqrt{9} < \sqrt{13.69} < \sqrt{16}$
    $\sqrt{3^2} < \sqrt{13.69} < \sqrt{4^2}$
    $3 < \sqrt{13.69} < 4$
    $\quad\quad 4$
    Check: $\sqrt{13.69} \approx 3.7$

37. $-\sqrt{25} < -\sqrt{26.79} < -\sqrt{36}$
    $-\sqrt{5^2} < -\sqrt{26.79} < -\sqrt{6^2}$
    $-5 < -\sqrt{26.79} < -6$
    $\quad\quad -5$
    Check: $-\sqrt{26.79} \approx -5.2$

38. $-\sqrt{144} < -\sqrt{156.25} < -\sqrt{169}$

$-\sqrt{12^2} < -\sqrt{156.25} < -\sqrt{13^2}$

$-12 < -\sqrt{156.25} < -13$

-12

Check: $-\sqrt{156.25} \approx -12.5$

39. Since $a \cdot a = a^2$, $\sqrt{a^2} = a$.

40. $\sqrt{169} - (-\sqrt{121}) = \sqrt{13^2} - (-\sqrt{11^2})$
$= 13 - (-11)$
$= 13 + 11$
$= 24$

41. $\sqrt{\sqrt{81}} = \sqrt{\sqrt{9^2}}$
$= \sqrt{9}$
$= \sqrt{3^2}$
$= 3$

42. Error message is given; the square root of a negative number is not a real number.

43. Yes; because when a negative number is squared the result is positive.

44. a. $R = \dfrac{s^2}{A}$

$R \cdot A = \dfrac{s^2}{A} \cdot A$

$RA = s^2$

$\sqrt{RA} = \sqrt{s^2}$

$\sqrt{RA} = s$

b. $s = \sqrt{RA}$

$s = \sqrt{(2.7)(30)}$

$s = \sqrt{81}$

$s = \sqrt{9^2}$

$s = 9$

The glider has a wingspan of 9 feet.

45. Area needed: $4 \cdot 100$ or 400 ft^2

$A = s^2$

$400 = s^2$

$\sqrt{400} = \sqrt{s^2}$

$20 = s$

Each side should be 20 feet.

46. $A = \pi r^2$

$0.442 = \pi r^2$

$\dfrac{0.442}{\pi} = \dfrac{\pi r^2}{\pi}$

$0.14 \approx r^2$

$\sqrt{0.14} \approx \sqrt{r^2}$

$0.374 \approx r$

The radius of the pipe is about 0.374 inches. So, the proper size of pipe for the water heater is $2(0.374)$ or about 0.75 inches.

47. $V = \frac{1}{3}Bh$

$V = \frac{1}{3} \cdot 8 \cdot 8 \cdot 9$

$V = 192 \text{ in}^3$

48. $7 \cdot 6 \cdot 5 \cdot 4 \cdot 3 \cdot 2 \cdot 1 = 5040$
5040 ways

49. $28\% = \dfrac{28}{100}$
$= \dfrac{7}{25}$

50. $18 \div 2\frac{1}{2} = \dfrac{18}{1} \div \dfrac{5}{2}$

$= \dfrac{18}{1} \times \dfrac{2}{5}$

$= \dfrac{18 \times 2}{1 \times 5}$

$= \dfrac{36}{5}$

$= 7\frac{1}{5}$

7 boards

51. Sample answer:
$9.2 \times 3.86 \rightarrow 9 \times 4 = 36$
9.2×3.86 is about 36.

52. $2160 = 2 \cdot 1080$
$= 2 \cdot 2 \cdot 540$
$= 2 \cdot 2 \cdot 2 \cdot 270$
$= 2 \cdot 2 \cdot 2 \cdot 2 \cdot 135$
$= 2 \cdot 2 \cdot 2 \cdot 2 \cdot 3 \cdot 45$
$= 2 \cdot 2 \cdot 2 \cdot 2 \cdot 3 \cdot 3 \cdot 15$
$= 2 \cdot 2 \cdot 2 \cdot 2 \cdot 3 \cdot 3 \cdot 3 \cdot 5$

$2160 = 2^4 \times 3^3 \times 5$

53. $a = -15 + (-5)$
$a = -20$

54.

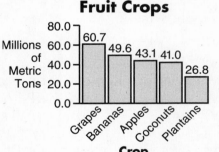

Fruit Crops

Millions of Metric Tons

Grapes 60.7, Bananas 49.6, Apples 43.1, Coconuts 41.0, Plantains 26.8

Crop

Page 668　From the Funny Paper

1. Sample answer: $6 + 3$ can be modeled by adding a length of 6 units and a length of 3 units, but it has nothing to do with the diagonal of a square.

2. No; a square has four equal sides.

3. Sample answer: Use 6 tiles to represent 6 and use 3 tiles to represent 3. There is a total of 9 tiles.

13-2　Problem-Solving Strategy: Use Venn Diagrams

Page 670　Checking Your Understanding

1. States that produce more than 100 million bushels of all three crops.

2. 16 states

3. **Dessert Preference**

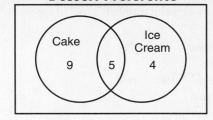

$9 + 5 + 4 = 18$
18 people

4. $5 + 4 + 15 + 3 + 8 + 2 + 7 = 44$
44 communities

Pages 670–671   Exercises

5.

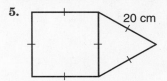

20 cm

$20 + 20 + 20 + 20 + 20 = 100$
The perimeter is 100 cm.

6. **TV Preference**

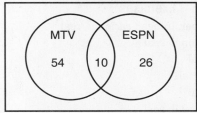

MTV: $64 - 10 = 54$
ESPN: $36 - 10 = 26$
$150 - (54 + 26 + 10) = 150 - 90$
$ = 60$

60 people

7.

6 cuts

10 cuts

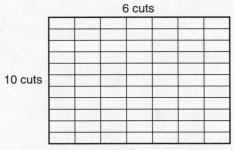

6 cuts: 7 pieces along the length
10 cuts: 11 pieces along the width
$7 \cdot 11 = 77$
77 pieces

8.
Pages yet to read ⟶ 20
Undo the half ⟶ $\times\ 2$
 40
Undo the 6 ⟶ $+\ 6$
 46
Undo the 30 ⟶ $+\ 30$
 76
Undo the half ⟶ $+\ 2$
 152

There are 152 pages in the book.

9. $85 + 65 + 110 = 260$; So, the area where the circles for *Seventeen* and *Elle* overlap contains $260 - 250$ or 10. Therefore, 10 girls read both.

Magazine Preference

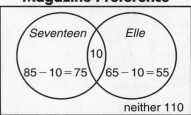

neither 110

10. **Pet Preference**

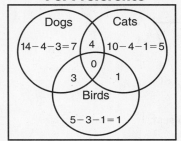

Students without pets = (total students)
 − (students with pets)

Students with pets:
$7 + 5 + 1 + 4 + 3 + 1 = 21$
So, $26 - 21$ or 5 students do not have pets.

11. **Vacation Preference**

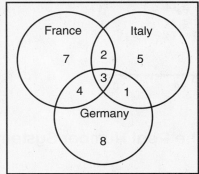

$11 - (2 + 3 + 5)$ or 1 student wanted to visit Italy and Germany. $16 - (8 + 1 + 3)$ or 4 students wanted to visit Germany and France. So, $16 - (4 + 2 + 3)$ or 7 students wanted to visit France.

12.

Quadrilaterals

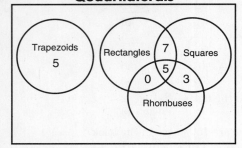

$5 + 7 + 5 + 3 = 20$
Least number of figures is 20.

13.

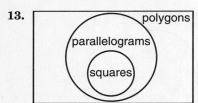

14. Since $11 \cdot 11 = 121$, $-\sqrt{121} = -11$.

15. A rhombus is a quadrilateral with four congruent sides.

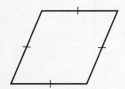

16. 6 months = 0.5 year
$I = prt$
$I = (800)(0.0575)(0.5)$
$I = \$23$

17. $\quad 2x - 5 = 48$
$2x - 5 + 5 = 48 + 5$
$\quad\quad 2x = 53$
$\quad\quad \frac{2x}{2} = \frac{53}{2}$
$\quad\quad\quad x = 26.5$

18. $\quad n - (-20) \geq 14$
$\quad\quad n + 20 \geq 14$
$n + 20 - 20 \geq 14 - 20$
$\quad\quad\quad n \geq -6$

```
  <-+--+--+--+--+--+--+--+->
   -8   -6   -4   -2    0
```

13-3 | **The Real Number System**

Page 674   Checking Your Understanding

1. Sample answer: Rational numbers can be named by terminating or repeating decimals and irrational numbers cannot.

2. Sample answer: Yes; $\sqrt{16}$ is 4 which is both an integer and a rational number. Also, all integers are rational numbers.

3. Sample answer: $-\sqrt{111}$

4. rational, real

5. whole, integer, rational, real

6. irrational, real

7. rational, real

8. $m^2 = 49$
$m = \sqrt{49}$ or $m = -\sqrt{81}$
$m = 7$ or $m = -7$

9. $r^2 = 361$
$r = \sqrt{361}$ or $r = -\sqrt{361}$
$r = 19$ or $r = -19$

10. $t^2 = 1$
$t = \sqrt{1}$ or $t = -\sqrt{1}$
$t = 1$ or $t = -1$

11. $n^2 = 17$
$n = \sqrt{17}$ or $n = -\sqrt{17}$
$n \approx 4.1$ or $n \approx -4.1$

12. $\quad R = \frac{s^2}{A}$
$\quad 2.5 = \frac{s^2}{120}$
$(2.5)120 = \left(\frac{s^2}{120}\right)120$
$\quad\quad 300 = s^2$
$\quad \sqrt{300} = s$
$\quad 17.3 \approx s$
The wingspan is about 17.3 feet.

Pages 674–675   Exercises

13. whole number, integer, rational, real

14. integer, rational, real

15. rational, real

16. irrational, real

17. rational, real

18. integer, rational, real

19. irrational, real

20. rational, real

21. irrational, real

22. integer, rational, real

23. rational, real

24. irrational, real

25. $r^2 = 36$
$r = \sqrt{36}$ or $r = -\sqrt{36}$
$r = 6$ or $r = -6$

26. $x^2 = 64$
$x = \sqrt{64}$ or $x = -\sqrt{64}$
$x = 8$ or $x = -8$

27. $y^2 = 12$
$y = \sqrt{12}$ or $y = -\sqrt{12}$
$y \approx 3.5$ or $y \approx -3.5$

28. $169 = m^2$
$m^2 = 169$
$m = \sqrt{169}$ or
$\quad\quad m = -\sqrt{169}$
$m = 13$ or -13

29. $n^2 = 120$
$n = \sqrt{120}$ or $n = -\sqrt{120}$
$n \approx 11.0$ or $n \approx -11.0$

30. $f^2 = 200$
$f = \sqrt{200}$ or $f = -\sqrt{200}$
$f \approx 14.1$ or $f \approx -14.1$

31. $180 = j^2$
$j^2 = 180$
$j = \sqrt{180}$ or $j = -\sqrt{180}$
$j \approx 13.4$ or $j \approx -13.4$

32. $p^2 = 1.44$
$p = \sqrt{1.44}$ or $p = -\sqrt{1.44}$
$p = 1.2$ or $p = -1.2$

33. $0.0004 = s^2$
$s^2 = 0.004$
$s = \sqrt{0.004}$ or $s = \sqrt{-0.004}$
$s = 0.02$ or $s = -0.02$

34. $h^2 = 240$
$h = \sqrt{240}$ or $h = \sqrt{-240}$
$h \approx 15.5$ or $h \approx -15.5$

35. $400 = q^2$
$q^2 = 400$
$q = \sqrt{400}$ or $q = -\sqrt{400}$
$q = 20$ or $q = -20$

36. $a^2 = 90{,}000$
$a = \sqrt{90{,}000}$ or $a = -\sqrt{90{,}000}$
$a = 300$ or $a = -300$

37. $(-b)^2 = 81$
$b^2 = 81$
$b = \sqrt{81}$ or $b = -\sqrt{81}$
$b = 9$ or $b = -9$

38. $c^2 - 3^2 = \sqrt{16^2}$
$c^2 - 9 = 16$
$c^2 - 9 + 9 = 16 + 9$
$c^2 = 25$
$c = \sqrt{25}$ or $c = \sqrt{-25}$
$c = 5$ or $c = -5$

39. $\sqrt{81} = d^2$
$d^2 = \sqrt{81}$
$d^2 = 9$
$d = \sqrt{9}$ or $d = -\sqrt{9}$
$d = 3$ or $d = -3$

40. Let $x =$ width, then $3x =$ length
$A = \ell \cdot w$
$192 = 3x \cdot x$
$192 = 3x^2$
$\frac{192}{3} = \frac{3x^2}{3}$
$64 = x^2$
$\sqrt{64} = x$
$8 = x$
$x = 8, 3x = 24$
The rectangle is 8 ft by 24 ft.

41. Yes; Sample answer: $\sqrt{2} \times \sqrt{2} = 2$

42. $t^2 = \frac{d^3}{216}$
$t^2 = \frac{6^3}{216}$
$t^2 = \frac{216}{216}$
$t^2 = 1$
$t = \sqrt{1}$
$t = 1$
The storm will last 1 hour.

43. $100 + 80 + 60 = 240;$

So, $s = \frac{1}{2}(240)$ or 120.
Let $a = 60$, $b = 80$, and $c = 100$.
$A = \sqrt{s(s - a)(s - b)(s - c)}$
$A = \sqrt{120(120 - 60)(120 - 80)(120 - 100)}$
$A = \sqrt{120(60)(40)(20)}$
$A = \sqrt{5{,}760{,}000}$
$A = 2400$
The area of the triangle is 2400 ft^2.

44. $d = 0.5gt^2$
$55 = (0.5)(32)t^2$
$55 = 16t^2$
$\frac{55}{16} = \frac{16t^2}{16}$
$3.43 = t^2$
$\sqrt{3.43} = t$
$1.85 \approx t$
It will take about 1.85 seconds for the ball to hit the ground.

45. See students' work.

46.

Program Preference

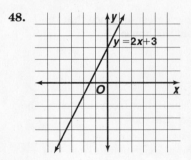

News: $46 - 15 = 31$
Game shows: $34 - 15 = 19$
$120 - (31 + 19 + 15) = 55$
55 people

47. $V = \pi r^2 h$
$V = \pi \cdot (12.5)^2 \cdot 10$
$V = \pi \cdot 156.25 \cdot 10$
$V \approx 4908.7$ cm^3

48.

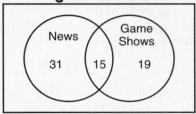

49. $v = \left(\frac{3}{7}\right)\left(-\frac{14}{15}\right)$
$v = \frac{-42}{105}$
$v = -\frac{2}{5}$

50. $36 = 2 \cdot 2 \cdot 3 \cdot 3$
$-30ab = -1 \cdot 2 \cdot 3 \cdot 5 \cdot a \cdot b$
The GCF is $2 \cdot 3$ or 6.

51. $4cd = 4(-2)(-9)$
$= 72$

52. $7(a + b) - 2(3a + 4b) = 7a + 7b - 6a - 8b$
$= 7a - 6a + 7b - 8b$
$= (7 - 6)a + (7 - 8)b$
$= 1a + (-1)b$
$= 1a - 1b$
$= a - b$

13-4   The Pythagorean Theorem

Page 676   Your Turn

See students' work.

a. Draw a 3-by-3 square around the given square so that the sides of the larger square contain the vertices of the given square. The area of the 3-by-3 square is 9 square units. The four triangles that are formed by the sides of the squares each have an area of $\frac{1}{2}(1 \cdot 2)$ or 1 square unit. Thus, the area of the square is $9 - 4(1)$ or 5 square units.

b. right triangle

c. 1 square unit; 4 square units

d. The area of the larger square equals the sum of the areas of the two smaller areas.

e. $\sqrt{5}$

Page 679   Checking Your Understanding

1. Sample answer: Square the hypotenuse and subtract the square of the leg, then find the square root of the result.

2. yes; $6^2 + 8^2 = 10^2$

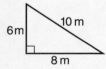

3. Let x represent the greatest distance that the ladder could be from the house.
$x^2 + 24^2 = 26^2$
$x^2 + 576 = 676$
$x^2 = 100$
$x = 10$
If the ladder is placed 10 feet from the house, the ladder will just reach the roof.

4. See students' diagrams.
Sample formula: length of hypotenuse $= \sqrt{(4 + 4)}$

5. $x^2 = 12^2 + 16^2$
$x^2 = 144 + 256$
$x^2 = 400$
$x = \sqrt{400}$
$x \approx 20$ in.

6. $4^2 = x^2 + 2^2$
$16 = x^2 + 4$
$16 - 4 = x^2 + 4 - 4$
$12 = x^2$
$\sqrt{12} = x$
$3.5 \text{ ft} \approx x$

7. $30^2 = 21^2 + b^2$
$900 = 441 + b^2$
$900 - 441 = 441 + b^2 - 441$
$459 = b^2$
$\sqrt{459} = b$
$21.4 \text{ km} \approx b$

8. $12^2 = a^2 + 10^2$
$144 = a^2 + 100$
$144 - 100 = a^2 + 100 - 100$
$44 = a^2$
$\sqrt{44} = a$
$6.6 \text{ in.} \approx a$

9. $c^2 = a^2 + b^2$
$c^2 = 3^2 + 4^2$
$c^2 = 9 + 16$
$c^2 = 25$
$c = \sqrt{25}$
$c = 5$

10. $c^2 = a^2 + b^2$
$7^2 = 3^2 + b^2$
$49 = 9 + b^2$
$49 - 9 = 9 + b^2 - 9$
$40 = b^2$
$\sqrt{40} = b$
$6.3 \approx b$

11. $c^2 = a^2 + b^2$
$35^2 = a^2 + 12^2$
$1225 = a^2 + 144$
$1225 - 144 = a^2 + 144 - 144$
$1081 = a^2$
$\sqrt{1081} = a$
$32.9 \approx a$

12. $c^2 = a^2 + b^2$
$c^2 = 15^2 + (16.7)^2$
$c^2 = 225 + 278.89$
$c^2 = 503.89$
$c = \sqrt{503.89}$
$c \approx 22.4$

13. $c^2 = a^2 + b^2$
$15^2 \stackrel{?}{=} 9^2 + 12^2$
$225 \stackrel{?}{=} 81 + 144$
$225 = 225$
yes

14. $c^2 = a^2 + b^2$
$12^2 \stackrel{?}{=} 6^2 + 7^2$
$144 \stackrel{?}{=} 36 + 49$
$144 \neq 85$
no

15. $c^2 = a^2 + b^2$
$c^2 = 90^2 + 90^2$
$c^2 = 8100 + 8100$
$c^2 = 16{,}200$
$c = \sqrt{16{,}200}$
$c \approx 127.3$
The distance between home and second base is about 127.3 ft.

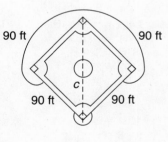

Pages 680–681   Exercises

16. $x^2 = 60^2 + 35^2$
$x^2 = 3600 + 1225$
$x^2 = 4825$
$x = \sqrt{4825}$
$x \approx 69.5$

17. $4^2 = x^2 + 2^2$
$16 = x^2 + 4$
$16 - 4 = x^2 + 4 - 4$
$12 = x^2$
$\sqrt{12} = x$
$3.5 = x$

18.
$$x^2 = 5^2 + 6^2$$
$$x^2 = 25 + 36$$
$$x^2 = 61$$
$$x = \sqrt{61}$$
$$x \approx 7.8$$

19.
$$c^2 = a^2 + b^2$$
$$40^2 = a^2 + 30^2$$
$$1600 = a^2 + 900$$
$$1600 - 900 = a^2 + 900 - 900$$
$$700 = a^2$$
$$\sqrt{700} = a$$
$$26.5 \text{ m} \approx a$$

20.
$$c^2 = a^2 + b^2$$
$$c^2 = 8^2 + (7.5)^2$$
$$c^2 = 64 + 56.25$$
$$c^2 = 120.25$$
$$c = \sqrt{120.25}$$
$$c \approx 11.0 \text{ ft}$$

21.
$$c^2 = a^2 + b^2$$
$$20^2 = 4^2 + b^2$$
$$400 = 16 + b^2$$
$$400 - 16 = 16 + b^2 - 16$$
$$384 = b^2$$
$$\sqrt{384} = b$$
$$19.6 \text{ ft} \approx b$$

22.
$$c^2 = a^2 + b^2$$
$$c^2 = 5^2 + 8^2$$
$$c^2 = 25 + 64$$
$$c^2 = 89$$
$$c = \sqrt{89}$$
$$c \approx 9.4 \text{ mi}$$

23.
$$c^2 = a^2 + b^2$$
$$c^2 = 12^2 + 16^2$$
$$c^2 = 144 + 256$$
$$c^2 = 400$$
$$c = \sqrt{400}$$
$$c = 20$$

24.
$$c^2 = a^2 + b^2$$
$$29^2 = a^2 + 21^2$$
$$841 = a^2 + 441$$
$$841 - 441 = a^2 + 441 - 441$$
$$400 = a^2$$
$$\sqrt{400} = a$$
$$20 = a$$

25.
$$c^2 = a^2 + b^2$$
$$c^2 = 2^2 + 5^2$$
$$c^2 = 4 + 25$$
$$c^2 = 29$$
$$c = \sqrt{29}$$
$$c \approx 5.4$$

26.
$$c^2 = a^2 + b^2$$
$$10^2 = 5^2 + b^2$$
$$100 = 25 + b^2$$
$$100 - 25 = 25 + b^2 - 25$$
$$75 = b^2$$
$$\sqrt{75} = b$$
$$8.7 \approx b$$

27.
$$c^2 = a^2 + b^2$$
$$9^2 = 7^2 + b^2$$
$$81 = 49 + b^2$$
$$81 - 49 = 49 + b^2 - 49$$
$$32 = b^2$$
$$\sqrt{32} = b$$
$$5.7 \approx b$$

28.
$$c^2 = a^2 + b^2$$
$$7^2 = a^2 + 3^2$$
$$49 = a^2 + 9$$
$$49 - 9 = a^2 + 9 - 9$$
$$40 = a^2$$
$$\sqrt{40} = a$$
$$6.3 \approx a$$

29.
$$c^2 = a^2 + b^2$$
$$c^2 = 7^2 + 7^2$$
$$c^2 = 49 + 49$$
$$c^2 = 98$$
$$c = \sqrt{98}$$
$$c \approx 9.9$$

30.
$$c^2 = a^2 + b^2$$
$$85^2 = a^2 + 36^2$$
$$7225 = a^2 + 1296$$
$$7225 - 1296 = a^2 + 1296 - 1296$$
$$5929 = a^2$$
$$\sqrt{5929} = a$$
$$77 = a$$

31.
$$c^2 = a^2 + b^2$$
$$c^2 = 14^2 + 15^2$$
$$c^2 = 196 + 225$$
$$c^2 = 421$$
$$c = \sqrt{421}$$
$$c \approx 20.5$$

32.
$$c^2 = a^2 + b^2$$
$$181^2 = 180^2 + b^2$$
$$32{,}761 = 32{,}400 + b^2$$
$$32{,}761 - 32{,}400 = 32{,}400 + b^2 - 32{,}400$$
$$361 = b^2$$
$$\sqrt{361} = b$$
$$19 = b$$

33.
$$c^2 = a^2 + b^2$$
$$6^2 = \left(\sqrt{11}\right)^2 + b^2$$
$$36 = 11 + b^2$$
$$36 - 11 = 11 + b^2 - 11$$
$$25 = b^2$$
$$\sqrt{25} = b$$
$$5 = b$$

34.
$$c^2 = a^2 + b^2$$
$$\left(\sqrt{233}\right)^2 = a^2 + 13^2$$
$$233 = a^2 + 169$$
$$233 - 169 = a^2 + 169 - 169$$
$$64 = a^2$$
$$\sqrt{64} = a$$
$$8 = a$$

35.
$$c^2 = a^2 + b^2$$
$$10^2 \stackrel{?}{=} 8^2 + 9^2$$
$$100 \stackrel{?}{=} 64 + 81$$
$$100 \neq 145$$
no

36.
$$c^2 = a^2 + b^2$$
$$26^2 \stackrel{?}{=} 10^2 + 24^2$$
$$676 \stackrel{?}{=} 100 + 576$$
$$676 = 676$$
yes

37.
$$c^2 = a^2 + b^2$$
$$15^2 \stackrel{?}{=} 12^2 + 9^2$$
$$225 \stackrel{?}{=} 144 + 81$$
$$225 = 225$$
yes

38.
$$c^2 = a^2 + b^2$$
$$8^2 \stackrel{?}{=} 6^2 + 7^2$$
$$64 \stackrel{?}{=} 36 + 49$$
$$64 \neq 85$$
no

39.
$$c^2 = a^2 + b^2$$
$$30^2 \stackrel{?}{=} 18^2 + \left(\sqrt{24}\right)^2$$
$$900 \stackrel{?}{=} 324 + 24$$
$$900 \neq 348$$
no

40.
$$c^2 = a^2 + b^2$$
$$16^2 \stackrel{?}{=} \left(\sqrt{31}\right)^2 + 15^2$$
$$256 \stackrel{?}{=} 31 + 225$$
$$256 = 256$$
yes

41.
$A = s^2$
$72 = s^2$
$\sqrt{72} = s$
If the area is 72 m², then the length of the sides of the square is $\sqrt{72}$ m.

So,
$c^2 = a^2 + b^2$
$c^2 = \left(\sqrt{72}\right)^2 + \left(\sqrt{72}\right)^2$
$c^2 = 72 + 72$
$c^2 = 144$
$c = \sqrt{144}$
$c = 12$
The diagonal is 12 m.

42. First, find the diagonal of a side.
$c^2 = a^2 + b^2$
$c^2 = 3^2 + 3^2$
$c^2 = 9 + 9$
$c^2 = 18$
$c = \sqrt{18}$

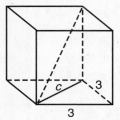

Then, find the diagonal of the cube.
$c^2 = a^2 + b^2$
$c^2 = \left(\sqrt{18}\right)^2 + 3^2$
$c^2 = 18 + 9$
$c^2 = 27$
$c = \sqrt{27}$
$c \approx 5.2$

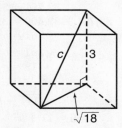

The diagonal of the cube is $\sqrt{27}$ or about 5.2 feet.

43.
$m\overline{BC} = 8 - 5 = 3$
$m\overline{BD} = 5 - 1 = 4$
$c^2 = a^2 + b^2$
$\left(m\overline{CD}\right)^2 = \left(m\overline{BC}\right)^2 + \left(m\overline{BD}\right)^2$
$\left(m\overline{CD}\right)^2 = 3^2 + 4^2$
$\left(m\overline{CD}\right)^2 = 9 + 16$
$\left(m\overline{CD}\right)^2 = 25$
$m\overline{CD} = \sqrt{25}$
$m\overline{CD} = 5$

44. a.
$\frac{1}{3} = \frac{x}{15}$
$1 \cdot 15 = 3 \cdot x$
$15 = 3x$
$\frac{15}{3} = \frac{3x}{3}$
$5 = x$
5 feet

b.
$c^2 = a^2 + b^2$
$15^2 = 5^2 + b^2$
$225 = 25 + b^2$
$225 - 25 = 25 + b^2 - 25$
$200 = b^2$
$\sqrt{200} = b$
$14.1 \approx b$
The ladder can safely reach about 14.1 feet.

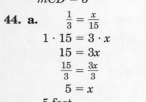

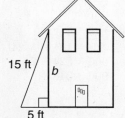

45.
$c^2 = a^2 + b^2$
$c^2 = 20^2 + 15^2$
$c^2 = 400 + 225$
$c^2 = 625$
$c = \sqrt{625}$
$c = 25$
Gracia is 25 km from the starting point of her hike.

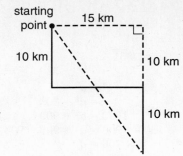

46.
$c^2 = a^2 + b^2$
$24^2 = 6^2 + b^2$
$576 = 36 + b^2$
$576 - 36 = 36 + b^2 - 36$
$540 = b^2$
$\sqrt{540} = b$
$23.2 \approx b$
The height of the mast is about 23.2 feet.

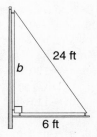

47.
$x^2 = 2.5$
$x = \sqrt{2.5}$
$x \approx 1.6$

48.

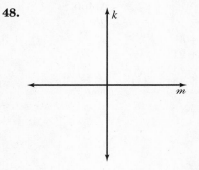

49.
$g(x) = -x + 4$
$g(-1) = -(-1) + 4$
$\quad = 1 + 4$
$\quad = 5$

50.
$5 - 2n = 4n + 41$
$5 - 2n - 4n = 4n - 4n + 41$
$5 - 6n = 41$
$5 - 5 - 6n = 41 - 5$
$-6n = 36$
$\frac{-6n}{-6} = \frac{36}{-6}$
$n = -6$

51.
$\left(\frac{2}{3}\right)^2 = x$
$\left(\frac{2}{3}\right)\left(\frac{2}{3}\right) = x$
$\frac{4}{9} = x$

52.

Day	Number of Laps
1	1 or 2^0
2	2 or 2^1
3	4 or 2^2
4	8 or 2^3
5	16 or 2^4
6	32 or 2^5
7	64 or 2^6

She should swim 64 laps on the seventh day.

53. $6b = 120$ What number
$6(20) = 120$ times 6 is 120?
$b = 20$

54. $3[4(6-2)-5] = 3[4(4)-5]$
$= 3[16-5]$
$= 3 \cdot 11$
$= 33$

Page 681   Self Test

1. Since $6 \cdot 6 = 36$, $\sqrt{36} = 6$.

2. Since $11 \cdot 11 = 121$, $\sqrt{121} = 11$.

3. Since $10 \cdot 10 = 100$, $-\sqrt{100} = -10$.

4.

Sports Preference

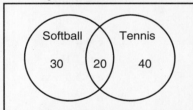

Tennis: $60 - 20 = 40$
Softball: $50 - 20 = 30$
$120 - (40 + 30 + 20) = 120 - 90$
$= 30$

30 students

5. $x^2 = 144$
$x = \sqrt{144}$ or $x = -\sqrt{144}$
$x = 12$ or $x = -12$

6. $y^2 = 50$
$y = \sqrt{50}$ or $y = -\sqrt{50}$
$y \approx 7.1$ or $y \approx -7.1$

7. $g^2 = 40$
$g = \sqrt{40}$ or $g = -\sqrt{40}$
$g \approx 6.3$ or $g \approx -6.3$

8. $c^2 = a^2 + b^2$
$c^2 = 12^2 + 16^2$
$c^2 = 144 + 256$
$c^2 = 400$
$c = \sqrt{400}$
$c = 20$

9. $c^2 = a^2 + b^2$
$65^2 = a^2 + 63^2$
$4225 = a^2 + 3969$
$4225 - 3969 = a^2 + 3969 - 3969$
$256 = a^2$
$\sqrt{256} = a$
$16 = a$

10. $c^2 = a^2 + b^2$
$39^2 = 15^2 + b^2$
$1521 = 225 + b^2$
$1521 - 225 = 225 + b^2 - 225$
$1296 = b^2$
$\sqrt{1296} = b$
$36 = b$

13-4B   Math Lab: Graphing Irrational Numbers

Pages 682   Your Turn

$\sqrt{8}$:

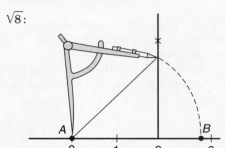

1. Sample answer: Use the procedure in the activity, drawing a right triangle with legs 1 and 3 units long. Then use a compass to find the distance $-\sqrt{10}$ on the x-axis.

2. Sample answer: Use the procedure in the activity, drawing a right triangle with both legs 1 unit long.

3. Sample answer: Use the procedure in the activity, drawing a right triangle with legs 1 unit and 2 units long; or use the procedure in the activity to find the lengths $\sqrt{2}$ and $\sqrt{3}$ and then use those lengths as the legs of a right triangle.

4. Sample asnwer: Use $\sqrt{2}$ as one leg of a right triangle and 1 unit as the other leg in the procedure in the activity.

5. Step 1: Draw a triangle with legs 2 and 4 units long.

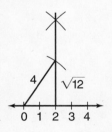

Step 2: Transfer $\sqrt{12}$ to the number line.

13-5 Special Right Triangles

Page 683 Your Turn

See students' work.

a. The length of the hypotenuse is $\sqrt{2}$ times the length of a leg.

b. They are opposite each other.

c. The hypotenuse is twice as long.

Pages 684–685 Checking Your Understanding

1. Sample answer: Multiply the measure of a leg by $\sqrt{2}$.

2. The length of the side opposite the 30° angle is one-half the length of the hypotenuse. So, the length of the hypotenuse is 2(5) or 10 m.

The length of the side opposite the 60° angle is $\sqrt{3}$ times the length of the other leg. So, the length of the side opposite the 60° angle is $\sqrt{3} \cdot 5$ or about 8.66 m.

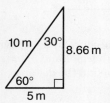

3. $c = a\sqrt{2}$
$c = 1\sqrt{2}$
$c \approx 1.4$ yd

4. $c = a\sqrt{2}$
$c = 9.5\sqrt{2}$
$c \approx 13.4$ m

5. $a = \frac{1}{2}c$
$a = \frac{1}{2}(18)$
$a = 9$ m

6. $a = \frac{1}{2}c$
$a = \frac{1}{2}(6\frac{1}{2})$
$a = \frac{1}{2}(\frac{13}{2})$
$a = \frac{13}{4}$
$a = 3\frac{1}{4}$ in.

7. In a 45°–45° right triangle the lengths of the legs are congruent. So, $a = 3$.
$c = a\sqrt{2}$
$c = 3\sqrt{2}$
$c \approx 4.2$
$a = 3$ m, $c \approx 4.2$ m

8. $a = \frac{1}{2}c$
$5 = \frac{1}{2}c$
$2(5) = 2(\frac{1}{2})c$
$10 = c$
$b = a\sqrt{3}$
$b = 5\sqrt{3}$
$b \approx 8.7$
$c = 10$ yd, $b \approx 8.7$ yd

9. $a = \frac{1}{2}c$
$a = \frac{1}{2}(12)$
$a = 6$
$b = a\sqrt{3}$
$b = 6\sqrt{3}$
$b \approx 10.4$
$a = 6$ m, $b \approx 10.4$ m

10. a. $a = \frac{1}{2}c$
$4 = \frac{1}{2}c$
$2(4) = 2(\frac{1}{2})c$
$8 = c$
The rope is 8 feet long.

b. $b = a\sqrt{3}$
$b = 4\sqrt{3}$
$b \approx 7.0$

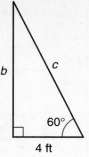

The tent pole is about 7 feet tall.

Pages 685–686 Exercises

11. In a 45°–45° right triangle the lengths of the legs are congruent. So, the length of the other leg is 15 cm.

12. a. $a = \frac{1}{2}c$
$3 = \frac{1}{2}c$
$2(3) = 2(\frac{1}{2})c$
$6 = c$
6 inches

b. $b = a\sqrt{3}$
$b = 3\sqrt{3}$
$b \approx 5.2$
about 5.2 inches

13. $c = a\sqrt{2}$
$c = 15\sqrt{2}$
$c = 21.2$ cm

14. $c = a\sqrt{2}$
$c = 7\sqrt{2}$
$c \approx 9.9$ yd

15. $c = a\sqrt{2}$
$c = 5.2\sqrt{2}$
$c \approx 7.4$ m

16. $c = a\sqrt{2}$
$c = 2\frac{1}{2}\sqrt{2}$
$c \approx 3.5$ ft

17. $c = a\sqrt{2}$
$c = 6.9\sqrt{2}$
$c \approx 9.8$ in.

18. $c = a\sqrt{2}$
$c = 4.1\sqrt{2}$
$c \approx 5.8$ mm

19. $a = \frac{1}{2}c$
$a = \frac{1}{2}(48)$
$a = 24$ in.

20. $a = \frac{1}{2}c$
$a = \frac{1}{2}(11)$
$a = 5.5$ yd

21. $a = \frac{1}{2}c$
$a = \frac{1}{2}(\frac{1}{4})$
$a = \frac{1}{8}$ mi

22. $a = \frac{1}{2}c$
$a = \frac{1}{2}(3000)$
$a = 1500$ m

23. $a = \frac{1}{2}c$
$a = \frac{1}{2}(4.63)$
$a = 2.315$ cm

24. $a = \frac{1}{2}c$
$a = \frac{1}{2}(13)$
$a = 6.5$ mm

25. $b = a\sqrt{3}$

$14 = a\sqrt{3}$

$\dfrac{14}{\sqrt{3}} = \dfrac{a\sqrt{3}}{\sqrt{3}}$

$8.1 \approx a$

$a = \dfrac{1}{2}c$

$8.1 \approx \dfrac{1}{2}c$

$2(8.1) \approx 2\left(\dfrac{1}{2}\right)c$

$16.2 \approx c$

$a \approx 8.1$ cm, $c \approx 16.2$ cm

26. In a 45°–45° right triangle the lengths of the legs are congruent. So, $b = 8.5$.

$c = a\sqrt{2}$

$c = 8.5\sqrt{2}$

$c \approx 12.0$

$b = 8.5$ m, $c \approx 12.0$ m

27. $a = \dfrac{1}{2}c$

$a = \dfrac{1}{2}(12)$

$a = 6$

$b = a\sqrt{3}$

$b = 6\sqrt{3}$

$b \approx 10.4$

$a = 6$ in., $b \approx 10.4$ in.

28. $a = \dfrac{1}{2}c$

$a = \dfrac{1}{2}(8)$

$a = 4$

$b = a\sqrt{3}$

$b = 4\sqrt{3}$

$b \approx 6.9$

$a = 4$ ft, $b \approx 6.9$ ft

29. In a 45°–45° right triangle the lengths of the legs are congruent. So, $b = 5$.

$c = a\sqrt{2}$

$c = 5\sqrt{2}$

$c \approx 7.1$

$b = 5$ yd, $c \approx 7.1$ yd

30. $c = a\sqrt{2}$

$c = 4\sqrt{2}$

$c \approx 5.7$

Since the lengths of the legs in a 45°–45° right triangle are congruent, $b = a = 4$.

$b = 4$ cm, $c \approx 5.7$ cm

31. $c = a\sqrt{2}$

$5.6 = a\sqrt{2}$

$\dfrac{5.6}{\sqrt{2}} = a\dfrac{\sqrt{2}}{\sqrt{2}}$

$4 \approx a$

Since the triangle is a 45°–45° right triangle, they legs are congruent. So, $b \approx 4$.

$a \approx 4$ m, $b \approx 4$m

32. $a = \dfrac{1}{2}c$

$a = \dfrac{1}{2}(3)$

$a = 1.5$

$b = a\sqrt{3}$

$b = 1.5\sqrt{3}$

$b \approx 2.6$

$a = 1.5$ in., $b \approx 2.6$ in.

33. $a = \dfrac{1}{2}c$

$a = \dfrac{1}{2}(11)$

$a = \dfrac{11}{2}$

$a = 5.5$

$b = a\sqrt{3}$

$b = 5.5\sqrt{3}$

$b \approx 9.5$

$a = 5.5$ km, $b \approx 9.5$ km

34. In a 45°–45° right triangle the lengths of the legs are congruent. So, $a = b$.

$c^2 = a^2 + b^2$

$c^2 = a^2 + a^2$

$12^2 = 2a^2$

$144 = 2a^2$

$\dfrac{144}{2} = \dfrac{2a^2}{2}$

$72 = a^2$

$\sqrt{72} = a$

$8.5 \approx a$

The length of each of the other sides is about 8.5 cm long.

35. The altitude of the triangle forms two 30°–60° right triangles, $\triangle KXL$ and $\triangle JXK$.

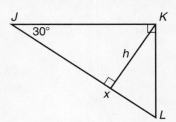

In $\triangle JXK$, if h represents the side opposite the 30° angle then the hypotenuse, $\overline{JK}$, is twice as long as h. So, $\overline{JK} = 2(5)$ or 10 yds. In $\triangle JKL$, $\overline{KL}$ is the side opposite the 30° angle. Therefore,

$\overline{JK} = \sqrt{3} \cdot \overline{KL}$

$10 = \sqrt{3} \cdot \overline{KL}$

$\dfrac{10}{\sqrt{3}} = \dfrac{\sqrt{3} \cdot \overline{KL}}{\sqrt{3}}$

$5.8 \approx \overline{KL}$

The length of $\overline{KL}$ is about 5.8 yards.

36. First, find the length of the sides of the square.

$A = s^2$

$900 = s^2$

$\sqrt{900} = s$

$30 = s$

Find the length of the diagonal.

$c^2 = a^2 + b^2$

$c^2 = 30^2 + 30^2$

$c^2 = 900 + 900$

$c^2 = 1800$

$c = \sqrt{1800}$

$c \approx 42.4$

The length of each of the diagonals is about 42.4 ft.

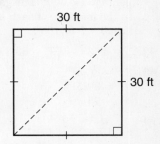

30 ft

30 ft

37. Let a = height of swing set

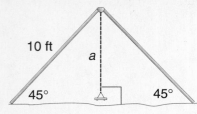

$$c = a\sqrt{2}$$
$$10 = a\sqrt{2}$$
$$\frac{10}{\sqrt{2}} = \frac{a\sqrt{2}}{\sqrt{2}}$$
$$7.07 \approx a$$

The height of the swing set is about 7.07 feet.

38. Let b = height of house

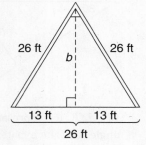

$$c^2 = a^2 + b^2$$
$$26^2 = 13^2 + b^2$$
$$676 = 169 + b^2$$
$$676 - 169 = 169 + b^2$$
$$\qquad\qquad - 169$$
$$507 = b^2$$
$$\sqrt{507} = b$$
$$22.5 \approx b$$

The height of the house is about 22.5 feet.

39. $c^2 = a^2 + b^2$
$c^2 = 20^2 + 12^2$
$c^2 = 400 + 144$
$c^2 = 544$
$c = \sqrt{544}$
$c \approx 23.3$

Both diagonals should be about 23.3 feet.

40. $A = \pi r^2$
$A = \pi\left(4\frac{1}{4}\right)^2$
$A = \pi\left(18\frac{1}{16}\right)$
$A \approx 56.7\ \text{in}^2$

41. The sum of the measures of the interior angles of a pentagon is 540°. The gazebo is a regular pentagon so the measure of each interior angle of the gazebo is 540 ÷ 5 or 108°.

42. $\frac{5}{6} = 0.83\overline{3} \rightarrow \frac{83.\overline{3}}{100} = 83.3\%$

43. $3c^2 = 3(-5)^2$
$\quad\ = 3(25)$
$\quad\ = 75$

44. $\qquad f + 19 = 4$
$f + 19 - 19 = 4 - 19$
$\qquad\qquad f = -15$

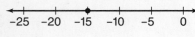

45. $s \geq 50$

Math Lab: Ratios in Right Triangles

Pages 687   Your Turn
See students' work.
1. The ratios are the same.
2. The ratios will be the same.
3. The ratios of the given angles are the same no matter how long the sides are.

13-6

The Sine, Cosine, and Tangent Ratios

Pages 688   Your Turn
See students' work.

a. second ratio = $\dfrac{\text{measure of the leg adjacent to } \angle A}{\text{measure of the hypotenuse}}$

b. third ratio = $\dfrac{\text{measure of the leg opposite } \angle A}{\text{measure of the leg adjacent to } \angle A}$

c. They were the same.

Page 690   Checking Your Understanding
1. Sample answer: The sine ratio of an acute angle equals the measure of the leg opposite that angle divided by the measure of the hypotenuse.

2. Sample answer: Both ratios use the measure of the hypotenuse for the denominator. The sine ratio uses the measure of the side opposite the acute angle for the numerator and the cosine ratio uses the measure of the side adjacent to the acute angle for the numerator.

3. Sample answer: To find the degree measure of an acute angle using the tangent ratio, divide the measure of the side opposite the angle by the measure of the side adjacent to the angle. Then press $\boxed{\text{TAN}^{-1}}$.

4. Sample answer:

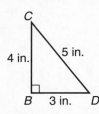

5. Derice. The value of sin 30° is constant.
6. See students' work.

7. $\frac{24}{25}$	**8.** $\frac{7}{25}$	**9.** $\frac{7}{25}$
10. $\frac{24}{25}$	**11.** $\frac{24}{7}$	**12.** $\frac{7}{24}$

13. $\cos 71° \approx 0.3256$ **14.** $\tan 2° \approx 0.0349$

15. $\sin 25° \approx 0.4226$ **16.** $\sin M = 0.4$
$\qquad\qquad\qquad\qquad\qquad\qquad \angle M \approx 24°$

17. $\cos N = 0.18$ **18.** $\tan F = 0.64$
$\quad\ \angle N \approx 80°$ $\qquad\ \angle F \approx 33°$

---

19. Let x = length of ramp

$$\sin 6° = \frac{2}{x}$$
$$x \sin 6° = 2$$
$$x = \frac{2}{\sin 6°}$$
$$x \approx 19$$

The ramp needs to be about 19 feet.

Pages 691–692   Exercises

20. $\sin B = \frac{55}{73}$
≈ 0.753
$\cos B = \frac{48}{73}$
≈ 0.658
$\tan B = \frac{55}{48}$
≈ 1.146

21. $\sin B = \frac{21}{29}$
≈ 0.724
$\cos B = \frac{20}{29}$
≈ 0.690
$\tan B = \frac{21}{20}$
≈ 1.05

22. $\sin B = \frac{8}{17}$
≈ 0.471
$\cos B = \frac{15}{17}$
≈ 0.882
$\tan B = \frac{8}{15}$
≈ 0.533

23. $\sin B = \frac{6}{10}$
$= 0.6$
$\cos B = \frac{8}{10}$
$= 0.8$
$\tan B = \frac{6}{8}$
$= 0.75$

24. $\sin B = \frac{35}{37}$
≈ 0.946
$\cos B = \frac{12}{37}$
≈ 0.324
$\tan B = \frac{35}{12}$
≈ 2.917

25. $\sin B = \frac{16}{65}$
≈ 0.246
$\cos B = \frac{63}{65}$
≈ 0.969
$\tan B = \frac{16}{63}$
≈ 0.254

26. $\tan 45° = 1.0000$

27. $\sin 30° = 0.5000$

28. $\cos 60° = 0.5000$

29. $\cos 25° \approx 0.9063$

30. $\tan 31° \approx 0.6009$

31. $\sin 71° \approx 0.9455$

32. $\tan J = 0.6$
$\angle J \approx 31°$

33. $\sin R = 0.8$
$\angle R \approx 53°$

34. $\cos F = 0.866$
$\angle F \approx 30°$

35. $\sin E = 0.6897$
$\angle E \approx 44°$

36. $\cos B = 0.4706$
$\angle B \approx 62°$

37. $\tan K = 1.8$
$\angle K \approx 61°$

38. $\tan x = \frac{9}{2}$
$\tan x = 4.5$
$x \approx 77°$

39. $\tan x = \frac{2}{11}$
$\tan x \approx 0.1818$
$x \approx 10°$

40. $\cos x = \frac{17}{21}$
$\cos x \approx 0.8095$
$x \approx 36°$

41. $\cos x = \frac{13.4}{18}$
$\cos x \approx 0.7444$
$x \approx 42°$

42. $\sin x = \frac{22.7}{50}$
$\sin x = 0.454$
$x \approx 27°$

43. Let y = measure of larger angle.
Find the measure of the larger angle.

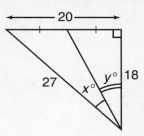

$\tan y = \frac{10}{18}$
$\tan y \approx 0.5556$
$y \approx 29$
Find $x° + y°$.
$\sin (x° + y°) = \frac{20}{27}$
$\sin (x° + y°) \approx 0.7407$
$x° + y° \approx 48$
So, $x° = 48 - 29$ or $19°$.

44. Sample answer: The sine of an angle is equal to the cosine of its complement.

45. $\tan x = \frac{55}{5}$
$\tan x = 11$
$x \approx 84.8°$

The measure of the angle should be about 84.8°.

46. $\tan x = \frac{1}{3.17}$
$\tan x = 0.3155$
$x \approx 17.5°$

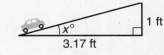

These streets form an angle about 17.5° with the horizontal.

47. $a = \frac{1}{2}c$
$a = \frac{1}{2}(20)$
$a = 10$ yd

48.

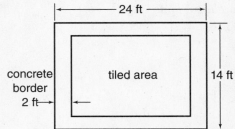

length of tiled area: $24 - 2(2) = 20$ ft
width of tiled area: $14 - 2(2) = 10$ ft
Area to be covered by tile: $A = \ell \cdot w$
$$A = 20 \cdot 10$$
$$A = 200 \text{ ft}^2$$

49. $3 \cdot 3 = 9$
9 ways

50. $2.5 \times 1000 = 2500$
2.5 g $= 2500$ mg

51. deductive

52. $(2b^3)(-6b^4) = (2 \cdot -6)(b^3 \cdot b^4)$
$= (-12)(b^{3+4})$
$= -12b^7$

53. $22 = \frac{n}{-11}$

$-11(22) = -11\left(\frac{n}{-11}\right)$

$-242 = n$

54. false

Page 692   The Shape of Things To Come
See students' work.

13-6B   ## Math Lab: Slope and Tangent

Pages 693   Your Turn
Slope $= \frac{6-3}{6-0}$ or $\frac{1}{2}$; See students' work for graphs.

1. $\frac{1}{2}$ **2.** $\frac{1}{2}$

3. They are the same.

4. Enter: `Y=` 3 `X,T,θ` `+` 4 `GRAPH` ; 3

5.
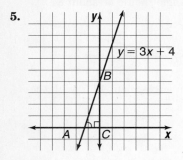

The leg opposite the angle is 4 units long, and the leg adjacent is $\frac{4}{3}$ units long.

So,

$\tan A = \frac{4}{\frac{4}{3}}$

$\tan A = 3$

6. $\tan A = 3$
$\angle A \approx 71.6°$

13-7   ## Using Trigonometric Ratios

Page 694   Your Turn
See students' work.

a.
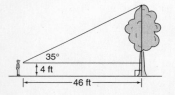

b. See students' work. If the given measures are used, the height of the tree is about 36.2 feet.

Page 696   Checking Your Understanding

1. See students' work.

2. If you know the measure of the hypotenuse and the measure of the side opposite the angle, use the sine ratio. If you know the measure of the hypotenuse and the measure of the side adjacent to the angle, use the cosine ratio. If you know the measures of the two legs, use the tangent ratio.

3. See students' work.

4. $\sin 46° = \frac{x}{15}$ **5.** $\tan 39° = \frac{10}{x}$
$(15)(\sin 46°) = x$ $x \tan 39° = 10$
$10.8 \approx x$ $x = \frac{10}{\tan 39°}$
$x \approx 12.3$

6. $\cos x° = \frac{12}{16}$
$\cos x° = 0.75$
$x \approx 41.4°$

7.
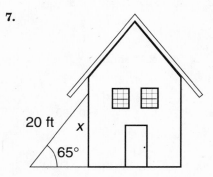

$\sin 65° = \frac{x}{20}$
$(20)(\sin 65°) = x$
$18.1 \approx x$
The ladder reaches about 18.1 feet.

Pages 696–697   Exercises

8. $\tan x° = \frac{28}{54}$ **9.** $\sin 60° = \frac{x}{16}$
$\tan x° \approx 0.5185$ $(16)(\sin 60°) = x$
$x \approx 27.4$ $13.9 \approx x$

10. $\tan 71° = \frac{6.3}{x}$ **11.** $\cos 30° = \frac{9}{x}$
$x \tan 71° = 6.3$ $x \cos 30° = 9$
$x = \frac{6.3}{\tan 71°}$ $x = \frac{9}{\cos 30°}$
$x \approx 2.2$ $x \approx 10.4$

12. $\cos 45° = \frac{x}{16}$ **13.** $\sin x° = \frac{8}{10}$
$(16)(\cos 45°) = x$ $\sin x° = 0.8$
$11.3 \approx x$ $x \approx 53.1$

14. $\sin x° = \frac{24}{26}$ **15.** $\sin x° = \frac{15}{21.2}$
$\sin x° \approx 0.9231$ $\sin x° \approx 0.7075$
$x \approx 67.4$ $x \approx 45.0$

16. $\cos 67° = \frac{x}{13}$
$(13)(\cos 67°) = x$
$5.1 \approx x$

17. Let h represent the distance from the ground to the kite.

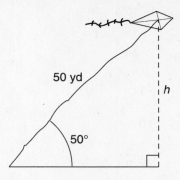

$$\sin 50° = \frac{h}{50}$$
$$(50)(\sin 50°) = h$$
$$38.3 \approx h$$

The kite is about 38.3 yards above the ground.

18. Let t represent the height of the flagpole.

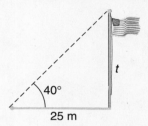

$$\tan 40° = \frac{t}{25}$$
$$(25)(\tan 40°) = t$$
$$21 \approx t$$

The flagpole is about 21 meters tall.

19. Let w represent the length of the wire.

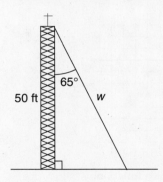

$$\cos 65° = \frac{50}{w}$$
$$w \cos 65° = 50$$
$$w = \frac{50}{\cos 65°}$$
$$w \approx 118$$

The guy wire is about 118 feet long.

20. Let x represent the length of the adjacent sides.

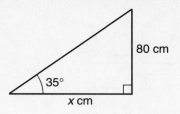

$$\tan 35° = \frac{80}{x}$$
$$x \tan 35° = 80$$
$$x = \frac{80}{\tan 35°}$$
$$x \approx 114.3$$

The adjacent side is about 114 cm long.

Therefore, $A = \frac{1}{2}bh$

$$A \approx \frac{1}{2}(114.25)(80)$$
$$A \approx \frac{1}{2}(9140)$$
$$A \approx 4570 \text{ cm}^2$$

21. Let h represent the height of the building from eye level.

$$\tan 26.5° = \frac{h}{85}$$
$$(85)(\tan 26.5°) = h$$
$$42.4 \approx h$$

The building is about $42.4 + 1.6$ or about 44 meters.

22. Let x represent the distance from the Sears Tower to the first sailboat. Let y represent the distance from the Sears Tower to the second sailboat.

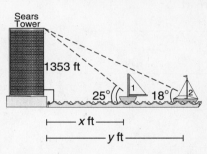

$\tan 25° = \frac{1353}{x}$	$\tan 18° = \frac{1353}{y}$
$x \tan 25° = 1353$	$y \tan 18° = 1353$
$x = \frac{1353}{\tan 25°}$	$y = \frac{1353}{\tan 18°}$
$x \approx 2901.5$	$y \approx 4164.1$

The boats are about $4164.1 - 2901.5$ or about 1262.6 feet apart.

23. Let x represent the altitude from B to D.

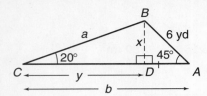

$$\sin 45° = \frac{x}{6}$$
$$(6)(\sin 45°) = x$$
$$4.24 \approx x$$

The altitude is about 4.24 yd.

To find a:
$$\sin 20° = \frac{4.24}{a}$$
$$a \sin 20° = 4.24$$
$$a = \frac{4.24}{\sin 20°}$$
$$a \approx 12.4 \text{ yd}$$

Let y represent the length of $\overline{CD}$.
$$a^2 = x^2 + y^2$$
$$(12.4)^2 \approx (4.24)^2 + y^2$$
$$153.8 \approx 18.0 + y^2$$
$$153.8 - 18.0 \approx y^2$$
$$135.8 \approx y^2$$
$$\sqrt{135.8} \approx y$$
$$11.7 \text{ yd} \approx y$$

To find b:
$$b \approx 11.7 + 4.24$$
$$b \approx 15.9 \text{ yd}$$

24. Let d represent the distance between the plane and the airport.

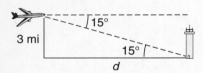

$$\tan 15° = \frac{3}{d}$$
$$d \tan 15° = 3$$
$$d = \frac{3}{\tan 15°}$$
$$d \approx 11.2$$

The distance between the plane and the airport is about 11.2 miles.

25. Let h represent the height of the wall.
$$\tan 75° = \frac{h}{10}$$
$$(10)(\tan 75°) = h$$
$$37 \approx h$$

The wall is about 37 feet high.

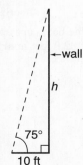

26. Let h represent the height of the cloud ceiling.

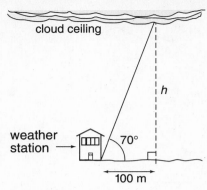

$$\tan 70° = \frac{h}{100}$$
$$(100)(\tan 70°) = h$$
$$275 \approx h$$

The cloud is about 275 meters high.

27. $\sin B = 0.8829$
$$\angle B \approx 62°$$

28. See students' work.

29. 45 47 50 51 62 68 69 72 75

      ↑   ↑   ↑

     LQ   Median   UQ

range: $75 - 45 = 30$

median: 62

upper quartile: $\frac{69 + 72}{2} = 70.5$

lower quartile: $\frac{47 + 50}{2} = 48.5$

interquartile range: $70.5 - 48.5 = 22$

30. $P(\text{March or April}) = \frac{25 + 13}{100}$
$$= \frac{38}{100}$$
$$= 38\%$$

31.

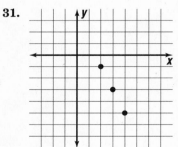

The relation is a function.

Chapter 13 Study Guide and Assessment

Page 699 Understanding and Using Vocabulary

1. square   **2.** radical sign

3. rational   **4.** hypotenuse

5. 30°–60°   **6.** elevation

Pages 700–702 Skills and Concepts

7. Since $3 \cdot 3 = 9$, $\sqrt{9} = 3$.

8. Since $11 \cdot 11 = 121$, $\sqrt{121} = 11$.

9. Since $5 \cdot 5 = 25$, $-\sqrt{25} = -5$.

10. Since $9 \cdot 9 = 81$, $-\sqrt{81} = -9$.

11. Since $15 \cdot 15 = 225$, $\sqrt{225} = 15$.

12. Since $30 \cdot 30 = 900$, $-\sqrt{900} = -30$.

13. $\sqrt{81} < \sqrt{83} < \sqrt{100}$
$\sqrt{9^2} < \sqrt{83} < \sqrt{10^2}$
$9 < \sqrt{83} < 10$
$\qquad 9 \qquad\qquad$ Check: $\sqrt{83} \approx 9.1$

14. $\sqrt{49} < \sqrt{54} < \sqrt{64}$
$\sqrt{7^2} < \sqrt{54} < \sqrt{8^2}$
$7 < \sqrt{54} < 8$
$\qquad 7 \qquad\qquad$ Check: $\sqrt{54} \approx 7.3$

15. $\sqrt{196} < \sqrt{220} < \sqrt{225}$
$\sqrt{14^2} < \sqrt{220} < \sqrt{15^2}$
$14 < \sqrt{220} < 15$
$\qquad 15$
Check: $\sqrt{220} \approx 14.8$

16. Since $30 \cdot 30 = 900$, $-\sqrt{900} = -30$.

17. $-\sqrt{36} < -\sqrt{39} < -\sqrt{49}$
$-\sqrt{6^2} < -\sqrt{39} < -\sqrt{7^2}$
$-6 < -\sqrt{39} < -7$
$\qquad -6$
Check: $-\sqrt{39} \approx 6.2$

18. $\sqrt{9} < \sqrt{9.61} < \sqrt{16}$
$\sqrt{3^2} < \sqrt{9.61} < \sqrt{4^2}$
$3 < \sqrt{9.61} < 4$
$\qquad 3$
Check: $\sqrt{9.61} \approx 3.1$

19. whole, integer, rational, real

20. rational, real

21. rational, real

22. irrational, real

23. $x^2 = 196$
$x = \sqrt{196}$ or $x = -\sqrt{196}$
$x = 14$ or $x = -14$

24. $n^2 = 160$
$n = \sqrt{160}$ or $n = -\sqrt{160}$
$n \approx 12.6$ or $n \approx -12.6$

25. $t^2 = 15$
$t = \sqrt{15}$ or $t = -\sqrt{15}$
$t \approx 3.9$ or $t \approx -3.9$

26. $a^2 = 0.04$
$a = \sqrt{0.04}$ or $a = -\sqrt{0.04}$
$a = 0.2$ or $a = -0.2$

27. $c^2 = a^2 + b^2$
$c^2 = 12^2 + 16^2$
$c^2 = 144 + 256$
$c^2 = 400$
$c = \sqrt{400}$
$c = 20$

28. $c^2 = a^2 + b^2$
$c^2 = 14^2 + 40^2$
$c^2 = 196 + 1600$
$c^2 = 1796$
$c = \sqrt{1796}$
$c \approx 42.4$

29. $c^2 = a^2 + b^2$
$c^2 = 30^2 + 16^2$
$c^2 = 900 + 256$
$c^2 = 1156$
$c = \sqrt{1156}$
$c = 34$

30. $\qquad c^2 = a^2 + b^2$
$\qquad 15^2 = 8^2 + b^2$
$\qquad 225 = 64 + b^2$
$225 - 64 = 64 + b^2 - 64$
$\qquad 161 = b^2$
$\sqrt{161} = b$
$\qquad 12.7 \approx b$

31. $\qquad c^2 = a^2 + b^2$
$\qquad 65^2 = a^2 + 63^2$
$\qquad 4225 = a^2 + 3969$
$4225 - 3969 = a^2 + 3969 - 3969$
$\qquad 256 = a^2$
$\sqrt{256} = a$
$\qquad 16 = a$

32. $\qquad c^2 = a^2 + b^2$
$\qquad 39^2 = 15^2 + b^2$
$\qquad 1521 = 225 + b^2$
$1521 - 225 = 225 + b^2 - 225$
$\qquad 1296 = b^2$
$\sqrt{1296} = b$
$\qquad 36 = b$

33. $x = \frac{1}{2}(6)$
$x = 6$ m

34. $x = 7\sqrt{2}$
$x \approx 9.9$ ft

35. $\qquad 1.5 = \frac{1}{2}x$
$\qquad 2(1.5) = 2\left(\frac{1}{2}\right)x$
$\qquad 3$ cm $= x$

36. $\sin x = \frac{40}{50}$
$\quad = 0.8$
$\cos x = \frac{30}{50}$
$\quad = 0.6$
$\tan x = \frac{40}{30}$
$\quad = 1.333$

37. $\sin x = \frac{30}{34}$
$\quad \approx 0.882$
$\cos x = \frac{16}{34}$
$\quad \approx 0.471$
$\tan x = \frac{30}{16}$
$\quad = 1.875$

38. $\tan C = 2.145$
$\angle C \approx 65°$

39. $\sin H = 0.9945$
$\angle H \approx 84°$

40. $\cos M = 0.2588$
$\angle M \approx 75°$

41. $\qquad \tan 35° = \frac{x}{15}$
$(15)(\tan 35°) = x$
$\qquad 10.5 \approx x$

42. $\cos x° = \frac{6}{11}$
$\cos x° \approx 0.5454$
$\qquad x \approx 56.9$

43. $\qquad \sin 25° = \frac{15}{x}$
$\quad x \sin 25° = 15$
$\qquad x = \frac{15}{\sin 25°}$
$\qquad x \approx 35.5$

Page 702　Applications and Problem Solving

44. $20 + 15 + 8 = 43$; So, the area where the circles overlap contains $43 - 32$ or 11. Therefore, 11 students chose both activities.

Favorite Activities

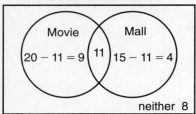

45. Let ℓ represent the length of the wire.

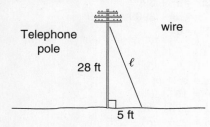

$\ell^2 = 28^2 + 5^2$
$\ell^2 = 784 + 25$
$\ell^2 = 809$
$\ell = \sqrt{809}$
$\ell \approx 28.4$
The wire is about 28.4 ft.

46. $d = s\sqrt{2}$

47. Let x represent the distance from the buoy to the foot of the lighthouse.
$\tan 25° = \frac{150}{x}$
$x \tan 25° = 150$
$x = \frac{150}{\tan 25°}$
$x \approx 321.68$

The buoy is about 321.68 feet from the foot of the lighthouse.

Page 703　Alternative Assessment

1.

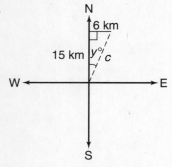

$\tan y° = \frac{6}{15}$
$\tan y° = 0.4$
$y \approx 22°$

The hikers are about 22° northeast from their starting point.
$c^2 = 15^2 + 6^2$
$c^2 = 225 + 36$
$c^2 = 261$
$c = \sqrt{261}$
$c \approx 16$ km
The hikers are about 16 km from the starting point.

2.

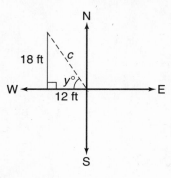

$\tan y° = \frac{18}{12}$
$\tan y° = 1.5$
$y \approx 56°$
The ball is about 56° northwest from the starting point.
$c^2 = 18^2 + 12^2$
$c^2 = 324 + 144$
$c^2 = 468$
$c = \sqrt{468}$
$c \approx 22$ ft
The ball is about 22 feet from the starting point.

Page 703　Thinking Critically

- when $m\angle A < 45°$
- when $m\angle A = 45°$
- $\tan A > 1$
- $0 \le \sin A \le 1$, $0 \le \cos A \le 1$

Page 703　Portfolio

See students' work.

Page 703　Self Evaluation

See students' work.

Chapter 14   Polynomials

Pages 707–708   Checking Your Understanding

1. No, because there is a variable in the denominator.

2. Sample answers: $4x + 7$; $15y^2 + 22x$; $\frac{1}{2}a - 6$;

   These are binomials because they are sums or differences of two monomials.

3. The degree of a monomial is the sum of the exponents of its variables. The degree of a polynomial is the same as the degree of the term with the greatest degree.

4. See students' work.

5. yes; monomial   6. yes; monomial

7. no; because there is a variable in the denominator.

8. yes; trinomial because it is the sum of three monomials.

9. $-2xy^2$ has degree $1 + 2$ or 3.

10. $12x^3y^2$ has degree $3 + 2$ or 5.

11. x^3 has degree 3.
    $7x$ has degree 1.
    So, the degree of $x^3 + 7x$ is 3.

12. x^2 has degree 2.
    xy^2 has degree $1 + 2$ or 3.
    $-y^4$ has degree 4.
    So, the degree of $x^2 + xy^2 - y^4$ is 4.

13. $3x - 5y + z^2 = 3(3) - 5(-5) + (-1)^2$
    $= 3(3) - 5(-5) + 1$
    $= 9 + 25 + 1$
    $= 35$

14. $x^3 + 2y^2 - z = (3)^3 + 2(-5)^2 - (-1)$
    $= 27 + 2(25) - (-1)$
    $= 27 + 50 + 1$
    $= 78$

15. $x^3 - 2xy = (3)^3 - 2(3)(-5)$
    $= 27 - 2(-15)$
    $= 27 + 30$
    $= 57$

16. $2xy + 6yz^2 = 2(3)(-5) + 6(-5)(-1)^2$
    $= 2(3)(-5) + 6(-5)(1)$
    $= -30 - 30$
    $= -60$

17. $12b + 11f + 5s = 12(1.79) + 11(0.99) + 5(1.29)$
    $= 21.48 + 10.89 + 6.45$
    $= \$38.82$

Pages 708–709   Exercises

18. yes; monomial

19. yes; binomial because it is the sum of two monomials.

20. yes; binomial because it is the difference of two monomials.

21. yes; trinomial because it is the sum of three monomials.

22. no; because there is a variable in the denominator.

23. yes; monomial   24. yes; monomial

25. yes; trinomial because it is the sum of three monomials.

26. yes; binomial because it is the sum of two monomials.

27. yes; monomial   28. yes; monomial

29. yes; trinomial because it is the sum of three monomials.

30. $11c^2$ has degree 2.
    4 has degree 0.
    So, the degree of $11c^2 + 4$ is 2.

31. $3x$ has degree 1.
    5 has degree 0.
    So, the degree of $3x + 5$ is 1.

32. 121 has degree 0.

33. $4x^3$ has degree 3.
    xy has degree $1 + 1$ or 2.
    $-y^2$ has degree 2.
    So, the degree of $4x^3 + xy - y^2$ is 3.

34. x^6 has degree 6.
    y^6 has degree 6.
    So, the degree of $x^6 + y^6$ is 6.

35. d^4 has degree 4.
    c^4d^2 has degree $4 + 2$ or 6.
    So, the degree of $d^4 + c^4d^2$ is 6.

36. $16y^2$ has degree 2.
    mnp has degree $1 + 1 + 1$ or 3.
    So, the degree of $16y^2 + mnp$ is 3.

37. x^3 has degree 3.
    $-x^2y^3$ has degree $2 + 3$ or 5.
    8 has degree 0.
    So, the degree of $x^3 - x^2y^3 + 8$ is 5.

38. $-7x^3y^4$ has degree $3 + 4$ or 7.

39. $-x^2yz^4$ has degree $2 + 1 + 4$ or 7.

40. $14c^5$ has degree 5.
    $-16c^6d$ has degree $6 + 1$ or 7.
    So, the degree of $14c^5 - 16c^6d$ is 7.

41. $2x^5$ has degree 5.
    $9x$ has degree 1.
    1 has degree 0.
    So, the degree of $2x^5 + 9x + 1$ is 5.

42. $a^3 - 2bc = (2)^3 - 2(-3)(4)$
    $= 8 - 2(-3)(4)$
    $= 8 - 2(-12)$
    $= 8 + 24$
    $= 32$

43. $ab + cd = (2)(-3) + (4)(-5)$
    $= -6 - 20$
    $= -26$

44. $2abc + 3a^2b = 2(2)(-3)(4) + 3(2)^2(-3)$
    $= 2(2)(-3)(4) + 3(4)(-3)$
    $= -48 - 36$
    $= -84$

45. $b^3 - 2ac + d^2 = (-3)^2 - 2(2)(4) + (-5)^2$
$= -27 - 2(2)(4) + 25$
$= -27 - 16 + 25$
$= -18$

46. $b^2 + a^2b = (-3)^2 + (2)^2(-3)$
$= 9 + 4(-3)$
$= 9 - 12$
$= -3$

47. $a^5 + bd^2 = (2)^5 + (-3)(-5)^2$
$= 32 + (-3)(25)$
$= 32 - 75$
$= -43$

48. $a^2 + b^2 - c^2 + d^2 = (2)^2 + (-3)^2 - (4)^2 + (-5)^2$
$= 4 + 9 - 16 + 25$
$= 22$

49. $abcd - 25 + a = (2)(-3)(4)(-5) - 25 + 2$
$= 120 - 25 + 2$
$= 97$

50. $5ad^2 - 2a + (bc)^2 = 5(2)(-5)^2 - 2(2) + [(-3)(4)]^2$
$= 5(2)(25) - 2(2) + [-12]^2$
$= 5(2)(25) - 2(2) + 144$
$= 250 - 4 + 144$
$= 390$

51. $-(-ac)^2 - cd = -[(-2)(4)]^2 - (4)(-5)$
$= -[-8]^2 - (4)(-5)$
$= -64 + 20$
$= -44$

52. $\sqrt{c} - b^2d = \sqrt{4} - (-3)^2(-5)$
$= 2 - 9(-5)$
$= 2 + 45$
$= 47$

53. $d - abc^2 - \sqrt{-27b} = -5 - (2)(-3)(4)^2 - \sqrt{-27(-3)}$
$= -5 - (2)(-3)(16) - \sqrt{81}$
$= -5 + 96 - 9$
$= 82$

54. $x + 3$; since it will be the largest exponent for all values of x.

55. a. $2x + 2y + z + xy$

b. $2x$ has degree 1.
$2y$ has degree 1.
z has degree 1.
xy has degree $1 + 1$ or 2.
So, the degree of $2x + 2y + z + xy$ is 2.

56. a. $-0.125x^5$ has degree 5.
$3.125x^4$ has degree 4.
4000 has degree 0.
So, the degree of $-0.125x^5 + 3.125x^4 + 4000$ is 5.

b. Since 1920 is 20 years from 1900, $x = 20$.
$-0.125x^5 + 3.125x^4 + 4000$
$= -0.125(20)^5 + 3.125(20)^4 + 4000$
$= -0.125(3,200,000) + 3.125(160,000) + 4000$
$= -400,000 + 500,000 + 4000$
$= 104,000$

57. See students' work.

58. $\tan 40° = \frac{10}{\overline{XY}}$
$\overline{XY} \tan 40° = 10$
$\overline{XY} = \frac{10}{\tan 40°}$
$\overline{XY} \approx 11.9$ ft

59. Find the area of each side of the top of the tent.
side: $A = \frac{1}{2}bh$
$A = \frac{1}{2}(8)(4.2)$
$A = \frac{1}{2}(33.6)$
$A = 16.8$ m
Find the area of each hanging side.
side: $A = \ell \cdot w$
$A = 2.8 \cdot 8$
$A = 22.4$
The tent requires $4(16.8) + 4(22.4)$ or 156.8 m^2 of canvas.

60. a. The range is $525 - 198$ or 327.

b. The median is $\frac{308 + 312}{2}$ or 310.

c. The upper quartile is 375 and the lower quartile is 278. So, the interquartile range is $375 - 278$ or 97.

d. $1.5(97) = 145.5$; So, the limits for the outliers are $278 - 145.5$ or 132.5 and $375 + 145.5$ or 520.5. There is one outlier, 525.

61. $0.065 \times 98 = 6.37$
The tax is $6.37.
So, the total cost is $98 + 6.37$ or $104.37.

62. $\frac{2x}{5} - 3 > -5$
$\frac{2x}{5} - 3 + 3 > -5 + 3$
$\frac{2x}{5} > -2$
$\frac{5}{2}\left(\frac{2}{5}\right)x > \frac{5}{2}(-2)$
$x > -5$

63. yes; 3; 81, 243, 729

64. $P = 2(\ell + w)$
$P = 2(3.5 + 1.75)$
$P = 2(5.25)$
$P = 10.5$ m

65. $x > 8$

66. $\frac{48}{-3} = -16$

67. $|-8| + |5| = 8 + 5$
$= 13$

Math Lab: Representing Polynomials with Algebra Tiles

Page 710   Your Turn

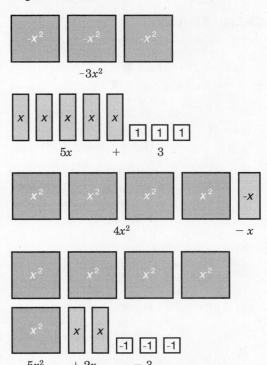

1. A monomial uses just one size of tiles, a binomial uses two different sizes, and a trinomial uses three different sizes.

2. $-x^2 + 3x - 5$

3. The degree of the polynomial is determined by the size of the largest algebra tile.

14-2   **Adding Polynomials**

Page 711   Your Turn

See students' work.

a. $8x^2 + 2x + 5$

b. The concept of the zero pairs is the same, but there are tiles that represent different terms in algebra tiles, and counters all represent 1 unit.

Page 713   Checking Your Understanding

1. x^2 and $2x^2$; $7x$ and $-3x$; 1 and 5

2. Sample answer: group like terms and add.
$(5x^2 + 6x + 4) + (2x^2 + 3x + 1)$
$= (5x^2 + 2x^2) + (6x + 3x) + (4 + 1)$
$= 7x^2 + 9x + 5$

3. Caroline; the variables are the same in both terms, they are just in a different order.

4.

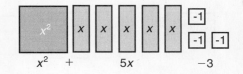

$3x^2 \qquad - \quad 2x \quad +1$

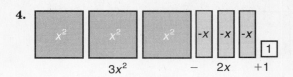

$x^2 \quad + \qquad 5x \qquad -3$

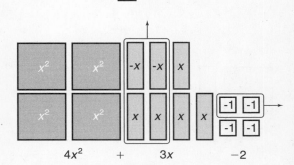

$4x^2 \qquad + \qquad 3x \qquad -2$

5.

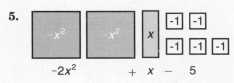

$-2x^2 \qquad + \quad x \ - \quad 5$

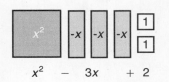

$x^2 \quad - \quad 3x \quad + \ 2$

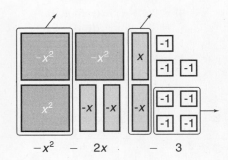

$-x^2 \ - \quad 2x \qquad - \quad 3$

6.

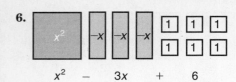

$$x^2 \quad - \quad 3x \quad + \quad 6$$

$$+$$

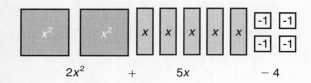

$$2x^2 \quad + \quad 5x \quad - 4$$

$$+$$

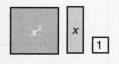

$$x^2 \quad + \quad x + 1$$

$$=$$

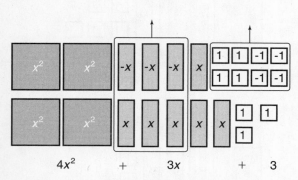

$$4x^2 \quad + \quad 3x \quad + \quad 3$$

7. $(x + 3) + (2x + 5) = (x + 2x) + (3 + 5)$
$= (1 + 2)x + (3 + 5)$
$= 3x + 8$

8. $(4x + 3) + (x - 1) = (4x + x) + (3 + (-1))$
$= (4 + 1)x + [3 + (-1)]$
$= 5x + 2$

9. $(3x - 5) + (x + 9) = (3x + x) + ((-5) + 9)$
$= (3 + 1)x + [(-5) + 9]$
$= 4x + 4$

10. $(2x - 3) + (x - 1) = (2x + x) + ((-3) + (-1))$
$= (2 + 1)x + [(-3) + (-1)]$
$= 3x + [-4]$
$= 3x - 4$

11. $\quad 2x^2 + 4x + 5$
$\underline{(+) \ x^2 - \ x - 3}$
$\quad 3x^2 + 3x + 2$

12. $\quad 2x^2 - 5x + 4$
$\underline{(+) \ 3x^2 + 8x - 1}$
$\quad 5x^2 + 3x + 3$

13. $P = 2(\ell + w)$
$P = 2((2x + 7) + (x + 5))$
$P = 2((2x + x) + (7 + 5))$
$P = 2(3x + 12)$
$P = 2(3x) + 2(12)$
$P = 6x + 24$ units

Pages 713–714 Exercises

14. $(6y - 5r) + (2y - 7r) = (6y + 2y) + [(-5r) + 7r)]$
$= (6 + 2)y + [(-5) + 7]r$
$= 8y + 2r$

15. $(3x + 9) + (x + 5) = (3x + x) + (9 + 5)$
$= (3 + 1)x + (9 + 5)$
$= 4x + 14$

16. $(11x + 2y) + (x - 5y) = (11x + x) + [2y + (-5y)]$
$= (11 + 1)x + [2 + (-5)]y$
$= 12x + (-3)y$
$= 12x - 3y$

17. $(8m - 2n) + (3m + n) = (8m + 3m) + [(-2n) + n]$
$= (8 + 3)m + [(-2) + 1]n$
$= 11m + (-1)n$
$= 11m - n$

18. $(13x - 7y) + 3y = 13x + [(-7y) + 3y]$
$= 13x + [(-7) + 3]y$
$= 13x + (-4)y$
$= 13x - 4y$

19. $(2x^2 + 5x) + (9 - 7x) = 2x^2 + [5x + (-7x)] + 9$
$= 2x^2 + [5 + (-7)]x + 9$
$= 2x^2 + (-2)x + 9$
$= 2x^2 - 2x + 9$

20. $(3r + 6s) + (5r - 9s) = (3r + 5r) + [6s + (-9s)]$
$= (3 + 5)r + [6 + (-9)]s$
$= 8r + (-3)s$
$= 8r - 3s$

21. $(5m + 3n) + 12m = (5m + 12m) + 3n$
$= (5 + 12)m + 3n$
$= 17m + 3n$

22. $(3x^2 - 9x + 5) + (5x^2 + 5x - 11)$
$= (3x^2 + 5x^2) + [(-9x) + 5x] + [5 + (-11)]$
$= (3 + 5)x^2 + [(-9) + 5]x + [5 + (-11)]$
$= 8x^2 + (-4)x + (-6)$
$= 8x^2 - 4x - 6$

23. $(5x^2 - 7x + 9) + (3x^2 + 4x - 6)$
$= (5x^2 + 3x^2) + [(-7x) + 4x] + [9 + (-6)]$
$= (5 + 3)x^2 + [(-7) + 4]x + [9 + (-6)]$
$= 8x^2 + (-3)x + 3$
$= 8x^2 - 3x + 3$

24. $(6x^2 + 15x - 9) + (5 - 8x - 8x^2)$
$= [6x^2 + (-8x^2)] + [15x + (-8x)] + [(-9) + 5]$
$= [6 + (-8)]x^2 + [15 + (-8)]x + [(-9) + 5]$
$= (-2)x^2 + 7x + (-4)$
$= -2x^2 + 7x - 4$

25. $(a^3 - b^3) + (3a^3 + 2a^2b - b^2 + 2b^3)$
$= (a^3 + 3a^3) + 2a^2b + (-b^2) + [(-b^3) + 2b^3]$
$= (1 + 3)a^3 + 2a^2b + (-b^2) + [(-1) + 2]b^3$
$= 4a^3 + 2a^2b + (-b^2) + (1)b^3$
$= 4a^3 + 2a^2b - b^2 + b^3$

26. $-6y^2 + 7b - 5$
$\underline{(+)\ 2y^2 - 9b + 8}$
$-4y^2 - 2b + 3$

27. $3a + 5b - 4c$
$2a - 3b + 7c$
$\underline{(+)\ -a + 4b - 2c}$
$4a + 6b + \ c$

28. $3x^2 - 7x + 9$
$-2x^2 + x - 4$
$\underline{(+)\ \ x^2 + 3x - 1}$
$2x^2 - 3x + 4$

29. $(3a + 5ab - 3b^2) + (7b^2 - 8ab) + (2 - 5a)$
$= [3a + (-5a)] + [5ab + (-8ab)] + [(-3b^2) + 7b^2] + 2$
$= [3 + (-5)]a + [5 + (-8)]ab + [(-3) + 7]b^2 + 2$
$= (-2)a + (-3)ab + 4b^2 + 2$
$= -2a - 3ab + 4b^2 + 2$

30. $(x^2 + x + 5) + (3x^2 - 4x - 2) + (2x^2 + 2x - 1)$
$= (x^2 + 3x^2 + 2x^2) + [x + (-4x) + 2x] +$
$\quad [5 + (-2) + (-1)]$
$= (1 + 3 + 2)x^2 + [1 + (-4) + 2]x +$
$\quad [5 + (-2) + (-1)]$
$= 6x^2 + (-1)x + 2$
$= 6x^2 - x + 2$

31. $(3x^2 + 7) + (4x - 2) + (x^2 - 3x - 6)$
$= (3x^2 + x^2) + [4x + (-3x)] + [7 + (-2) + (-6)]$
$= (3 + 1)^2 + [4 + (-3)]x + [7 + (-2) + (-6)]$
$= 4x^2 + (1)x + (-1)$
$= 4x^2 + x - 1$

32. $(3a + 5b) + (2a - 9b) = (3a + 2a) + [5b + (-9b)]$
$= (3 + 2)a + [5 + (-9)]b$
$= 5a + (-4)b$
$= 5a - 4b$
$= 5(-3) - 4(4)$
$= -15 - 16$
$= -31$

33. $(a^2 - 3ab + b^2) + (3a^2 - 2b - 5b^2)$
$= (a^2 + 3a^2) + (-3ab) + (-2b) + [b^2 + (-5b^2)]$
$= (1 + 3)a^2 + (-3ab) + (-2b) + [1 + (-5)]b^2$
$= 4a^2 + (-3ab) + (-2b) + (-4)b^2$
$= 4a^2 - 3ab - 2b - 4b^2$
$= 4(-3)^2 - 3(-3)(4) - 2(4) - 4(4)^2$
$= 4(9) - 3(-3)(4) - 2(4) - 4(16)$
$= 36 + 36 - 8 - 64$
$= 0$

34. $(a^2 + 7b^2) + (5 - 3b^2) + (2a^2 - 7)$
$= (a^2 + 2a^2) + [7b^2 + (-3b^2)] + [5 + (-7)]$
$= (1 + 2)a^2 + [7 + (-3)]b^2 + [5 + (-7)]$
$= 3a^2 + 4b^2 + (-2)$
$= 3a^2 + 4b^2 - 2$
$= 3(-3)^2 + 4(4)^2 - 2$
$= 3(9) + 4(16) - 2$
$= 27 + 64 - 2$
$= 89$

35. $\qquad\qquad (4r + 3s) + (6r - 5s) = (10r - 2s)$
$(4r + 3s) + (6r - 5s) - (6r - 5s) = (10r - 2s) -$
$\qquad\qquad\qquad\qquad\qquad\qquad (6r - 5s)$
$\qquad\qquad\ (4r + 3s) = (10r - 2s) -$
$\qquad\qquad\qquad\qquad\qquad\qquad (6r - 5s)$
So, $(10r - 2s) - (6r - 5s) = (4r + 3s)$.

36. a. $(2x - 2) + (x + 10) + x = (2x + x + x) +$
$\qquad\qquad\qquad\qquad\qquad\qquad [(-2) + 10]$
$\qquad\qquad\qquad\qquad\ = (2 + 1 + 1)x +$
$\qquad\qquad\qquad\qquad\qquad\quad [(-2) + 10]$
$\qquad\qquad\qquad\qquad\ = 4x + 8$

b. $\qquad 4x + 8 = 180$
$4x + 8 - 8 = 180 - 8$
$\qquad\quad 4x = 172$
$\qquad\ \dfrac{4x}{4} = \dfrac{172}{4}$
$\qquad\quad\ x = 43°$

c. $x = 43$, $43 + 10 = 53$, and $2(43) - 2 = 84$.
So, the measures of the angles of the triangle
are $43°$, $53°$, and $84°$.

37. $(3x - 5) + (x + 7) = (3x + x) + [(-5) + 7]$
$\qquad\qquad\qquad\qquad = (3 + 1)x + [(-5) + 7]$
$\qquad\qquad\qquad\qquad = 4x + 2$
The window is $4x + 2$ united inches.

38. yes; binomial because it is the difference of two
monomials.

39. $A = \frac{1}{2}bh$
$A = \frac{1}{2}(5)(3)$
$A = \frac{1}{2}(15)$
$A = 7.5$ cm^2

40. 20% of $15.98 = d$
$0.20 \times 15.98 = 3.196$
The discount is $3.20.

41. a. $t + h > 130$

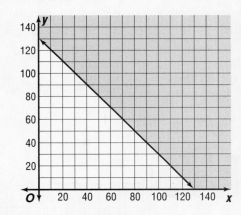

b. the area above the boundary line.

c. No points with $h > 100$ are included in the
graph.

42. a. 10

b. 2, 6, 11, 17, 24, 32, 41, 51
$\quad\ \ _{+4}\ _{+5}\ _{+6}\ _{+7}\ _{+8}\ _{+9}\ _{+10}$

43. $\quad\ A = \ell \cdot w$
$150 = \ell \cdot w$
$150 = 10\ell$
$\dfrac{150}{10} = \dfrac{10\ell}{10}$
$\ \ 15 = \ell$

The length is 15 ft.

44.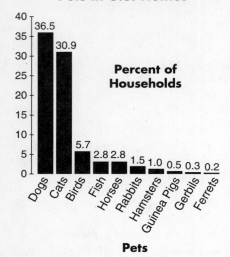

Pets in U.S. Homes

Percent of Households

Pets

45. $236 + n = 298$
$n = 298 - 236$
$n = 62$
There were 62 more women on the 1996 team.

| 14-3 | Subtracting Polynomials |

Page 717 Checking Your Understanding

1. Addition and subtraction are inverse operations.

2. Multiply by -1. The additive inverse of $3x^2 - 5x + 7$ is $-3x^2 + 5x - 7$.

3. 0

4. Sample answer:
$(5m^2 + 2m + 7) - (2m^2 + 7m + 3) = 3m^2 - 5m + 4$

5.

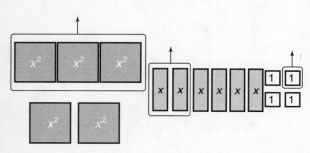

$(5x^2 + 6x + 4) - (3x^2 + 2x + 1) = 2x^2 + 4x + 3$

6. To subtract $(x^2 - 2x + 3)$, add its additive inverse.
$(-1)(x^2 - 2x + 3) = -x^2 + 2x - 3$

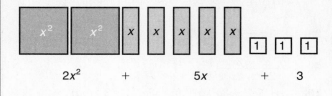

$2x^2 \quad + \quad 5x \quad + \quad 3$

$+$

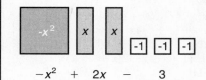

$-x^2 + 2x - 3$

$=$

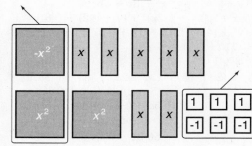

$x^2 + 7x$

7.

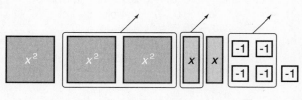

$(3x^2 + 2x - 5) \quad - \quad (2x^2 + x - 4) \quad = \quad x^2 + x - 1$

8.

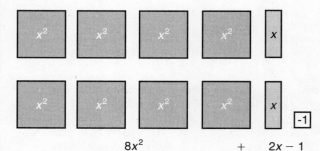

$8x^2 \qquad + \quad 2x - 1$

To subtract $(2x^2 + x + 5)$, you need to remove five 1-tiles. Since there are no 1-tiles, add five zero pairs of 1-tiles. Then remove five 1-tiles.

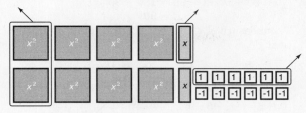

$$(8x^2 + 2x - 1) - (2x^2 + x + 5) = 6x^2 + x - 6$$

9. $-1(2abc) = -2abc$ **10.** $-1(3x + 2y) = -3x - 2y$

11. $-1(x^2 + 5x + 1) = -x^2 - 5x - 1$

12. $-1(3x^2 - 2x + 5) = -3x^2 + 2x - 5$

13. $-1(-8m + 7n) = 8m - 7n$

14. $-1(-4h^2 - 5hk - k^2) = 4h^2 + 5hk + k^2$

15. $(3x + 4) - (x + 2) = (3x + 4) + (-1)(x + 2)$
$$= 3x + 4 + (-x - 2)$$
$$= 3x + 4 - x - 2$$
$$= 3x - x + 4 + 2$$
$$= 2x + 2$$

16. $(4x + 5) - (2x + 3) = (4x + 5) + (-1)(2x + 3)$
$$= 4x + 5 + (-2x - 3)$$
$$= 4x + 5 - 2x - 3$$
$$= 4x - 2x + 5 - 3$$
$$= 2x + 2$$

17. $(5x - 7) - (3x - 4) = (5x - 7) + (-1)(3x - 4)$
$$= 5x - 7 + (-3x + 4)$$
$$= 5x - 7 - 3x + 4$$
$$= 5x - 3x - 7 + 4$$
$$= 2x - 3$$

18. $(2x - 5) - (3x + 1) = (2x - 5) + (-1)(3x + 1)$
$$= 2x - 5 + (-3x - 1)$$
$$= 2x - 5 - 3x - 1$$
$$= 2x - 3x - 5 - 1$$
$$= -1x - 6$$
$$= -x - 6$$

19.
$$\begin{array}{r} 5x^2 + 4x - 1 \\ (-)4x^2 + x + 2 \\ \end{array} \rightarrow \begin{array}{r} 5x^2 + 4x - 1 \\ (+)\,-4x^2 - x - 2 \\ \hline x^2 + 3x - 3 \end{array}$$

20.
$$\begin{array}{r} 3x^2 + 5x + 4 \\ (-)x^2 - 1 \\ \end{array} \rightarrow \begin{array}{r} 3x^2 + 5x + 4 \\ (+)\,-x^2 + 1 \\ \hline 2x^2 + 5x + 5 \end{array}$$

21. $(6x - 3) - (2x + 3) = (6x - 3) + (-1)(2x + 3)$
$$= 6x - 3 + (-2x - 3)$$
$$= 6x - 3 - 2x - 3$$
$$= 6x - 2x - 3 - 3$$
$$= 4x - 6$$

The hypotenuse is $4x - 6$ longer than the shorter leg.

22. $(9x + 5) - (4x + 3) = (9x + 5) + (-1)(4x + 3)$
$$= 9x + 5 + (-4x - 3)$$
$$= 9x + 5 - 4x - 3$$
$$= 9x - 4x + 5 - 3$$
$$= 5x + 2$$

23. $(2x + 5) - (x + 8) = (2x + 5) + (-1)(x + 8)$
$$= 2x + 5 + (-x - 8)$$
$$= 2x + 5 - x - 8$$
$$= 2x - x + 5 - 8$$
$$= 1x - 3$$
$$= x - 3$$

24. $(3x - 2) - (5x - 4) = (3x - 2) + (-1)(5x - 4)$
$$= 3x - 2 + (-5x + 4)$$
$$= 3x - 2 - 5x + 4$$
$$= 3x - 5x - 2 + 4$$
$$= -2x + 2$$

25. $(6x - 5) - (4x + 3) = (6x - 5) + (-1)(4x + 3)$
$$= 6x - 5 + (-4x - 3)$$
$$= 6x - 5 - 4x - 3$$
$$= 6x - 4x - 5 - 3$$
$$= 2x - 8$$

26. $(2x + 3y) - (x - y) = (2x + 3y) + (-1)(x - y)$
$$= 2x + 3y + (-x + y)$$
$$= 2x + 3y - x + y$$
$$= 2x - x + 3y + y$$
$$= 1x + 4y$$
$$= x + 4y$$

27. $(9x - 4y) - (12x - 9y) = (9x - 4y) - (-1)(12x - 9y)$
$$= 9x - 4y + (-12x + 9y)$$
$$= 9x - 4y - 12x + 9y$$
$$= 9x - 12x - 4y + 9y$$
$$= -3x + 5y$$

28. $(5x^2 - 3) - (2x^2 - 7) = (5x^2 - 3) + (-1)(2x^2 - 7)$
$$= 5x^2 - 3 + (-2x^2 + 7)$$
$$= 5x^2 - 3 - 2x^2 + 7$$
$$= 5x^2 - 2x^2 - 3 + 7$$
$$= 3x^2 + 4$$

29. $(x^2 + 6x) - (3x^2 + 7) = (x^2 + 6x) + (-1)(3x^2 + 7)$
$$= x^2 + 6x + (-3x^2 - 7)$$
$$= x^2 + 6x - 3x^2 - 7$$
$$= x^2 - 3x^2 + 6x - 7$$
$$= -2x^2 + 6x - 7$$

30.
$$\begin{array}{r} 5a^2 + 7a + 9 \\ (-)3a^2 + 4a + 1 \\ \end{array} \rightarrow \begin{array}{r} 5a^2 + 7a + 9 \\ (+)\,-3a^2 - 4a - 1 \\ \hline 2a^2 + 3a + 8 \end{array}$$

31.
$$\begin{array}{r} 6m^2 - 5m + 3 \\ (-)5m^2 + 2m - 7 \\ \end{array} \rightarrow \begin{array}{r} 6m^2 - 5m + 3 \\ (+)\,-5m^2 - 2m + 7 \\ \hline m^2 - 7m + 10 \end{array}$$

32.
$$\begin{array}{r} 5x^2 - 4xy \\ (-) - 3xy + 2y^2 \\ \end{array} \rightarrow \begin{array}{r} 5x^2 - 4xy \\ (+) + 3xy - 2y^2 \\ \hline 5x^2 - xy - 2y^2 \end{array}$$

33.
$$\begin{array}{r} 9m^2 + 7 \\ (-)\,-6m^2 + 2m - 3 \\ \end{array} \rightarrow \begin{array}{r} 9m^2 + 7 \\ (+)\,6m^2 - 2m + 3 \\ \hline 15m^2 - 2m + 10 \end{array}$$

34.
$$\begin{array}{r} 15x^2y^2 + 11xy - 9 \\ (-)9x^2y^2 - 13xy + 6 \\ \end{array} \rightarrow \begin{array}{r} 15x^2y^2 + 11xy - 9 \\ (+)\,-9x^2y^2 + 13xy - 6 \\ \hline 6x^2y^2 + 24xy - 15 \end{array}$$

35.
$$14a + 10b - 18c \quad \rightarrow \quad 14a + 10b - 18c$$
$$\underline{(-)5a + 7b - 11c} \qquad \underline{(+)-5a - 7b + 11c}$$
$$\qquad\qquad\qquad\qquad 9a + 3b - 7c$$

36. $(10x^2 + 8x - 6) - (3x^2 + 2x - 9)$
$= (10^2 + 8x - 6) + (-1)(3x^2 + 2x - 9)$
$= 10x^2 + 8x - 6 + (-3x^2 - 2x + 9)$
$= 10x^2 + 8x - 6 - 3x^2 - 2x + 9$
$= 10x^2 - 3x^2 + 8x - 2x - 6 + 9$
$= 7x^2 + 6x + 3$

37. $(5y^2 + 9y - 12) - (-3y^2 + 5y - 7)$
$= (5y^2 + 9y - 12) + (-1)(-3y^2 + 5y - 7)$
$= 5y^2 + 9y - 12 + (3y^2 - 5y + 7)$
$= 5y^2 + 9y - 12 + 3y^2 - 5y + 7$
$= 5y^2 + 3y^2 + 9y - 5y - 12 + 7$
$= 8y^2 + 4y - 5$

38. $(6a^2 + 7ab - 3b^2) - (2a^2 + 3ab - b^2)$
$= (6a^2 + 7ab - 3b^2) + (-1)(2a^2 + 3ab - b^2)$
$= 6a^2 + 7ab - 3b^2 + (-2a^2 - 3ab + b^2)$
$= 6a^2 + 7ab - 3b^2 - 2a^2 - 3ab + b^2$
$= 6a^2 - 2a^2 + 7ab - 3ab - 3b^2 + b^2$
$= 4a^2 + 4ab - 2b^2$

39. $(x^3 - 3x^2y + 4xy^2 + y^3) - (7x^3 - 9xy^2 + x^2y + y^3)$
$= (x^3 - 3x^2y + 4xy^2 + y^3) + (-1)(7x^3 - 9xy^2 + x^2y + y^3)$
$= x^3 - 3x^2y + 4xy^2 + y^3 + (-7x^3 + 9xy^2 - x^2y - y^3)$
$= x^3 - 3x^2y + 4xy^2 + y^3 - 7x^3 + 9xy^2 - x^2y - y^3$
$= x^3 - 7x^3 - 3x^2y - x^2y + 4xy^2 + 9xy^2 + y^3 - y^3$
$= -6x^3 - 4x^2y + 13xy^2$

40. $(A + B) + (A - B) = 2A$, so $(3x^2 + 2x - 2) + (-x^2 + 4x - 8) = 2A$. $(3x^2 + 2x - 2) + (-x^2 + 4x - 8) = 2x^2 + 6x - 10$, so $A = x^2 + 3x - 5$.
$A + B = 3x^2 + 2x - 2$, substitute for A.
$(x^2 + 3x - 5) + B = (3x^2 + 2x - 2)$, so $B = (3x^2 + 2x - 2) - (x^2 + 3x - 5)$. Therefore, $B = 2x^2 - x + 3$.

41. a. Let n represent the Nugget's score.
Nugget's score + Piston's score = total score
$$n \qquad + \qquad 186 \qquad = 2n + 2$$
$$186 = n + 2$$
$$184 = n$$
The Nugget's scored 184 points.

b. The total score was $184 + 186$ or 370 points.

42. $(16x + 1) - [(2x - 3) + (5x + 2) + (2x - 3)]$
$= (16x + 1) - [(2x + 5x + 2x) + ((-3) + 2 + (-3))]$
$= (16x + 1) - [(2 + 5 + 2)x + ((-3) + 2 + (-3))]$
$= (16x + 1) - [9x + (-4)]$
$= (16x + 1) - (9x - 4)$
$= (16x + 1) - (-1)(9x - 4)$
$= (16x + 1) + (-9x + 4)$
$= 16x + 1 - 9x + 4$
$= 16x - 9x + 1 + 4$
$= 7x + 5$
The length of the missing base is $7x + 5$ units.

43. $(2a^2 + 3a - 4) + (6a^2 - a + 5)$
$= (2a^2 + 6a^2) + [3a + (-a)] + [(-4) + 5]$
$= (2 + 6)a^2 + [3 + (-1)]a + [(-4) + 5]$
$= 8a^2 + 2a + 1$

44. $n^2 = 18$
$n = \sqrt{18}$
$n \approx 4.2$

45. $m\angle C + m\angle D + m\angle E = 180$
$35 + 55 + m\angle E = 180$
$90 + m\angle E = 180$
$90 + m\angle E - 90 = 180 - 90$
$m\angle E = 90$
The measure of $\angle E$ is 90°. The triangle is a right triangle.

46. $y = -x + 5$
Let $y = 0$:
$0 = -x + 5$
$0 - 5 = -x + 5 - 5$
$-5 = -x$
$-1(-5) = -1(-x)$
$5 = x$
The x-intercept is 5.
The ordered pair is $(5, 0)$.
Let $x = 0$;
$y = 0 + 5$
$y = 5$
The y-intercept is 5.
The ordered pair is $(0, 5)$.

47. Days debate team meets: 0, 3, 6, 9, ⑫, 15, 18, 21, ㉔, . . .
Days dance committee meets: 0, 4, 8, ⑫, 16, 20, ㉔, 28, 32, . . .
The patterns show that both groups meet on the same day every 12 school days.

48. $x = 32 + 56 + (-18)$
$x = 88 + (-18)$
$x = 70$

49. Quadrant II

50. $8c = 72$ What number
$8(9) = 72$ times 8 is 72?
$C = 9$

Page 718   Self Test

1. yes, binomial because it is the sum of two monomials.
ax^2 has degree $1 + 2$ or 3.
$6x$ has degree 1.
So, the degree of $ax^2 + 6x$ is 3.

2. yes, trinomial because it is the sum of three monomials.
$4b^2$ has degree 2.
c^3d^4 has degree $3 + 4$ or 7.
x has degree 1.
So, the degree of $4b^2 + c^3d^4 + x$ is 7.

3. yes, monomial;
$a^3b^4c^5$ has degree $3 + 4 + 5$ or 12.

4. $(4x + 5y) + (7x - 3y) = (4x + 7x) + [5y + (-3y)]$
$= (4 + 7)x + [5 + (-3)]y$
$= 11x + 2y$

5. $(2x^2 + 5) + (-3x^2 + 7) = [2x^2 + (-3x^2)] + (5 + 7)$
$= [2 + (-3)]x^2 + (5 + 7)$
$= (-1)x^2 + 12$
$= -x^2 + 12$

6. $(9m - 3n) + (10m + 4n) = (9m + 10m) + [(-3n) + 4n]$
$= (9 + 10)m + [(-3) + 4]n$
$= 19m + (1)n$
$= 19m + n$

7. $(7x + 2y) - [(2x + y) + (3x - 5y)]$
$= (7x + 2y) - [(2x + 3x) + (y + (-5y))]$
$= (7x + 2y) - [(2 + 3)x + (1 + (-5))y]$
$= (7x + 2y) - [5x + (-4)y]$
$= (7x + 2y) - (5x - 4y)$
$= (7x + 2y) + (-1)((5x - 4y)$
$= 7x + 2y + (-5x + 4y)$
$= 7x + 2y - 5x + 4y$
$= 7x - 5x + 2y + 4y$
$= 2x + 6y$
The length of the third side is $2x + 6y$ units.

8. $(11p + 5r) - (2p + r) = (11p + 5r) + (-1)(2p + r)$
$= 11p + 5r + (-2p - r)$
$= 11p + 5r - 2p - r$
$= 11p - 2p + 5r - r$
$= 9p + 4r$

9. $(7a + 6d) - (6a - 7d) = (7a + 6d) + (-1)(6a - 7d)$
$= 7a + 6d + (-6a + 7d)$
$= 7a + 6d - 6a + 7d$
$= 7a - 6a + 6d + 7d$
$= 1a + 13d$
$= a + 13d$

10. $(4t + 11r) - (t + 2r) = (4t + 11r) + (-1)(t + 2r)$
$= 4t + 11r + (-t - 2r)$
$= 4t + 11r - t - 2r$
$= 4t - t + 11r - 2r$
$= 3t + 9r$

| 14-4 | **Powers of Monomials** |

Page 719 Your Turn

Power	Value	Power	Value
3^1	3	$(3^2)^1$	9
3^2	9	$(3^2)^2$	81
3^3	27	$(3^2)^3$	729
3^4	81	$(3^2)^4$	6561
3^5	243	$(3^2)^5$	59,049
3^6	729	$(3^2)^6$	531,441

a. They are the same.

b. $6 = 2 \cdot 3$

c. 3^8 or 6561

d. Sample answer: Keep the base and multiply the exponents.

Pages 721–722 Checking Your Understanding

1. Julie, $(5x)^3 = 5x \cdot 5x \cdot 5x$ or $125x^3$.

2. The area is $x \cdot x$ or x^2.
If doubled, the area would be $2x \cdot 2x$ or $4x^2$.
If tripled, the area would be $3x \cdot 3x$ or $9x^2$.

3. Sample answers:
  a. Power of a power: When you raise a power to a power, multiply the exponents and keep the base.
  Example: $(x^2)^4 = x^8$.
  b. Power of a product: When you raise a product to a power, distribute the exponent over each term.
  Example: $(4x)^4 = 256x^4$.
  c. Power of a monomial: When you raise a product involving powers to a power, multiply each power by the exponent.
  Example: $(x^2y^3)^4 = x^{2\cdot4}y^{3\cdot4}$ or x^8y^{12}.

4. $(y^5)^3 = y^{5\cdot3}$
$= y^{15}$

5. $(2^4)^3 = 2^{4\cdot3}$
$= 2^{12}$

6. $(2m)^4 = 2^4 m^4$
$= 16m^4$

7. $(3xy)^3 = 3^3 x^3 y^3$
$= 27x^3 y^3$

8. $(a^2 b^3)^2 = (a^2)^2(b^3)^2$
$= a^{2\cdot2} b^{3\cdot2}$
$= a^4 b^6$

9. $(-xy)^2 = (-x)^2 y^2$
$= x^2 y^2$

10. $a^2 b = (-1)^2(3)$
$= 1 \cdot 3$
$= 3$

11. $-ab^2 = -(-1)(3)^2$
$= -(1)(9)$
$= 9$

12. $(-4a^3 b)^2 = (-4)^2(a^3)^2 b^2$
$= 16a^6 b^2$
$= 16(-1)^6(3)^2$
$= 16(1)(9)$
$= 144$

13. $V = (2x^3)(6xy^2)(4x^2)$
$V = (2 \cdot 6 \cdot 4)(x^3 \cdot x \cdot x^2)(y^2)$
$V = (2 \cdot 6 \cdot 4)(x^6)(y^2)$
$V = 48x^6 y^2$

Pages 722–723 Exercises

14. $(7^3)^2 = 7^{3\cdot2}$
$= 7^6$

15. $(yz)^4 = y^4 z^4$

16. $(-3w)^3 = (-3)^3 w^3$
$= -27w^3$

17. $(-2rs)^4 = (-2)^4 r^4 s^4$
$= 16r^4 s^4$

18. $[(-4)^2]^2 = [16]^2$
$= 256$

19. $(m^2)^5 = m^{2\cdot5}$
$= m^{10}$

20. $(-y^3)^6 = (-y)^{3\cdot6}$
$= (-y)^{18}$
$= y^{18}$

21. $(-2x^2)^5 = (-2)^5(x^2)^5$
$= -32x^{2\cdot5}$
$= -32x^{10}$

22. $(x^2 y)^3 = (x^2)^3 y^3$
$= x^{2\cdot3} y^3$
$= x^6 y^3$

23. $(-xy^3)^4 = (-x)^4(y^3)^4$
$= x^4 y^{3\cdot4}$
$= x^4 y^{12}$

24. $(2a^3 b)^5 = (2)^5(a^3)^5 b^5$
$= 32a^{3\cdot5} b^5$
$= 32a^{15} b^5$

25. $3x(2x)^2 = 3x(2^2 x^2)$
$= 3x(4x^2)$
$= 3 \cdot 4 \cdot x \cdot x^2$
$= 12x^3$

26. $-5x(x^3)^2 = -5x(x^{3\cdot2})$
$= -5x(x^6)$
$= -5 \cdot x \cdot x^6$
$= -5x^7$

27. $(4x^2y^3)^2 = 4^2(x^2)^2(y^3)^2$
$\qquad = 16x^{2\cdot2}y^{3\cdot2}$
$\qquad = 16x^4y^6$

28. $[(-3)^2]^3 = [9]^3$
$\qquad = 729$

29. $(t^3)^{-4} = t^{3\cdot-4}$
$\qquad = t^{-12}$

30. $(-w^2)^{-5} = -w^{2\cdot-5}$
$\qquad = -w^{-10}$

31. $-2(x^3y)^{-2} = -2((x^3)^{-2}y^2)$
$\qquad = -2(x^{3\cdot-2}y^{-2})$
$\qquad = -2x^{-6}y^{-2}$

32. $2ab^2 = 2(-2)(3)^2$
$\qquad = 2(-2)(9)$
$\qquad = -36$

33. $-3a^2b = -3(-2)^2(3)$
$\qquad = -3(4)(3)$
$\qquad = -36$

34. $-(ab^2)^2 = -[(-2)(3)^2]^2$
$\qquad = -[(-2)(9)]^2$
$\qquad = -[-18]^2$
$\qquad = -[324]$
$\qquad = -324$

35. $(-2ab^3) = [-2(-2)(3)^3]$
$\qquad = [-2(-2)(27)]$
$\qquad = 108$

36. $(a^3b^2) = [(-2)^3(3)^2]$
$\qquad = [(-8)(3)]^2$
$\qquad = [-24]^2$
$\qquad = 576$

37. $-(3a^2b)^2 = -[3(-2)^2(3)]^2$
$\qquad = -[3(4)(3)]^2$
$\qquad = -[36]^2$
$\qquad = -[1296]$
$\qquad = -1296$

38. $-3b(2a)^{-2} = -3(3)[2(-2)]^{-2}$
$\qquad = -9[-4]^{-2}$
$\qquad = \dfrac{-9}{[-4]^2}$
$\qquad = \dfrac{-9}{16}$

39. $2b^2(-3ab)^{-3} = 2(3)^2[-3(-2)(3)]^{-3}$
$\qquad = 2(9)[-3(-2)(3)]^{-3}$
$\qquad = 18[18]^{-3}$
$\qquad = \dfrac{18}{[18]^3}$
$\qquad = \dfrac{18}{5832}$
$\qquad = \dfrac{1}{324}$

40. $2(3a^{-2})^2 = 2[3(-2)^{-2}]^2$
$\qquad = 2\left[\dfrac{3}{(-2)^2}\right]^2$
$\qquad = 2\left[\dfrac{3}{4}\right]^2$
$\qquad = 2\left[\dfrac{9}{16}\right]$
$\qquad = \dfrac{18}{16}$
$\qquad = 1\dfrac{1}{8}$

41.

Monomial	Value	Monomial	Value
$(2\cdot3)^2$	36	$2^2\cdot3^2$	36
$(4\cdot5)^3$	8000	$4^3\cdot5^3$	8000
$(6\cdot7)^4$	3,111,696	$6^4\cdot7^4$	3,111,696
$(8\cdot3)^5$	7,962,624	$8^5\cdot3^5$	7,962,624

a. The numbers in the values columns are the same.

b. The exponents are distributed across the factors.

c. When you raise a product to a power, distribute the exponent over each factor.

42. yes; $(2^6)^4 = 2^{6\cdot4}$ or 2^{24},
$(4^6)^2 = ((2^2)^6)^2$ or 2^{24}.

43. a. $1000(1.01^4)^6$
b. $1000(1.01^4)^6 = 1000(1.01^{24})$
$\qquad = 1000(1.26973)$
$\qquad = 1269.73$
$\qquad$ $1269.73

44. a. $(2^5)^2 = 2^{10}$
b. $(2^5)^2 = (32)^2$
$\qquad = 1024$

45. Since there are 5280 feet in a mile, there are 5280^3 feet in a cubic mile.

46. $(5x + 2) - [(2x - 1) + (x + 3)]$
$= (5x + 2) - [(2x + x) + ((-1) + 3)]$
$= (5x + 2) - [(2 + 1)x + ((-1) + 3)]$
$= (5x + 2) - [3x + 2]$
$= (5x + 2) - (3x + 2)$
$= (5x + 2) + (-1)(3x + 2)$
$= 5x + 2 + (-3x - 2)$
$= 5x + 2 - 3x - 2$
$= 5x - 3x + 2 - 2$
$= 2x$

47. $C^2 = a^2 + b^2$
$C^2 = 5^2 + 12^2$
$C^2 = 25 + 144$
$C^2 = 169$
$C = \sqrt{169}$
$C = 13$ in.

48. $\triangle GHI \cong \triangle LKJ$;
$\angle G \cong \angle L$;
$\angle H \cong \angle K$;
$\angle I \cong \angle J$;
$\overline{GH} \cong \overline{LK}$;
$\overline{HI} \cong \overline{KJ}$;
$\overline{GI} \cong \overline{LJ}$

49. Sample answer: A spinner divided into 10 sections, six of them being successes.

50. $\dfrac{2x}{-5} = -24$
$-5\left(\dfrac{2}{-5}\right)x = -5(-24)$
$\qquad 2x = 120$
$\qquad \dfrac{2x}{2} = \dfrac{120}{2}$
$\qquad x = 60$

51.

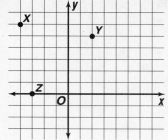

    a. Quadrant II
    b. Quadrant I
    c. none

52. a. $|2x| + yz = |2(-2)| + (4)(-1)$
             $= |-4| + (-4)$
             $= 4 + (-4)$
             $= 0$

    b. $\frac{4(x + y)}{2z} = \frac{4(-2 + 4)}{2(-1)}$
               $= \frac{4(2)}{-2}$
               $= \frac{8}{-2}$
               $= -4$

    c. $\frac{xyz}{8} = \frac{(-2)(4)(-1)}{8}$
           $= \frac{8}{8}$
           $= 1$

53. $xy \div 5$

Page 723   Earth Watch
See students' work.

| 14-5A | Math Lab: Multiplying Polynomials |

Page 724   Your Turn

1.

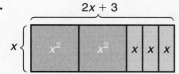

    $x(2x + 3)$
    $= 2x^2 + 3x$
    True

2.

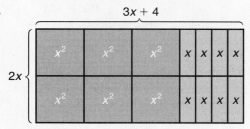

$2x(3x + 4)$
$= 6x^2 + 8x$
$\neq 6x^2 + 4x$
False

3.

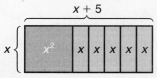

    $x(x + 5)$
    $= x^2 + 5x$

4.

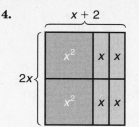

    $2x(x + 2)$
    $= 2x^2 + 4x$

5.

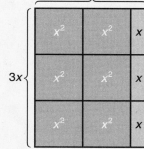

    $3x(2x + 1)$
    $= 6x^2 + 3x$

6. a.

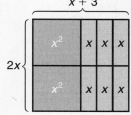

    $2x(x + 3)$;
    $2x^2 + 6x$

  b. $2(10)^2 + 6(10) = 2(100) + 60$
                   $= 200 + 60$
                   $= 260$
    260 ft^2

| 14-5 | Multiplying a Polynomial by a Monomial |

Page 726–727   Checking Your Understanding

  1. Multiply $2x$ and -1 by x.

  2. $x(2x + 3) = 2x^2 + 3x$

  3. The commutative property of multiplication says that the order of the multiplication is not important.

4.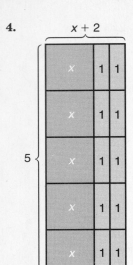

$x + 2$

$5(x + 2)$
$= 5x + 10$

5.

$x + 4$

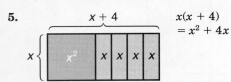

$x(x + 4)$
$= x^2 + 4x$

6.

$x - 1$

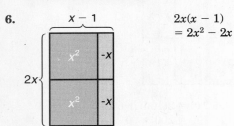

$2x(x - 1)$
$= 2x^2 - 2x$

7. $3(x + 4) = 3(x) + 3(4)$
$\qquad = 3x + 12$

8. $x(x + 5) = x(x) + x(5)$
$\qquad = x^2 + 5x$

9. $3(x - 2) = 3(x) - 3(2)$
$\qquad = 3x - 6$

10. $2x(x - 8) = 2x(x) - 2x(8)$
$\qquad = 2x^2 - 16x$

11. $4x(3x + 7) = 4x(3x) + 4x(7)$
$\qquad = 12x^2 + 28x$

12. $x(5x - 12) = x(5x) - x(12)$
$\qquad = 5x^2 - 12x$

13. Let w represent the width,
then the length is $3w - 120$.
$$P = 2(\ell + w)$$
$$1040 = 2[(3w - 120) + w]$$
$$1040 = 2[3w - 120 + w]$$
$$1040 = 2[3w + w - 120]$$
$$1040 = 2[4w - 120]$$
$$1040 = 2(4w) - 2(120)$$
$$1040 = 8w - 240$$
$$1040 + 240 = 8w - 240 + 240$$
$$1280 = 8w$$
$$\frac{1280}{8} = \frac{8w}{8}$$
$$160 = w$$
$w = 160$ and $3w - 120 = 360$.
The football field is 160 by 360 feet.

Page 727   Exercises

14. $7(3x + 5) = 7(3x) + 7(5)$
$\qquad = 21x + 35$

15. $-2(x + 8) = -2(x) + (-2)(8)$
$\qquad = -2 + (-16)$
$\qquad = -2x - 16$

16. $y(y - 9) = y(y) - y(9)$
$\qquad = y^2 - 9y$

17. $3x(2x - 1) = 3x(2x) - 3x(1)$
$\qquad = 6x^2 - 3x$

18. $-3x(x - 5) = -3x(x) - (-3x)(5)$
$\qquad = -3x^2 - (-15x)$
$\qquad = -3x^2 + 15x$

19. $c(a^2 + b) = c(a^2) + c(b)$
$\qquad = a^2c + bc$

20. $4m(m^2 - m) = 4m(m^2) - 4m(m)$
$\qquad = 4m^3 - 4m^2$

21. $pq(pq + 8) = pq(pq) + pq(8)$
$\qquad = p^2q^2 + 8pq$

22. $-3x(x^2 - 7x) = -3x(x^2) - (-3x)(7x)$
$\qquad = -3x^3 - (-21x^2)$
$\qquad = -3x^3 + 21x^2$

23. $-2a(9 - a^2) = -2a(9) - (-2a)(a^2)$
$\qquad = -18a - (-2a^3)$
$\qquad = -18a + 2a^3$

24. $7(-2a^2 + 5a - 11) = 7(-2a^2) + 7(5a) - 7(11)$
$\qquad = -14a^2 + 35a - 77$

25. $-5(3x^2 - 7x + 9) = -5(3x^2) - (-5)(7x) + (-5)(9)$
$\qquad = -15x^2 - (-35x) + (-45)$
$\qquad = -15x^2 + 35x - 45$

26. $-3y(6 - 9y + 4y^2) = -3y(6) - (-3y)(9y) + (-3y)(4y^2)$
$\qquad = -18y - (-27y^2) + (-12y^3)$
$\qquad = -18y + 27y^2 - 12y^3$

27. $4c(c^3 + 7c^2 - 10) = 4c(c^3) + 4c(7c^2) - 4c(10)$
$\qquad = 4c^4 + 28c^3 - 40c$

28. $-5x^2(3x^3 - 8x - 12) = -5x^2(3x^3) - (-5x^2)(8x) -$
$\qquad\qquad (-5x^2)(12)$
$\qquad = -15x^5 - (-40x^3) - (-60x^2)$
$\qquad = -15x^5 + 40x^3 + 60x^2$

29. $6x^2(-2x^3 + 8x^2 - 7) = 6x^2(-2x^3) + 6x^2(8x^2) - 6x^2(7)$
$\qquad = -12x^5 + 48x^4 - 42x^2$

30. $2x(5x^3 - 4x^2 + 6x - 9) = 2x(5x^3) - 2x(4x^2) +$
$\qquad\qquad 2x(6x) - 2x(9)$
$\qquad = 10x^4 - 8x^3 + 12x^2 - 18x$

31. $-x^2(x^3 - x^2 + 3x - 5) = -x^2(x^3) - (-x^2)(x^2) +$
$\qquad\qquad (-x^2)(3x) - (-x^2)(5)$
$\qquad = -x^5 - (-x^4) + (-3x^3) - (-5x^2)$
$\qquad = -x^5 + x^4 - 3x^3 + 5x^2$

32. $\qquad -3(2a - 12) + 48 = 3a + 3$
$-3(2a) - (-3)(12) + 48 = 3a + 3$
$\qquad -6a - (-36) + 48 = 3a + 3$
$\qquad -6a + 36 + 48 = 3a + 3$
$\qquad -6a + 84 = 3a + 3$
$\qquad -6a + 84 - 84 = 3a + 3 - 84$
$\qquad -6a = 3a - 81$
$\qquad -6a - 3a = 3a - 3a - 81$
$\qquad -9a = -81$
$\qquad \frac{-9a}{-9} = \frac{-81}{-9}$
$\qquad a = 9$

33.
$$2(5w - 12) = 6(-2w + 3) + 2$$
$$2(5w) - 2(12) = 6(-2w) + 6(3) + 2$$
$$10w - 24 = -12w + 18 + 2$$
$$10w - 24 = -12w + 20$$
$$10w - 24 + 24 = -12w + 20 + 24$$
$$10w = -12w + 44$$
$$10w + 12w = -12w + 12w + 44$$
$$22w = 44$$
$$\frac{22w}{22} = \frac{44}{22}$$
$$w = 2$$

34.

x	1	1	1
x	1	1	1

The factors of $2x + 6$ are 2 and $x + 3$. You can find the factors of a binomial by dividing each term by its greatest common factor. Then the greatest common factor and the result are the factors of the binomials.

35. a. The measures of the sides of the box are equal.
side: $A = x(2x + 1)$
$$A = x(2x) + x(1)$$
$$A = 2x^2 + x$$
The total area of the sides is $4(2x^2 + x)$
or $8x^2 + 4x$.
bottom: $A = (2x + 1)(2x + 1)$
$$A = 2x(2x) + 2x(1) + 1(2x) + 1(1)$$
$$A = 4x^2 + 2x + 2x + 1$$
$$A = 4x^2 + 4x + 1$$
So, $8x^2 + 4x + 4x^2 + 4x + 1$ or $12x^2 + 8x + 1$ square inches of cardboard is needed.
b. $12x^2 + 8x + 1 = 12(2.5)^2 + 8(2.5) + 1$
$$= 12(6.25) + 8(2.5) + 1$$
$$= 75 + 20 + 1$$
$$= 96$$
The surface area is 96 in^2.

36. Area (shaded region) = area (large region)
                                                            − area (small region)
$$A = s(2s + s) - 3s$$
$$A = s(2s) + s(s) - 3s$$
$$A = 2s^2 + s^2 - 3s$$
$$A = 3s^2 - 3s$$
The area of the shaded region is $3s^2 - 3s$.

37. $-4b(2b)^3 = -4b(2^3 b^3)$
$$= -4b(8b^3)$$
$$= -32b^4$$

38. $-\sqrt{144} < -\sqrt{150} < -\sqrt{169}$
$$-\sqrt{12^2} < -\sqrt{150} < -\sqrt{13^2}$$
$$-12 < -\sqrt{150} < -13$$
$$-12$$
Check: $-\sqrt{150} \approx -12.2$

39. Sample answers: Choose a scale that makes one product look much better than the other; omit some information or labels.

40.

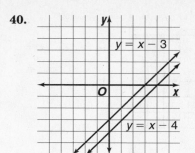

There is no solution.

41. The area of the background is 130×90 or 11,700 square feet. The sprinkler can water an area of 30×30 or 900 square feet. $11,700 \div 900 = 13$. Therefore, the sprinkler will need to be moved 13 times.

42. 2, 3, 6

43. $d = rt$
$$d = (55)\left(3\frac{1}{2}\right)$$
$$d = 192.5 \text{ miles}$$

14-6   **Multiplying Binomials**

Page 730   Checking Your Understanding

1.

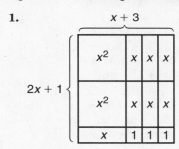

$(x + 3)(2x + 1) = 2x^2 + 7x + 3$

2. Sample answer: The distributive property is used to multiply both two binomials and a binomial and a monomial. But when you multiply two binomials there are four multiplications, and with a binomial and a monomial there are only two multiplications to perform.

3.

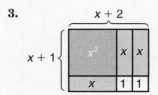

$(x + 1)(x + 2) = x^2 + 3x + 2$

4.

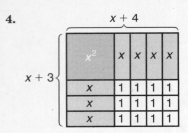

$$(x + 3)(x + 4) = x^2 + 7x + 12$$

5.

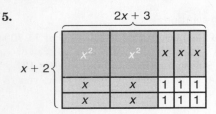

$$(2x + 3)(x + 2) = 2x^2 + 7x + 6$$

6. $2x + 2, x + 2; 2x^2 + 6x + 4$

7. $x + 3, 2x + 1; 2x^2 + 7x + 3$

8. $(x + 3)(2x + 5) = (x + 3)2x + (x + 3)5$
$\qquad = (x)2x + (3)2x + (x)5 + (3)5$
$\qquad = 2x^2 + 6x + 5x + 15$
$\qquad = 2x^2 + 11x + 15$

9. $(2x + 3)(x + 1) = (2x + 3)x + (2x + 3)1$
$\qquad = (2x)x + (3)x + (2x)1 + (3)1$
$\qquad = 2x^2 + 3x + 2x + 3$
$\qquad = 2x^2 + 5x + 3$

10. $(2x + 3)(3x + 2) = (2x + 3)3x + (2x + 3)2$
$\qquad = (2x)3x + (3)3x + (2x)2 + (3)2$
$\qquad = 6x^2 + 9x + 4x + 6$
$\qquad = 6x^2 + 13x + 6$

11. $(5x - 3)(2x + 1) = (5x - 3)2x + (5x - 3)1$
$\qquad = (5x)2x - (3)2x + (5x)1 - (3)1$
$\qquad = 10x^2 - 6x + 6x + 5x - 3$
$\qquad = 10x^2 - x - 3$

12. Let w represent the width of the court.

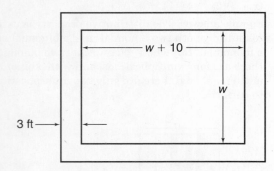

The width of the court and path is $3 + w + 3$ or $w + 6$. The length of the court and path is $3 + w + 10 + 3$ or $w + 16$. Therefore, the total area of the court and path is $(w + 6)(w + 16)$ or $w^2 + 22w + 96$ feet.

Pages 730–731 Exercises

13. $2x + 1, x + 2; 2x^2 + 5x + 2$

14. $2x + 2, x + 1; 2x^2 + 4x + 2$

15. $2x + 3, 2x + 2; 4x^2 + 10x + 6$

16. $2x + 2, x + 3; 2x^2 + 8x + 6$

17. $(x + 4)(x + 3) = (x + 4)x + (x + 4)3$
$\qquad = (x)x + (4)x + (x)3 + (4)3$
$\qquad = x^2 + 4x + 3x + 12$
$\qquad = x^2 + 7x + 12$

18. $(x + 5)(x + 2) = (x + 5)x + (x + 5)2$
$\qquad = (x)x + (5)x + (x)2 + (5)2$
$\qquad = x^2 + 5x + 2x + 10$
$\qquad = x^2 + 7x + 10$

19. $(x - 6)(x + 2) = (x - 6)x + (x - 6)2$
$\qquad = (x)x - (6)x + (x)2 - (6)2$
$\qquad = x^2 - 6x + 2x - 12$
$\qquad = x^2 - 4x - 12$

20. $(x + 7)(x - 5) = (x + 7)x + (x + 7)(-5)$
$\qquad = (x)x + (7)x + (x)(-5) + (7)(-5)$
$\qquad = x^2 + 7x + (-5x) + (-35)$
$\qquad = x^2 + 2x - 35$

21. $(x - 9)(x + 4) = (x - 9)x + (x - 9)4$
$\qquad = (x)x - (9)x + (x)4 - (9)4$
$\qquad = x^2 - 9x + 4x - 36$
$\qquad = x^2 - 5x - 36$

22. $(x + 2)(x + 2) = (x + 2)x + (x + 2)2$
$\qquad = (x)x + (2)x + x(2) + (2)2$
$\qquad = x^2 + 2x + 2x + 4$
$\qquad = x^2 + 4x + 4$

23. $(2x + 3)(x - 4) = (2x + 3)x + (2x + 3)(-4)$
$\qquad = (2x)x + (3)x + (2x)(-4) + (3)(-4)$
$\qquad = 2x^2 + 3x + (-8x) + (-12)$
$\qquad = 2x^2 - 5x - 12$

24. $(3x - 1)(x + 8) = (3x - 1)x + (3x - 1)8$
$\qquad = (3x)x - (1)x + (3x)8 - (1)8$
$\qquad = 3x^2 - 1x + 24x - 8$
$\qquad = 3x^2 + 23x - 8$

25. $(x + 3)(x + 3) = (x + 3)x + (x + 3)3$
$\qquad = (x)x + (3)x + (x)3 + 3(3)$
$\qquad = x^2 + 3x + 3x + 9$
$\qquad = x^2 + 6x + 9$

26. $(2x + 5)(3x + 1) = (2x + 5)3x + (2x + 5)1$
$\qquad = (2x)3x + 5(3x) + (2x)1 + (5)1$
$\qquad = 6x^2 + 15x + 2x + 5$
$\qquad = 6x^2 + 17x + 5$

27. $(5x + 2)(2x - 3) = (5x + 2)2x + (5x + 2)(-3)$
$\qquad = (5x)2x + (2)2x + (5x)(-3) + (2)(-3)$
$\qquad = 10x^2 + 4x + (-15x) + (-6)$
$\qquad = 10x^2 - 11x - 6$

28. $(x - 5)(x + 5) = (x - 5)x + (x - 5)5$
$\qquad = (x)x - (5)x + (x)5 - (5)5$
$\qquad = x^2 - 5x + 5x - 25$
$\qquad = x^2 - 25$

29. $\left(3x - \frac{1}{4}\right)\left(6x - \frac{1}{2}\right) = \left(3x - \frac{1}{4}\right)6x + \left(3x - \frac{1}{4}\right)\left(-\frac{1}{2}\right)$
$\qquad = (3x)6x - \left(\frac{1}{4}\right)6x + (3x)\left(-\frac{1}{2}\right) - \left(\frac{1}{4}\right)\left(-\frac{1}{2}\right)$
$\qquad = 18x^2 - \frac{3}{2}x + \left(-\frac{3}{2}x\right) - \left(-\frac{1}{8}\right)$
$\qquad = 18x^2 - 3x + \frac{1}{8}$

30. $(x - 2)(x^2 + 2x + 4)$
$= (x - 2)x^2 + (x - 2)2x + (x - 2)4$
$= (x)x^2 - (2)x^2 + (x)2x - (2)2 + (x)4 - (2)4$
$= x^3 - 2x^2 + 2x^2 - 4x + 4x - 8$
$= x^3 - 8$

31. $(x + 2)(x - 1); x^2 + x - 2$

32. a.

x^2
x
x

b.

x^2	x	x	x
x	1	1	1
x	1	1	1
x	1	1	1
x	1	1	1
x	1	1	1
x	1	1	1

c. full-sized: $x^2 + 9x + 18$;
baby quilt: $x^2 + 2x$

d. $(x^2 + 9x + 18) - (x^2 + 2x)$
$= (x^2 + 9x + 18) + (-1)(x^2 + 2x)$
$= x^2 + 9x + 18 + (-x^2 - 2x)$
$= x^2 + 9x + 18 - x^2 - 2x$
$= x^2 - x^2 + 9x - 2x + 18$
$= 7x + 18$

33. a. Let w represent the width of the small
rectangle. Then $2w - 1$ represents the length
of the small rectangle, $w + 2$ represents the
width of the large rectangle and $(2w - 1) + 2$
or $2w + 1$ represents the length of the large
rectangle.
Area(shaded region) = Area(large) − Area(small)
area(large): $A = (2w + 1)(w + 2)$
$A = (2w + 1)w + (2w + 1)2$
$A = (2w)w + (1)w + (2w)2 + (1)2$
$A = 2w^2 + 1w + 4w + 2$
$A = 2w^2 + 5w + 2$
area(small): $A = (2w - 1)w$
$A = (2w)w - (1)w$
$A = 2w^2 - w$
So,
$86 = (2w^2 + 5w + 2) - (2w^2 - w)$
$86 = (2w^2 + 5w + 2) + (-1)(2w^2 - w)$
$86 = 2w^2 + 5w + 2 + (-2w^2 + w)$
$86 = 2w^2 + 5w + 2 - 2w^2 + w$
$86 = 6w + 2$
$86 - 2 = 6w + 2 - 2$
$84 = 6w$
$14 = w$
$w = 14$ and $2(14) - 1 = 27$.
The dimensions of the smaller rectangle are
14 in. and 27 in.

b. The area of the smaller rectangle is 14×27
or 378 in^2.

c. The length of the larger rectangle is
$((2(14) - 1) + 2)$ or 29 inches. The width is
$14 + 2$ or 16 inches. Therefore, the area of the
larger rectangle is $16(29)$ or 464 in^2.

34. $-2(4c^2 - 3c + 5) = -2(4c^2) - (-2)(3c) + (-2)(5)$
$= -8c^2 - (-6c) + (-10)$
$= -8c^2 + 6c - 10$

35. Let x represent height of tree.
$\frac{x}{60} = \frac{3}{2}$
$x \cdot 2 = 60 \cdot 3$
$2x = 180$
$\frac{2x}{2} = \frac{180}{2}$
$x = 90$
The height of the tree is 90 ft.

36. $0.12 \times 360 = 43.2 \rightarrow 43.2°$

37. $C = 2\pi r$
$C = 2 \cdot \pi \cdot 0.5$
$C \approx 3.14$ m

38. $60 = 2 \cdot 2 \cdot 3 \cdot 5$
$25 = 5 \cdot 5$
The GCF of 60 and 25 is 5.

39. $6x < -84$
$\frac{6x}{6} < \frac{-84}{6}$
$x < -14$

14-6B Math Lab: Factoring

Page 732 Your Turn
See students' work

1.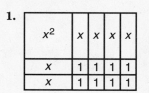
yes;
$x^2 + 6x + 8$
$= (x + 2)(x + 4)$

2.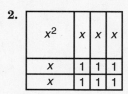
yes;
$x^2 + 5x + 6$
$= (x + 2)(x + 3)$

3.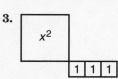
$x^2 + 7x + 3$ is
not factorable.

4.

x^2	x
x^2	x
x^2	x
x	1
x	1
x	1
x	1
x	1

yes;
$3x^2 + 8x + 5$
$= (3x + 5)(x + 1)$

5.

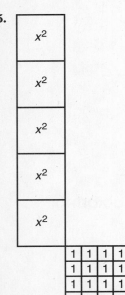

$5x^2 - x + 16$ is not factorable.

6.

x^2	$-x$	$-x$	$-x$	$-x$
x^2	$-x$	$-x$	$-x$	$-x$
x^2	$-x$	$-x$	$-x$	$-x$
x^2	$-x$	$-x$	$-x$	$-x$
x^2	$-x$	$-x$	$-x$	$-x$
x^2	$-x$	$-x$	$-x$	$-x$
x^2	$-x$	$-x$	$-x$	$-x$
x^2	$-x$	$-x$	$-x$	$-x$
x	1	1	1	1

yes;
$8x^2 - 31x - 4$
$= (8x + 1)(x - 4)$

7. Sample answer: A trinomial can be factored if you can make a rectangle with algebra tiles that represent that trinomial.

$x^2 + 5x + 6$ can be factored, but $x^2 + 6x + 6$ cannot.

x^2	x	x
x	1	1
x	1	1
x	1	1

Chapter 14   Study Guide and Assessment

Page 733   Understanding and Using Vocabulary

1. sum
2. trinomial
3. greatest
4. coefficient
5. additive inverse
6. distributive property
7. false
8. false
9. true
10. true

Pages 734–736   Skills and Concepts

11. yes; binomial because it is the difference of two monomials.
12. no; because there is a variable in the denominator.
13. yes; monomial

14. yes; trinomial because it is the sum of three monomials.

15. yes; binomial because it is the difference of two monomials.

16. no; because there is a variable in the denominator.

17. $4x$ has degree 1.

18. $5a^2b$ has degree $2 + 1$ or 3.

19. $3x$ has degree 1.
y^2 has degree 2.
So, the degree of $3x + y^2$ is 2.

20. $19m^2n^3$ has degree $2 + 3$ or 5.
$-14mn^4$ has degree $1 + 4$ or 5.
So, the degree of $19m^2n^3 - 14mn^4$ is 5.

21. x^2 has degree 2.
$-6xy$ has degree $1 + 1$ or 2.
xy^2 has degree $1 + 2$ or 3.
So, the degree of $x^2 - 6xy + xy^2$ is 3.

22. $12rs^2$ has degree $1 + 2$ or 3.
$3r^2s$ has degree $2 + 1$ or 3.
$5r^4s$ has degree $4 + 1$ or 5.
So, the degree of $12rs^2 + 3r^2s + 5r^4s$ is 5.

23. $(2x^2 - 5x) + (3x^2 + x) = (2x^2 + 3x^2) + [(-5x) + x]$
$= (2 + 3)x^2 + [(-5) + 1]x$
$= 5x^2 + (-4)x$
$= 5x^2 - 4x$

24. $(a^2 - 6ab) + (3a^2 + ab) = (a^2 + 3a^2) + [(-6ab) + ab]$
$= (1 + 3)a^2 + [(-6) + 1]ab$
$= 4a^2 + (-5)ab$
$= 4a^2 - 5ab$

25. $(x^2 - 5x + 3) + (4x + 3) = x^2 + [(-5x) + 4x] + [3 + (-3)]$
$= x^2 + [(-5) + 4]x + [3 + (-3)]$
$= x^2 + (-1)x + 0$
$= x^2 - x$

26. $(-3y^2 + 2) + (4y^2 - 5y - 2\,) = [(-3y^2) + 4y^2] +$
$\qquad\qquad (-5y) + [2 + (-2)]$
$= [(-3) + 4]y^2 +$
$\qquad\qquad (-5y) + [2 + (-2)]$
$= (1)y^2 + (-5y) + 0$
$= y^2 - 5y$

27.
$$\begin{array}{r} 4x^2 + 3x + 2 \\ (+)\ x^2 \qquad\ -1 \\ \hline 5x^2 + 3x + 1 \end{array}$$

28.
$$\begin{array}{r} 16x^2y - 2xy + \ xy^2 \\ (+)\ 4x^2y + 6xy - 8xy^2 \\ \hline 20x^2y + 4xy - 7xy^2 \end{array}$$

29. $(7a - 11b) - (3a + 4b) = (7a - 11b) + (-1)(3a + 4b)$
$= 7a - 11b + (-3a - 4b)$
$= 7a - 11b - 3a - 4b$
$= 7a - 3a - 11b - 4b$
$= 4a - 15b$

30. $(6y - 8z) - (6y + 4z) = (6y - 8z) + (-1)(6y + 4z)$
$= 6y - 8z + (-6y - 4z)$
$= 6y - 8z - 6y - 4z$
$= 6y - 6y - 8z - 4z$
$= 0 - 12z$
$= -12z$

31. $(3a^2 - b^2 + c^2) - (a^2 + 2b^2)$
$= (3a^2 - b^2 + c^2) + (-1)(a^2 + 2b^2)$
$= 3a^2 - b^2 + c^2 + (-a^2 - 2b^2)$
$= 3a^2 - b^2 + c^2 - a^2 - 2b^2$
$= 3a^2 - a^2 - b^2 - 2b^2 + c^2$
$= 2a^2 - 3b^2 + c^2$

32. $(14a^2 - 3a) - (6a^2 + 5a + 17)$
$= (14a^2 - 3a) + (-1)(6a^2 + 5a + 17)$
$= 14a^2 - 3a + (-6a^2 - 5a - 17)$
$= 14a^2 - 3a - 6a^2 - 5a - 17$
$= 14a^2 - 6a^2 - 3a - 5a - 17$
$= 8a^2 - 8a - 17$

33.
$$\begin{array}{r} 18x^2 + 3x - 1 \\ (-)\,2x^2 + 4x + 6 \end{array} \rightarrow \begin{array}{r} 18x^2 + 3x - 1 \\ (+)\,-2x^2 - 4x - 6 \\ \hline 16x^2 - \ x - 7 \end{array}$$

34.
$$\begin{array}{r} 12m^2 - \ mn + 9n^2 \\ (-)\,7m^2 + 2mn - 4n^2 \end{array} \rightarrow \begin{array}{r} 12m^2 - \ mn + \ 9n^2 \\ (+)\,-7m^2 - 2mn + \ 4n^2 \\ \hline 5m^2 - 3mn + 13n^2 \end{array}$$

35. $(a^2)^3 = a^{2\cdot3}$
$\quad = a^6$

36. $(-2x)^3 = (-2)^3x^3$
$\quad = -8x^3$

37. $(p^2q)^3 = (p^2)^3q^3$
$= p^{2\cdot3}q^3$
$= p^6q^3$

38. $-5c(2cd)^3 = -5c(2^3c^3d^3)$
$= -5c(8c^3d^3)$
$= -5 \cdot 8 \cdot c \cdot c^3 \cdot d$
$= -40c^4d^3$

39. $4y(y^2z)^3 = 4y((y^2)^3z^3)$
$= 4y(y^{2\cdot3}z^3)$
$= 4y(y^6z^3)$
$= 4 \cdot y \cdot y^6 \cdot z^3$
$= 4y^7z^3$

40. $(12a^5)^2b^3 = 12^2(a^5)^2b^3$
$= 144a^{5\cdot2}b^3$
$= 144a^{10}b^3$

41. $6a(-ab)^7 = 6a((-a)^7b^7)$
$= 6a(-a^7b^7)$
$= -1 \cdot 6 \cdot a \cdot a^7 \cdot b^7$
$= -6a^8b^7$

42. $(-2d^2)^6(-3)^3 = (-2)^6(d^2)^6(-3)^3$
$= 64d^{12}(-27)$
$= 64(-27)d^{12}$
$= -1728d^{12}$

43. $4d(2d - 5) = 4d(2d) - 4d(5)$
$= 8d^2 - 20d$

44. $x(-5x + 3) = x(-5x) + x(3)$
$= -5x^2 + 3x$

45. $a^2(2a^3 + a - 5) = a^2(2a^3) + a^2(a) - a^2(5)$
$= 2a^5 + a^3 - 5a^2$

46. $3y(-y^2 - 8y + 4) = 3y(-y^2) - 3y(8y) + 3y(4)$
$= -3y^3 - 24y^2 + 12y$

47. $-2g(g^3 + 6g + 3) = -2g(g^3) + (-2g)(6g) + (-2g)(3)$
$= -2g^4 + (-12g^2) + (-6g)$
$= -2g^4 - 12g^2 - 6g$

48. $-3az(2z^2 + 4az + a^2) = -3az(2z^2) + (-3az)(4az) +$
$\qquad\qquad (-3az)(a^2)$
$= -6az^3 + (-12a^2z^2) + (-3a^3z)$
$= -6az^3 - 12a^2z^2 - 3a^3z$

49. $2x + 1, x + 3; 2x^2 + 7x + 3$

50. $(x + 3)(x + 1) = (x + 3)x + (x + 3)1$
$= (x)x + (3)x + (x)1 + (3)1$
$= x^2 + 3x + 1x + 3$
$= x^2 + 4x + 3$

51. $(2x + 1)(x + 1) = (2x + 1)x + (2x + 1)1$
$= (2x)x + (1)x + (2x)1 + (1)1$
$= 2x^2 + 1x + 2x + 1$
$= 2x^2 + 3x + 1$

52. $(3x + 2)(2x + 2) = (3x + 2)2x + (3x + 2)2$
$= (3x)2x + (2)2x + (3x)2 + (2)2$
$= 6x^2 + 4x + 6x + 4$
$= 6x^2 + 10x + 4$

Page 736   Applications and Problem Solving

53. dining room: $(2y)(y) = 2y^2$
kitchen: $(2y)(z - x) = 2yz - 2xy$
living room: $(4y)(x) = 4xy$

total area of first floor: $4xy - 2xy + 2y^2 + 2yz$
$$= 2xy + 2y^2 + 2yz$$

54. $(4x - 2y) - [(x + y) + (x - y)]$
$= (4x - 2y) - [(x + x) + (y + (-y))]$
$= (4x - 2y) - [(1 + 1)x + (1 + (-1))y]$
$= (4x - 2y) - [2x + (0)y]$
$= 4x - 2y - 2x$
$= 4x - 2x - 2y$
$= 2x - 2y$
$2x - 2y$ units

55. $V = Bh$
$V = \left(\frac{1}{2} \cdot x \cdot 2x\right) \cdot 3x$
$V = x^2 \cdot 3x$
$V = 3x^3$

56. Let w represent the width of the field. Then $2w + 40$ represents the length of the field.
$$P = 2(\ell + w)$$
$1040 = 2((2w + 40) + w)$
$1040 = 2(2w + w + 40)$
$1040 = 2(3w + 40)$
$1040 = 2(3w) + 2(40)$
$1040 = 6w + 80$
$1040 - 80 = 6w + 80 - 80$
$960 = 6w$
$160 = w$
$w = 160$ and $2w + 40 = 360$.
The field is 160 ft by 360 ft.

Page 737   Alternative Assessment

Power	Product	Coefficients of the Terms
$(x + y)^2$	$x^2 + 2xy + y^2$	1, 2, 1
$(x + y)^3$	$x^3 + 3x^2y + 3xy^2 + y^3$	1, 3, 3, 1
$(x + y)^4$	$x^4 + 4x^3y + 6x^2y^2 + 4xy^3 + y^4$	1, 4, 6, 4, 1
$(x + y)^5$	$x^5 + 5x^4y + 10x^3y^2 + 10x^2y^3 + 5xy^4 + y^5$	1, 5, 10, 10, 5, 1

The sixth row of Pascal's Triangle is the coefficients of the expansion of $(x + y)^5$
$(x + y)^6 = x^6 + 6x^5y + 15x^4y^2 + 20x^3y^3 +$
$\qquad 15x^2y^4 + 6xy^5 + y^6$.

Page 737   Thinking Critically

- yes
- Let a represent the upper base. Then $2a - 5$ represents the lower base.
$$A = \frac{1}{2}h(a + b)$$
$425 = \frac{1}{2} \cdot 10(a + (2a - 5))$
$425 = \frac{1}{2} \cdot 10(a + 2a - 5)$
$425 = \frac{1}{2} \cdot 10(3a - 5)$
$425 = 5(3a - 5)$
$425 = 5(3a) - 5(5)$
$425 = 15a - 25$
$425 + 25 = 15a - 25 + 25$
$450 = 15a$
$30 = a$

The upper base is 30 in. and the lower base is $2(30) - 5$ or 55 in.

Page 737   Portfolio

See students' work.

Page 737   Self Evaluation

See students' work.

Ongoing Assessment

Pages 738–739

1. B; $\frac{3^6}{3^2} = 3^{6-2}$
$\qquad = 3^4$

2. C; $\tan \angle D = \frac{12}{9}$
$\qquad = \frac{4}{3}$

3. C; front and back: $2(6 \times 12) = 144$
top and bottom: $2(6 \times 2) = 24$
two sides: $2(2 \times 12) = 48$
The surface area is
$144 + 24 + 48$ or 216 in^2.

4. A; $(7x^2 + 3y) - (3x^2 + 5y)$
$= (7x^2 + 3y) + (-1)(3x^2 + 5y)$
$= 7x^2 + 3y + (-3x^2 - 5y)$
$= 7x^2 + 3y - 3x^2 - 5y$
$= 7x^2 - 3x^2 + 3y - 5y$
$= 4x^2 - 2y$

5. C; $0.25 \times 35 = 8.75$
The discount is \$8.75.
The sale price is $35 - 8.75$ or \$26.25.
So, \$26 is the best estimate.

6. C; $c^2 = a^2 + b^2$
$c^2 = (30)^2 + (40)^2$
$c^2 = 900 + 1600$
$c^2 = 2500$
$c = \sqrt{2500}$
$c = 50$
The diagonal is 50 in.

7. B; $SA = \pi r^2 + \pi rs$
$SA = \pi(6)^2 + \pi(6)(18)$
$SA = \pi(36) + \pi(6)(18)$
$SA \approx 113.0 + 339.2$
$SA \approx 452.2 \text{ m}^2$

8. A; $(-2x)^3 = (-2)^3 x^3$
$= -8x^3$

9. B; Since $\angle M \cong \angle F$, $m\angle M = 60°$.

10. C; $\sin 30° = \frac{15}{x}$
$x \sin 30° = 15$
$x = \frac{15}{\sin 30°}$
$x \approx 30 \text{ in.}$

11. A regular hexagon has 6 sides. Therefore, the perimeter is 6(12.6) or 75.6 m.

12.

Nickel	Dime	Quarter	Half Dollar	Amount
∣	∣			15¢
∣		∣		30¢
∣			∣	55¢
	∣	∣		30¢
	∣		∣	60¢
		∣	∣	75¢

He can choose 15¢, 30¢, 35¢, 55¢, 60¢, or 75¢.

13.

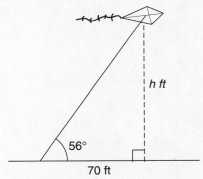

Let h represent the height of the kite.
$\tan 56° = \frac{h}{70}$
$(70)(\tan 56°) = h$
$103.8 \approx h$
The kite is 103.8 feet high.

14. $a^4 - 2a^3 + 4b^2 - c = (2)^4 - 2(2)^3 + 4(-6)^2 - (-2)$
$= 16 - 2(8) + 4(36) - (-2)$
$= 16 - 16 + 144 + 2$
$= 146$

15. $A = \pi r^2$
$A = \pi(6)^2$
$A = \pi(36)$
$A \approx 113 \text{ cm}^2$

16.

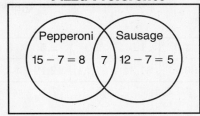

Pizza Preference

Pepperoni $15 - 7 = 8$ | 7 | Sausage $12 - 7 = 5$

$25 - (8 + 7 + 5) = 25 - 20$
$= 5$
5 people

17. $\frac{15}{50} = \frac{x}{1000}$
$15 \cdot 1000 = 50 \cdot x$
$15,000 = 50x$
$\frac{15,000}{50} = \frac{50x}{50}$
$300 = x$
Expect 300 people to like country music.

18. $(4x^3 + 2x^2) + (-2x^3 - 7x^2)$
$= [4x^2 + (-2x^3)] + [2x^2 + (-7x^2)]$
$= [4 + (-2)]x^3 + [2 + (-7)]x^2$
$= 2x^3 + (-5)x^2$
$= 2x^3 - 5x^2$

19. $\sqrt{45} \approx 6.7$

20. Let x represent the area of Canada.
$2x - 110,416 = 6,590,876$
$2x - 110,416 + 110,416 = 6,590,876 + 110,416$
$2x = 6,701,292$
$\frac{2x}{2} = \frac{6,701,292}{2}$
$x = 3,350,646$
Canada is 3,350,646 square miles.

21. $2.25 = 2\frac{25}{100}$
$= 2\frac{1}{4}$

22. A trapezoid has 4 sides.
Therefore, $n = 4$.
$(n - 2)180 = (4 - 2)180$
$= 2(180)$ or 360
The sum of the measures of the interior angles of a trapezoid is 360°.

23. See students' work.

24. See students' work.

25. See students' work.

Extra Practice

Pages 740 Lesson 1-1

1. a. know other rates, need to find rate for 5.5 oz

   b. sample answer: look for a pattern
   By looking at the table, the rate should be about $4.50.

   c.

0.5	1.0	1.5	2.0	2.5	3.0
$0.50	$0.95	$1.34	$1.73	$2.12	$2.51

$\overset{+0.45}{\smile}\ \overset{+0.39}{\smile}\ \overset{+0.39}{\smile}\ \overset{+0.39}{\smile}\ \overset{+0.39}{\smile}$

3.5	4.0	4.5	5.0	5.5
$2.90	$3.29	$3.68	$4.07	$4.46

$\overset{+0.39}{\smile}\ \overset{+0.39}{\smile}\ \overset{+0.39}{\smile}\ \overset{+0.39}{\smile}$

The air mail rate for a package that weighs 5.5 ounces is $4.46.

   d. See students' work.

2. a. sample answer: estimation since the problem says "about"

   b. Explore—We know the cost of one stamp and the number of stamps issued. We need to know how much postage the stamps represented.

   Plan—Multiply the cost of one stamp by the number of stamps issued. Since an exact answer is not necessary, solve by using estimation.

   Solve—$0.32 \times 90,000,000 \rightarrow$
   $0.30 \times 100,000,000 = 30,000,000$
   The stamps represented about $30 million in postage.

   Examine—The actual answer is $0.32 \times 90,000,000$ or $28,800,000$. So, the estimate of $30 million is reasonable.

Page 740 Lesson 1-2

1. $8 + 7 + 12 \div 4 = 8 + 7 + 3$
$= 15 + 3$
$= 18$

2. $20 \div 4 - 5 + 12 = 5 - 5 + 12$
$= 0 + 12$
$= 12$

3. $(25 \cdot 3) + (10 \cdot 3) = 75 + 30$
$= 105$

4. $36 \div 6 + 7 - 6 = 6 + 7 - 6$
$= 13 - 6$
$= 7$

5. $30 \cdot (6 - 4) = 30 \cdot 2$
$= 60$

6. $(40 \cdot 2) - (6 \cdot 11) = 80 - 66$
$= 14$

7. $\frac{86 - 11}{11 + 4} = (86 - 11) \div (11 + 4)$
$= 75 \div 15$
$= 5$

8. $\frac{12 + 84}{11 + 13} = (12 + 84) \div (11 + 13)$
$= 96 \div 24$
$= 4$

9. $\frac{5 \cdot 5 + 5}{5 \cdot 5 - 15} = (5 \cdot 5 + 5) \div (5 \cdot 5 - 15)$
$= (25 + 5) \div (25 - 15)$
$= 30 \div 10$
$= 3$

10. $(19 - 8)4 = (11)4$
$= 44$

11. $75 - 5(2 \cdot 6) = 75 - 5(12)$
$= 75 - 60$
$= 15$

12. $81 \div 27 \times 6 - 2 = 3 \times 6 - 2$
$= 18 - 2$
$= 16$

Page 740 Lesson 1-3

1. $ba - ac = 4 \cdot 2 - 2 \cdot 3$
$= 8 - 2 \cdot 3$
$= 8 - 6$
$= 2$

2. $4b + a \cdot a = 4 \cdot 4 + 2 \cdot 2$
$= 16 + 2 \cdot 2$
$= 16 + 4$
$= 20$

3. $11 \cdot c - ab = 11 \cdot 3 - 2 \cdot 4$
$= 33 - 2 \cdot 4$
$= 33 - 8$
$= 25$

4. $4b - (a + c) = 4 \cdot 4 - (2 + 3)$
$= 4 \cdot 4 - 5$
$= 16 - 5$
$= 11$

5. $7(a + b) - c = 7(2 + 4) - 3$
$= 7 \cdot 6 - 3$
$= 42 - 3$
$= 39$

6. $8a + 8b = 8 \cdot 2 + 8 \cdot 4$
$= 16 + 8 \cdot 4$
$= 16 + 32$
$= 48$

7. $\frac{8(a + b)}{4c} = \frac{8(2 + 4)}{4 \cdot 3}$
$= [8(2 + 4)] \div [4 \cdot 3]$
$= [8 \cdot 6] \div [4 \cdot 3]$
$= 48 \div 12$
$= 4$

8. $36 - 12c = 36 - 12 \cdot 3$
$= 36 - 36$
$= 0$

9. $\frac{9(b + a)}{c - 1} = \frac{9(4 + 2)}{3 - 1}$
$= [9(4 + 2)] \div [3 - 1]$
$= [9 \cdot 6] \div [3 - 1]$
$= 54 \div 2$
$= 27$

10. $abc - bc = (2)(4)(3) - (4)(3)$
$$= 24 - 12$$
$$= 12$$

11. $28 - bc + a = 28 - 4 \cdot 3 + 2$
$$= 28 - 12 + 2$$
$$= 16 + 2$$
$$= 18$$

12. $a(b - c) = 2(4 - 3)$
$$= 2 \cdot 1$$
$$= 2$$

13. $a + 9$ **14.** $k - 11$

15. $3p$ **16.** $5n$

17. $2s - 18$ **18.** $16 \div n$

Page 741   Lesson 1-4

1. multiplicative identity
2. associative, addition
3. associative, multiplication
4. commutative, multiplication
5. multiplication property of zero
6. commutative, addition
7. $6 + 8 + 14 = (6 + 14) + 8$
$$= 20 + 8$$
$$= 28$$
8. $5 \cdot 18 \cdot 2 = (5 \cdot 2) \cdot 18$
$$= 10 \cdot 18$$
$$= 180$$
9. $0(13 \cdot 6) = 0$
10. $8 + 4 + 12 + 16 = (8 + 12) + (4 + 16)$
$$= 20 + 20$$
$$= 40$$
11. $8 \cdot 20 \cdot 10 = (8 \cdot 20) \cdot 10$
$$= 160 \cdot 10$$
$$= 1600$$
12. $4 \cdot 14 \cdot 5 = (4 \cdot 5) \cdot 14$
$$= 20 \cdot 14$$
$$= 280$$
13. 5 rows with 6 stars

Page 741   Lesson 1-5

1. $8k + 2k + 7 = (8 + 2)k + 7$
$$= 10k + 7$$
2. $3 + 2b + b = 3 + (2 + 1)b$
$$= 3 + 3b$$
3. $t + 2t = (1 + 2)t$
$$= 3t$$
4. $9(3 + 2x) = 9 \cdot 3 + 9 \cdot 2x$
$$= 27 + 18x$$
5. $4(xy + 2) - 2 = 4xy + 4 \cdot 2 - 2$
$$= 4xy + 8 - 2$$
$$= 4xy + 6$$
6. $(6 + 3e)4 = 4 \cdot 6 + 4 \cdot 3e$
$$= 24 + 12e$$
7. $4 + 9c + 3(c + 2) = 4 + 9c + 3c + 3 \cdot 2$
$$= 4 + 9c + 3c + 6$$
$$= 9c + 3c + 4 + 6$$
$$= (9 + 3)c + 4 + 6$$
$$= 12c + 10$$

8. $5(7 + 2s) + 3(s - 4) = 5 \cdot 7 + 5 \cdot 2s + 3s + 3 \cdot 4$
$$= 35 + 10s + 3s + 12$$
$$= 10s + 3s + 35 + 12$$
$$= (10 + 3)s + 35 + 12$$
$$= 13s + 47$$

9. $9(f + 2) + 14f = 9f + 9 \cdot 2 + 14f$
$$= 9f + 18 + 14f$$
$$= 9f + 14f + 18$$
$$= (9 + 14)f + 18$$
$$= 23f + 18$$

10. $\$0.35(23 + 20) = \$0.35(43)$
$$= \$15.05$$

Page 741   Lesson 1-6

1. $16 - f = 7$ $16 - f = 7$
$16 - 5 = 7$ $16 - 7 = 7$
$\quad\; 11 = 7$ $9 = 7$
This sentence is false.   This sentence is false.
$\quad 16 - f = 7$
$16 - 9 = 7$
$\qquad 7 = 7$
This sentence is true.
The solution is 9.

2. $9 = \frac{72}{m}$ $9 = \frac{72}{m}$
$9 = \frac{72}{8}$ $9 = \frac{72}{9}$
$9 = 9$ $9 = 8$
This sentence is true.   This sentence is false.
The solution is 8.
$9 = \frac{72}{m}$
$9 = \frac{72}{11}$
$9 = 6\frac{6}{11}$
This sentence is false.

3. $4b + 1 = 17$ $4b + 1 = 17$
$4(3) + 1 = 17$ $4(4) + 1 = 17$
$12 + 1 = 17$ $16 + 1 = 17$
$\quad\; 13 = 17$ $17 = 17$
This sentence is false.   This sentence is true.
                                  The solution is 4.
$\quad 4b + 1 = 17$
$4(5) + 1 = 17$
$20 + 1 = 17$
$\quad\; 21 = 17$
This sentence is false.

4. $17 + r = 25$ $17 + r = 25$
$17 + 6 = 25$ $17 + 7 = 25$
$\quad\; 23 = 25$ $24 = 25$
This sentence is false.   This sentence is false.
$17 + r = 25$
$17 + 8 = 25$
$\quad\; 25 = 25$
This sentence is true.
The solution is 8.

5. $9 = 7n - 12$
$9 = 7(3) - 12$
$9 = 21 - 12$
$9 = 9$
This sentence is true.
The solution is 3.
$9 = 7n - 12$
$9 = 7(7) - 12$
$9 = 49 - 12$
$9 = 37$
This sentence is true.

$9 = 7n - 12$
$9 = 7(5) - 12$
$9 = 35 - 12$
$9 = 23$
This sentence is false.

6. $67 = 98 - q$
$67 = 98 - 21$
$67 = 77$
This sentence is false.
$67 = 98 - q$
$67 = 98 - 31$
$67 = 67$
This sentence is true.
The solution is 31.

$67 = 98 - q$
$67 = 98 - 26$
$67 = 72$
This sentence is false.

7. $131 - u = 120$ 131 minus what
$131 - 11 = 120$ number is 120?
$u = 11$

8. $88 = 11d$ What number
$88 = 11 \cdot 8$ times 11 is 88?
$8 = d$

9. $\frac{84}{h} = 12$ What number
$\frac{84}{7} = 12$ times 12 is 84?
$h = 7$

10. $5t = 0$ What number
$5 \cdot 0 = 0$ times 5 is 0?
$t = 0$

11. $\frac{x}{2} = 8$ What number
$\frac{16}{2} = 8$ divided by 2 is 8?
$x = 16$

12. $88 + y = 96$ 88 plus what
$88 + 8 = 96$ number is 96?
$y = 8$

13. $13g = 39$ What number
$13 \cdot 3 = 39$ times 13 is 39?
$g = 3$

14. $23 = w + 6$ What number
$23 = 17 + 6$ plus 6 is 23?
$17 = w$

15. $9z = 45$ What number
$9 \cdot 5 = 45$ times 9 is 45?
$z = 5$

Page 742   Lesson 1-7

1. P **2.** N **3.** Q
4. B **5.** S **6.** T
7. $(4, 8)$ **8.** $(9, 7)$
9. $(5, 1)$ **10.** $(0, 6)$
11. $(0, 8)$ **12.** $(3, 4)$

Page 742   Lesson 1-8

1. $37 = b + 22$
$37 - 22 = b$
$15 = b$

2. $6 + u = 14$
$u = 14 - 6$
$u = 8$

3. $p - 19 = 3$
$p = 3 + 19$
$p = 22$

4. $6x = 30$
$x = 30 \div 6$
$x = 5$

5. $3v = 99$
$v = 99 \div 3$
$v = 33$

6. $48c = 192$
$c = 192 \div 48$
$c = 4$

7. $r \div 7 = 4$
$r = 4 \cdot 7$
$r = 28$

8. $12 = \frac{z}{3}$
$3 \cdot 12 = z$
$36 = z$

9. $6 \cdot 2 = 5.8 + g$
$6.2 - 5.8 = g$
$0.4 = g$

10. $x + 8 = 14$ **11.** $n - 12 = 50$
12. $10n = 70$ **13.** $n \div 3 = 9$

Page 742   Lesson 1-9

1. true   **2.** true   **3.** open
4. open   **5.** false   **6.** true

7. $5 \geq 2t - 12$
$5 \geq 2(11) - 12$
$5 \geq 22 - 12$
$5 \geq 10$
This sentence is false.

8. $7 + n < 25$
$7 + 4 < 25$
$11 < 25$
This sentence is true.

9. $6r - 18 > 0$
$6(3) - 18 > 0$
$18 - 18 > 0$
$0 > 0$
This sentence is false.

10. $3n + 2 < 26$
$3(3) + 2 < 26$
$9 + 2 < 26$
$11 < 26$
This sentence is true.

11. $h - 19 < 13$
$28 - 19 < 13$
$9 < 13$
This sentence is true.

12. $20m \geq 10$
$20(0) \geq 10$
$0 \geq 10$
This sentence is false.

13. $n > 50$

Page 743   Lesson 1-10

1. Pink Floyd, *Dark Side of the Moon*
2. 302
3. $490 - 295$ or 195 weeks

4.

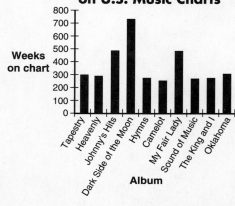

Albums with Longest Stays on U.S. Music Charts

Page 743   Lesson 2-1

1. $|-3| + |9| = 3 + 9$
   $ = 12$

2. $|-18| - |5| = 18 - 5$
   $ = 13$

3. $|12 + 7| = |19|$
   $ = 19$

4. $-|6| = -6$

5. $|-8| + |4| = 8 + 4$
   $ = 12$

6. $-|-20| = -20$

7. $|15 - 12| = |3|$
   $ = 3$

8. $|8 + 9| = |17|$
   $ = 17$

9. $-|4| \cdot |-5| = -4 \cdot 5$
   $ = -20$

10. $|-6| \cdot 8 = 6 \cdot 8$
    $ = 48$

11. $-|12| \cdot |9| = -12 \cdot 9$
    $ = -108$

12. $-||-16| + |-22|| = -|16 + 22|$
    $ = -|38|$
    $ = -38$

Page 743   Lesson 2-2

1. D 2. J 3. C
4. L 5. B 6. N

7. Quadrant III
8. Quadrant I
9. Quadrant II
10. Quadrant IV
11. Quadrant II
12. Quadrant IV

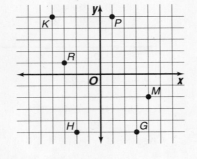

Page 744   Lesson 2-3

1. $\{-5, -1, 2\}$
2. $\{-9, -2, 0, 5, 8\}$
3. $\{-86, -34, 0, 21, 100\}$
4. $\{-43, -40, -1, 8, 16, 27\}$
5. $\{-23, -15, 0, 24, 75\}$
6. $\{-6, -5, 6, 18\}$
7. $130{,}119 > 40{,}953$ 8. $1050 > 940$
9. $24 < 26$ 10. $0.03 < 70$
11. $227.9 > 149.6$

Page 744   Lesson 2-4

1. $n = 5 + (-6)$
   $n = (-6) + 5$
   $n = -(|-6| - |5|)$
   $n = -(6 - 5)$
   $n = -1$

2. $-17 + 24 = y$
   $24 + (-17) = y$
   $+(|24| - |-17|) = y$
   $+(24 - 17) = y$
   $7 = y$

3. $k = 15 + (-29)$
   $k = (-29) + 15$
   $k = -(|-29| - |15|)$
   $k = -(29 - 15)$
   $k = -14$

4. $m = -6 + 13$
   $m = 13 + (-6)$
   $m = +(|13| - |-6|)$
   $m = +(13 - 6)$
   $m = 7$

5. $50 + (-14) = x$
   $+(|50| - |-14|) = x$
   $+(50 - 14) = x$
   $36 = x$

6. $w = -(|-21| + |-4|)$
   $w = -(21 + 4)$
   $w = -25$

7. $30 + (-7) = t$
   $+(|30| - |-7|) = t$
   $+(30 - 7) = t$
   $23 = t$

8. $z = (-3) + (-10)$
   $z = -(|-3| + |-10|)$
   $z = -(3 + 10)$
   $z = -13$

9. $-15 + 26 = q$
   $26 + (-15) = q$
   $+(|26| - |-15|) = q$
   $+(26 - 15) = q$
   $11 = q$

10. $b = -17 + 4 + (-2)$
    $b = -17 + (-2) + 4$
    $b = -(|-17| + |-2|) + 4$
    $b = -(17 + 2) + 4$
    $b = -19 + 4$
    $b = -(|-19| - |4|)$
    $b = -(19 - 4)$
    $b = -15$

11. $d = 50 + (-16) + (-11)$
    $d = (-16) + (-11) + 50$
    $d = -(|-16| + |-11|) + 50$
    $d = -(16 + 11) + 50$
    $d = -27 + 50$
    $d = 50 + (-27)$
    $d = +(|50| - |-27|)$
    $d = +(50 - 27)$
    $d = 23$

12. $-17 + 8 + (-14) = f$
    $-17 + (-14) + 8 = f$
    $-(|-17| + |-14|) + 8 = f$
    $-(17 + 14) + 8 = f$
    $-31 + 8 = f$
    $-(|-31| - |8|) = f$
    $-(31 - 8) = f$
    $-23 = f$

Page 744   Lesson 2-5

1. $8 - 17 = f$
   $8 + (-17) = f$
   $-9 = f$

2. $-15 - 3 = r$
   $-15 + (-3) = r$
   $-18 = r$

3. $10 - 21 = a$
   $10 + (-21) = a$
   $-11 = a$

4. $20 - (-5) = m$
   $20 + 5 = m$
   $25 = m$

5. $5 - (-9) = g$
   $5 + 9 = g$
   $14 = g$

6. $-12 - (-7) = v$
   $-12 + 7 = v$
   $-5 = v$

7. $-19 - (-6) = k$
   $-19 + 6 = k$
   $-13 = k$

8. $-16 - (-23) = b$
   $-16 + 23 = b$
   $7 = b$

9. $-56 - 32 = z$
   $-56 + (-32) = z$
   $-88 = z$

10. $-49 - (-52) = h$
    $-49 + 52 = h$
    $3 = h$

11. $-6 - 9 - (-7) = d$
    $-6 + (-9) + 7 = d$
    $-15 + 7 = d$
    $-8 = d$

12. $6 - (-10) - 7 = n$
    $6 + 10 + (-7) = n$
    $16 + (-7) = n$
    $9 = n$

Page 744 Lesson 2-6

1. 2 3 5 9 17 33 65
    +1 +2 +4 +8 +16 +32

2. F is the sixth letter of the alphabet, L is the twelfth letter of the alphabet, and J is the tenth letter of the alphabet. Thus, if FOG = 6 − 15 − 7 and LOG = 12 − 15 − 7, then JOG = 10 − 15 − 7.

3. F is the sixth letter of the alphabet and L is the twelfth. These letters are the only difference between "FOG" and "LOG." The 6 and the 12 are the only difference between the expressions. Thus, since J is the tenth letter, JOG = 10 − 15 − 7.

Page 745 Lesson 2-7

1. $n = 4(-2)$
$n = -8$

2. $-8(-5) = h$
$40 = h$

3. $r = 13(-4)$
$r = -52$

4. $-5 \cdot 6 \cdot 10 = c$
$(-5 \cdot 6) \cdot 10 = c$
$-30 \cdot 10 = c$
$-300 = c$

5. $-6(-2)(-14) = w$
$[-6(-2)](-14) = w$
$12(-14) = w$
$-168 = w$

6. $u = 18(-3)(6)$
$u = [18(-3)](6)$
$u = -54(6)$
$u = -324$

7. $-6t = -6(15)$
$= -90$

8. $7p = 7(-9)$
$= -63$

9. $-4k = -4(-16)$
$= 64$

10. $aw = (0)(-72)$
$= 0$

11. $dk = (-12)(11)$
$= -132$

12. $st = (-8)(-10)$
$= 80$

13. $3hp = 3(9)(-3)$
$= 3[(9)(-3)]$
$= 3(-27)$
$= -81$

14. $5bc = -5(-6)(2)$
$= -5[(-6)(2)]$
$= -5(-12)$
$= 60$

15. $-4wx = -4(-1)(-8)$
$= -4[(-1)(-8)]$
$= -4(8)$
$= -32$

Page 745 Lesson 2-8

1. $-36 \div 9 = -4$

2. $112 \div (-8) = -14$

3. $-72 \div 2 = -36$

4. $-26 \div (-13) = 2$

5. $-144 \div 6 = -24$

6. $-180 \div (-10) = 18$

7. $304 \div (-8) = -38$

8. $-216 \div (-9) = 24$

9. $80 \div (-5) = -16$

10. $-105 \div 15 = -7$

11. $120 \div (-30) = -4$

12. $-200 \div (-8) = 25$

Page 745 Lesson 3-1

1.

	Lindsay	Lee	Ann	Marcos
Art	X	X	X	O
Math	X	O	X	X
Music	X	X	O	X
Physics	O	X	X	X

Lindsay: Physics, Lee: Math,
Ann: Music, Marcos: Art

2.

	Nancy	Pete	Jeff	Gina	Tom
First	O	X	X	X	X
Second	X	O	X	X	X
Third	X	X	X	X	O
Fourth	X	X	O	X	X
Fifth	X	X	X	O	X

Nancy: First, Pete: Second, Jeff: Fourth, Gina: Fifth, and Tom: Third. Therefore, the correct answer is c.

Page 745 Lesson 3-2

1.
$$y + 49 = 26$$
$$y + 49 - 49 = 26 - 49$$
$$y = -23$$
Check: $y + 49 = 26$
$$-23 + 49 \overset{?}{=} 26$$
$$26 = 26 \checkmark$$

2.
$$d - (-31) = -24$$
$$d + 31 = -24$$
$$d + 31 - 31 = -24 - 31$$
$$d = -55$$
Check: $d - (-31) = -24$
$$-55 - (-31) \overset{?}{=} -24$$
$$-55 + 31 \overset{?}{=} -24$$
$$-24 = -24 \checkmark$$

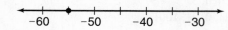

3.
$$q - 8 = 16$$
$$q - 8 + 8 = 16 + 8$$
$$q = 24$$
Check: $q - 8 = 16$
$$24 - 8 \overset{?}{=} 16$$
$$16 = 16 \checkmark$$

4.
$$x - 16 = 32$$
$$x - 16 + 16 = 32 + 16$$
$$x = 48$$
Check: $x - 16 = 32$
$$48 - 16 \stackrel{?}{=} 32$$
$$32 = 32 ✔$$

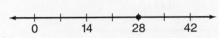

5.
$$40 = a + 12$$
$$40 - 12 = a + 12 - 12$$
$$28 = a$$
Check: $40 = a + 12$
$$40 \stackrel{?}{=} 28 + 12$$
$$40 = 40 ✔$$

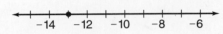

6.
$$b + 12 = -1$$
$$b + 12 - 12 = -1 - 12$$
$$b = -13$$
Check: $\quad b + 12 = -1$
$$-13 + 12 \stackrel{?}{=} -1$$
$$-1 = -1 ✔$$

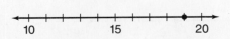

7.
$$21 = u - (-6)$$
$$21 = u + 6$$
$$21 - 6 = u + 6 - 6$$
$$15 = u$$
Check: $21 = u - (-6)$
$$21 \stackrel{?}{=} 15 - (-6)$$
$$21 \stackrel{?}{=} 15 + 6$$
$$21 = 21 ✔$$

8.
$$-52 = p + 5$$
$$-52 - 5 = p + 5 - 5$$
$$-57 = p$$
Check: $-52 = p + 5$
$$-52 \stackrel{?}{=} -57 + 5$$
$$-52 = -52 ✔$$

9.
$$-14 = 5 - g$$
$$-14 - 5 = 5 - g - 5$$
$$-19 = -g$$
$$(-1)(-19) = (-1)(-g)$$
$$19 = g$$
Check: $-14 = 5 - g$
$$-14 \stackrel{?}{=} 5 - 19$$
$$-14 = -14 ✔$$

10.
$$121 = k + (-12)$$
$$121 = k - 12$$
$$121 + 12 = k - 12 + 12$$
$$133 = k$$
Check: $121 = k + (-12)$
$$121 \stackrel{?}{=} 133 + (-12)$$
$$121 = 121 ✔$$

11.
$$-234 = m - 94$$
$$-234 + 94 = m - 94 + 94$$
$$-140 = m$$
Check: $-234 = m - 94$
$$-234 \stackrel{?}{=} -140 - 94$$
$$-234 = -234 ✔$$

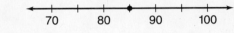

12.
$$110 = x + 25$$
$$110 - 25 = x + 25 - 25$$
$$85 = x$$
Check: $110 = x + 25$
$$110 \stackrel{?}{=} 85 + 25$$
$$110 = 110 ✔$$

13.
$$f - 7 = 84$$
$$f - 7 + 7 = 84 + 7$$
$$f = 91$$
Check: $\quad f - 7 = 84$
$$91 - 7 \stackrel{?}{=} 84$$
$$84 = 84 ✔$$

14.
$$y - 864 = -652$$
$$y - 864 + 864 = -652 + 864$$
$$y = 212$$
Check: $\quad y - 864 \stackrel{?}{=} -652$
$$212 - 864 \stackrel{?}{=} -652$$
$$-652 = -652 ✔$$

15.
$$475 + z = -18$$
$$475 + z - 475 = -18 - 475$$
$$z = -493$$
Check: $\quad 475 + z \stackrel{?}{=} -18$
$$475 + (-493) \stackrel{?}{=} -18$$
$$-18 = -18 ✔$$

1. $-y = -32$

$\frac{-y}{-1} = \frac{-32}{-1}$

$y = 32$

Check: $-y = -32$

$-32 = -32$ ✔

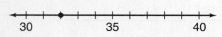

2. $7r = -56$

$\frac{7r}{7} = \frac{-56}{7}$

$r = -8$

Check: $7r = -56$

$7(-8) \stackrel{?}{=} -56$

$-56 = -56$ ✔

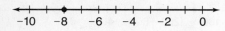

3. $\frac{t}{-3} = 12$

$\frac{t}{-3}(-3) = 12(-3)$

$t = -36$

Check: $\frac{t}{-3} = 12$

$\frac{-36}{-3} \stackrel{?}{=} 12$

$12 = 12$ ✔

4. $4 = \frac{s}{-14}$

$4(-14) = \frac{s}{-14}(-14)$

$-56 = s$

Check: $4 = \frac{s}{-14}$

$4 \stackrel{?}{=} \frac{-56}{-14}$

$4 = 4$ ✔

5. $\frac{b}{47} = -2$

$\frac{b}{47}(47) = -2(47)$

$b = -94$

Check: $\frac{b}{47} = -2$

$\frac{-94}{47} \stackrel{?}{=} -2$

$-2 = -2$ ✔

6. $64 = -4n$

$\frac{64}{-4} = \frac{-4n}{-4}$

$-16 = n$

Check: $64 = -4n$

$64 \stackrel{?}{=} -4(-16)$

$64 = 64$ ✔

7. $-144 = 12q$

$\frac{-144}{12} = \frac{12q}{12}$

$-12 = q$

Check: $-144 = 12q$

$-144 \stackrel{?}{=} 12(-12)$

$-144 = -144$ ✔

8. $\frac{r}{11} = -132$

$\frac{r}{11}(11) = -132(11)$

$r = -1452$

Check: $\frac{r}{11} = -132$

$\frac{-1452}{11} \stackrel{?}{=} -132$

$-132 = -132$ ✔

9. $-5g = -385$

$\frac{-5g}{-5} = \frac{-385}{-5}$

$g = 77$

Check: $-5g = -385$

$-5(77) \stackrel{?}{=} -385$

$-385 = -385$ ✔

10. $-16x = -176$

$\frac{-16x}{-16} = \frac{-176}{-16}$

$x = 11$

Check: $-16x = -176$

$-16(11) \stackrel{?}{=} -176$

$-176 = -176$ ✔

11. $-21 = \frac{y}{-4}$

$-21(-4) = \frac{y}{-4}(-4)$

$84 = y$

Check: $-21 = \frac{y}{-4}$

$-21 \stackrel{?}{=} \frac{84}{-4}$

$-21 = -21$ ✔

12. $-372 = 31k$

$$\frac{-372}{31} = \frac{31k}{31}$$

$$-12 = k$$

Check: $-372 = 31k$

$$-372 \stackrel{?}{=} 31(-12)$$

$$-372 = -372 \;✔$$

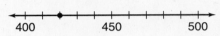

13. $84 = \frac{k}{5}$

$$84(5) = \frac{k}{5}(5)$$

$$420 = k$$

Check: $84 = \frac{k}{5}$

$$84 \stackrel{?}{=} \frac{420}{5}$$

$$84 = 84 \;✔$$

14. $-b = 19$

$$\frac{-b}{-1} = \frac{19}{-1}$$

$$b = -19$$

Check: $-b = 19$

$$-(-19) \stackrel{?}{=} 19$$

$$19 = 19 \;✔$$

15. $\frac{y}{112} = -9$

$$\frac{y}{112}(112) = -9(112)$$

$$y = -1008$$

Check: $\frac{y}{112} = -9$

$$\frac{-1008}{112} = -9$$

$$-9 = -9 \;✔$$

Page 746   Lesson 3-4

1. $A = \pi \cdot r^2$
$A = 3.14 \cdot 5^2$
$A = 3.14 \cdot 25$
$A = 78.5$

2. $\frac{5}{9}(F - 32) = C$
$\frac{5}{9}(86 - 32) = C$
$\frac{5}{9}(54) = C$
$30 = C$

3. $d = r \cdot t$
$366 = r \cdot 3$
$366 = 3r$
$\frac{366}{3} = \frac{3r}{3}$
$122 = r$

4. $S = (n - 2) \cdot 180$
$S = (8 - 2) \cdot 180$
$S = 6 \cdot 180$
$S = 1080$

5. $A = \frac{1}{2}bh$
$36 = \frac{1}{2} \cdot b \cdot 12$
$36 = 6b$
$\frac{36}{6} = \frac{6b}{6}$
$6 = b$

6. $P = 4s$
$108 = 4s$
$\frac{108}{4} = \frac{4s}{4}$
$27 = s$

7. $V = \frac{1}{3}(B \cdot H)$
$V = \frac{1}{3}(27 \cdot 5)$
$V = \frac{1}{3}(135)$
$V = 45$

8. $h = 69 + 2.2F$
$h = 69 + 2.2(42)$
$h = 69 + 92.4$
$h = 161.4$

Page 746   Lesson 3-5

1. $P = 2(\ell + w)$
$P = 2(23 + 9)$
$P = 2(32)$
$P = 64$ cm

$A = \ell \cdot w$
$A = 23 \cdot 9$
$A = 207$ cm^2

2. $P = 2(\ell + w)$
$P = 2(16 + 14)$
$P = 2(30)$
$P = 60$ ft

$A = \ell \cdot w$
$A = 16 \cdot 14$
$A = 224$ ft^2

3. $P = 2(\ell + w)$
$P = 2(31 + 3)$
$P = 2(34)$
$P = 68$ m

$A = \ell \cdot w$
$A = 31 \cdot 3$
$A = 93$ m^2

4. $P = 2(\ell + w)$
$P = 2(7.5 + 7.5)$
$P = 2(15)$
$P = 30$ m

$A = \ell \cdot w$
$A = 7.5 \cdot 7.5$
$A = 56.25$ m^2

5. $A = \ell \cdot w$
$126 = 9 \cdot w$
$\frac{126}{9} = \frac{9w}{9}$
$14 = w$
The width is 14 ft.

6. $A = \ell \cdot w$
$108 = \ell \cdot 18$
$\frac{108}{18} = \frac{18\ell}{18}$
$6 = \ell$
The length is 6 in.

7. $A = \ell \cdot w$
$273 = 13 \cdot w$
$\frac{273}{13} = \frac{13w}{13}$
$21 = w$
The width is 21 yd.

8. $A = \ell \cdot w$
$168 = \ell \cdot 12$
$\frac{168}{12} = \frac{12\ell}{12}$
$14 = \ell$
The length is 14 cm.

9. $A = \ell \cdot w$
$162 = \ell \cdot 3$
$\frac{162}{3} = \frac{3\ell}{3}$
$54 = \ell$
The length is 54 m.

10. $A = \ell \cdot w$
$720 = 18 \cdot w$
$\frac{720}{18} = \frac{18w}{18}$
$40 = w$
The width is 40 mi.

Page 747   Lesson 3-6

1. $m + 9 < 14$

$$m + 9 - 9 < 14 - 9$$

$$m < 5$$

Check: Try 3, a number less than 5.

$$m + 9 < 14$$

$$3 + 9 \stackrel{?}{<} 14$$

$$12 < 14 \;✔$$

2. $k + (-5) < -12$

$k - 5 < -12$

$k - 5 + 5 < -12 + 5$

$k < -7$

Check: Try -9, a number less than -7.

$k + (-5) < -12$

$-9 + (-5) \overset{?}{<} -12$

$-14 < -12$ ✔

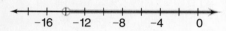

3. $-15 < v - 1$

$-15 + 1 < v - 1 + 1$

$-14 < v$

Check: Try 0, a number greater than -14.

$-15 < v - 1$

$-15 \overset{?}{<} 0 - 1$

$-15 < -1$ ✔

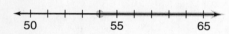

4. $-7 + f \ge 47$

$-7 + f + 7 \ge 47 + 7$

$f \ge 54$

Check: Try 55, a number greater than or equal to 54.

$-7 + f \ge 47$

$-7 + 55 \overset{?}{\ge} 47$

$48 \ge 47$ ✔

5. $r > -15 - 8$

$r > -23$

Check: Try -20, a number greater than -23.

$r > -15 - 8$

$-20 \overset{?}{>} -15 - 8$

$-20 > -23$ ✔

6. $18 \ge s - (-4)$

$18 \ge s + 4$

$18 - 4 \ge s + 4 - 4$

$14 \ge s$

Check: Try 8, a number less than or equal to 14.

$18 \ge s - (-4)$

$18 \overset{?}{\ge} 8 - (-4)$

$18 \overset{?}{\ge} 8 + 4$

$18 \ge 12$ ✔

7. $38 < r - (-6)$

$38 < r + 6$

$38 - 6 < r + 6 - 6$

$32 < r$

Check: Try 35, a number greater than 32.

$38 < r - (-6)$

$38 \overset{?}{<} 35 - (-6)$

$38 \overset{?}{<} 35 + 6$

$38 < 41$ ✔

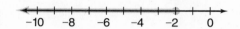

8. $z - 9 \le -11$

$z - 9 + 9 \le -11 + 9$

$z \le -2$

Check: Try -4, a number less than or equal to -2.

$z - 9 \le -11$

$-4 - 9 \overset{?}{\le} -11$

$-13 \le -11$ ✔

9. $-16 + c \ge 1$

$-16 + c + 16 \ge 1 + 16$

$c \ge 17$

Check: Try 20, a number greater than or equal to 17.

$-16 + c \ge 1$

$-16 + 20 \overset{?}{\ge} 1$

$4 \ge 1$ ✔

10. $24 < a + -3$

$24 < a - 3$

$24 + 3 < a - 3 + 3$

$27 < a$

Check: Try 30, a number greater than 27.

$24 < a + (-3)$

$24 \overset{?}{<} 30 + (-3)$

$24 \overset{?}{<} 30 - 3$

$24 < 27$ ✔

11. $-52 \ge d + (-6)$

$-52 \ge d - 6$

$-52 + 6 \ge d - 6 + 6$

$-46 \ge d$

Check: Try -50, a number less than or equal to -46.

$-52 \ge d + (-6)$

$-52 \overset{?}{\ge} -50 + (-6)$

$-52 \ge -56$ ✔

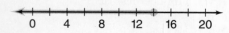

12.
$$24 < -2 + b$$
$$24 + 2 < -2 + b + 2$$
$$26 < b$$

Check: Try 28, a number greater than 26.
$$24 < -2 + b$$
$$24 \overset{?}{<} -2 + 28$$
$$24 < 26 \; \checkmark$$

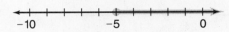

13.
$$n - (-17) \geq 12$$
$$n + 17 \geq 12$$
$$n + 17 - 17 \geq 12 - 17$$
$$n \geq -5$$

Check: Try 1, a number greater than or equal to -5.
$$n - (-17) \geq 12$$
$$1 - (-17) \overset{?}{\geq} 12$$
$$1 + 17 \overset{?}{\geq} 12$$
$$18 \geq 12 \; \checkmark$$

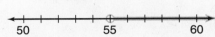

14.
$$31 < x - 24$$
$$31 + 24 < x - 24 + 24$$
$$55 < x$$

Check: Try 60, a number greater than 55.
$$31 < x - 24$$
$$31 \overset{?}{<} 60 - 24$$
$$31 < 36 \; \checkmark$$

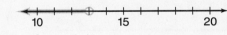

15.
$$-20 \leq n + (-3)$$
$$-20 \leq n - 3$$
$$-20 + 3 \leq n - 3 + 3$$
$$-17 \leq n$$

Check: Try -15, a number greater than or equal to -17.
$$-20 \leq n + (-3)$$
$$-20 \overset{?}{\leq} -15 + (-3)$$
$$-20 \leq -18 \; \checkmark$$

16.
$$p + (-11) < -37$$
$$p - 11 < -37$$
$$p - 11 + 11 < -37 + 11$$
$$p < -26$$

Check: Try -30, a number less than -26.
$$p + (-11) < -37$$
$$-30 + (-11) \overset{?}{<} -37$$
$$-41 < -37 \; \checkmark$$

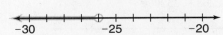

17.
$$-40 \leq -72 + w$$
$$-40 + 72 \leq -72 + w + 72$$
$$32 \leq w$$

Check: Try 35, a number greater than or equal to 32.
$$-40 \leq -72 + w$$
$$-40 \overset{?}{\leq} -72 + 35$$
$$-40 \leq -37 \; \checkmark$$

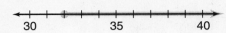

18.
$$72 > a + 88$$
$$72 - 88 > a + 88 - 88$$
$$-16 > a$$

Check: Try -20, a number less than -16.
$$72 > a + 88$$
$$72 \overset{?}{>} -20 + 88$$
$$72 > 68 \; \checkmark$$

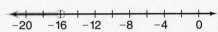

Page 747   Lesson 3-7

1.
$$6p < 78$$
$$\frac{6p}{6} < \frac{78}{6}$$
$$p < 13$$

Check: Try 10, a number less than 13.
$$6p < 78$$
$$6 \cdot 10 \overset{?}{<} 78$$
$$60 < 78 \; \checkmark$$

2.
$$\frac{m}{-3} > 24$$
$$\frac{m}{-3}(-3) < 24(-3)$$
$$m < -72$$

Check: Try -75, a number less than -72.
$$\frac{m}{-3} > 24$$
$$\frac{-75}{-3} \overset{?}{>} 24$$
$$25 > 24 \; \checkmark$$

3.
$$-18 < 3b$$
$$\frac{-18}{3} < \frac{3b}{3}$$
$$-6 < b$$

Check: Try 0, a number greater than -6.
$$-18 < 3b$$
$$-18 \overset{?}{<} 3 \cdot 0$$
$$-18 < 0 \; \checkmark$$

4. $-5k \geq 125$

$\dfrac{-5k}{-5} \leq \dfrac{125}{-5}$

$k \leq -25$

Check: Try -30, a number less than or equal
to -25.

$-5k \geq 125$

$-5(-30) \overset{?}{\geq} 125$

$150 \geq 125$ ✔

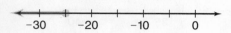

5. $-75 > \dfrac{a}{5}$

$-75(5) > \dfrac{a}{5}(5)$

$-375 > a$

Check: Try -380, a number less than -375.

$-75 > \dfrac{a}{5}$

$-75 \overset{?}{>} \dfrac{-380}{5}$

$-75 > -76$ ✔

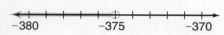

6. $\dfrac{w}{6} < -5$

$\dfrac{w}{6}(6) < -5(6)$

$w < -30$

Check: Try -42, a number less than -30.

$\dfrac{w}{6} < -5$

$\dfrac{-42}{6} \overset{?}{<} -5$

$-7 < -5$ ✔

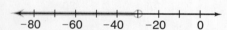

7. $\dfrac{y}{-13} > -20$

$\dfrac{y}{-13}(-13) < -20(-13)$

$y < 260$

Check: Try 247, a number less than 260.

$\dfrac{y}{-13} > -20$

$\dfrac{247}{-13} \overset{?}{>} -20$

$-19 > -20$ ✔

8. $14t < 266$

$\dfrac{14t}{14} < \dfrac{266}{14}$

$t < 19$

Check: Try 15, a number less than 19.

$14t < 266$

$14 \cdot 15 \overset{?}{<} 266$

$210 < 266$ ✔

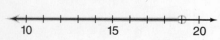

9. $\dfrac{g}{-25} \geq 8$

$\dfrac{g}{-25}(-25) \leq 8(-25)$

$g \leq -200$

Check: Try -225, a number less than or equal
to -200.

$\dfrac{g}{-25} \geq 8$

$\dfrac{-225}{-25} \overset{?}{\geq} 8$

$9 \geq 8$ ✔

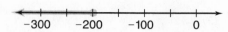

10. $-216 \leq 9h$

$\dfrac{-216}{9} \leq \dfrac{9h}{9}$

$-24 \leq h$

Check: Try 0, a number greater than or equal
to -24.

$-216 \leq 9h$

$-216 \overset{?}{\leq} 9 \cdot 0$

$-216 \leq 0$ ✔

11. $\dfrac{g}{-9} < -8$

$\dfrac{g}{-9}(-9) > -8(-9)$

$g > 72$

Check: Try 81, a number greater than 72.

$\dfrac{g}{-9} < -8$

$\dfrac{81}{-9} \overset{?}{<} -8$

$-9 < -8$ ✔

12. $-18d > 108$

$\dfrac{-18d}{-18} < \dfrac{108}{-18}$

$d < -6$

Check: Try -8, a number less than -6.

$-18d > 108$

$-18(-8) \overset{?}{>} 108$

$144 > 108$ ✔

13. $2268 < -63a$

$\dfrac{2268}{-63} > \dfrac{-63a}{-63}$

$-36 > a$

Check: Try -40, a number less than -36.

$2268 < -63a$

$2268 \overset{?}{<} -63(-40)$

$2268 < 2520$ ✔

14. $52 \leq \frac{p}{4}$

$52(4) \leq \frac{p}{4}(4)$

$208 \leq p$

Check: Try 220, a number greater than or equal to 208.

$52 \leq \frac{p}{4}$

$52 \overset{?}{\leq} \frac{220}{4}$

$52 \leq 55$ ✔

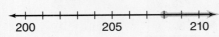

15. $42n \leq -210$

$\frac{42n}{42} \leq \frac{-210}{42}$

$n \leq -5$

Check: Try -7, a number less than or equal to -5.

$-42n \leq -210$

$42(-7) \overset{?}{\leq} -210$

$-294 \leq -210$ ✔

16. $-60 > -4d$

$\frac{-60}{-4} < \frac{-4d}{-4}$

$15 < d$

Check: Try 20, a number greater than 15.

$-60 > -4d$

$-60 \overset{?}{>} -4 \cdot 20$

$-60 > -80$ ✔

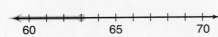

17. $\frac{k}{-3} \geq -21$

$\frac{k}{-3}(-3) \leq -21(-3)$

$k \leq 63$

Check: Try 60, a number less than or equal to 63.

$\frac{k}{-3} \geq -21$

$\frac{60}{-3} \overset{?}{\geq} -21$

$-20 \geq -21$ ✔

18. $\frac{v}{-8} < 0$

$\frac{v}{-8}(-8) > 0(-8)$

$v > 0$

Check: Try 1, a number greater than 0.

$\frac{v}{-8} < 0$

$\frac{1}{-8} \overset{?}{<} 0$

$-0.125 < 0$ ✔

Page 747 Lesson 3-8

1. x = number

$3x = 36$

$\frac{3x}{3} = \frac{36}{3}$

$x = 12$

2. y = number

$y + 5 < 12$

$y + 5 - 5 < 12 - 5$

$y < 7$

3. r = number of points

$r - 6 = 2377$

$r - 6 + 6 = 2377 + 6$

$r = 2383$

4. s = number of students

$6s < 38{,}958$

$\frac{6s}{6} < \frac{38{,}958}{6}$

$s < 6493$

Page 748 Lesson 4-1

1. 2   **2.** 3   **3.** 2, 5, 10

4. 2, 3, 6   **5.** 3, 5   **6.** 2, 3, 5, 6, 10

7. none   **8.** 2, 3, 6   **9.** 3, 5

10. yes; product of an integer and a variable

11. no; involves subtraction

12. yes; product of an integer and a variable

Page 748 Lesson 4-2

1. $(-6)^5$ **2.** y^7

3. 9^1 **4.** $(3q)^6$

5. n^{17} **6.** 8^4

7. $13 \cdot 13 \cdot 13$ **8.** $(-4)(-4)(-4)(-4)(-4)$

9. $k \cdot k \cdot k \cdot k \cdot k \cdot k \cdot k \cdot k$

10. $(2 - w)(2 - w)$

11. $\underbrace{3m \cdot 3m \cdot \ldots \cdot 3m}_{\text{15 factors}}$

12. $(-x)(-x)(-x)(-x)$

1. Let A, B, C, and D represent the four people who are eligible to be officers.

President   Treasurer
         VP   Secretary

```
            C ——— D ——————→ ABCD
        B <
            D ——— C ——————→ ABDC
            B ——— D ——————→ ACBD
A <     C <
            D ——— B ——————→ ACDB
            B ——— C ——————→ ADBC
        D <
            C ——— B ——————→ ADCB

            A ——— D ——————→ BCAD
        C <
            D ——— A ——————→ BCDA
            A ——— C ——————→ BDAC
B <     D <
            C ——— A ——————→ BDCA
            C ——— D ——————→ BACD
        A <
            D ——— C ——————→ BADC

            A ——— B ——————→ CDAB
        D <
            B ——— A ——————→ CDBA
            B ——— D ——————→ CABD
C <     A <
            D ——— B ——————→ CADB
            A ——— D ——————→ CBAD
        B <
            D ——— A ——————→ CBDA

            B ——— C ——————→ DABC
        A <
            C ——— B ——————→ DACB
            A ——— C ——————→ DBAC
D <     B <
            C ——— A ——————→ DBCA
            A ——— B ——————→ DCAB
        C <
            B ——— A ——————→ DCBA
```

24 ways

2.

0	12	12	0
8	4	4	8
4	8	8	4
12	0	0	12

The sum of the numbers on each row, column, and diagonal is 24.

3.

Sections Painted		
Pam	**Beverly**	
3	5	
6	10	← 1 hour
9	15	
12	20	← 2 hours
15	25	
18	30	← 3 hours

Pam will paint 18 sections in 3 hours.

4.

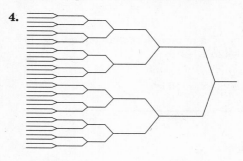

31 games

1. prime   **2.** composite   **3.** composite

4. $40 = 2 \cdot 20$
$ = 2 \cdot 2 \cdot 10$
$ = 2 \cdot 2 \cdot 2 \cdot 5$

5. $630a = 2 \cdot 315 \cdot a$
$ = 2 \cdot 3 \cdot 105 \cdot a$
$ = 2 \cdot 3 \cdot 3 \cdot 35 \cdot a$
$ = 2 \cdot 3 \cdot 3 \cdot 5 \cdot 7 \cdot a$

6. $187 = 11 \cdot 17$

7. $310 = 2 \cdot 155$
$ = 2 \cdot 5 \cdot 31$

8.

9. $1589 = 7 \cdot 227$

10. $f \cdot f \cdot g$
$f \cdot f \cdot g$
$f \cdot f \cdot g$

11.

12.

Page 749   Lesson 4-5

1. $112 = \boxed{2} \cdot \boxed{2} \cdot \boxed{2} \cdot 2 \cdot 7$
   $216 = \boxed{2} \cdot \boxed{2} \cdot \boxed{2} \cdot 3 \cdot 3 \cdot 3$
   The GCF is $2 \cdot 2 \cdot 2$ or 8.

2. $120 = 2 \cdot 2 \cdot 2 \cdot 3 \cdot \boxed{5}$
   $245 = \boxed{5} \cdot 7 \cdot 7$
   The GCF is 5.

3. $84k = \boxed{2} \cdot \boxed{2} \cdot \boxed{3} \cdot 7 \cdot \boxed{k}$
   $108k^2 = \boxed{2} \cdot \boxed{2} \cdot \boxed{3} \cdot 3 \cdot 3 \cdot \boxed{k} \cdot k$
   The GCF is $2 \cdot 2 \cdot 3 \cdot k$ or $12k$.

4. $135ab = 3 \cdot \boxed{3} \cdot \boxed{3} \cdot 5 \cdot a \cdot \boxed{b}$
   $-171b = -1 \cdot \boxed{3} \cdot \boxed{3} \cdot 19 \cdot \boxed{b}$
   The GCF is $3 \cdot 3 \cdot b$ or $9b$.

5. $185fg = 5 \cdot \boxed{37} \cdot \boxed{f} \cdot \boxed{g}$
   $74f^2g = 2 \cdot \boxed{37} \cdot \boxed{f} \cdot f \cdot \boxed{g}$
   The GCF is $37 \cdot f \cdot g$ or $37fg$.

6. $44m = \boxed{2} \cdot \boxed{2} \cdot 11 \cdot m$
   $60n = \boxed{2} \cdot \boxed{2} \cdot 3 \cdot 5 \cdot n$
   The GCF is $2 \cdot 2$ or 4.

7. $90gh = 2 \cdot \boxed{3} \cdot \boxed{3} \cdot \boxed{5} \cdot g \cdot h$
   $225k = \boxed{3} \cdot \boxed{3} \cdot \boxed{5} \cdot 5 \cdot k$
   The GCF is $3 \cdot 3 \cdot 5$ or 45.

8. $8 = 2 \cdot \boxed{2} \cdot \boxed{2}$
   $-28h = -1 \cdot \boxed{2} \cdot \boxed{2} \cdot 7 \cdot h$
   The GCF is $2 \cdot 2$ or 4.

9. $-16w = -1 \cdot \boxed{2} \cdot \boxed{2} \cdot 2 \cdot 2 \cdot \boxed{w}$
   $-28w^3 = 1 \cdot \boxed{2} \cdot \boxed{2} \cdot 7 \cdot \boxed{w} \cdot w \cdot w$
   The GCF is $2 \cdot 2 \cdot w$ or $4w$.

10. $24a = \boxed{2} \cdot 2 \cdot 2 \cdot \boxed{3} \cdot \boxed{a}$
    $30ab = \boxed{2} \cdot \boxed{3} \cdot 5 \cdot \boxed{a} \cdot b$
    $66a^2 = \boxed{2} \cdot \boxed{3} \cdot 11 \cdot \boxed{a} \cdot a$
    The GCF is $2 \cdot 3 \cdot a$ or $6a$.

11. $-13z = -1 \cdot \boxed{13} \cdot z$
    $39yz = 3 \cdot \boxed{13} \cdot y \cdot z$
    $52y = 2 \cdot 2 \cdot \boxed{13} \cdot y$
    The GCF is 13.

12. $60a^3b = \boxed{2} \cdot 2 \cdot \boxed{3} \cdot 5 \cdot \boxed{a} \cdot \boxed{a} \cdot a \cdot \boxed{b}$
    $150a^2b^2 = \boxed{2} \cdot \boxed{3} \cdot 5 \cdot 5 \cdot \boxed{a} \cdot \boxed{a} \cdot \boxed{b} \cdot b$
    $360a^2b = \boxed{2} \cdot 2 \cdot \boxed{3} \cdot 3 \cdot \boxed{a} \cdot \boxed{a} \cdot \boxed{b}$
    The GCF is $2 \cdot 3 \cdot a \cdot a \cdot b$ or $6a^2b$.

Page 749   Lesson 4-6

1. $\dfrac{3}{54} = \dfrac{\cancel{3}^{1}}{2 \cdot \cancel{3} \cdot 9}$
   $= \dfrac{1}{18}$

2. simplified

3. $\dfrac{6}{58} = \dfrac{\cancel{2} \cdot 3}{\cancel{2} \cdot 29}$
   $= \dfrac{3}{29}$

4. $\dfrac{15}{55} = \dfrac{3 \cdot \cancel{5}^{1}}{\cancel{5} \cdot 11}$
   $= \dfrac{3}{11}$

5. $\dfrac{10}{90} = \dfrac{\cancel{2}^{1} \cdot \cancel{5}^{1}}{\cancel{2} \cdot 3 \cdot 3 \cdot \cancel{5}}$
   $= \dfrac{1}{9}$

6. simplified

7. $\dfrac{8}{20} = \dfrac{\cancel{2} \cdot \cancel{2} \cdot 2}{\cancel{2} \cdot \cancel{2} \cdot 5}$
   $= \dfrac{2}{5}$

8. $\dfrac{99}{9} = \dfrac{\cancel{9} \cdot \cancel{9} \cdot 11}{\cancel{9} \cdot \cancel{9}}$
   $= 11$

9. $\dfrac{18}{54} = \dfrac{\cancel{2}^{1} \cdot \cancel{3}^{1} \cdot \cancel{3}^{1}}{\cancel{2} \cdot \cancel{3} \cdot \cancel{3} \cdot 3}$
   $= \dfrac{1}{3}$

10. simplified

11. $\dfrac{40}{76} = \dfrac{\cancel{2}^{1} \cdot \cancel{2}^{1} \cdot 2 \cdot 5}{\cancel{2} \cdot \cancel{2} \cdot 19}$
    $= \dfrac{10}{19}$

12. $\dfrac{49}{56} = \dfrac{7 \cdot \cancel{7}^{1}}{2 \cdot 2 \cdot 2 \cdot \cancel{7}}$
    $= \dfrac{7}{8}$

Page 749   Lesson 4-7

1. $30 = \boxed{2} \cdot \boxed{3} \cdot 5$
   $18 = \boxed{2} \cdot \boxed{3} \cdot 3$
   The LCM is $2 \cdot 3 \cdot 3 \cdot 5$ or 90.

2. $3m = 1 \cdot \boxed{3} \cdot m$
   $12 = 2 \cdot 2 \cdot \boxed{3}$
   The LCM is $1 \cdot 2 \cdot 2 \cdot 3 \cdot m$ or $12m$.

3. $6a = 2 \cdot 3 \cdot \boxed{a}$
   $17a^5 = 1 \cdot 17 \cdot \boxed{a} \cdot a \cdot a \cdot a \cdot a$
   The LCM is $1 \cdot 2 \cdot 3 \cdot 17 \cdot a \cdot a \cdot a \cdot a \cdot a$ or $102a^5$.

4. $2 = \boxed{1} \cdot 2$
   $5 = \boxed{1} \cdot 5$
   $7 = \boxed{1} \cdot 7$
   The LCM is $1 \cdot 2 \cdot 5 \cdot 7$ or 70.

5. $5 = 1 \cdot \boxed{5}$
   $25 = 5 \cdot \boxed{5}$
   The LCD is $1 \cdot 5 \cdot 5$ or 25.

6. $12 = 2 \cdot 2 \cdot 3$
   $5 = 1 \cdot 5$
   The LCD is $1 \cdot 2 \cdot 2 \cdot 3 \cdot 5$ or 60.

7. $6 = 2 \cdot \boxed{3}$
   $9 = 3 \cdot \boxed{3}$
   The LCD is $2 \cdot 3 \cdot 3$ or 18.

8. $4 = \boxed{2} \cdot 2$
   $6 = \boxed{2} \cdot \boxed{3}$
   $9 = 3 \cdot \boxed{3}$
   The LCD is $2 \cdot 2 \cdot 3 \cdot 3$ or 36.

9. $\dfrac{5}{11} < \dfrac{6}{13}$

10. $\dfrac{15}{34} < \dfrac{4}{8}$

11. $\dfrac{8}{18} > \dfrac{5}{16}$

12. $\dfrac{3}{14} < \dfrac{5}{20}$

Page 750   Lesson 4-8

1. $r^4 \cdot r^2 = r^{4+2}$
   $= r^6$

2. $\dfrac{2^9}{2^3} = 2^{9-3}$
   $= 2^6$

3. $\dfrac{b^{18}}{b^5} = b^{18-5}$
   $= b^{13}$

4. $12^3 \cdot 12^8 = 12^{3+8}$
   $= 12^{11}$

5. $x \cdot x^9 = x^1 \cdot x^9$
   $= x^{1+9}$
   $= x^{10}$

6. $(2s^6)(4s^2) = (2 \cdot 4)(s^6 \cdot s^2)$
   $= (8)(s^{6+2})$
   $= 8s^8$

7. $w^3 \cdot w^4 \cdot w^2 = w^{3+4+2}$
   $= w^9$

8. $(-2)^2(-2)^5(-2) = (-2)^2(-2)^5(-2)^1$
   $= (-2)^{2+5+1}$
   $= (-2)^8$

9. $\dfrac{4^7}{4^6} = 4^{7-6}$
$= 4^1$
$= 4$

10. $3(f^{17})(f^2) = 3(f^{17+2})$
$= 3f^{19}$

11. $(5k)^2 \cdot k^7 = 5k \cdot 5k \cdot k^7$
$= 5k^1 \cdot 5k^1 \cdot k^7$
$= (5 \cdot 5)(k^1 \cdot k^1 \cdot k^7)$
$= (25)(k^{1+1+7})$
$= 25k^9$

12. $\dfrac{6m^8}{3m^2} = 2m^{8-2}$
$= 2m^6$

13. $(2^4)(2^2) = 2^6$

14. $y(y^3)(y^4) = y^8$

15. $\dfrac{5^7}{5^3} = 5^4$

16. $12^9 \cdot 12^5 = 12^{14}$

17. $\dfrac{b^{10}}{b^9} = b$

18. $\dfrac{2^7}{8^2} = 2^1$

Page 750   Lesson 4-9

1. $\dfrac{1}{y^9}$

2. $\dfrac{3}{m^4}$

3. $\dfrac{-a}{5^3}$

4. $\left(\dfrac{x}{2}\right)^7$

5. p^{-4}

6. $6ab^{-9}$

7. $\dfrac{2}{27} = \dfrac{2}{3^3}$
$= 2 \cdot 3^{-3}$

8. $17a^{-1}$

9. $5^n = 5^{-2}$
$= \dfrac{1}{5^2}$
$= \dfrac{1}{25}$

10. $(2a^{-2}b)^2 = (2 \cdot 3^{-2} \cdot 6)^2$
$= \left(\dfrac{2 \cdot 6}{3^2}\right)^2$
$= \left(\dfrac{12}{9}\right)^2$
$= \dfrac{144}{81}$
$= 1\dfrac{7}{9}$

11. $15n^{-3} = 15 \cdot 5^{-3}$
$= \dfrac{15}{5^3}$
$= \dfrac{15}{125}$
$= \dfrac{3}{25}$

12. $9x^{-6} = 9(-3)^{-6}$
$= \dfrac{9}{(-3)^6}$
$= \dfrac{9}{729}$
$= \dfrac{1}{81}$

13. $(x^8)(x^{-2}) = x^{8+(-2)}$
$= x^6$

14. $(g^{-12})(g^9) = g^{-12+9}$
$= g^{-3}$
$= \dfrac{1}{g^3}$

15. $\dfrac{r^{14}}{r^{-2}} = r^{14-(-2)}$
$= r^{14+2}$
$= r^{16}$

16. $\dfrac{y^7}{y^{10}} = y^{7-10}$
$= y^{-3}$
$= \dfrac{1}{y^3}$

Page 750   Lesson 5-1

1. Rational

2. Whole, Integer, Rational

3. Integer, Rational

4. $\dfrac{3}{4} > \dfrac{2}{5}$

5. $\dfrac{-13}{25} > \dfrac{-3}{5}$

6. $\dfrac{9}{10} > \dfrac{7}{8}$

7. $5\dfrac{2}{9} = \dfrac{47}{9}$

8. $\dfrac{5}{26} < \dfrac{4}{13}$

9. $\dfrac{-11}{4} < -2\dfrac{1}{2}$

10. $0.38 = \dfrac{38}{100}$
$= \dfrac{19}{50}$

11. $2.346 = 2\dfrac{346}{1000}$
$= 2\dfrac{173}{500}$

12. Let $N = -0.444\ldots$ Then $10N = -4.444\ldots$
$10N = -4.444\ldots$
$\underline{-\ 1N = -0.444\ldots}$
$9N = -4$
$N = \dfrac{-4}{9}$
Therefore, $-0.\overline{4} = -\dfrac{4}{9}$.

Page 751   Lesson 5-2

1. 7   **2.** 5   **3.** 42

4. 1   **5.** 0   **6.** 1

7. Sample answer:
$9.9 - 3.2 \to 10 - 3 = 7$
$9.9 - 3.2$ is about 7.

8. Sample answer:
$16.2 + 9.31 \to 16 + 9 = 25$
$16.2 + 9.31$ is about 25.

9. Sample answer:
$1.3 + 2.8 - 3.4 \to 1 + 3 - 3 = 1$
$1.3 + 2.8 - 3.4$ is about 1.

10. Sample answer:
$8\dfrac{3}{5} - 2\dfrac{1}{6} \to 8\dfrac{1}{2} - 2 = 6\dfrac{1}{2}$
$8\dfrac{3}{5} - 2\dfrac{1}{6}$ is about $6\dfrac{1}{2}$.

11. Sample answer:
$19\dfrac{4}{10} + 13\dfrac{8}{11} \to 19\dfrac{1}{2} + 14 = 33\dfrac{1}{2}$
$19\dfrac{4}{10} + 13\dfrac{8}{11}$ is about $33\dfrac{1}{2}$.

12. Sample answer:
$863\dfrac{1}{12} - 241\dfrac{189}{221} \to 863 - 242 = 621$
$863\dfrac{1}{12} - 241\dfrac{189}{221}$ is about 621.

Page 751   Lesson 5-3

1. $b = 5.8 + 9.3$
$\begin{array}{r} 9.3 \\ +\ 5.8 \\ \hline 15.1 \end{array}$
$b = 15.1$

2. $s = 12.4 - 4.52$
$\begin{array}{r} 12.40 \\ -\ 4.52 \\ \hline 7.88 \end{array}$
$s = 7.88$

3. $-4.9 + 8.4 = k$
$\begin{array}{r} 8.4 \\ -4.9 \\ \hline 3.5 \end{array}$
$k = 3.5$

4. $-5.2 - 7.8 = q$
$-5.2 + (-7.8) = q$
$\begin{array}{r} 7.8 \\ +\ 5.2 \\ \hline 13.0 \end{array}$
$q = -13$

5. $p = 14.8 - 29.46$
$p = -|129.46 - 14.81|$
$\begin{array}{r} 29.46 \\ -14.80 \\ \hline 14.66 \end{array}$
$p = -14.66$

6. $-4.25 + 11.2 = t$
$\begin{array}{r} 11.20 \\ -\ 4.25 \\ \hline 6.95 \end{array}$
$t = 6.95$

7. $21.4 - 9.2 = z$
$\begin{array}{r} 21.4 \\ -\ 9.2 \\ \hline 12.2 \end{array}$
$z = 12.2$

8. $45.26 - (-6.1) = y$
$45.26 + 6.1 = y$
$\begin{array}{r} 45.26 \\ +\ 6.10 \\ \hline 51.36 \end{array}$
$y = 51.36$

9. $x = -9.27 - 8.1$
$x = -9.27 + (-8.1)$

$$\begin{array}{r} 9.27 \\ +\ 8.10 \\ \hline 17.37 \end{array}$$

$x = -17.37$

10. $-28.94 + 3.48 = u$
$-|28.94 - 3.48| = u$

$$\begin{array}{r} 28.94 \\ -\ 3.48 \\ \hline 25.46 \end{array}$$

$u = -25.46$

Page 751   Lesson 5-4

1. $\frac{2}{7} + \frac{3}{7} = g$
$\frac{5}{7} = g$

2. $\frac{8}{15} - \frac{4}{15} = y$
$\frac{4}{15} = y$

3. $\frac{3}{7} + \frac{4}{7} = w$
$\frac{7}{7} = w$
$1 = w$

4. $\frac{5}{6} - \frac{1}{6} = t$
$\frac{4}{6} = t$
$\frac{2}{3} = t$

5. $\frac{7}{12} - \frac{5}{12} = r$
$\frac{2}{12} = r$
$\frac{1}{6} = r$

6. $\frac{5}{12} + \frac{11}{12} = w$
$\frac{16}{12} = w$
$1\frac{4}{12} = w$
$1\frac{1}{3} = w$

7. $12\frac{7}{8}s - 7\frac{3}{8}s + 2\frac{5}{8}s = \left(12\frac{7}{8} - 7\frac{3}{8} + 2\frac{5}{8}\right)s$
$= \left(12\frac{7}{8} + 2\frac{5}{8} - 7\frac{3}{8}\right)s$
$= \left(14\frac{12}{8} - 7\frac{3}{8}\right)s$
$= \left(15\frac{4}{8} - 7\frac{3}{8}\right)s$
$= \left[(15 - 7) + \left(\frac{4}{8} - \frac{3}{8}\right)\right]s$
$= \left(8 + \frac{1}{8}\right)s$
$= 8\frac{1}{8}s$

8. $-6\frac{4}{9}t - \left(-4\frac{5}{9}t\right) + 3\frac{2}{9}t = -6\frac{4}{9}t + 4\frac{5}{9}t + 3\frac{2}{9}t$
$= \left(-6\frac{4}{9} + 4\frac{5}{9} + 3\frac{2}{9}\right)t$
$= \left(-6\frac{4}{9} + 7\frac{7}{9}\right)t$
$= \left[(-6 + 7) + \left(-\frac{4}{9} + \frac{7}{9}\right)\right]t$
$= \left(1 + \frac{3}{9}\right)t$
$= \left(1 + \frac{1}{3}\right)t$
$= 1\frac{1}{3}t$

9. $6\frac{1}{4}g + \left(-6\frac{3}{4}g\right) = 6\frac{1}{4}g - 6\frac{3}{4}g$
$= \left(6\frac{1}{4} - 6\frac{3}{4}\right)g$
$= \left[(6 - 6) + \left(\frac{1}{4} - \frac{3}{4}\right)\right]g$
$= \left[0 + \left(-\frac{2}{4}\right)\right]g$
$= -\frac{2}{4}g$
$= -\frac{1}{2}g$

10. $7\frac{2}{5}n - \left(-4\frac{2}{5}n\right) = 7\frac{2}{5}n + 4\frac{2}{5}n$
$= \left(7\frac{2}{5} + 4\frac{2}{5}\right)n$
$= \left[(7 + 4) + \left(\frac{2}{5} + \frac{2}{5}\right)\right]n$
$= \left(11 + \frac{4}{5}\right)n$
$= 11\frac{4}{5}n$

Page 751   Lesson 5-5

1. $\frac{1}{5} + \frac{2}{7} = d$
$\frac{7}{35} + \frac{10}{35} = d$
$\frac{17}{35} = d$

2. $a = \frac{4}{5} + \frac{7}{9}$
$a = \frac{36}{45} + \frac{35}{45}$
$a = \frac{71}{45}$
$a = 1\frac{26}{45}$

3. $\frac{1}{9} - \frac{7}{12} = n$
$\frac{4}{36} - \frac{21}{36} = n$
$\frac{-17}{36} = n$

4. $z = \frac{8}{11} - \frac{4}{5}$
$z = \frac{40}{55} - \frac{44}{55}$
$z = \frac{-4}{55}$

5. $\frac{7}{12} - \left(\frac{-4}{11}\right) = y$
$\frac{7}{12} + \frac{4}{11} = y$
$\frac{77}{132} + \frac{48}{132} = y$
$\frac{125}{132} = y$

6. $\ell = \frac{-9}{14} + \frac{15}{16}$
$\ell = \frac{-72}{112} + \frac{105}{112}$
$\ell = \frac{33}{112}$

7. $3\frac{2}{5} + 2\frac{4}{7} = k$
$3\frac{14}{35} + 2\frac{20}{35} = k$
$5\frac{34}{35} = k$

8. $r = -4\frac{1}{8} + 2\frac{5}{9}$
$r = -4\frac{9}{72} + 2\frac{40}{72}$
$r = 2\frac{40}{72} - 4\frac{9}{72}$
$r = 2\frac{40}{72} - 3\frac{81}{72}$
$r = -1\frac{41}{72}$

9. $-3\frac{3}{7} - 5\frac{1}{14} = g$
$-3\frac{3}{7} + \left(-5\frac{1}{14}\right) = g$
$-3\frac{6}{14} + \left(-5\frac{1}{14}\right) = g$
$-8\frac{7}{14} = g$
$-8\frac{1}{2} = g$

Page 752   Lesson 5-6

1. $a - 4.86 = 7.2$
$a - 4.86 + 4.86 = 7.2 + 4.86$
$a = 12.06$
Check: $a - 4.86 = 7.2$
$12.06 - 4.86 \stackrel{?}{=} 7.2$
$7.2 = 7.2$ ✔

2. $n + 6.98 = 10.3$
$n + 6.98 - 6.98 = 10.3 - 6.98$
$n = 3.32$
Check: $n + 6.98 = 10.3$
$3.32 + 6.98 \stackrel{?}{=} 10.3$
$10.3 = 10.3$ ✔

3. $87.64 = f - (-8.5)$
$87.64 = f + 8.5$
$87.64 - 8.5 = f + 8.5 - 8.5$
$79.14 = f$
Check: $87.64 = f - (-8.5)$
$87.64 \stackrel{?}{=} 79.14 - (-8.5)$
$87.64 \stackrel{?}{=} 79.14 + 8.5$
$87.64 = 87.64$ ✔

4.
$$x - \frac{2}{5} = -\frac{8}{15}$$
$$x - \frac{2}{5} + \frac{2}{5} = -\frac{8}{15} + \frac{2}{5}$$
$$x = -\frac{8}{15} + \frac{6}{15}$$
$$x = -\frac{2}{15}$$

Check: $x - \frac{2}{5} = -\frac{8}{15}$

$$-\frac{2}{15} - \frac{2}{5} \overset{?}{=} -\frac{8}{15}$$
$$-\frac{2}{15} - \frac{6}{15} \overset{?}{=} \frac{-8}{15}$$
$$\frac{-8}{15} = \frac{-8}{15} ✔$$

5.
$$3\frac{3}{4} + m = 6\frac{5}{8}$$
$$3\frac{3}{4} + m - 3\frac{3}{4} = 6\frac{5}{8} - 3\frac{3}{4}$$
$$m = 6\frac{5}{8} - 3\frac{6}{8}$$
$$m = 5\frac{13}{8} - 3\frac{6}{8}$$
$$m = 2\frac{7}{8}$$

Check: $3\frac{3}{4} + m = 6\frac{5}{8}$

$$3\frac{3}{4} + 2\frac{7}{8} \overset{?}{=} 6\frac{5}{8}$$
$$3\frac{6}{8} + 2\frac{7}{8} \overset{?}{=} 6\frac{5}{8}$$
$$5\frac{13}{8} \overset{?}{=} 6\frac{5}{8}$$
$$6\frac{5}{8} = 6\frac{5}{8} ✔$$

6.
$$4\frac{1}{6} = r + 6\frac{1}{4}$$
$$4\frac{1}{6} - 6\frac{1}{4} = r + 6\frac{1}{4} - 6\frac{1}{4}$$
$$4\frac{2}{12} - 6\frac{3}{12} = r$$
$$\frac{50}{12} - \frac{75}{12} = r$$
$$\frac{-25}{12} = r$$
$$-2\frac{1}{2} = r$$

Check: $4\frac{1}{6} = r + 6\frac{1}{4}$

$$4\frac{1}{6} \overset{?}{=} -2\frac{1}{12} + 6\frac{1}{4}$$
$$4\frac{1}{6} \overset{?}{=} -2\frac{1}{12} + 6\frac{3}{12}$$
$$4\frac{1}{6} \overset{?}{=} 4\frac{2}{12}$$
$$4\frac{1}{6} = 4\frac{1}{6} ✔$$

7.
$$7\frac{1}{3} = c - \frac{4}{5}$$
$$7\frac{1}{3} + \frac{4}{5} = c - \frac{4}{5} + \frac{4}{5}$$
$$7\frac{5}{15} + \frac{12}{15} = c$$
$$7\frac{17}{15} = c$$
$$8\frac{2}{15} = c$$

Check: $7\frac{1}{3} = c - \frac{4}{5}$

$$7\frac{1}{3} \overset{?}{=} 8\frac{2}{15} - \frac{4}{5}$$
$$7\frac{1}{3} \overset{?}{=} 8\frac{2}{15} - \frac{12}{15}$$
$$7\frac{1}{3} \overset{?}{=} 7\frac{17}{15} - \frac{12}{15}$$
$$7\frac{1}{3} \overset{?}{=} 7\frac{5}{15}$$
$$7\frac{1}{3} = 7\frac{1}{3} ✔$$

8.
$$-4.62 = h + (-9.4)$$
$$-4.62 = h - 9.4$$
$$-4.62 + 9.4 = h - 9.4 + 9.4$$
$$4.78 = h$$

Check: $-4.62 = h + (-9.4)$

$$-4.62 \overset{?}{=} 4.78 + (-9.4)$$
$$-4.62 \overset{?}{=} 4.78 - 9.4$$
$$-4.62 = -4.62 ✔$$

9.
$$w - 1\frac{1}{5} = \frac{2}{9}$$
$$w - 1\frac{1}{5} + 1\frac{1}{5} = \frac{2}{9} + 1\frac{1}{5}$$
$$w = \frac{10}{45} + 1\frac{9}{45}$$
$$w = 1\frac{19}{45}$$

Check: $w - 1\frac{1}{5} = \frac{2}{9}$

$$1\frac{19}{45} - 1\frac{1}{5} \overset{?}{=} \frac{2}{9}$$
$$1\frac{19}{45} - 1\frac{9}{45} \overset{?}{=} \frac{2}{9}$$
$$\frac{10}{45} \overset{?}{=} \frac{2}{9}$$
$$\frac{2}{9} = \frac{2}{9} ✔$$

Page 752   Lesson 5-7

1.
$$h + 5.7 > 21.3$$
$$h + 5.7 - 5.7 > 21.3 - 5.7$$
$$h > 15.6$$
Check: Try 16, a number greater than 15.6.
$$h + 5.7 > 21.3$$
$$16 + 5.7 \overset{?}{>} 21.3$$
$$21.7 > 21.3 ✔$$

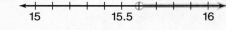

2.
$$78.26 \le v - (-65.854)$$
$$78.26 \le v + 65.854$$
$$78.26 - 65.854 \le v + 65.854 - 65.854$$
$$12.406 \le v$$
Check: Try 13, a number greater than or equal to 12.406.
$$78.26 \le v - (-65.854)$$
$$78.26 \overset{?}{\le} 13 - (-65.854)$$
$$78.26 \overset{?}{\le} 13 + 65.854$$
$$78.26 \le 78.854 ✔$$

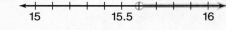

3.
$$\frac{2}{3} \le a - \frac{5}{6}$$
$$\frac{2}{3} + \frac{5}{6} \le a - \frac{5}{6} + \frac{5}{6}$$
$$\frac{4}{6} + \frac{5}{6} \le a$$
$$\frac{9}{6} \le a$$
$$1\frac{3}{6} \le a$$
$$1\frac{1}{2} \le a$$

Check: Try 2, a number greater than or equal to $1\frac{1}{2}$.

$$\frac{2}{3} \leq a - \frac{5}{6}$$

$$\frac{2}{3} \overset{?}{\leq} 2 - \frac{5}{6}$$

$$\frac{2}{3} \overset{?}{\leq} \frac{12}{6} - \frac{5}{6}$$

$$\frac{2}{3} \overset{?}{\leq} \frac{7}{6}$$

$$\frac{2}{3} \leq 1\frac{1}{6} \ \checkmark$$

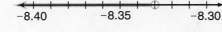

4.
$$-13.2 > w - 4.87$$
$$-13.2 + 4.87 > w - 4.87 + 4.87$$
$$-8.33 > w$$

Check: Try -10, a number less than -8.33.
$$-13.2 > w - 4.87$$
$$-13.2 \overset{?}{>} -10 - 4.87$$
$$-13.2 > -14.87 \ \checkmark$$

$-8.40 \quad -8.35 \quad -8.30$

5.
$$a + \frac{5}{12} \geq \frac{7}{18}$$
$$a + \frac{5}{12} - \frac{5}{12} \geq \frac{7}{18} - \frac{5}{12}$$
$$a \geq \frac{14}{36} - \frac{15}{36}$$
$$a \geq -\frac{1}{36}$$

Check: Try 0, a number greater than or equal to $-\frac{1}{36}$.
$$a + \frac{5}{12} \geq \frac{7}{18}$$
$$0 + \frac{5}{12} \overset{?}{\geq} \frac{7}{18}$$
$$\frac{5}{12} \geq \frac{7}{18} \ \checkmark$$

$-\frac{1}{2} \qquad 0 \qquad \frac{1}{2}$

6.
$$7\frac{1}{2} < n - \left(-\frac{7}{8}\right)$$
$$7\frac{1}{2} < n + \frac{7}{8}$$
$$7\frac{1}{2} - \frac{7}{8} < n + \frac{7}{8} - \frac{7}{8}$$
$$7\frac{4}{8} - \frac{7}{8} < n$$
$$6\frac{12}{8} - \frac{7}{8} < n$$
$$6\frac{5}{8} < n$$

Check: Try 9, a number greater than $6\frac{5}{8}$.
$$7\frac{1}{2} < n - \left(-\frac{7}{8}\right)$$
$$7\frac{1}{2} \overset{?}{<} 9 - \left(-\frac{7}{8}\right)$$
$$7\frac{1}{2} \overset{?}{<} 9 + \frac{7}{8}$$
$$7\frac{1}{2} < 9\frac{7}{8} \ \checkmark$$

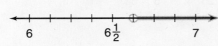

7.
$$t - 8.5 > -4.2$$
$$t - 8.5 + 8.5 > -4.2 + 8.5$$
$$t > 4.3$$

Check: Try 5, a number greater than 4.3.
$$t - 8.5 > -4.2$$
$$5 - 8.5 \overset{?}{>} -4.2$$
$$-3.5 > -4.2 \ \checkmark$$

$4.0 \qquad 4.5 \qquad 5.0$

8.
$$-7.42 \leq d - 5.9$$
$$-7.42 + 5.9 \leq d - 5.9 + 5.9$$
$$-1.52 \leq d$$

Check: Try 0, a number greater than or equal to -1.52.
$$-7.42 \leq d - 5.9$$
$$-7.42 \overset{?}{\leq} 0 - 5.9$$
$$-7.42 \leq -5.9 \ \checkmark$$

$-1.60 \qquad\qquad\qquad -1.50$

9.
$$m - (-18.4) < -17.6$$
$$m + 18.4 < -17.6$$
$$m + 18.4 - 18.4 < -17.6 - 18.4$$
$$m < -36$$

Check: Try -40, a number less than -36.
$$m - (-18.4) \overset{?}{<} -17.6$$
$$-40 - (-18.4) \overset{?}{<} -17.6$$
$$-40 + 18.4 \overset{?}{<} -17.6$$
$$-21.6 < -17.6 \ \checkmark$$

$-40 \qquad\qquad\qquad -30$

10.
$$s - \frac{2}{3} \geq 9\frac{4}{5}$$
$$s - \frac{2}{3} + \frac{2}{3} \geq 9\frac{4}{5} + \frac{2}{3}$$
$$s \geq 9\frac{12}{15} + \frac{10}{15}$$
$$s \geq 9\frac{22}{15}$$
$$s \geq 10\frac{7}{15}$$

Check: Try 12, a number greater than or equal to $10\frac{7}{15}$.
$$s - \frac{2}{3} \geq 9\frac{4}{5}$$
$$12 - \frac{2}{3} \overset{?}{\geq} 9\frac{4}{5}$$
$$\frac{36}{3} - \frac{2}{3} \overset{?}{\geq} 9\frac{4}{5}$$
$$\frac{34}{3} \overset{?}{\geq} 9\frac{4}{5}$$
$$11\frac{1}{3} \geq 9\frac{4}{5} \ \checkmark$$

$10 \qquad\qquad\qquad 11$

Page 752   Lesson 5-8
1. Sample answer: inductive
   See students' explanations.
2. Sample answer: inductive
   See students' explanations.

3. Sample answer: deductive
See students' explanations.
4. Sample answer: deductive
See students' explanations.

Page 752   Lesson 5-9

1. 3.5 4.3 5.1
+0.8 +0.8
yes; 5.9, 6.7, 7.5

2. 5 10 20
+5 +10
no; 40, 80, 160

3. $\frac{1}{2}$ $\frac{5}{6}$ $1\frac{1}{6}$
+$\frac{1}{3}$ +$\frac{1}{3}$
yes; $1\frac{1}{2}$, $1\frac{5}{6}$, $2\frac{1}{6}$

4. $\frac{1}{4}$ $\frac{1}{2}$ 1 2
+$\frac{1}{4}$ +$\frac{1}{2}$ +1
no; 4, 8, 16

5. 23 18 13
-5 -5
yes; 8, 3, -2

6. 45 43 39 33
-2 -4 -6
no; 25, 15, 3

Page 753   Lesson 6-1

1. $\frac{6}{10} \rightarrow 10\overline{)6.0}$
0.6
$\underline{-6\,0}$
0
$\frac{6}{10} = 0.6$

2. $-4\frac{7}{12} = -\left(4 + \frac{7}{12}\right)$
$\frac{7}{12} \rightarrow 12\overline{)7.0000}$
0.5833
$\underline{-6\,0}$
$1\,00$
$\underline{-96}$
40
$\underline{-36}$
40
$\underline{-36}$
4
$-(4 + 0.58\overline{3}) = -4.58\overline{3}$
$-4\frac{7}{12} = -4.58\overline{3}$

3. $\frac{8}{11} \rightarrow 11\overline{)8.0000}$
0.7272
$\underline{-7\,7}$
30
$\underline{-22}$
80
$\underline{-77}$
30
$\underline{-22}$
8
$\frac{8}{11} = 0.\overline{72}$

4. $3\frac{4}{18} = 3 + \frac{4}{18}$
$\frac{4}{18} \rightarrow 18\overline{)4.000}$
0.222
$\underline{-3\,6}$
40
$\underline{-36}$
40
$\underline{-36}$
4
$3 + 0.\overline{2} = 3.\overline{2}$
$3\frac{4}{18} = 3.\overline{2}$

5. $-\frac{3}{16} \rightarrow 16\overline{)3.0000}$
0.1875
$\underline{-1\,6}$
$1\,40$
$\underline{-1\,28}$
120
$\underline{-112}$
80
$\underline{-80}$
0
$-\frac{3}{16} = -0.1875$

6. $8\frac{36}{44} \rightarrow 8 + \frac{36}{44}$
$\frac{36}{44} \rightarrow 44\overline{)36.0000}$
0.8181
$\underline{-35\,2}$
80
$\underline{-44}$
360
$\underline{-352}$
80
$\underline{-44}$
36
$8 + 0.\overline{81} = 8.\overline{81}$
$8\frac{36}{44} = 8.\overline{81}$

7. $\frac{9}{37} \rightarrow 37\overline{)9.000000}$
0.243243
$\underline{-74}$
160
$\underline{-148}$
120
$\underline{-111}$
90
$\underline{-74}$
160
$\underline{-148}$
120
$\underline{-111}$
9
$\frac{9}{37} = 0.\overline{243}$

8. $\frac{6}{15} \rightarrow 15\overline{)6.0}$
0.4
$\underline{-6\,0}$
0
$\frac{6}{15} = 0.4$

9. $\frac{7}{8} > \frac{5}{6}$ because
$0.875 > 0.83\overline{3}$

10. $0.04 < \frac{5}{9}$ because
$0.04 < 0.5\overline{5}$

11. $\frac{1}{3} > \frac{2}{7}$ because
$0.33\overline{3} > 0.286$

12. $\frac{3}{5} = \frac{12}{20}$ because
$\frac{12}{20} = \frac{12}{20}$

13. $\frac{1}{2} > 0.75$ because
$0.50 > 0.75$

14. $0.3 < \frac{1}{3}$ because
$0.3 < 0.3\overline{3}$

15. $\frac{2}{3} > 0.64$ because
$0.\overline{66} > 0.64$

16. $\frac{2}{20} = 0.10$ because
$0.10 = 0.10$

Page 753   Lesson 6-2

1. Sample answer:
$16.38 \times 1.5 \rightarrow 16 \times 2 = 32$
16.38×1.5 is about 32.

2. Sample answer:
$35.54 \div 4.1 \rightarrow 36 \div 4 = 9$
$35.54 \div 4.1$ is about 9.

3. Sample answer:
$6\frac{4}{9} \cdot 7.09 \rightarrow 6 \cdot 7 = 42$
$6\frac{4}{9} \cdot 7.09$ is about 42.

4. Sample answer:
$18.24 \cdot 3.25 \rightarrow 18 \cdot 3 = 54$
$18.24 \cdot 3.25$ is about 54.

314

5. Sample answer:

$\frac{6}{13} \times 150 \to \frac{1}{2} \times 150 = 75$

$\frac{6}{13} \times 150$ is about 75.

6. Sample answer:

$\left(\frac{1}{4}\right)(15) \to \left(\frac{1}{4}\right)(16) = 4$

$\left(\frac{1}{4}\right)(15)$ is about 4.

7. Sample answer:

$78 \div 1\frac{11}{12} \to 78 \div 2 = 39$

$78 \div 1\frac{11}{12}$ is about 39.

8. Sample answer:

$1\frac{7}{8} \cdot 40 \to 2 \cdot 40 = 80$

$1\frac{7}{8} \cdot 40$ is about 80.

9. Sample answer:

$\frac{1}{3} \cdot 37 \to \frac{1}{3} \cdot 36 = 12$

$\frac{1}{3} \cdot 37$ is about 12.

10. Sample answer:

$75 \div 1\frac{7}{16} \to 75 \cdot 1\frac{1}{2} = 50$

$75 \div 1\frac{7}{16}$ is about 50.

11. Sample answer:

$88 \div \frac{3}{8} \to 88 \div \frac{1}{2} = 44$

$88 \div \frac{3}{8}$ is about 44.

12. Sample answer:

$71.99 \div 5.7 \to 72 \div 6 = 12$

$71.99 \div 5.7$ is about 12.

13. Sample answer:

$\frac{4}{9} \cdot 20 \to \frac{1}{2} \cdot 20 = 10$

$\frac{4}{9} \cdot 20$ is about 10.

14. Sample answer:

$65.46 \div 5.6 \to 63 \div 7 = 9$

$65.46 \div 5.6$ is about 9.

15. Sample answer:

$32 \times \$5.49 \to 30 \times 6 = 180$

$32 \times \$5.49$ is about \$180.

16. Sample answer:

$45 \div \frac{6}{13} \to 45 \div \frac{1}{2} = 90$

$45 \div \frac{6}{13}$ is about 90.

Page 753   Lesson 6-3

1. $d = \frac{2}{5} \cdot \frac{3}{16}$

$d = \frac{2 \cdot 3}{5 \cdot 16}$

$d = \frac{1 \cdot 3}{5 \cdot 8}$

$d = \frac{3}{40}$

2. $u = 3\frac{1}{4} \cdot \frac{2}{11}$

$u = \frac{13}{4} \cdot \frac{2}{11}$

$u = \frac{13 \cdot 2}{4 \cdot 11}$

$u = \frac{13 \cdot 1}{2 \cdot 11}$

$u = \frac{13}{22}$

3. $\left(\frac{3}{5}\right)\left(-\frac{5}{12}\right) = g$

$\left(\frac{3}{5}\right)\left(-\frac{5}{12}\right) = g$

$\frac{1 \cdot -1}{1 \cdot 4} = g$

$\frac{-1}{4} = g$

4. $t = \left(\frac{4}{5}\right)^3$

$t = \left(\frac{4}{5}\right)\left(\frac{4}{5}\right)\left(\frac{4}{5}\right)$

$t = \frac{64}{125}$

5. $s = 2\frac{2}{6} \cdot 6\frac{2}{7}$

$s = \frac{14}{6} \cdot \frac{44}{7}$

$s = \frac{14 \cdot 44}{6 \cdot 7}$

$s = \frac{2 \cdot 22}{3 \cdot 1}$

$s = \frac{44}{3}$

$s = 14\frac{2}{3}$

6. $2\left(-\frac{7}{12}\right) = r$

$\frac{2}{1}\left(-\frac{7}{12}\right) = r$

$\frac{2}{1}\left(-\frac{7}{12}\right) = r$

$\frac{1 \cdot -7}{1 \cdot 6} = r$

$-\frac{7}{6} = r$

$-1\frac{1}{6} = r$

7. $1\frac{3}{7} \cdot \left(-9\frac{4}{5}\right) = c$

$\frac{10}{7} \cdot \left(-\frac{49}{5}\right) = c$

$\frac{10}{7} \cdot \left(-\frac{49}{5}\right) = c$

$\frac{2 \cdot -7}{1 \cdot 1} = c$

$-14 = c$

8. $h = \left(-\frac{6}{7}\right)^2$

$h = \left(-\frac{6}{7}\right)\left(-\frac{6}{7}\right)$

$h = \frac{36}{49}$

9. $rx = -\frac{1}{5} \cdot 1\frac{1}{4}$

$= -\frac{1}{5} \cdot \frac{5}{4}$

$= \frac{-1 \cdot 5}{5 \cdot 4}$

$= \frac{-1 \cdot 1}{1 \cdot 4}$

$= \frac{-1}{4}$

10. $5r^2 = 5\left(-\frac{1}{5}\right)^2$

$= 5\left(-\frac{1}{5}\right)\left(-\frac{1}{5}\right)$

$= 5\left(\frac{1}{25}\right)$

$= \frac{5}{1}\left(\frac{1}{25}\right)$

$= \frac{5}{1}\left(\frac{1}{25}\right)$

$= \frac{1 \cdot 1}{1 \cdot 5}$

$= \frac{1}{5}$

11. $s(x + y) = \frac{2}{3}\left(1\frac{1}{4} + \left(-2\frac{1}{8}\right)\right)$

$= \frac{2}{3}\left(1\frac{1}{4} - 2\frac{1}{8}\right)$

$= \frac{2}{3}\left(\frac{5}{4} - \frac{17}{8}\right)$

$= \frac{2}{3}\left(\frac{10}{8} - \frac{17}{8}\right)$

$= \frac{2}{3}\left(-\frac{7}{8}\right)$

$= \frac{2}{3}\left(-\frac{7}{8}\right)$

$= \frac{1 \cdot -7}{3 \cdot 4}$

$= \frac{-7}{12}$

12. $8y + 12x = 8\left(-2\frac{1}{8}\right) + 12\left(1\frac{1}{4}\right)$

$= 8\left(-\frac{17}{8}\right) + 12\left(\frac{5}{4}\right)$

$= \frac{8}{1}\left(-\frac{17}{8}\right) + \frac{12}{1}\left(\frac{5}{4}\right)$

$= \frac{8}{1}\left(-\frac{17}{8}\right) + \frac{12}{1}\left(\frac{5}{4}\right)$

$= \frac{1 \cdot -17}{1 \cdot 1} + \frac{3 \cdot 5}{1 \cdot 1}$

$= \frac{-17}{1} + \frac{15}{1}$

$= -17 + 15$

$= -2$

13. $x^2(s + 2) = \left(1\frac{1}{4}\right)^2\left(\frac{2}{3} + 2\right)$

$\quad = \left(\frac{5}{4}\right)^2\left(2\frac{2}{3}\right)$

$\quad = \left(\frac{5}{4}\right)\left(\frac{5}{4}\right)\left(\frac{8}{3}\right)$

$\quad = \frac{200}{48}$

$\quad = 4\frac{8}{48}$

$\quad = 4\frac{1}{6}$

14. $-x(x - 2s) = -1\frac{1}{4}\left(1\frac{1}{4} - 2\left(\frac{2}{3}\right)\right)$

$\quad = -1\frac{1}{4}\left(1\frac{1}{4} - \frac{4}{3}\right)$

$\quad = -1\frac{1}{4}\left(\frac{5}{4} - \frac{4}{3}\right)$

$\quad = -1\frac{1}{4}\left(\frac{15}{12} - \frac{16}{12}\right)$

$\quad = -1\frac{1}{4}\left(-\frac{1}{12}\right)$

$\quad = -\frac{5}{4}\left(-\frac{1}{12}\right)$

$\quad = \frac{-5 \cdot -1}{4 \cdot 12}$

$\quad = \frac{5}{48}$

Page 754   Lesson 6-4

1. $-\frac{9}{5}$ or $1\frac{4}{5}$

2. $\frac{8}{43}$

3. $\frac{10}{7}$ or $1\frac{3}{7}$

4. $\frac{20}{47}$

5. $-\frac{1}{18}$

6. $\frac{b}{a}$

7. $w = \frac{3}{4} \div \frac{15}{16}$

$\quad w = \frac{3}{4} \times \frac{16}{15}$

$\quad w = \frac{48}{60}$

$\quad w = \frac{4}{5}$

8. $16 \div 1\frac{7}{8} = m$

$\quad \frac{16}{1} \div \frac{15}{8} = m$

$\quad \frac{16}{1} \times \frac{8}{15} = m$

$\quad \frac{128}{15} = m$

$\quad 8\frac{8}{15} = m$

9. $q = 2\frac{1}{6} \div 1\frac{1}{5}$

$\quad q = \frac{13}{6} \div \frac{6}{5}$

$\quad q = \frac{13}{6} \times \frac{5}{6}$

$\quad q = \frac{65}{36}$

$\quad q = 1\frac{29}{36}$

10. $y = -11 \div 3\frac{1}{7}$

$\quad y = \frac{-11}{1} \div \frac{22}{7}$

$\quad y = \frac{-11}{1} \times \frac{7}{22}$

$\quad y = \frac{-77}{22}$

$\quad y = -3\frac{11}{22}$

$\quad y = -3\frac{1}{2}$

11. $a = \frac{8}{45} \div \frac{10}{27}$

$\quad a = \frac{8}{45} \times \frac{27}{10}$

$\quad a = \frac{216}{450}$

$\quad a = \frac{12}{25}$

12. $220 \div -5\frac{1}{2} = p$

$\quad \frac{220}{1} \div -\frac{11}{2} = p$

$\quad \frac{220}{1} \times -\frac{2}{11} = p$

$\quad \frac{-440}{11} = p$

$\quad -40 = p$

Page 754   Lesson 6-5

1. $7.3017 \div 0.57 = a$

$$0.57\overline{)7.3017}$$

$$\begin{array}{r} 12.81 \\ 57\overline{)730.17} \\ -57 \\ \hline 160 \\ -114 \\ \hline 46\,1 \\ -45\,6 \\ \hline 57 \\ -57 \\ \hline 0 \end{array}$$

$a = 12.81$

2. $13.42 \div 67.1 = d$

$$67.1\overline{)13.42}$$

$$\begin{array}{r} 0.2 \\ 671\overline{)134.2} \\ -134\,2 \\ \hline 0 \end{array}$$

$d = 0.2$

3. $x = 80 \div -3.2$

$$3.2\overline{)80.0}$$

$$\begin{array}{r} 25 \\ 32\overline{)800} \\ -64 \\ \hline 160 \\ -160 \\ \hline 0 \end{array}$$

$x = -25$

4. $m = -2.016 \div (-0.13)$

$$0.13\overline{)2.016}$$

$$\begin{array}{r} 15.5076 \\ 13\overline{)201.6000} \\ -13 \\ \hline 71 \\ -65 \\ \hline 6\,6 \\ -6\,5 \\ \hline 100 \\ -\,91 \\ \hline 90 \\ -\,78 \\ \hline 12 \end{array}$$

$m \approx 15.508$

5. $3.8 \cdot 2.9 = k$

$$\begin{array}{r} 3.8 \\ \times\,2.9 \\ \hline 342 \\ +\,760 \\ \hline 11.02 \end{array}$$

$k = 11.02$

6. $85 \cdot 0.07 = w$

$$\begin{array}{r} 0.07 \\ \times\,85 \\ \hline 035 \\ +0560 \\ \hline 5.95 \end{array}$$

$w = 5.95$

7. $r = 15.32(0.0015)$

$$\begin{array}{r} 0.0015 \\ \times\,15.32 \\ \hline 00030 \\ 000450 \\ 0\,007500 \\ +00\,015000 \\ \hline 00.022980 \end{array}$$

$r = 0.02298$

8. $(16.2)(0.013) = b$

$$\begin{array}{r} 0.013 \\ \times\,16.2 \\ \hline 0026 \\ 0\,0780 \\ +00\,1300 \\ \hline 00.2106 \end{array}$$

$b = 0.2106$

9. $c = 5.4 \cdot 9.7$

$$\begin{array}{r} 9.7 \\ \times\,5.4 \\ \hline 38\,8 \\ +48\,50 \\ \hline 52.38 \end{array}$$

$c = 52.38$

10. $4y^3 = 4(0.6)^3$

$\quad = 4(0.216)$

$\quad = 0.864$

11. $xy = (0.348)(-6.4)$

$\quad = -2.2272$

12. $\dfrac{3a}{w} = \dfrac{3(0.4)}{2}$

$\phantom{\dfrac{3a}{w}} = \dfrac{1.2}{2}$

$\phantom{\dfrac{3a}{w}} = 0.6$

Page 754   Lesson 6-6

1. 79, 82, 91, 93, 95

mean: $\dfrac{79 + 82 + 91 + 93 + 95}{5} = 88$

median: 91

mode: none

2. 76, 85, 85, 88, 94, 97

mean: $\dfrac{76 + 85 + 85 + 88 + 94 + 97}{6} = 87.5$

median: $\dfrac{85 + 88}{2} = 86.5$

mode: 85

3. 0.57, 0.96, 0.96, 4.1, 6.1, 12.6, 12.81, 12.81, 14.3

mean: $\dfrac{65.21}{9} \approx 7.2$

median: 6.1

mode: 0.96 and 12.81

4. mean: $\dfrac{67.7 + 68.2 + 71.1 + 70.4 + 63.9 + 67.4}{6} \approx 68.1$

5. 20.3, 20.5, 22.2, 22.7, 23.9, 24.1

median: $\dfrac{22.2 + 22.7}{2} = 22.45$

6. mode: 11.5

Page 755   Lesson 6-7

1. $3.5a = 7$

$\dfrac{3.5a}{3.5} = \dfrac{7}{3.5}$

$a = 2$

Check: $3.5a = 7$

$3.5(2) \overset{?}{=} 7$

$7 = 7$ ✔

2. $0.8 = -0.8b$

$\dfrac{0.8}{-0.8} = \dfrac{-0.8b}{0.8}$

$-1 = b$

Check: $0.8 = -0.8b$

$0.8 \overset{?}{=} -0.8(-1)$

$0.8 = 0.8$ ✔

3. $8 < \dfrac{2}{3}c$

$\left(\dfrac{3}{2}\right)8 < \left(\dfrac{3}{2}\right)\dfrac{2}{3}c$

$12 < c$

Check: Try 15, a number greater than 12.

$8 < \dfrac{2}{3}c$

$8 \overset{?}{<} \dfrac{2}{3}(15)$

$8 < 10$ ✔

4. $\dfrac{m}{13} \geq 0.5$

$\dfrac{m}{13}(13) \geq 0.5(13)$

$m \geq 6.5$

Check: Try 13, a number greater than or equal to 6.5.

$\dfrac{m}{13} \geq 0.5$

$\dfrac{13}{13} \overset{?}{\geq} 0.5$

$1 \geq 0.5$ ✔

5. $-9 = \dfrac{3}{4}g$

$\left(\dfrac{4}{3}\right)(-9) = \left(\dfrac{4}{3}\right)\dfrac{3}{4}g$

$-12 = g$

Check: $-9 = \dfrac{3}{4}g$

$-9 \overset{?}{=} \dfrac{3}{4}(-12)$

$-9 = -9$ ✔

6. $0.4y > -2$

$\dfrac{0.4y}{0.4} > \dfrac{-2}{0.4}$

$y > -5$

Check: Try 0, a number greater than -5.

$0.4y > -2$

$0.4(0) \overset{?}{>} -2$

$0 > -2$ ✔

7. $-\dfrac{1}{2}d \leq -5\dfrac{1}{2}$

$(-2)\left(-\dfrac{1}{2}\right)d \geq (-2)\left(-5\dfrac{1}{2}\right)$

$d \geq \left(-\dfrac{2}{1}\right)\left(-\dfrac{11}{2}\right)$

$d \geq \dfrac{22}{2}$

$d \geq 11$

Check: Try 12, a number greater than or equal to 11.

$-\dfrac{1}{2}d \leq -5\dfrac{1}{2}$

$-\dfrac{1}{2}(12) \overset{?}{\leq} -5\dfrac{1}{2}$

$-6 \leq -5\dfrac{1}{2}$ ✔

8. $-3.5 = 0.07z$

$\dfrac{-3.5}{0.07} = \dfrac{0.07z}{0.07}$

$-50 = z$

Check: $-3.5 = 0.07z$

$-3.5 \overset{?}{=} 0.07(-50)$

$-3.5 = -3.5$ ✔

9. $-\dfrac{1}{6}s = 15$

$(-6)\left(-\dfrac{1}{6}\right)s = (-6)15$

$s = -90$

Check: $-\dfrac{1}{6}s = 15$

$-\dfrac{1}{6}(-90) \overset{?}{=} 15$

$15 = 15$ ✔

10. $\dfrac{2}{7}t < 4$

$\left(\dfrac{7}{2}\right)\dfrac{2}{7}t < \left(\dfrac{7}{2}\right)4$

$t < 14$

11. $8.37 = 2.7d$

$\dfrac{8.37}{2.7} = \dfrac{2.7d}{2.7}$

$3.1 = d$

12. $\dfrac{1}{5}m \geq 4\dfrac{3}{5}$

$(5)\dfrac{1}{5}m \geq (5)4\dfrac{3}{5}$

$m \geq (5)\dfrac{23}{5}$

$m \geq 23$

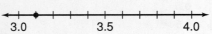

Page 755   Lesson 6-8

1. 2 4 8 16
  ×2 ×2 ×2

yes: 2; 32, 64, 128

2. 125 75 45
    ×$\frac{3}{5}$ ×$\frac{3}{5}$

yes; $\frac{3}{5}$; 27, $16\frac{1}{5}$, $9\frac{18}{25}$

3. 100 75 50
   −25 −25

no

4. $\frac{1}{5}$ 1 5 25
    ×5 ×5 ×5

yes; 5; 125, 625, 3125

5. 2401 49 7
    ÷7^2 ÷7^1

no

6. $-\frac{4}{5}$ 2 −5 $12\frac{1}{2}$
   × $-2\frac{1}{2}$ × $-2\frac{1}{2}$ × $-2\frac{1}{2}$

yes; $-2\frac{1}{2}$; $31\frac{1}{4}$, $78\frac{1}{8}$,

$-195\frac{5}{16}$

7. $-4(3) = -12$; $-12(3) = -36$; $-36(3) = -108$;
$-108(3) = -324$
$-4, -12, -36, -108, -324$

8. $-12\left(\frac{1}{2}\right) = -6$; $-6\left(\frac{1}{2}\right) = -3$; $-3\left(\frac{1}{2}\right) = -\frac{3}{2}$; $-\frac{3}{2}\left(\frac{1}{2}\right) = -\frac{3}{4}$
$-12, -6, -3, -\frac{3}{2}, -\frac{3}{4}$

9. $1.8(-3) = -5.4$; $-5.4(-3) = 16.2$; $16.2(-3) = -48.6$;
$-48.6(-3) = 145.8$
$1.8, -5.4, 16.2, -48.6, 145.8$

10. $ar^{n-1} = (-8)\left(-\frac{3}{2}\right)^{8-1}$

$= (-8)\left(-\frac{3}{2}\right)^{7}$

$= (-8)\left(-\frac{2187}{128}\right)$

$= \frac{17{,}496}{128}$

$= 136\frac{88}{128}$

$= 136\frac{11}{16}$

Page 755   Lesson 6-9

1. $6{,}184{,}000 = 6.184 \times 10^6$

2. $27{,}210{,}000 = 2.721 \times 10^7$

3. $0.00004637 = 4.637 \times 10^{-5}$

4. $0.00546 = 5.46 \times 10^{-3}$

5. $500{,}300{,}100 = 5.003001 \times 10^8$

6. $0.00000321 = 3.21 \times 10^{-6}$

7. $9.562 \times 10^{-3} = 9.562 \times \left(\frac{1}{10}\right)^3$

$= 9.562 \times \frac{1}{1000}$

$= 0.009562$

8. $8.2453 \times 10^{-7} = 8.2453 \times \left(\frac{1}{10}\right)^7$

$= 8.2453 \times \frac{1}{10{,}000{,}000}$

$= 0.00000082453$

9. $8.2 \times 10^4 = 8.2 \times 10{,}000$

$= 82{,}000$

10. $9.102040 \times 10^2 = 9.102040 \times 100$

$= 910.204$

11. $2.41023 \times 10^6 = 2.41023 \times 1{,}000{,}000$

$= 2{,}410{,}230$

12. $4.21 \times 10^{-5} = 4.21 \times \left(\frac{1}{10}\right)^5$

$= 4.21 \times \frac{1}{100{,}000}$

$= 0.0000421$

Page 756   Lesson 7-1

1. Doug left with 42 milk caps ⟶ 42
Undo 6 that he gave to Maria ⟶ + 6
 48
Undo 2 he received from Antonio ⟶ − 2
 46
Undo the third he traded ⟶ +23
(46 is $\frac{2}{3}$ of the remaining caps) ⟶ 69

Doug brought 69 milk bottle caps to Antonio's house.

2. Sandy has 3 cookies.

If Simon gave a third of his cookies to Sandy, then Simon had 9 cookies. (3 is $\frac{1}{3}$ of 9.)

If Justin gave half of his cookies to Simon, then Justin had 18 cookies. (9 is $\frac{1}{2}$ of 18.)

If Kwan gave a fourth of her cookies to Justin, then Kwan had 72 cookies. (18 is $\frac{1}{4}$ of 72.)

3.

Time	Number of Bacteria
After 3 full days ⟶	1600
	÷ 2
After $2\frac{1}{2}$ days ⟶	800
	÷ 2
After 2 full days ⟶	400
	÷ 2
After $1\frac{1}{2}$ days ⟶	200
	÷ 2
After 1 full day ⟶	100
	÷ 2
After $\frac{1}{2}$ day ⟶	50
	÷ 2
After 0 days ⟶	25

At the beginning of the first day, there were 25 bacteria in the culture.

4. Advance 5 spaces $\longrightarrow +5$

Back 4 spaces $\longrightarrow \underline{-4}$
$$+1$$

Advance 2 spaces $\longrightarrow \underline{+2}$
$$+3$$

Back 8 spaces $\longrightarrow \underline{-8}$
$$-5$$

Advance 2 spaces $\longrightarrow \underline{+2}$
$$-3$$

The piece moved back 3 places.

Page 756   Lesson 7-2

1.
$$3t - 13 = 2$$
$$3t + 13 + 13 = 2 + 13$$
$$3t = 15$$
$$\frac{3t}{3} = \frac{15}{3}$$
$$t = 5$$
Check: $3t - 13 = 2$
$$3(5) - 13 \stackrel{?}{=} 2$$
$$15 - 13 \stackrel{?}{=} 2$$
$$2 = 2 ✔$$

2.
$$-8j - 7 = 57$$
$$-8j - 7 + 7 = 57 + 7$$
$$-8j = 64$$
$$\frac{-8j}{-8} = \frac{64}{-8}$$
$$j = -8$$
Check: $-8j - 7 = 57$
$$-8(-8) - 7 \stackrel{?}{=} 57$$
$$64 - 7 \stackrel{?}{=} 57$$
$$57 = 57 ✔$$

3.
$$9d - 5 = 4$$
$$9d - 5 + 5 = 4 + 5$$
$$9d = 9$$
$$\frac{9d}{9} = \frac{9}{9}$$
$$d = 1$$
Check: $9d - 5 = 4$
$$9(1) - 5 \stackrel{?}{=} 4$$
$$9 - 5 \stackrel{?}{=} 4$$
$$4 = 4 ✔$$

4.
$$6 - 3w = -27$$
$$6 - 3w - 6 = -27 - 6$$
$$-3w = -33$$
$$\frac{-3w}{-3} = \frac{-33}{-3}$$
$$w = 11$$
Check: $6 - 3w = -27$
$$6 - 3(11) \stackrel{?}{=} -27$$
$$6 - 33 \stackrel{?}{=} -27$$
$$-27 = -27 ✔$$

5.
$$\frac{k}{6} + 8 = 12$$
$$\frac{k}{6} + 8 - 8 = 12 - 8$$
$$\frac{k}{6} = 4$$
$$6 \cdot \frac{k}{6} = 6 \cdot 4$$
$$k = 24$$
Check: $\frac{k}{6} + 8 = 12$
$$\frac{24}{6} + 8 \stackrel{?}{=} 12$$
$$4 + 8 \stackrel{?}{=} 12$$
$$12 = 12 ✔$$

6.
$$-4 = \frac{q}{8} - 19$$
$$-4 + 19 = \frac{q}{8} - 19 + 19$$
$$15 = \frac{q}{8}$$
$$8 \cdot 15 = 8 \cdot \frac{q}{8}$$
$$120 = q$$
Check: $-4 = \frac{q}{8} - 19$
$$-4 \stackrel{?}{=} \frac{120}{8} - 19$$
$$-4 \stackrel{?}{=} 15 - 19$$
$$-4 = -4 ✔$$

7.
$$15 - \frac{n}{7} = 13$$
$$15 - \frac{n}{7} - 15 = 13 - 15$$
$$-\frac{n}{7} = -2$$
$$(-7)\left(\frac{-n}{7}\right) = (-7)(-2)$$
$$n = 14$$
Check: $15 - \frac{n}{7} = 13$
$$15 - \frac{14}{7} \stackrel{?}{=} 13$$
$$15 - 2 \stackrel{?}{=} 13$$
$$13 = 13 ✔$$

8.
$$7.25 = 3r - 6.25$$
$$7.25 + 6.25 = 3r - 6.25 + 6.25$$
$$13.5 = 3r$$
$$\frac{13.5}{3} = \frac{3r}{3}$$
$$4.5 = r$$
Check: $7.25 = 3r - 6.25$
$$7.25 \stackrel{?}{=} 3(4.5) - 6.25$$
$$7.25 \stackrel{?}{=} 13.5 - 6.25$$
$$7.25 = 7.25 ✔$$

9.
$$21.63 - h = -32.7$$
$$21.63 - h - 21.63 = -32.7 - 21.63$$
$$-h = -54.33$$
$$\frac{-h}{-1} = \frac{-54.33}{-1}$$
$$h = 54.33$$
Check: $21.63 - h = -32.7$
$$21.63 - 54.33 \stackrel{?}{=} -32.7$$
$$-32.7 = -32.7 ✔$$

10.
$$-19 = 11b - (-3)$$
$$-19 = 11b + 3$$
$$-19 - 3 = 11b + 3 - 3$$
$$-22 = 11b$$
$$\frac{-22}{11} = \frac{11b}{11}$$
$$-2 = b$$
Check: $-19 = 11b - (-3)$
$$-19 \stackrel{?}{=} 11(-2) - (-3)$$
$$-19 \stackrel{?}{=} -22 + 3$$
$$-19 = -19 ✔$$

11.
$$6 = 20 + \frac{x}{3}$$
$$6 - 20 = 20 + \frac{x}{3} - 20$$
$$-14 = \frac{x}{3}$$
$$3 \cdot -14 = 3 \cdot \frac{x}{3}$$
$$-42 = x$$
Check: $6 = 20 + \frac{x}{3}$
$$6 \stackrel{?}{=} 20 + \frac{-42}{3}$$
$$6 \stackrel{?}{=} 20 + -14$$
$$6 \stackrel{?}{=} 20 - 14$$
$$6 = 6 ✔$$

12.
$$8.12 + 3a = -3.25$$
$$8.12 + 3a - 8.12 = -3.25 - 8.12$$
$$3a = -11.37$$
$$\frac{3a}{3} = \frac{-11.37}{3}$$
$$a = -3.79$$
Check: $8.12 + 3a = -3.25$
$$8.12 + 3(-3.79) \stackrel{?}{=} -3.25$$
$$8.12 + (-11.37) \stackrel{?}{=} -3.25$$
$$8.12 - 11.37 \stackrel{?}{=} -3.25$$
$$-3.25 = -3.25 ✔$$

Page 756   Lesson 7-3

1. Let q = number
$$29 + 3q = 44$$
$$29 + 3q - 29 = 44 - 29$$
$$3q = 15$$
$$\frac{3q}{3} = \frac{15}{3}$$
$$q = 5$$

2. Let m = number
$$-2m - 3 = 17$$
$$-2m - 3 + 3 = 17 + 3$$
$$-2m = 20$$
$$\frac{-2m}{-2} = \frac{20}{-2}$$
$$m = -10$$

3. Let x = first number
$x + 1$ = second number
$x + 2$ = third number
$x + 3$ = fourth number
$x + 4$ = fifth number
$$x + (x + 1) + (x + 2) + (x + 3) + (x + 4) = 95$$
$$x + x + 1 + x + 2 + x + 3 + x + 4 = 95$$
$$5x + 10 = 95$$
$$5x + 10 - 10 = 95 - 10$$
$$5x = 85$$
$$\frac{5x}{5} = \frac{85}{5}$$
$$x = 17$$
The numbers are 17, 18, 19, 20, and 21.

4. Let n = length of one side
$n + 2$ = length of second side
$n + 4$ = length of third side
$n + 6$ = length of fourth side
$$n + (n + 2) + (n + 4) + (n + 6) = 108$$
$$n + n + 2 + n + 4 + n + 6 = 108$$
$$4n + 12 = 108$$
$$4n + 12 - 12 = 108 - 12$$
$$4n = 96$$
$$\frac{4n}{4} = \frac{96}{4}$$
$$n = 24$$
The lengths of the sides of the quadrilateral are 24 yd, 26 yd, 28 yd, and 30 yd.

Page 757   Lesson 7-4

1. The diameter is twice the radius. So, the diameter is 2×5 or 10 cm.
$$C = 2\pi r$$
$$C = 2 \cdot \pi \cdot 5$$
$$C \approx 31.4 \text{ cm}$$
The circumference is about 31.4 cm.

2. The radius is half the diameter. So, the radius is $\frac{1}{2} \times 25$ or 12.5 mi.
$$C = \pi d$$
$$C = \pi \cdot 25$$
$$C \approx 78.5 \text{ mi.}$$
The circumference is about 78.5 mi.

3. The radius is half the diameter. So, the radius is $\frac{1}{2} \times 14$ or 7 in.
$$C = \pi d$$
$$C = \pi \cdot 14$$
$$C \approx 43.96 \text{ in.}$$
The circumference is about 43.96 in.

4.
$$C = \pi d$$
$$65.94 \approx \pi d$$
$$\frac{65.94}{\pi} \approx \frac{\pi d}{\pi}$$
$$21 \text{ mi} \approx d$$
The diameter is about 21 mi.
Since the radius is half the diameter, the radius is $\frac{1}{2} \times 21$ or about 10.5 mi.

320

5.
$$C = 2\pi r$$
$$56.52 \approx 2\pi r$$
$$\frac{56.52}{2\pi} \approx \frac{2\pi r}{2\pi}$$
$$9 \text{ ft} \approx r$$
The radius is about 9 ft.
Since the diameter is twice the radius, the diameter is 2×9 or about 18 ft.

6. $C = 2\pi r$
$C = 2 \cdot \pi \cdot 8$
$C \approx 50.24$ in.
The circumference is about 50.24 in.
$$C = \pi d$$
$$50.24 \approx \pi d$$
$$\frac{50.24}{\pi} \approx \frac{\pi d}{\pi}$$
$$16 \text{ in.} \approx d$$
The diameter is about 16 in.

7. $C = \pi d$
$C = \pi \cdot 17$
$C \approx 53.38$ m
The circumference is about 53.38m.
The radius is half the diameter. So, the radius is $\frac{1}{2} \times 17$ or 8.5 m.

8.
$$C = \pi d$$
$$100.48 \approx \pi d$$
$$\frac{100.48}{\pi} \approx \frac{\pi d}{\pi}$$
$$32 \text{ ft.} \approx d$$
The diameter is about 32 ft.
Since the radius is half the diameter, the radius is $\frac{1}{2} \times 32$ or about 16 ft.

9. $C = 2\pi r$
$C = 2 \cdot \pi \cdot 6$
$C \approx 37.68$ yds
The circumference is about 37.68 yds.
The diameter is twice the radius. So, the diameter is 2×6 or 12 yds.

10. $C = \pi d$
$C = \pi \cdot 22$
$C \approx 69.08$ cm
The circumference is about 69.08 cm.
Since the radius is half the diameter, the radius is $\frac{1}{2} \times 22$ or 11 cm.

11. $C = 2\pi r$
$C = 2 \cdot \pi \cdot 20$
$C \approx 125.6$ mm
The circumference is about 125.6 mm.
The diameter is twice the radius. So, the diameter is 2×20 or 40 mm.

12.
$$C = \pi d$$
$$81.64 \approx \pi d$$
$$\frac{81.64}{\pi} \approx \frac{\pi d}{\pi}$$
$$26 \text{ in.} \approx d$$
The diameter is about 26 in.
The radius is half the diameter. So, the radius is $\frac{1}{2} \times 26$ or about 13 in.

Page 757 Lesson 7-5

1.
$$-7h - 5 = 4 - 4h$$
$$-7h - 5 + 5 = 4 + 5 - 4h$$
$$-7h = 9 - 4h$$
$$-7h + 4h = 9 - 4h + 4h$$
$$-3h = 9$$
$$\frac{-3h}{-3} = \frac{9}{-3}$$
$$h = -3$$
Check: $\quad -7h - 5 = 4 - 4h$
$$-7(-3) - 5 \stackrel{?}{=} 4 - 4(-3)$$
$$21 - 5 \stackrel{?}{=} 4 + 12$$
$$16 = 16 ✔$$

2.
$$5t - 8 = 3t + 12$$
$$5t - 8 + 8 = 3t + 12 + 8$$
$$5t = 3t + 20$$
$$5t - 3t = 3t - 3t + 20$$
$$2t = 20$$
$$\frac{2t}{2} = \frac{20}{2}$$
$$t = 10$$
Check: $\quad 5t - 8 = 3t + 12$
$$5(10) - 8 \stackrel{?}{=} 3(10) + 12$$
$$50 - 8 \stackrel{?}{=} 30 + 12$$
$$42 = 42 ✔$$

3.
$$w + 6 = 2(w - 6)$$
$$w + 6 = 2w - 12$$
$$w + 6 - 6 = 2w - 12 - 6$$
$$w = 2w - 18$$
$$w - 2w = 2w - 2w - 18$$
$$-w = -18$$
$$-1(-w) = -1(-18)$$
$$w = 18$$
Check: $w + 6 = 2(w - 6)$
$$18 + 6 \stackrel{?}{=} 2(18 - 6)$$
$$24 \stackrel{?}{=} 36 - 12$$
$$24 = 24 ✔$$

4. $m + 2m + 1 = 7$
$$3m + 1 = 7$$
$$3m + 1 - 1 = 7 - 1$$
$$3m = 6$$
$$\frac{3m}{3} = \frac{6}{3}$$
$$m = 2$$
Check: $m + 2m + 1 = 7$
$$2 + 2(2) + 1 \stackrel{?}{=} 7$$
$$2 + 4 + 1 \stackrel{?}{=} 7$$
$$7 = 7 ✔$$

5.
$$3.21 - 7y = 10y - 1.89$$
$$3.21 - 3.21 - 7y = 10y - 1.89 - 3.21$$
$$-7y = 10y - 5.1$$
$$-7y - 10y = 10y - 10y - 5.1$$
$$-17y = -5.1$$
$$\frac{-17y}{-17} = \frac{-5.1}{-17}$$
$$y = 0.3$$
Check: $\quad 3.21 - 7y = 10y - 1.89$
$$3.21 - 7(0.3) \stackrel{?}{=} 10(0.3) - 1.89$$
$$3.21 - 2.1 \stackrel{?}{=} 3 - 1.89$$
$$1.11 = 1.11 ✔$$

6.
$$3(b + 1) = 4b - 1$$
$$3b + 3 = 4b - 1$$
$$3b + 3 - 3 = 4b - 1 - 3$$
$$3b = 4b - 4$$
$$3b - 4b = 4b - 4b - 4$$
$$-b = -4$$
$$-1(-b) = -1(-4)$$
$$b = 4$$

Check: $3(b + 1) = 4b - 1$

$$3(4 + 1) \stackrel{?}{=} 4(4) - 1$$
$$3(5) \stackrel{?}{=} 4(4) - 1$$
$$15 \stackrel{?}{=} 16 - 1$$
$$15 = 15 ✔$$

7.
$$\frac{5}{9}g + 8 = \frac{1}{6}g + 1$$
$$\frac{5}{9}g + 8 - 8 = \frac{1}{6}g + 1 - 8$$
$$\frac{5}{9}g = \frac{1}{6}g - 7$$
$$\frac{5}{9}g - \frac{1}{6}g = \frac{1}{6}g - \frac{1}{6}g - 7$$
$$\frac{10}{18}g - \frac{3}{18}g = -7$$
$$\frac{7}{18}g = -7$$
$$\frac{18}{7} \cdot \frac{7}{18}g = \frac{18}{7} \cdot -7$$
$$g = -18$$

Check: $\frac{5}{9}g + 8 = \frac{1}{6}g + 1$

$$\frac{5}{9}(-18) + 8 \stackrel{?}{=} \frac{1}{6}(-18) + 1$$
$$-10 + 8 \stackrel{?}{=} -3 + 1$$
$$-2 = -2 ✔$$

8.
$$\frac{s - 3}{7} = \frac{s + 5}{9}$$
$$63\left(\frac{s - 3}{7}\right) = 63\left(\frac{s + 5}{9}\right)$$
$$9(s - 3) = 7(s + 5)$$
$$9s - 27 = 7s + 35$$
$$9s - 27 + 27 = 7s + 35 + 27$$
$$9s = 7s + 62$$
$$9s - 7s = 7s - 7s + 62$$
$$2s = 62$$
$$\frac{2s}{2} = \frac{62}{2}$$
$$s = 31$$

Check: $\frac{s - 3}{7} = \frac{s + 5}{9}$

$$\frac{31 - 3}{7} \stackrel{?}{=} \frac{31 + 5}{9}$$
$$\frac{28}{7} \stackrel{?}{=} \frac{36}{9}$$
$$4 = 4 ✔$$

1.
$$2m + 1 < 9$$
$$2m + 1 - 1 < 9 - 1$$
$$2m < 8$$
$$\frac{2m}{2} < \frac{8}{2}$$
$$m < 4$$

Check: Try 0, a number less than 4.

$$2m + 1 < 9$$
$$2(0) + 1 \stackrel{?}{<} 9$$
$$0 + 1 \stackrel{?}{<} 9$$
$$1 < 9 ✔$$

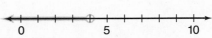

2.
$$-3k - 4 \leq -22$$
$$-3k - 4 + 4 \leq -22 + 4$$
$$-3k \leq -18$$
$$\frac{-3k}{-3} \geq \frac{-18}{-3}$$
$$k \geq 6$$

Check: Try 8, a number greater than or equal to 6.

$$-3k - 4 \leq -22$$
$$-3(8) - 4 \stackrel{?}{\leq} -22$$
$$-24 - 4 \stackrel{?}{\leq} -22$$
$$-28 \leq -22 ✔$$

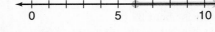

3.
$$-2 > 10 - 2x$$
$$-2 - 10 > 10 - 2x - 10$$
$$-12 > -2x$$
$$\frac{-12}{-2} < \frac{-2x}{-2}$$
$$6 < x$$

Check: Try 7, a number greater than 6.

$$-2 > 10 - 2x$$
$$-2 \stackrel{?}{>} 10 - 2(7)$$
$$-2 \stackrel{?}{>} 10 - 14$$
$$-2 > -4 ✔$$

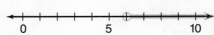

4.
$$-6a + 2 \geq 14$$
$$-6 + 2 - 2 \geq 14 - 2$$
$$-6a \geq 12$$
$$\frac{-6a}{-6} \leq \frac{12}{-6}$$
$$a \leq -2$$

Check: Try -4, a number less than or equal to -2.

$$-6a + 2 \geq 14$$
$$-6(-4) + 2 \stackrel{?}{\geq} 14$$
$$24 + 2 \stackrel{?}{\geq} 14$$
$$26 \geq 14 ✔$$

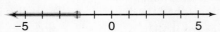

5.
$$3y + 2 < -7$$
$$3y + 2 - 2 < -7 - 2$$
$$3y < -9$$
$$\frac{3y}{3} < \frac{-9}{3}$$
$$y < -3$$

Check: Try -6, a number less than -3.
$$3y + 2 < -7$$
$$3(-6) + 2 \overset{?}{<} -7$$
$$-18 + 2 \overset{?}{<} -7$$
$$-16 < -7 \ \checkmark$$

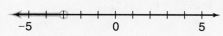

6.
$$\frac{d}{4} + 3 \geq -11$$
$$\frac{d}{4} + 3 - 3 \geq -11 - 3$$
$$\frac{d}{4} \geq -14$$
$$4 \cdot \frac{d}{4} \geq 4 \cdot -14$$
$$d \geq -56$$

Check: Try 0, a number greater than -56.
$$\frac{d}{4} + 3 \geq -11$$
$$\frac{0}{4} + 3 \overset{?}{\geq} -11$$
$$0 + 3 \overset{?}{\geq} -11$$
$$3 \geq -11 \ \checkmark$$

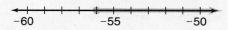

7.
$$\frac{x}{3} - 5 < 6$$
$$\frac{x}{3} - 5 + 5 < 6 + 5$$
$$\frac{x}{3} < 11$$
$$3 \cdot \frac{x}{3} < 3 \cdot 11$$
$$x < 33$$

Check: Try 3, a number less than 33.
$$\frac{x}{3} - 5 < 6$$
$$\frac{3}{3} - 5 \overset{?}{<} 6$$
$$1 - 5 \overset{?}{<} 6$$
$$-4 < 6 \ \checkmark$$

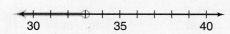

8.
$$-5g + 6 < 3g + 20$$
$$-5g + 6 - 6 < 3g + 20 - 6$$
$$-5g < 3g + 14$$
$$-5g - 3g < 3g - 3g + 14$$
$$-8g < 14$$
$$\frac{-8g}{-8} > \frac{14}{-8}$$
$$g > -1.75$$

Check: Try 1, a number greater than -1.75.
$$-5g + 6 < 3g + 20$$
$$-5(1) + 6 \overset{?}{<} 3(1) + 20$$
$$-5 + 6 \overset{?}{<} 3 + 20$$
$$1 < 23 \ \checkmark$$

9.
$$-3(m - 2) > 12$$
$$-3m + 6 > 12$$
$$-3m + 6 - 6 > 12 - 6$$
$$-3m > 6$$
$$\frac{-3m}{-3} > \frac{6}{-3}$$
$$m > -2$$

Check: Try -4, a number less than -2.
$$-3(m - 2) > 12$$
$$-3(-4 - 2) \overset{?}{>} 12$$
$$-3(-6) \overset{?}{>} 12$$
$$18 > 12 \ \checkmark$$

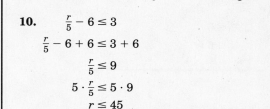

10.
$$\frac{r}{5} - 6 \leq 3$$
$$\frac{r}{5} - 6 + 6 \leq 3 + 6$$
$$\frac{r}{5} \leq 9$$
$$5 \cdot \frac{r}{5} \leq 5 \cdot 9$$
$$r \leq 45$$

Check: Try 0, a number less than or equal to 45.
$$\frac{r}{5} - 6 \leq 3$$
$$\frac{0}{5} - 6 \overset{?}{\leq} 3$$
$$0 - 6 \overset{?}{\leq} 3$$
$$-6 \leq 3 \ \checkmark$$

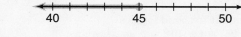

11.
$$\frac{3(n + 1)}{7} \geq \frac{n + 4}{5}$$
$$\frac{3n + 3}{7} \geq \frac{n + 4}{5}$$
$$35\left(\frac{3n + 3}{7}\right) \geq 35\left(\frac{n + 4}{5}\right)$$
$$5(3n + 3) \geq 7(n + 4)$$
$$15n + 15 \geq 7n + 28$$
$$15n + 15 - 15 \geq 7n + 28 - 15$$
$$15n \geq 7n + 13$$
$$15n - 7n \geq 7n - 7n + 13$$
$$8n \geq 13$$
$$\frac{8n}{8} \geq \frac{13}{8}$$
$$n \geq 1.625$$

Check: Try 2, a number greater than or equal to 1.625.

$$\frac{3(n+1)}{7} \geq \frac{n+4}{5}$$

$$\frac{3(2+1)}{7} \overset{?}{\geq} \frac{2+4}{5}$$

$$\frac{3(3)}{7} \overset{?}{\geq} \frac{6}{5}$$

$$\frac{9}{7} \overset{?}{\geq} \frac{6}{5}$$

$$1\frac{2}{7} \geq 1\frac{1}{5} \; ✔$$

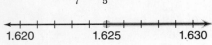

12.
$$\frac{n+10}{-3} \leq 6$$

$$-3\left(\frac{n+10}{-3}\right) \geq -3(6)$$

$$n + 10 \geq -18$$

$$n + 10 - 10 \geq -18 - 10$$

$$n \geq -28$$

Check: Try 2, a number greater than or equal to -28.

$$\frac{n+10}{-3} \leq 6$$

$$\frac{2+10}{-3} \overset{?}{\leq} 6$$

$$\frac{12}{-3} \overset{?}{\leq} 6$$

$$-4 \leq 6 \; ✔$$

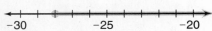

Page 757   Lesson 7-7

1. Let x = number

$$8x - 2 < 15$$
$$8x - 2 + 2 < 15 + 2$$
$$8x < 17$$
$$\frac{8x}{8} < \frac{17}{8}$$
$$x < \frac{17}{8}$$

2. Let t = amount to spend for ties

$$2(13.95) + t \leq 40$$
$$27.90 + t \leq 40$$
$$27.90 - 27.90 + t \leq 40 - 27.90$$
$$t \leq 12.10$$

George can spend at most $12.10.

3. Let x = amount to pay for the boat

$$350(36) - 2200 \geq x$$
$$12,600 - 2200 \geq x$$
$$10,400 \geq x$$

Mia can pay at most 10,400 dollars.

Page 758   Lesson 7-8

1. $8.2 \div 10 = 0.82$
   8.2 mm $= 0.82$ cm

2. $6.7 \times 1000 = 6700$
   6.7 km $= 6700$ m

3. $8.4 \times 1,000,000 = 8,400,000$
   8.4 kg $= 8,400,000$ mg

4. $18 \div 100 = 0.18$
   18 cm $= 0.18$ m

5. $250 \div 1000 = 0.25$
   250 mL $= 0.25$ L

6. $4 \times 1000 = 4000$
   4 g $= 4000$ mg

7. meters

8. kilograms

9. liter

10. grams

Page 758   Lesson 8-1

1. D = {1, 3, 21, 35};
   R = {1, 7, 6, 64}; yes

2. D = {27, 32, 36, 45};
   R = {24}; yes

3. D = {2, 3, 4};
   R = {9, 18, 27, 36}; no

4. D = $\left\{\frac{1}{10}, \frac{1}{8}, \frac{1}{6}, \frac{1}{4}, \frac{1}{2}\right\}$;
   R = {3, 5, 7, 9, 11}; yes

5. D = {1};
   R = {0, 9, 18}; no

6. D = {5, 6, 7, 8};
   R = {5, 6, 7}; yes

7. D = {8, 15, 22, 29};
   R = {8, 22, 51}; yes

8. D = {-3, 4};
   R = {-3, 2.5}; no

Page 758   Lesson 8-2

1. positive; See students' explanations.

2. negative; See students' explanations.

3. positive; See students' explanations.

4. none; See students' explanations.

5. positive; See students' explanations.

6. positive; See students' explanations.

7. positive; See students' explanations.

Page 759   Lesson 8-3

1.

x	y
4	2
4	3
4	5
4	6

Answers will vary.
Sample answer:
(4, 2), (4, 3),
(4, 5), (4, 6)

2.

x	y
1	0
5	0
6	0
0	0

Answers will vary.
Sample answer:
(1, 0), (5, 0),
(6, 0), (0, 0)

3. Rewrite $x + y = 2$ as $y = 2 - x$.

x	$2 - x$	y
2	$2 - 2$	0
1	$2 - 1$	1
0	$2 - 0$	2
-1	$2 - (-1)$	3

Answers will vary.
Sample answer:
(2, 0), (1, 1)
(0, 2), (-1, 3)

4.

x	$2x - 6$	y
0	$2(0) - 6$	-6
1	$2(1) - 6$	-4
2	$2(2) - 6$	-2
3	$2(3) - 6$	0

Answers will vary.
Sample answer:
(0, -6), (1, -4)
(2, -2), (3, 0)

5. Rewrite $x - y = 5$ as $y = -5 + x$.

x	$-5 + x$	y
8	$-5 + 8$	3
7	$-5 + 7$	2
6	$-5 + 6$	1
5	$-5 + 5$	0

Answers will vary.
Sample answer:
(8, 3), (7, 2)
(6, 1), (5, 0)

6. Rewrite $3x - y = 8$ as $y = -8 + 3x$.

x	$-8 + 3x$	y
3	$-8 + 3(3)$	1
4	$-8 + 3(4)$	4
0	$-8 + 3(0)$	-8
2	$-8 + 3(2)$	-2

Answers will vary.
Sample answer:
(3, 1), (4, 4)
(0, -8), (2, -2)

7.

x	$\frac{1}{2}x - 3$	y
0	$\frac{1}{2}(0) - 3$	-3
2	$\frac{1}{2}(2) - 3$	-2
4	$\frac{1}{2}(4) - 3$	-1
6	$\frac{1}{2}(6) - 3$	0

Answers will vary.
Sample answer:
(0, -3), (2, -2),
(4, -1), (6, 0)

8.

x	$\frac{1}{3}x + 1$	y
0	$\frac{1}{3}(0) + 1$	1
3	$\frac{1}{3}(3) + 1$	2
-3	$\frac{1}{3}(-3) + 1$	0
6	$\frac{1}{3}(6) + 1$	3

Answers will vary.
Sample answer:
(0, 1), (3, 2),
(-3, 0), (6, 3)

9. Rewrite $2x + y = -2$ as $y = -2 - 2x$.

x	$-2 - 2x$	y
1	$-2 - 2(1)$	-4
0	$-2 - 2(0)$	-2
-1	$-2 - 2(-1)$	0
-2	$-2 - 2(-2)$	2

Answers will vary.
Sample answer:
(1, -4), (0, -2),
(-1, 0), (-2, 2)

10. Rewrite $2x + 3y = 12$ as $y = 4 - \frac{2}{3}x$.

x	$4 - \frac{2}{3}x$	y
6	$4 - \frac{2}{3}(6)$	0
0	$4 - \frac{2}{3}(0)$	4
3	$4 - \frac{2}{3}(3)$	2
-3	$4 - \frac{2}{3}(-3)$	6

Answers will vary.
Sample answer:
(6, 0), (0, 4),
(3, 2), (-3, 6)

11. Rewrite $x + 2y = -4$ as $y = -2 - \frac{1}{2}x$.

x	$-2 - \frac{1}{2}x$	y
0	$-2 - \frac{1}{2}(0)$	-2
2	$-2 - \frac{1}{2}(2)$	-3
-2	$-2 - \frac{1}{2}(-2)$	-1
-4	$-2 - \frac{1}{2}(-4)$	0

Answers will vary.
Sample answer:
(0, -2), (2, -3),
(-2, -1), (-4, 0)

12. Rewrite $2x - 4y = 8$ as $y = -2 + \frac{1}{2}x$.

x	$-2 + \frac{1}{2}x$	y
4	$-2 + \frac{1}{2}(4)$	0
0	$-2 + \frac{1}{2}(0)$	-2
2	$-2 + \frac{1}{2}(2)$	-1
-2	$-2 + \frac{1}{2}(-2)$	-3

Answers will vary.
Sample answer:
(4, 0), (0, -2),
(2, -1), (-2, -3)

Page 759   Lesson 8-4

1. yes

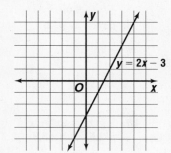

$y = 2x - 3$

2. no

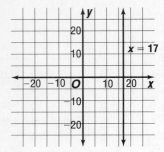

3. yes

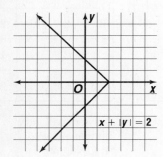

4. no

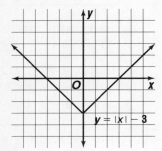

5. $f(x) = 3x + 2$
$f(3) = 3(3) + 2$
$\quad = 9 + 2$
$\quad = 11$

6. $g(x) = 2x^2 - x$
$g(-5) = 2(-5)^2 - (-5)$
$\quad = 2(25) - (-5)$
$\quad = 50 + 5$
$\quad = 55$

7. $g(x) = 2x^2 - x$
$g\left(\frac{1}{2}\right) = 2\left(\frac{1}{2}\right)^2 - \frac{1}{2}$
$\quad = 2\left(\frac{1}{4}\right) - \frac{1}{2}$
$\quad = \frac{1}{2} - \frac{1}{2}$
$\quad = 0$

8. $f(x) = 3x + 2$
$f\left(\frac{2}{3}\right) = 3\left(\frac{2}{3}\right) + 2$
$\quad = 2 + 2$
$\quad = 4$

9. $g(x) = 2x^2 - x$
$g(-1) = 2(-1)^2 - (-1)$
$\quad = 2(-1) - (-1)$
$\quad = 2 + 1$
$\quad = 3$

10. $g(x) = 2x^2 - x$
$g(2.5) = 2(2.5)^2 - 2.5$
$\quad = 2(6.25) - 2.5$
$\quad = 12.5 - 2.5$
$\quad = 10$

11. $f(x) = 3x + 2$
$f(-2) = 3(-2) + 2$
$\quad = -6 + 2$
$\quad = -4$

12. $2[f(x)] = 2[3x + 2]$
$2[f(3)] = 2[3(3) + 2]$
$\quad = 2(9 + 2)$
$\quad = 2(11)$
$\quad = 22$

Page 759 Lesson 8-5

1. Let the horizontal axis represent the month. Let the vertical axis represent the temperature. Graph (January, 41°) for 41° in January and (July, 74°) for 74° in July. Draw the line that contains these points. Thus, approximately 58° corresponds to April. In April, the average high temperature is approximately 58°.

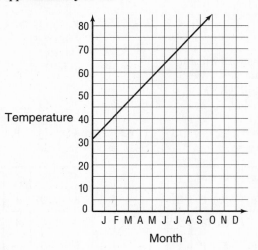

2. Let the horizontal axis represent time in minutes. Let the vertical axis represent the cost. Graph (23, 1.65) for 23 minutes and $1.65 and (18, 1.30) for 18 minutes and $1.30. Draw the line that contains these points. Thus, approximately $1.44 corresponds to 20 minutes. A 20-minute phone call would cost approximately $1.44.

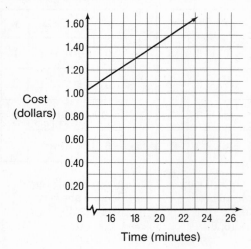

3. Let the horizontal axis represent distance in miles. Let the vertical axis represent distance in kilometers. Graph (5, 8) for 5 miles and 8 kilometers and (30, 48.2) for 30 miles and 48.2 kilometers. Draw the line that contains these points. Thus, 80.4 kilometers corresponds to 25 miles. A distance of 25 miles is equivalent to 80.4 kilometers.

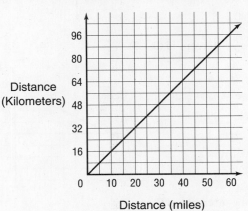

Page 760   Lesson 8-6

1. slope $= \frac{8 - (-3)}{3 - 4}$
$= \frac{11}{-1}$
$= -11$

2. slope $= \frac{5 - (-9)}{4 - (-3)}$
$= \frac{14}{7}$
$= 2$

3. slope $= \frac{2 - 5}{-1 - 0}$
$= \frac{-3}{-1}$
$= 3$

4. no slope

5. slope $= \frac{-3 - 1}{8 - (-4)}$
$= \frac{-4}{12}$
$= -\frac{1}{3}$

6. slope $= \frac{5 - 10}{1 - 3}$
$= \frac{-5}{-2}$
$= \frac{5}{2}$

7. slope $= \frac{2 - (-2)}{7 - (-2)}$
$= \frac{4}{9}$

8. slope $= \frac{-4 - (-19)}{2 - 5}$
$= \frac{15}{-3}$
$= -5$

9. slope $= \frac{6 - 6}{5 - 7}$
$= \frac{0}{-2}$
$= 0$

10. slope $= \frac{-3 - 4}{-6 - (-9)}$
$= \frac{-7}{3}$

11. slope $= \frac{-6 - (-10)}{-1 - (-5)}$
$= \frac{4}{4}$
$= 1$

12. slope $= \frac{9 - (-5)}{5 - (-4)}$
$= \frac{14}{9}$

Page 760   Lesson 8-7

1. Rewrite $2x + y = 6$ as $y = -2x + 6$.
Let $y = 0$:
$y = -2x + 6$
$0 = -2x + 6$
$0 - 6 = -2x + 6 - 6$
$-6 = -2x$
$3 = x$
The x-intercept is 3.

Let $x = 0$:
$y = -2x + 6$
$y = -2(0) + 6$
$y = 0 + 6$
$y = 6$
The y-intercept is 6.

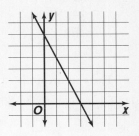

2. Rewrite $-4x + y = 8$ as $y = 4x + 8$.
Let $y = 0$:
$y = 4x + 8$
$0 = 4x + 8$
$0 - 8 = 4x + 8 - 8$
$-8 = 4x$
$-2 = x$
The x-intercept is -2.

Let $x = 0$:
$y = 4x + 8$
$y = 4(0) + 8$
$y = 0 + 8$
$y = 8$
The y-intercept is 8.

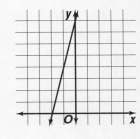

3. Rewrite $3x + 3y = -12$ as $y = x + 4$.
Let $y = 0$:
$y = x + 4$
$0 = x + 4$
$0 - 4 = x + 4 - 4$
$-4 = x$
The x-intercept is -4.

Let $x = 0$:
$y = x + 4$
$y = 0 + 4$
$y = 4$
The y-intercept is 4.

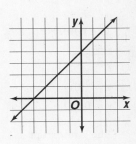

4. Rewrite $x + 2y = -4$ as $y = -\frac{1}{2}x - 2$.
Let $y = 0$:
$y = -\frac{1}{2}x - 2$
$0 = -\frac{1}{2}x - 2$
$0 + 2 = -\frac{1}{2}x - 2 + 2$
$2 = -\frac{1}{2}x$
$-4 = x$
The x-intercept is -4.

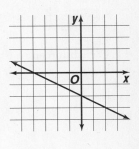

Let $x = 0$:
$y = -\frac{1}{2}x - 2$
$y = -\frac{1}{2}(0) - 2$
$y = 0 - 2$
$y = -2$
The y-intercept is -2.

5. Let $y = 0$:
$y = -\frac{1}{2}x - 6$
$0 = -\frac{1}{2}x - 6$
$0 + 6 = -\frac{1}{2}x - 6 + 6$
$6 = -\frac{1}{2}x$
$-12 = x$
The x-intercept is -12.
Let $x = 0$:
$y = -\frac{1}{2}x - 6$
$y = -\frac{1}{2}(0) - 6$
$y = 0 - 6$
$y = -6$
The y-intercept is -6.

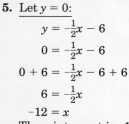

6. Let $y = 0$:
$y = \frac{5}{2}x - 1$
$0 = \frac{5}{2}x - 1$
$0 + 1 = \frac{5}{2}x - 1 + 1$
$1 = \frac{5}{2}x$
$\frac{2}{5} = x$
The x-intercept is $\frac{2}{5}$.
Let $x = 0$:
$y = \frac{5}{2}x - 1$
$y = \frac{5}{2}(0) - 1$
$y = 0 - 1$
$y = -1$
The y-intercept is -1.

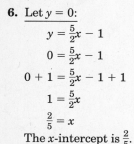

7. $y = 3x - 2$
slope $= m = 3$
Let $x = 0$:
$y = 3x - 2$
$y = 3(0) - 2$
$y = 0 - 2$
$y = -2$
The y-intercept is $(0, -2)$.

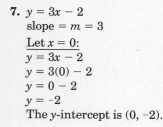

8. Rewrite $x - 3y = 9$
$y = \frac{1}{3}x - 3$.
slope $= m = \frac{1}{3}$
Let $x = 0$:
$y = \frac{1}{3}x - 3$
$y = \frac{1}{3}(0) - 3$
$y = 0 - 3$
$y = -3$
The y-intercept is $(0, -3)$.

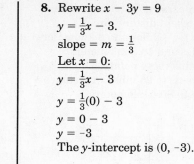

9. $y = \frac{1}{2}x + 4$
slope $= m = \frac{1}{2}$
Let $x = 0$:
$y = \frac{1}{2}x + 4$
$y = \frac{1}{2}(0) + 4$
$y = 0 + 4$
$y = 4$
The y-intercept is $(0, 4)$.

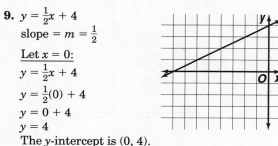

10. $y = -\frac{2}{3}x - 1$
slope $= m = -\frac{2}{3}$
Let $x = 0$:
$y = -\frac{2}{3}x - 1$
$y = -\frac{2}{3}(0) - 1$
$y = 0 - 1$
$y = -1$
The y-intercept is $(0, -1)$.

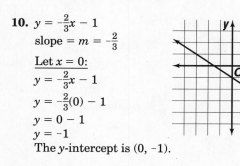

11. Rewrite $x - y = -4$
as $y = x + 4$.
slope $= m = 1$
Let $x = 0$:
$y = x + 4$
$y = 0 + 4$
$y = 4$
The y-intercept is $(0, 4)$.

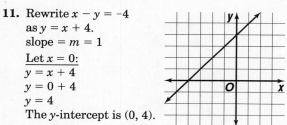

12. Rewrite $2x + 4y = -4$
as $y = -\frac{1}{2}x - 1$.
slope $= m = -\frac{1}{2}$
Let $x = 0$:
$y = -\frac{1}{2}x - 1$
$y = -\frac{1}{2}(0) - 1$
$y = 0 - 1$
$y = -1$

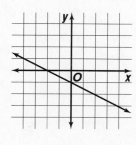

1.

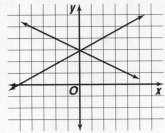

The solution is (0, 3).

2.

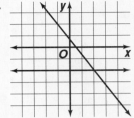

The solution is (2, –2).

3.

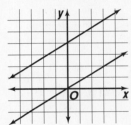

no solution

4.

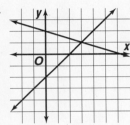

The solution is (3, 1).

5.

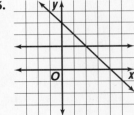

The solution is (2, 2).

6.

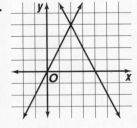

The solution is (2, 4).

7.

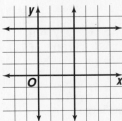

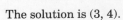

The solution is (3, 4).

8.

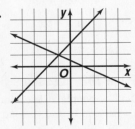

The solution is (1, –1).

1.

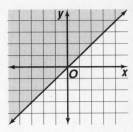

2.

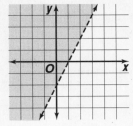

3.

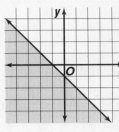

4.

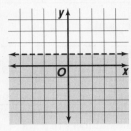

5.

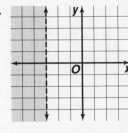

6.

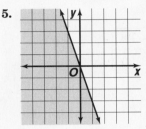

7.

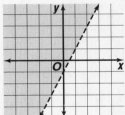

8.

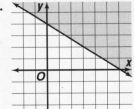

Page 761   Lesson 9-1

1. $\frac{15}{240} = \frac{1}{16}$

2. $\frac{140}{12} = \frac{35}{3}$

3. $\frac{98}{14} = \frac{7}{1}$

4. $\frac{6}{14} = \frac{3}{7}$

5. $\frac{30}{6} = \frac{5}{1}$

6. $\frac{18}{45} = \frac{2}{5}$

7. $\frac{321}{96} = \frac{107}{32}$

8. $\frac{3 \text{ cups}}{3 \text{ quarts}} = \frac{3 \text{ cups}}{12 \text{ cups}} = \frac{1}{4}$

9. $\frac{343.8 \text{ miles}}{9 \text{ gallons}} = \frac{38.2 \text{ miles}}{1 \text{ gallon}}$
38.2 mpg

10. $\frac{\$7.95}{5 \text{ pounds}} = \frac{\$1.59}{1 \text{ pound}}$
$1.59 per pound

11. $\frac{\$52}{8 \text{ tickets}} = \frac{\$6.50}{1 \text{ ticket}}$
$6.50 per ticket

12. $\frac{\$43.92}{4 \text{ CDs}} = \frac{\$10.98}{1 \text{ CD}}$
$10.98 per CD

Pre-Algebra Extra Practice

1. Try different combinations of 6 coins with a value of $1.15 to find a combination that does not include change for $1, 50¢, 10¢, or 5¢.

nickels	dimes	quarters	half-dollars	total	meet requirements?
1	1	4	0	$1.15	no
0	4	1	1	$1.15	yes

Susan has 4 dimes, 1 quarter, and 1 half-dollar.

2.

Prime Numbers	2	3	5	7	11	13	17	19
$12 + 3 + 5$	6	1	1					

There is 1 way to add 8 prime numbers to get a sum of 20.

3.

buys	sells	buys	sells
$100	$110	$120	$130

$(-\$100) + \$110 + (-\$120) + \$130 = \$20$
Ms. Zody gained $20.

4.

bought	sold	bought	sold
$230	$18	$35	$62

$(-\$230) + \$18 + (-\$35) + \$62 = -\$180$
Dwight lost $180.

5.

Reason for Change	Number of Employees
—	48
8 leave	$48 - 8 = 40$
2 transferred	$40 - 2 = 38$
17 hired	$38 + 17 = 55$
21 hired	$55 + 21 = 76$
3 leave	$76 - 3 = 73$

After 6 years, 73 people are employed by the company.

1. $P(\text{green}) = \frac{3}{12}$ or $\frac{1}{4}$ 2. $P(\text{blue}) = \frac{4}{12}$ or $\frac{1}{3}$

3. $P(\text{red}) = \frac{5}{12}$ 4. $P(\text{not green}) = \frac{9}{12}$ or $\frac{3}{4}$

5. $P(\text{white}) = 0$

6. $P(\text{blue or red}) = \frac{9}{12}$ or $\frac{3}{4}$

7. $P(\text{neither red nor green}) = \frac{4}{12}$ or $\frac{1}{3}$

8. $P(\text{not orange}) = 1$

1. $\frac{7}{k} = \frac{49}{63}$
$7 \cdot 63 = k \cdot 49$
$441 = 49k$
$\frac{441}{49} = \frac{49k}{49}$
$9 = k$

2. $\frac{s}{4.8} = \frac{30.6}{28.8}$
$s \cdot 28.8 = 4.8 \cdot 30.6$
$28.8s = 146.88$
$\frac{28.8s}{28.8} = \frac{146.88}{28.8}$
$s = 5.1$

3. $\frac{6}{11} = \frac{19.2}{g}$
$6 \cdot g = 11 \cdot 19.2$
$6g = 211.2$
$\frac{6g}{6} = \frac{211.2}{6}$
$g = 35.2$

4. $\frac{8}{13} = \frac{b}{65}$
$8 \cdot 65 = 13 \cdot b$
$520 = 13b$
$\frac{520}{13} = \frac{13b}{13}$
$40 = b$

5. $\frac{6}{1.00} = \frac{10}{d}$
$6 \cdot d = 1.00 \cdot 10$
$6d = 10$
$\frac{6d}{6} = \frac{10}{6}$
$d = \$1.67$

6. $\frac{8}{9.36} = \frac{f}{17.55}$
$8 \cdot 17.55 = 9.36 \cdot f$
$140.4 = 9.36f$
$\frac{140.4}{9.36} = \frac{9.36f}{9.36}$
$15 = f$

7. $\frac{3}{53.67} = \frac{7}{m}$
$3 \cdot m = 53.67 \cdot 7$
$3m = 375.69$
$\frac{3m}{3} = \frac{375.69}{3}$
$m = \$125.23$

8. $\frac{10}{7.50} = \frac{p}{18}$
$10 \cdot 18 = 7.50 \cdot p$
$180 = 7.50p$
$\frac{180}{7.50} = \frac{7.50p}{7.50}$
$24 = p$

1. $\frac{p}{134} = \frac{81}{100}$
$p \cdot 100 = 134 \cdot 81$
$100p = 10,854$
$\frac{100p}{100} = \frac{10,854}{100}$
$p = 108.54$
81% of 134 is 108.54.

2. $\frac{52.08}{B} = \frac{21}{100}$
$52.08 \cdot 100 = B \cdot 21$
$5208 = 21B$
$\frac{5208}{21} = \frac{21B}{21}$
$248 = B$
52.08 is 21% of 248.

3. $\frac{11.18}{86} = \frac{r}{100}$
$11.18 \cdot 100 = 86 \cdot r$
$1118 = 86r$
$\frac{1118}{86} = \frac{86r}{86}$
$13 = r$
11.18 is 13% of 86.

4. $\frac{p}{312} = \frac{120}{100}$
$p \cdot 100 = 312 \cdot 120$
$100p = 37,440$
$\frac{100p}{100} = \frac{37,440}{100}$
$p = 374.4$
120% of 312 is 374.4.

5. $\frac{140}{400} = \frac{r}{100}$
$140 \cdot 100 = 400 \cdot r$
$14,000 = 400r$
$\frac{14,000}{400} = \frac{400r}{400}$
$35 = r$
140 is 35% of 400.

6. $\frac{430.2}{B} = \frac{60}{100}$
$430.2 \cdot 100 = B \cdot 60$
$43,020 = 60B$
$\frac{43,020}{60} = \frac{60B}{60}$
$717 = B$
430.2 is 60% of 717.

1. The people at the candy counter were chosen randomly and the sample was large.

2. The people were chosen at a candy counter, so they will probably prefer the types of candy sold at that candy counter.

3.
$$\frac{5}{100} = \frac{r}{100}$$
$$5 \cdot 100 = 100 \cdot r$$
$$500 = 100r$$
$$\frac{500}{100} = \frac{100r}{100}$$
$$5 = r$$

5% of the people preferred Giggles Bar.

4.
$$\frac{21}{100} = \frac{x}{600}$$
$$21 \cdot 600 = 100 \cdot x$$
$$12,600 = 100x$$
$$\frac{12,600}{100} = \frac{100x}{100}$$
$$126 = x$$

126 customers would prefer a Venus Bar.

5.
$$\frac{37}{100} = \frac{x}{600}$$
$$37 \cdot 600 = 100 \cdot x$$
$$22,200 = 100x$$
$$\frac{22,200}{100} = \frac{100x}{100}$$
$$222 = x$$

222 customers would prefer a Galaxy Bar.

6. Galaxy Bar

Page 763   Lesson 9-7

1. $0.06 \rightarrow \frac{0.06}{1} = \frac{6}{100}$ or 6%

2. $0.374 \rightarrow \frac{0.374}{1} = \frac{37.4}{100}$ or 37.4%

3. $0.0095 \rightarrow \frac{0.0095}{1} = \frac{0.95}{100}$ or 0.95%

4. $56.71 \rightarrow \frac{56.71}{1} = \frac{5671}{100}$ or 5671%

5. $\frac{3}{4} = 0.75 \rightarrow \frac{75}{100} = 75\%$

6. $3\frac{1}{4} = 3.25 \rightarrow \frac{325}{100} = 325\%$

7. $\frac{45}{50} = 0.9 \rightarrow \frac{90}{100} = 90\%$

8. $\frac{3}{1000} = 0.003 \rightarrow \frac{0.3}{100} = 0.3\%$

9. $17\% = \frac{17}{100}$

10. $0.8\% = \frac{0.8}{100}$
$$= \frac{8}{1000}$$

11. $5268\% = \frac{5268}{100}$
$$= 52\frac{68}{100}$$
$$= 52\frac{17}{25}$$

12. $\frac{15}{4}\% = 3.75\%$
$$= \frac{3.75}{100}$$
$$= \frac{375}{10,000}$$

Page 763   Lesson 9-8

1. 28% is about 25% or $\frac{1}{4}$.

$\frac{1}{4}$ of 500 is 125.

So, the correct choice is c.

2. 96% is about 100% or 1.

1 of 900 is 900.

So, the correct choice is b.

3. 148% is about 150% or $1\frac{1}{2}$.

$1\frac{1}{2}$ of 350 is 525.

So, the correct choice is c.

4. $\frac{1}{3}\% = \frac{\frac{1}{3}}{100} = \frac{1}{300}$.

360 is about 324.

$\frac{1}{300}$ of 324 is 1.08.

So, the correct choice is a.

5. 72% is about 70% or $\frac{7}{10}$.

$\frac{7}{10}$ of 250 is 175.

6. 47% is about 50% or $\frac{1}{2}$.

$\frac{1}{2}$ of 198 is 99.

7. 0.8% is about 1% or $\frac{1}{100}$.

$\frac{1}{100}$ of 380 is 3.8.

8. 98% is about 100% or 1.

1 of 32 is 32.

9. $12\frac{1}{2}\%$ is about 10% or $\frac{1}{10}$.

$\frac{1}{10}$ of 130 is 13.

10. 122% is about 120% or $1\frac{1}{5}$.

$1\frac{1}{5}$ of 84 is 100.8.

11. Sample answer:
$\frac{12}{20} = \frac{3}{5}$
$\frac{3}{5} = 60\%$

12. Sample answer:
$\frac{14}{40}$ is about $\frac{12}{40}$ or $\frac{3}{10}$.
$\frac{3}{10} = 30\%$

13. Sample answer:
$\frac{3}{75}$ is about $\frac{4}{80}$ or $\frac{1}{20}$.
$\frac{1}{20} = 5\%$

14. Sample answer:
$\frac{75}{179}$ is about $\frac{81}{180}$.
$\frac{81}{180} = 45\%$

15. Sample answer:
$\frac{19}{96}$ is about $\frac{20}{100}$ or $\frac{1}{5}$.
$\frac{1}{5} = 20\%$

16. Sample answer:
$\frac{1.6}{88}$ is about $\frac{1.5}{150}$ or $\frac{1}{100}$.
$\frac{1}{100} = 1\%$

17. Sample answer:
$\frac{5}{9}$ is about $\frac{5}{10}$ or $\frac{1}{2}$.
$\frac{1}{2} = 50\%$

18. Sample answer:

$\frac{6}{210}$ is about $\frac{6}{200}$ or $\frac{3}{100}$.

$\frac{3}{100} = 3\%$

19. Sample answer:

$\frac{12}{2250}$ is about $\frac{12}{2400}$ or $\frac{1}{200}$.

$\frac{1}{200} = 0.5\%$

Page 763   Lesson 9-9

1. $9.28 = R \cdot 58$

$\frac{9.28}{58} = \frac{58R}{58}$

$0.16 = R$

9.28 is 16% of 58.

2. $P = 0.43 \cdot 110$

$P = 47.3$

43% of 110 is 47.3.

3. $396 = 0.88 \cdot B$

$\frac{396}{0.88} = \frac{0.88B}{0.88}$

$450 = B$

396 is 88% of 450.

4. $P = 0.61 \cdot 524$

$P = 319.64$

61% of 524 is 319.64.

5. $126 = R \cdot 90$

$\frac{126}{90} = \frac{90R}{90}$

$1.4 = R$

126 is 140% of 90.

6. $109.2 = 0.52 \cdot B$

$\frac{109.2}{0.52} = \frac{0.52B}{0.52}$

$210 = B$

109.2 is 52% of 210.

7. 32% of $64.98 = d$

$(0.32)(64.98) = 20.7936$

The discount is $20.79.

8. $I = prt$

$I = (1000)(0.04)(2)$

$I = \$80$

9. 20% of $589 = d$

$(0.20)(589) = 117.80$

The discount is $117.80.

10. $I = prt$; 18 months $= 1\frac{1}{2}$ years

$I = (500)(0.025)(1.5)$

$I = \$18.75$

11. $I = prt$; 15 months $= 1\frac{1}{4}$ years

$I = (800)(0.075)(1.25)$

$I = \$75$

12. 40% of $2148 = d$

$(0.40)(2148) = 859.20$

The discount is $859.20.

Page 764   Lesson 9-10

1. decrease;

$42 - 56 = -14$

$-14 = R \cdot 56$

$\frac{-14}{56} = \frac{56R}{56}$

$0.25 = R$

The percent of decrease is 25%.

2. increase;

$29.64 - 26 = 3.64$

$3.64 = R \cdot 26$

$\frac{3.64}{26} = \frac{26R}{26}$

$0.14 = R$

The percent of increase is 14%.

3. increase;

$37.18 - 22 = 15.18$

$15.18 = R \cdot 22$

$\frac{15.18}{22} = \frac{22R}{22}$

$0.69 = R$

The percent of increase is 69%.

4. decrease;

$85.25 - 137.50 = -52.25$

$-52.25 = R \cdot 137.50$

$\frac{-52.25}{137.50} = \frac{137.50R}{137.50}$

$-0.38 = R$

The percent of decrease is 38%.

5. increase;

$955.50 - 455 = 500.50$

$500.50 = R \cdot 455$

$\frac{500.50}{455} = \frac{455R}{455}$

$1.10 = R$

The percent of increase is 110%.

6. increase;

$15 - 3 = 12$

$12 = R \cdot 3$

$\frac{12}{3} = \frac{3R}{3}$

$4 = R$

The percent of increase is 400%.

7. increase;

$765.51 - 750.75 = 14.76$

$14.76 = R \cdot 750.75$

$\frac{14.76}{750.75} = \frac{750.75R}{750.75}$

$0.0196 = R$

The percent of increase is about 2%.

8. decrease;

$476.5 - 953 = -476.5$

$-476.5 = R \cdot 953$

$\frac{-476.5}{953} = \frac{953R}{953}$

$-0.5 = R$

The percent of decrease is 50%.

9. increase;

$379.69 - 101.25 = 278.44$

$278.44 = R \cdot 101.25$

$\frac{278.44}{101.25} = \frac{101.25R}{101.25}$

$2.750 = R$

The percent of increase is about 275%.

10. increase;

$842.27 - 836 = 6.27$

$6.27 = R \cdot 836$

$\frac{6.27}{836} = \frac{836R}{836}$

$0.0075 = R$

The percent of increase is 0.75% or $\frac{3}{4}\%$.

Page 764   Lesson 10-1

1.

3	2 7
4	4 9
5	3 9
6	1 9

$3 | 2 = 32$

2.

0	3 5 8
1	
2	1 4 6
3	0 5 5 8 9

$0 | 3 = 3$

3.
```
 0 | 5 6
 1 |
 2 |
 3 |
 4 |
 5 |
 6 |
 7 | 3 4 9
 8 |
 9 |
10 |
11 |
12 |
13 |
14 |
15 | 3 7
```
$0|6 = 0.6$

4.
```
17 | 1 2 9
18 | 1 1 2 6
19 | 3 8
```
$17|1 = 171$

5.
```
100 | 1 5 5 5
101 | 0 6 8
102 | 1
```
$100|1 = 100.1$

Page 764   Lesson 10-2

1. 23   35   37   44   49   61   95   96
        ↑LQ   ↑Median ↑UQ

The range is $96 - 23$ or 73.

The median is $\frac{44 + 49}{2}$ or 46.5.

The upper quartile is $\frac{61 + 95}{2}$ or 78 and the lower

quartile is $\frac{35 + 37}{2}$ or 36.

The interquartile range is $78 - 36$ or 42.

2. 12   24   30   30   35   38   39   53   62   80
          ↑LQ   ↑Median ↑UQ

The range is $80 - 12$ or 68.

The median is $\frac{35 + 38}{2}$ or 36.5.

The upper quartile is 53 and the lower quartile is 30.
The interquartile range is $53 - 30$ or 23.

3. 3.2   4.7   5.3   6   7.15   9.19   30.1
      ↑LQ ↑Median ↑UQ

The range is $30.1 - 3.2$ or 26.9.
The median is 6.
The upper quartile is 9.19 and the lower quartile is 4.7.
The interquartile range is $9.19 - 4.7$ or 4.49.

4. 181   193   271   711   791   818   861   891
        ↑LQ   ↑Median ↑UQ

The range is $891 - 181$ or 710.

The median is $\frac{711 + 791}{2}$ or 751.

The upper quartile is $\frac{818 + 861}{2}$ or 839.5

and the lower quartile is $\frac{193 + 271}{2}$ or 232.

The interquartile range is $839.5 - 232$ or 607.5.

Page 764   Lesson 10-3

1.

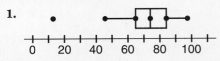

2. The range is $97 - 12$ or 85.

3. 73   **4.** 84.5

5. 62.5   **6.** $84.5 - 62.5$ or 22

7. 12 and 97   **8.** yes; 12

9. $1.5(22) = 33$, so $62.5 - 33$ or 29.5 and $84.5 + 33$ or 117.5 are the limits for the outliers.

Page 765   Lesson 10-4

1. The ranges on the vertical axis are different.

2. The graph on the left makes the income look more consistent because the scale has a shorter distance between large numbers.

3. The graph on the right makes it appear that the family expenses have risen sharply.

Page 765   Lesson 10-5

1. $3 \times 3 \times 4 = 36$
36 outcomes

2. $4 \times 2 \times 2 = 16$
16 outcomes

3. $1 \cdot 10 \cdot 10 \cdot 10 \cdot 10 \cdot 10 \cdot 1 = 100{,}000$
100,000 outcomes

4. A chair can be a rocker, recliner, swivel, straight back, rocker/recliner, rocker/swivel, or recliner/swivel. 7 outcomes

Page 765   Lesson 10-6

1. $C(7, 5) = \frac{P(7, 5)}{5!}$
$= \frac{7 \cdot 6 \cdot 5 \cdot 4 \cdot 3}{5 \cdot 4 \cdot 3 \cdot 2 \cdot 1}$
$= 21$
21 ways

2. $6! = 6 \cdot 5 \cdot 4 \cdot 3 \cdot 2 \cdot 1$
$= 720$
720 ways

3. $C(5, 3) = \frac{P(5, 3)}{3!}$
$= \frac{5 \cdot 4 \cdot 3}{3 \cdot 2 \cdot 1}$
$= 10$
10 ways

4. $7! = 7 \cdot 6 \cdot 5 \cdot 4 \cdot 3 \cdot 2 \cdot 1$
$= 5040$

5. $P(3, 2) = 3 \cdot 2$
$= 6$

6. $C(9, 4) = \frac{P(9, 4)}{4!}$
$= \frac{9 \cdot 8 \cdot 7 \cdot 6}{4 \cdot 3 \cdot 2 \cdot 1}$
$= 126$

7. $P(10, 5) = 10 \cdot 9 \cdot 8 \cdot 7 \cdot 6$
$= 30{,}240$

8. $10! = 10 \cdot 9 \cdot 8 \cdot 7 \cdot 6 \cdot 5 \cdot 4 \cdot 3 \cdot 2 \cdot 1$
$= 3{,}628{,}800$

9. $\frac{6!2!}{5!} = \frac{6 \cdot 2 \cdot 1}{1}$
$= 12$

Page 766   Lesson 10-7

1. odds of landing on blue
$= 1:5$
The odds of landing on blue are 1:5.

2. odds of landing on a color with less than 5 letters
$= 2:4$
The odds of landing on a color with less than 5 letters are 2:4.

3. odds of landing on a color that begins with a consonant
$= 5:1$
The odds of landing on a color that begins with a consonant are 5:1.

4. odds of landing on red, yellow, or blue
$= 3:3$
The odds of landing on red, yellow, or blue are 3:3.

5. odds of rolling a number less than 7
$= 6:4$
The odds of rolling a number less than 7 are 6:4.

6. odds of rolling an odd number
$= 5:5$
The odds of rolling an odd number are 5:5.

7. odds of rolling a composite number
$= 5:5$
The odds of rolling a composite number are 5:5.

8. odds of rolling a number divisible by 3
$= 3:7$
The odds of rolling a number divisible by 3 are 3:7.

Page 766   Lesson 10-8

1. Sample answer: Roll one die ten times. If the result on the first die is 1, 2, 3, or 4, she has made a shot from the field. Then roll the die five times. If the result is 1, 2, 3, 4, or 5, she has made a free throw. The sum of 2(the number of field shots) + (the number of free throws) is the probable number of points Laneeda will make in the game.

2. Sample answer: Roll a die fourteen times. Each time the die shows 1, Ted wins a soft drink.

Page 766   Lesson 10-9

1. dependent

2. independent

3. dependent

4. dependent

5. independent

6. $P(\text{3 nines in a row}) = \frac{4}{24} \cdot \frac{3}{23} \cdot \frac{2}{22}$
$= \frac{24}{12,144} \text{ or } \frac{1}{506}$

7. $P(\text{a black jack and then a red queen})$
$= \frac{2}{24} \cdot \frac{2}{23}$
$= \frac{4}{552}$
$= \frac{1}{138}$

8. $P(\text{a nine of clubs, a black king, and a red ace})$
$= \frac{1}{24} \cdot \frac{2}{23} \cdot \frac{2}{22}$
$= \frac{4}{12,144}$
$= \frac{1}{3036}$

9. $P(\text{4 face cards in a row})$
$= \frac{12}{24} \cdot \frac{11}{23} \cdot \frac{10}{22} \cdot \frac{9}{21}$
$= \frac{11,880}{255,024}$
$= \frac{15}{322}$

10. $P(\text{2 cards lower than a jack})$
$= \frac{8}{24} \cdot \frac{7}{23}$
$= \frac{56}{552}$
$= \frac{7}{69}$

Page 767   Lesson 10-10

1. inclusive;
$P(\text{12 or even}) = \frac{1}{14} + \frac{7}{14} - \frac{1}{14}$
$= \frac{7}{14} \text{ or } \frac{1}{2}$

2. exclusive;
$P(\text{13 or less than 7}) = \frac{1}{14} + \frac{1}{14}$
$= \frac{2}{14} \text{ or } \frac{1}{7}$

3. exclusive;
$P(\text{even or odd}) = \frac{7}{14} + \frac{7}{14}$
$= \frac{14}{14} \text{ or } 1$

4. exclusive;
$P(\text{14 or greater than 20}) = \frac{1}{14} + 0$
$= \frac{1}{14}$

5. inclusive;
$P(\text{even or less than 10}) = \frac{7}{14} + \frac{4}{14} - \frac{2}{14}$
$= \frac{9}{14}$

6. inclusive;
$P(\text{odd or greater than 10}) = \frac{7}{14} + \frac{9}{14} - \frac{5}{14}$
$= \frac{11}{14}$

7. inclusive;
$P(\text{divisible by 3 or even}) = \frac{5}{14} + \frac{7}{14} - \frac{3}{14}$
$= \frac{9}{14}$

8. exclusive;
$P(\text{prime or even}) = \frac{5}{14} + \frac{7}{14}$
$= \frac{12}{14} \text{ or } \frac{6}{7}$

Page 767   Lesson 11-1

1. 120°; obtuse

2. 26°; acute

3. 90°; right

4. 140°; obtuse

5. 40°; acute

6. 154°; obtuse

Page 767   Lesson 11-2

1. There are $169 + 86 + 70 + 42 + 18$ or 385 items.

Canned Goods:	$169 \div 385 = 0.44 \rightarrow 44\%$
Pasta:	$86 \div 385 = 0.22 \rightarrow 22\%$
Cereal:	$70 \div 385 = 0.18 \rightarrow 18\%$
Peanut Butter:	$42 \div 385 = 0.11 \rightarrow 11\%$
Condiments:	$18 \div 385 = 0.05 \rightarrow 5\%$

Canned Goods:	$0.44 \times 360 = 158.4 \rightarrow 158.4°$
Pasta:	$0.22 \times 360 = 79.2 \rightarrow 79.2°$
Cereal:	$0.18 \times 360 = 64.8 \rightarrow 64.8°$
Peanut Butter:	$0.11 \times 360 = 39.6 \rightarrow 39.6°$
Condiments:	$0.05 \times 360 = 18.0 \rightarrow 18.0°$

Items Donated for Food Drive

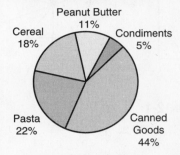

2. The total monthly expenditures is $800 + 600 + 350 + 200 + 150 + 100$ or $2200.

Housing:	$800 \div 2200 = 0.36 \rightarrow 36\%$
Taxes:	$600 \div 2200 = 0.27 \rightarrow 27\%$
Food:	$350 \div 2200 = 0.16 \rightarrow 16\%$
Clothing:	$200 \div 2200 = 0.09 \rightarrow 9\%$
Insurance:	$150 \div 2200 = 0.07 \rightarrow 7\%$
Savings:	$100 \div 2200 = 0.05 \rightarrow 5\%$

Housing:	$0.36 \times 360 = 129.6 \rightarrow 129.6°$
Taxes:	$0.27 \times 360 = 97.2 \rightarrow 97.2°$
Food:	$0.16 \times 360 = 57.6 \rightarrow 57.6°$
Clothing:	$0.09 \times 360 = 32.4 \rightarrow 32.4°$
Insurance:	$0.07 \times 360 = 25.2 \rightarrow 25.2°$
Savings:	$0.05 \times 360 = 18.0 \rightarrow 18.0°$

Davis Family Monthly Expenditures

Page 767   Lesson 11-3

1. $\angle 1$ and $\angle 2$ are supplementary.
$180 - 38 = 142$. So, $m\angle 1 = 42°$.

2. Since $\angle 2$ and $\angle 3$ are vertical angles, they are congruent. So, $m\angle 3 = 38°$.

3. $\angle 4$ and $\angle 2$ are supplementary.
$180 - 38 = 142$. So, $m\angle 4 = 142°$.

4. Since $\angle 5$ and $\angle 2$ are corresponding angles, they are congruent. So, $m\angle 5 = 38°$.

5. $\angle 6$ and $\angle 5$ are supplementary.
$180 - 38 = 142$. So, $m\angle 6 = 142°$.

6. Since $\angle 8$ and $\angle 6$ are vertical angles, they are congruent. So, $m\angle 8 = 142°$.

Page 768   Lesson 11-4

1. Let x represent the measure of one angle, $2x$ the measure of a second angle, and $3x$ the measure of the third angle.
$$x + 2x + 3x = 180$$
$$6x = 180$$
$$\frac{6x}{6} = \frac{180}{6}$$
$$x = 30$$
$x = 30$, $2x = 60$, and $3x = 90$.
The measures of the angles are 30°, 60°, and 90°.

2. Let x represent the measure of the first and the second angle, and $2x$ the measure of the third angle.
$$x + x + 2x = 180$$
$$4x = 180$$
$$\frac{4x}{4} = \frac{180}{4}$$
$$x = 45$$
$x = 45$ and $2x = 90$.
The measures of the angles are 45°, 45°, and 90°.

3. Let x represent the measure of one angle, $9x$ the measure of the second angle, and $26x$ the measure of the third angle.
$$x + 9x + 26x = 180$$
$$36x = 180$$
$$\frac{36x}{36} = \frac{180}{36}$$
$$x = 5$$
$x = 5$, $9x = 45$, and $26x = 130$.
The measures of the angles are 5°, 45°, and 130°.

Page 768   Lesson 11-5

1. $\angle K \cong \angle G$

2. $\overline{WG} \cong \overline{LK}$

3. $\angle D \cong \angle J$

4. $\overline{KL} \cong \overline{GW}$

5. $\overline{DG} \cong \overline{JK}$

Page 768   Lesson 11-6

1.
$$\frac{x}{4} = \frac{9}{6}$$
$$x \cdot 6 = 4 \cdot 9$$
$$6x = 36$$
$$\frac{6x}{6} = \frac{36}{6}$$
$$x = 6$$

2.
$$\frac{x}{12} = \frac{10}{18}$$
$$x \cdot 18 = 12 \cdot 10$$
$$18x = 120$$
$$\frac{18x}{18} = \frac{120}{18}$$
$$x = 6\frac{2}{3}$$

Page 768   Lesson 11-7

1. $x + (2x - 5) + (2x + 5) + (x - 30) = 360$
$x + 2x - 5 + 2x + 5 + x - 30 = 360$
$6x - 30 = 360$
$6x - 30 + 30 = 360 + 30$
$6x = 390$
$\frac{6x}{6} = \frac{390}{6}$
$x = 65$
So, $x = 65°$, $2x - 5 = 125°$, $2x + 5 = 135°$, and $x - 30 = 35°$.

2. $x + (2x + 15) + x + (2x + 15) = 360$
$x + 2x + 15 + x + 2x + 15 = 360$
$6x + 30 = 360$
$6x + 30 - 30 = 360 - 30$
$6x = 330$
$\frac{6x}{6} = \frac{330}{6}$
$x = 55$
So, $x = 55°$, $2x + 15 = 125°$, $x = 55°$, and $2x + 15 = 125°$.

3. $x + 90 + \left(\frac{1}{2}x + 10\right) + (x + 10) = 360$
$x + 90 + \frac{1}{2}x + 10 + x + 10 = 360$
$2\frac{1}{2}x + 110 = 360$
$2\frac{1}{2}x + 110 - 110 = 360 - 110$
$2\frac{1}{2}x = 250$
$\frac{2\frac{1}{2}x}{2\frac{1}{2}} = \frac{250}{2\frac{1}{2}}$
$x = 100$
So, $x = 100°$, $\frac{1}{2}x + 10 = 60°$, and $x + 10 = 110°$.

Page 768   Lesson 11-8

1. $360 \div 3 = 120$
So, the measure of each exterior angle is 120°.
$180 - 120 = 60$
So, the measure of each interior angle is 60°.

2. $360 \div 5 = 72$
So, the measure of each exterior angle is 72°.
$180 - 72 = 108$
So, the measure of each interior angle is 108°.

3. $360 \div 8 = 45$
So, the measure of each exterior angle is 45°.
$180 - 45 = 135$
So, the measure of each interior angle is 135°.

4. $360 \div 9 = 40$
So, the measure of each exterior angle is 40°.
$180 - 40 = 140$
So, the measure of each interior angle is 140°.

Page 769   Lesson 11-9

1.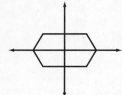

2.

3.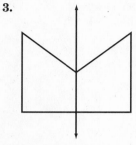

4.

Page 769   Lesson 12-1

1. $A = \frac{1}{2}bh$
$A = \frac{1}{2}(6)(11)$
$A = \frac{1}{2}(66)$
$A = 33$
The area is 33 cm^2.

2. $A = bh$
$A = 9 \cdot 12$
$A = 108$
The area is 108 m^2.

3. $A = \frac{1}{2}h(a + b)$
$A = \frac{1}{2} \cdot 5(7 + 16.5)$
$A = \frac{1}{2} \cdot 5 \cdot 23.5$
$A = 58.75$
The area is 58.75 ft^2.

Page 769   Lesson 12-2

1. $A = \pi r^2$
$A = \pi \cdot 5^2$
$A = \pi \cdot 25$
$A \approx 78.5$ in^2

2. $A = \pi r^2$
$A = \pi \cdot 8^2$
$A = \pi \cdot 64$
$A \approx 201.1$ mm^2

3. $A = \pi r^2$
$A = \pi \cdot (7.7)^2$
$A = \pi \cdot 59.29$
$A \approx 186.3$ m^2

Page 769   Lesson 12-3

1. Area of shaded region = (area of square)
　　　　　　　　　　　　 − (area of circle)

area of square: $A = s^2$
$A = 16^2$
$A = 256$ in^2

area of circle: $A = \pi r^2$
$A = \pi \cdot 8^2$
$A = \pi \cdot 64$
$A \approx 201.1$ in^2

The area of the shaded region is about $256 - 201.1$ or 54.9 in^2.

So, $P(\text{shaded}) = \frac{\text{shaded area}}{\text{area of target}}$

$\approx \frac{54.9}{256}$

≈ 0.21

2. The dartboard is a circle with radius 15.

Area of dartboard: $A = \pi r^2$

$A = \pi \cdot 15^2$

$A = \pi \cdot 225$

$A \approx 706.9$

Area of shaded region

= (area of circle with radius 10)

  − (area of circle with radius 5)

area of circle with radius 10: $A = \pi r^2$

$A = \pi \cdot 10^2$

$A = \pi \cdot 100$

$A \approx 314.2$

area of circle with radius 5: $A = \pi r^2$

$A = \pi \cdot 5^2$

$A = \pi \cdot 25$

$A \approx 78.5$

The area of the shaded region is $314.2 - 78.5$ or 235.7.

So, $P(\text{shaded}) = \frac{\text{shaded area}}{\text{area of target}}$

$\approx \frac{235.7}{706.9}$

≈ 0.33 or $\frac{1}{3}$

3. The dartboard is a 24 by 8 centimeter rectangle and a circle with radius of 4 cm.

Area of dartboard = (area of rectangle)

$\qquad\qquad\qquad$ + (area of circle)

area of rectangle: $A = \ell \cdot w$

$A = 24 \cdot 8$

$A = 192 \text{ cm}^2$

area of circle: $A = \pi r^2$

$A = \pi \cdot 4^2$

$A = \pi \cdot 16$

$A \approx 50.3 \text{ cm}^2$

The area of the dartboard is about $192 + 50.3$ or 242.3 cm^2.

Area of shaded region

= (area of circle) + (area of two triangles)

area of circle: $A = \pi r^2$

$A = \pi \cdot 4^2$

$A = \pi \cdot 16$

$A \approx 50.3 \text{ cm}^2$

area of two triangles: $A = 2\left(\frac{1}{2}bh\right)$

$A = 2\left(\frac{1}{2} \cdot 24 \cdot 4\right)$

$A = 2(48)$

$A = 96 \text{ cm}^2$

The area of the shaded region is about $50.3 + 96$ or 146.3 cm^2.

So, $P(\text{shaded}) = \frac{\text{shaded area}}{\text{area of target}}$

$\approx \frac{146.3}{242.3}$

≈ 0.6

1.

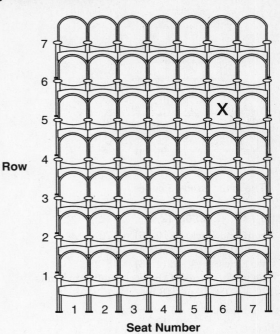

Row

Seat Number

There are 49 seats in this section of the theater.

2.

The winner of the tournament will play 4 games.

3.

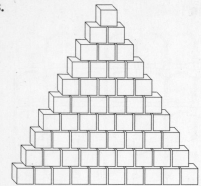

The artist used 55 cubes.

Page 770   Lesson 12-5

1. Front and Back: $2(10 \cdot 6) = 120$
Top and Bottom: $2(10 \cdot 4) = 80$
Two Sides: $2(4 \cdot 6) = 48$
The surface area of the rectangular prism is
$120 + 80 + 48$ or 248 in^2.

2. Two Bases: $2\left(\frac{1}{2} \cdot 15 \cdot 8\right) = 120$
Front: $17 \cdot 12 = 204$
Bottom: $15 \cdot 12 = 180$
Back: $12 \cdot 8 = 96$
The surface area of the triangular prism is
$120 + 204 + 180 + 96$ or 600 ft^2.

3. $2(\pi r^2) + 2\pi rh = 2(\pi \cdot 5^2) + 2 \cdot \pi \cdot 5 \cdot 3.5$
$\qquad = 2(\pi \cdot 25) + 2 \cdot \pi \cdot 5 \cdot 3.5$
$\qquad \approx 157.1 + 109.9$
$\qquad \approx 267.0$
The surface area of the cylinder is about 267.0 cm^2.

Page 770   Lesson 12-6

1. Base: $A = s^2$
$\quad A = 24^2$
$\quad A = 576$ mm^2
Side: $A = \frac{1}{2}bh$
$\quad A = \frac{1}{2}(24)(26)$
$\quad A = \frac{1}{2}(624)$
$\quad A = 312$ mm^2
The surface area is $576 + 4(312)$ or 1824 mm^2.

2. Base: $A = \pi r^2$
$\quad A = \pi \cdot 8^2$
$\quad A = \pi \cdot 64$
$\quad A \approx 201.1$ in^2
Surface: $A = \pi rs$
$\quad A = \pi \cdot 8 \cdot 14$
$\quad A \approx 351.8$ in^2
The surface area is $201.1 + 351.8$ or 552.96 in^2.

3. Base: $A = \pi r^2$
$\quad A = \pi \cdot (2.3)^2$
$\quad A = \pi \cdot 5.29$
$\quad A \approx 16.6$ m^2
Surface: $A = \pi rs$
$\quad A = \pi \cdot (2.3) \cdot (5.2)$
$\quad A \approx 37.6$ m^2
The surface area is about $16.6 + 37.6$ or 54.2 m^2.

Page 770   Lesson 12-7

1. $V = Bh$
$V = 24 \cdot 7$
$V = 168$ cm^3

2. $V = Bh$
$V = \left(\frac{1}{2} \cdot 22 \cdot 26\right) \cdot 10$
$V = 286 \cdot 10$
$V = 2860$ cm^3

3. $V = \pi r^2 h$
$V = \pi \cdot 4^2 \cdot 11$
$V = \pi \cdot 16 \cdot 11$
$V \approx 552.9$ in^3

Page 771   Lesson 12-8

1. $V = \frac{1}{3}\pi r^2 h$
$V = \frac{1}{3} \cdot \pi \cdot (3.3)^2 \cdot 3$
$V = \frac{1}{3} \cdot \pi \cdot (10.89) \cdot 3$
$V \approx 34.2$ ft^3

2. $V = \frac{1}{3}\pi r^2 h$
$V = \frac{1}{3} \cdot \pi \cdot 3^2 \cdot 7$
$V = \frac{1}{3} \cdot \pi \cdot 9 \cdot 7$
$V \approx 66.0$ m^3

3. $V = \frac{1}{3}Bh$
$V = \frac{1}{3} \cdot 11 \cdot 3 \cdot 8$
$V = 88$ in^3

Page 771   Lesson 13-1

1. $\sqrt{16} < \sqrt{21} < \sqrt{25}$
$\quad 4^2 < \sqrt{21} < \sqrt{5^2}$
$\quad 4 < \sqrt{21} < 5$
$\qquad 5$
Check: $\sqrt{21} \approx 4.6$

2. $-\sqrt{81} < -\sqrt{85} < -\sqrt{100}$
$\quad -\sqrt{9^2} < -\sqrt{85} < -\sqrt{10^2}$
$\quad -9 < -\sqrt{85} < -10$
$\qquad -9$
Check: $-\sqrt{85} \approx -9.2$

3. $\sqrt{4} < \sqrt{7.3} < \sqrt{9}$
$\quad \sqrt{2^2} < \sqrt{7.3} < \sqrt{3^2}$
$\quad 2 < \sqrt{7.3} < 3$
$\qquad 3$
Check: $\sqrt{7.3} \approx 2.7$

4. $\sqrt{1} < \sqrt{1.99} < \sqrt{4}$
$\quad \sqrt{1^2} < \sqrt{1.99} < \sqrt{2^2}$
$\quad 1 < \sqrt{1.99} < 2$
$\qquad 1$
Check: $\sqrt{1.99} \approx 1.4$

5. $-\sqrt{49} < -\sqrt{62} < -\sqrt{64}$
$\quad -\sqrt{7^2} < -\sqrt{62} < -\sqrt{8^2}$
$\quad -7 < -\sqrt{62} < -8$
$\qquad -8$
Check: $-\sqrt{62} \approx -7.9$

6. $\sqrt{64} = \sqrt{74.1} = \sqrt{81}$
$\quad \sqrt{8^2} = \sqrt{74.1} = \sqrt{9^2}$
$\quad 8 = \sqrt{74.1} = 9$
$\qquad 9$
Check: $\sqrt{74.1} \approx 8.6$

7. $\sqrt{784} < \sqrt{810} < \sqrt{841}$
$\quad \sqrt{28^2} < \sqrt{810} < \sqrt{29^2}$
$\quad 28 < \sqrt{810} < 29$
$\qquad 28$
Check: $\sqrt{810} \approx 28.4$

8. $-\sqrt{81} < -\sqrt{88.8} < -\sqrt{100}$
$-\sqrt{9^2} < -\sqrt{88.8} < -\sqrt{10^2}$
$\quad -9 < -\sqrt{88.8} < -10$
$\qquad\qquad -9$
Check: $-\sqrt{88.8} \approx -9.4$

Page 771 Lesson 13-2

1.
Cereal Preference

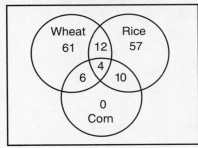

2.
Cooking Preference

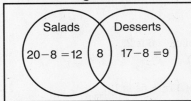

a. members who like to mix salads:
$20 - 8 = 12$
12 people

b. members who do not like either baking desserts or mixing salads:
$30 - (12 + 8 + 9) = 30 - 29$
$\qquad\qquad\qquad\qquad\quad = 1$
1 person

Page 771 Lesson 13-3

1. $x^2 = 14$
$x = \sqrt{14}$ or $x = -\sqrt{14}$
$x \approx 3.7$ or $x \approx -3.7$

2. $y^2 = 25$
$y = \sqrt{25}$ or $y = -\sqrt{25}$
$y = 5$ or $y = -5$

3. $34 = p^2$
$p^2 = 34$
$p = \sqrt{34}$ or $p = -\sqrt{34}$
$p \approx 5.8$ or $p \approx -5.8$

4. $55 = h^2$
$h^2 = 55$
$h = \sqrt{55}$ or $h = -\sqrt{55}$
$h \approx 7.4$ or $h \approx -7.4$

5. $225 = k^2$
$k^2 = 225$
$k = \sqrt{225}$ or $k = -\sqrt{225}$
$k = 15$ or $k = -15$

6. $324 = m^2$
$m^2 = 324$
$m = \sqrt{324}$ or $m = -\sqrt{324}$
$m = 18$ or $m = -18$

7. $d^2 = 441$
$d = \sqrt{441}$ or $d = -\sqrt{441}$
$d = 21$ or $d = -21$

8. $r^2 = 25,000$
$r = \sqrt{25,000}$ or $r = -\sqrt{25,000}$
$r \approx 158.1$ or $r \approx -158.1$

Page 771 Lesson 13-4

1. $c^2 = a^2 + b^2$
$c^2 = 7^2 + 24^2$
$c^2 = 49 + 576$
$c^2 = 625$
$c = \sqrt{625}$
$c = 25$ m

2. $\quad c^2 = a^2 + b^2$
$\quad 30^2 = 18^2 + b^2$
$\quad 900 = 324 + b^2$
$900 - 324 = 324 + b^2 - 324$
$\quad 576 = b^2$
$\quad \sqrt{576} = b$
$\quad 24$ in. $= b$

3. $\quad c^2 = a^2 + b^2$
$\quad 20^2 = a^2 + 10^2$
$\quad 400 = a^2 + 100$
$400 - 100 = a^2 + 100 - 100$
$\quad 300 = a^2$
$\quad \sqrt{300} = a$
$\quad 17.3$ ft $\approx a$

4. $\quad c^2 = a^2 + b^2$
$\quad 9^2 = 3^2 + b^2$
$\quad 81 = 9 + b^2$
$81 - 9 = 9 + b^2 - 9$
$\quad 72 = b^2$
$\quad \sqrt{72} = b$
$\quad 8.5$ cm $\approx b$

5. $\quad c^2 = a^2 + b^2$
$\quad 32^2 = a^2 + 8^2$
$\quad 1024 = a^2 + 64$
$1024 - 64 = a^2 + 64 - 64$
$\quad 960 = a^2$
$\quad \sqrt{960} = a$
$\quad 31.0$ m $\approx a$

6. $\quad c^2 = a^2 + b^2$
$\quad 65^2 = 32^2 + b^2$
$\quad 4225 = 1024 + b^2$
$4225 - 1024 = 1024 + b^2 - 1024$
$\quad 3201 = b^2$
$\quad \sqrt{3201} = b$
$\quad 56.6$ yd $\approx b$

Page 772 Lesson 13-5

1. In a 45°–45° right triangle the lengths of the legs are congruent. So, $b = 3$.
$c = a\sqrt{2}$
$c = 3\sqrt{2}$
$c \approx 4.2$
$b = 3$ ft, $c \approx 4.2$ ft

2. $b = a\sqrt{3}$
$b = 8\sqrt{3}$
$b = 13.9$
$a = \frac{1}{2}c$
$8 = \frac{1}{2}c$
$2(8) = 2\left(\frac{1}{2}\right)c$
$16 = c$
$b \approx 13.9$ m, $c = 16$ m

3. $c = a\sqrt{2}$
$10 = a\sqrt{2}$
$\frac{10}{\sqrt{2}} = \frac{a\sqrt{2}}{\sqrt{2}}$
$7.1 \approx a$
$a \approx 7.1$ cm, $b \approx 7.1$ cm

4. $a = b\sqrt{3}$
$12 = b\sqrt{3}$
$\frac{12}{\sqrt{3}} = \frac{b\sqrt{3}}{\sqrt{3}}$
$6.9 \approx b$
$b = \frac{1}{2}c$
$6.9 \approx \frac{1}{2}c$
$2(6.9) \approx 2\left(\frac{1}{2}\right)c$
$13.9 \approx c$
$b \approx 6.9$ in., $c \approx 13.9$ in.

Page 772   Lesson 13-6

1. $\cos x = \frac{5}{6.3}$
$\cos x \approx 0.7937$
$x \approx 38°$

2. $\tan y = \frac{20.8}{8}$
$\tan y = 2.6$
$y \approx 69°$

3. $\sin y = \frac{7.7}{10}$
$\sin y = 0.77$
$y \approx 50°$

4. $\tan x = \frac{12}{8.4}$
$\tan x \approx 1.4286$
$x \approx 55°$

Page 772   Lesson 13-7

1. Let d represent the distance from the boat to the base of the falls.

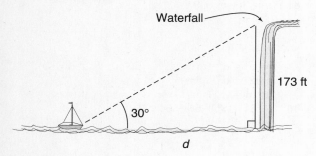

Waterfall
173 ft
30°
d

$\tan 30° = \frac{173}{d}$
$d \tan 30° = 173$
$d = \frac{173}{\tan 30°}$
$d \approx 299.6$
The boat is about 299.6 ft from the base of the falls.

2. Let h represent the height of the monument.

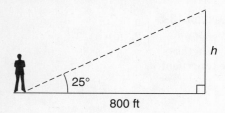

h
25°
800 ft

$\tan 25° = \frac{h}{800}$
$(800)(\tan 25°) = h$
$373.0 \approx h$
The height of the monument is about 373.0 ft.

---

3. Let d represent the distance from the boat to the cliff.

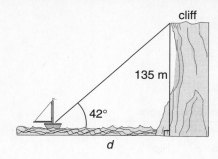

cliff
135 m
42°
d

$\tan 42° = \frac{135}{d}$
$d \tan 42° = 135$
$d = \frac{135}{\tan 42°}$
$d \approx 149.9$
The boat is about 149.9 m from the cliff.

Page 772   Lesson 14-1

1. $4x$ has degree 1.

2. a^2 has degree 2.
-6 has degree 0.
So, the degree of $a^2 - 6$ is 2.

3. $11r$ has degree 1.
$5s$ has degree 1.
So, the degree of $11r + 5s$ is 1.

4. $3y^24y$ has degree 2 + 1 or 3.
-2 has degree 0.
So, the degree of $3y^24y - 2$ is 3.

5. $9cd^3$ has degree 1 + 3 or 4.
-5 has degree 0.
So, the degree of $9cd^3 - 5$ is 4.

6. $-5p^3$ has degree 3.
$8q^2$ has degree 2.
So, the degree of $-5p^3 + 8q^2$ is 3.

7. w^2 has degree 2.
$2x$ has degree 1.
$-3y^3$ has degree 3.
$-7z$ has degree 1.
So, the degree of $w^2 + 2x - 3y^3 - 7z$ is 3.

8. $\frac{x^3}{6}$ has degree 3.
$-x$ has degree 1.
So, the degree of $\frac{x^3}{6} - x$ is 3.

9. $-17n^2p$ has degree 2 + 1 or 3.
$-11np^3$ has degree 1 + 3 or 4.
So, the degree of $-17n^2p - 11np^3$ is 4.

Page 773   Lesson 14-2

1. $(3a + 4) + (a + 2) = (3a + a) + (4 + 2)$
$= (3 + 1)a + (4 + 2)$
$= 4a + 6$

2. $(8m - 3) + (4m + 1) = (8m + 4m) + ((-3) + 1)$
$= (8 + 4)m + ((-3) + 1)$
$= 12m + (-2)$
$= 12m - 2$

3. $(5x - 3y) + (2x - y) = (5x + 2x) + ((-3y) + (-y))$
$= (5 + 2)x + [(-3) + (-1)]y$
$= 7x + [-4]y$
$= 7x - 4y$

4. $(8p^2 - 2p + 3) + (-3p^2 - 2)$
$= (8p^2 + (-3p^2)) + (-2p) + (3 + (-2))$
$= [8 + (-3)]p^2 + (-2p) + (3 + (-2))$
$= 5p^2 + (-2p) + 1$
$= 5p^2 - 2p + 1$

5. $(-11r^2 + 3s) + (5r^2 - s) = (-11r^2 + 5r^2) + (3s + (-s))$
$= [(-11) + 5]r^2 + [3 + (-1)]s$
$= (-6)r^2 + 2s$
$= -6r^2 + 2s$

6. $(3a^2 + 5a + 1) + (2a^2 - 3a - 6)$
$= (3a^2 + 2a^2) + (5a + (-3a)) + (1 + (-6))$
$= (3 + 2)a^2 + [5 + (-3)]a + (1 + (-6))$
$= 5a^2 + 2a + (-5)$
$= 5a^2 + 2a - 5$

Page 773   Lesson 14-3

1. $(3n + 2) - (n + 1) = (3n + 2) + (-1)(n + 1)$
$= 3n + 2 + (-1n - 1)$
$= 3n + 2 - 1n - 1$
$= 3n - 1n + 2 - 1$
$= 2n + 1$

2. $(-3c + 2d) - (7c - 6d) = (-3c + 2d) + (-1)(7c - 6d)$
$= -3c + 2d + (-7c + 6d)$
$= -3c + 2d - 7c + 6d$
$= -3c - 7c + 2d + 6d$
$= -10c + 8d$

3. $(4x^2 + 1) - (3x^2 - 4) = (4x^2 + 1) + (-1)(3x^2 - 4)$
$= 4x^2 + 1 + (-3x^2 + 4)$
$= 4x^2 + 1 - 3x^2 + 4$
$= 4x^2 - 3x^2 + 1 + 4$
$= x^2 + 5$

4. $(5a - 4b) - (-a + b) = (5a - 4b) + (-1)(-a + b)$
$= 5a - 4b + (a - b)$
$= 5a - 4b + a - b$
$= 5a + a - 4b - b$
$= 6a - 5b$

5. $\begin{array}{r} 6x^2 - 4x + 11 \\ (-)5x^2 + 5x - 4 \\ \hline \end{array}$ $\rightarrow$ $\begin{array}{r} 6x^2 - 4x + 11 \\ (+)-5x^2 - 5x + 4 \\ \hline x^2 - 9x + 15 \end{array}$

6. $\begin{array}{r} 8n^2 + 3mn \\ (-)4n^2 - 2mn - 9 \\ \hline \end{array}$ $\rightarrow$ $\begin{array}{r} 8n^2 + 3mn \\ (+)-4n^2 - 2mn + 9 \\ \hline 4n^2 - mn + 9 \end{array}$

Page 773   Lesson 4-4

1. $(a^2)^3 = a^{2 \cdot 3}$
$= a^6$

2. $(-2x)^3 = (-2)^3 x^3$
$= -8x^3$

3. $(p^2 q)^3 = (p^2)^3 q^3$
$= p^{2 \cdot 3} q^3$
$= p^6 q^3$

4. $-5c(2cd)^3 = -5c(2^3 c^3 d^3)$
$= -5c(8c^3 d^3)$
$= -5 \cdot 8 \cdot c \cdot c^3 \cdot d^3$
$= -40c^4 d^3$

5. $4y(y^2 z)^3 = 4y((y^2)^3 z^3)$
$= 4y(y^{2 \cdot 3} z^3)$
$= 4y \cdot y^6 \cdot z^3$
$= 4y^7 z^3$

6. $6a(-ab)^7 = 6a((-a)^7 b^7)$
$= 6a(-a^7 b^7)$
$= -6a^8 b^7$

Page 773   Lesson 14-5

1. $4n(5n - 3) = 4n(5n) - 4n(3)$
$= 20n^2 - 12n$

2. $-3x(4 - x) = -3x(4) - (-3x)(x)$
$= -12x - (-3x^2)$
$= -12x + 3x^2$

3. $6m(-m^2 + 3) = 6m(-m^2) + 6m(3)$
$= -6m^3 + 18m$

4. $-5x(2x^2 - 3x + 1) = -5x(2x^2) - (-5x)(3x) + (-5x)(1)$
$= -10x^3 - (-15x^2) + (-5x)$
$= -10x^3 + 15x^2 - 5x$

5. $7r(r^2 - 3r + 7) = 7r(r^2) - 7r(3r) + 7r(7)$
$= 7r^3 - 21r^2 + 49r$

6. $-3az(2z^2 + 4az + a^2)$
$= -3az(2z^2) + (-3az)(4az) + (-3az)(a^2)$
$= -6az^3 + (-12a^2 z^2) + (-3a^3 z)$
$= -6az^3 - 12a^2 z^2 - 3a^3 z$

Page 773   Lesson 14-6

1. $(2x + 2)(3x + 1) = (2x + 2)3x + (2x + 2)1$
$= (2x)3x + (2)3x + (2x)1 + (2)1$
$= 6x^2 + 6x + 2x + 2$
$= 6x^2 + 8x + 2$

2. $(x + 4)(3x + 1) = (x + 4)3x + (x + 4)1$
$= (x)3x + (4)3x + (x)1 + (4)1$
$= 3x^2 + 12x + 1x + 4$
$= 3x^2 + 13x + 4$

3. $(7x + 4)(3x - 11)$
$= (7x + 4)3x + (7x + 4)(-11)$
$= (7x)3x + (4)3x + (7x)(-11) + (4)(-11)$
$= 21x^2 + 12x + (-77x) + (-44)$
$= 21x^2 + 12x - 77x - 44$
$= 21x^2 - 65x - 44$

4. $(x + 3)(x + 1) = (x + 3)x + (x + 3)1$
$= (x)x + (3)x + (x)1 + (3)1$
$= x^2 + 3x + 1x + 3$
$= x^2 + 4x + 3$

5. $(2x + 1)(x + 1) = (2x + 1)x + (2x + 1)1$
$= (2x)x + (1)x + (2x)1 + (1)1$
$= 2x^2 + 1x + 2x + 1$
$= 2x^2 + 3x + 1$

6. $(3x + 2)(2x + 2) = (3x + 2)2x + (3x + 2)2$
$= (3x)2x + (2)2x + (3x)2 + (2)2$
$= 6x^2 + 4x + 6x + 4$
$= 6x^2 + 10x + 4$

1. Explore—We know the distance between the two houses and the time it takes Jackie to walk ten feet. We need to determine how long it will take her to walk to Roberta's house.

   Plan—Divide the distance between the two houses by ten and then multiply the answer by three to find how long it will take to walk to Roberta's house.
   Estimate:
   $90 \div 10 \rightarrow 100 \div 10 = 10; 10 \times 3 = 30$

   Solve—$90 \div 10 = 9$
   $9 \times 3 = 27$
   It will take 27 seconds to walk to Roberta's house.

   Examine—The time of 27 seconds makes sense with the estimate.

2. $7 \cdot 4 + 6 \cdot 5 = 28 + 30$
   $= 58$

3. $8 + 3(16 - 12) = 8 + 3(4)$
   $= 8 + 12$
   $= 20$

4. $6[4 \cdot (72 - 63) \div 3] = 6[4 \cdot 9 \div 3]$
   $= 6[36 \div 3]$
   $= 6[12]$
   $= 72$

5. $6[5 \times (41 - 36) - (8 + 14)] = 6[5 \times 5 - (8 + 14)]$
   $= 6[5 \times 5 - 22]$
   $= 6[25 - 22]$
   $= 6[3]$
   $= 18$

6. $2c + 6bc - 7 = 2 \cdot 3 + 6 \cdot 4 \cdot 3 - 7$
   $= 6 + 72 - 7$
   $= 78 - 7$
   $= 71$

7. $15 \div c + 7b = 15 \div 3 + 7 \cdot 4$
   $= 5 + 7 \cdot 4$
   $= 5 + 28$
   $= 33$

8. $6b \div a + 5c = 6 \cdot 4 \div 8 + 5 \cdot 3$
   $= 24 \div 8 + 5 \cdot 3$
   $= 3 + 5 \cdot 3$
   $= 3 + 15$
   $= 18$

9. commutative, multiplication
10. associative, addition
11. identity, addition
12. distributive
13. associative, multiplication
14. identity, multiplication
15. $(b + 12) + 15 = b + (12 + 15)$
    $= b + 27$
16. $6(v \cdot 2) = (6 \cdot 2)v$
    $= 12v$
17. $18 + yz + 13yz = yz(18 + 13)$
    $= yz(31)$
    $= 31yz$

18. $5(2w + 3) + 7(w + 13) = 5 \cdot 2w + 5 \cdot 3 + 7 \cdot w + 7 \cdot 13$
    $= 10w + 15 + 7w + 91$
    $= 10w + 7w + 15 + 91$
    $= (10 + 7)w + 15 + 91$
    $= 17w + 106$

19. $5x = 25$ What number
    $5(5) = 25$ times 5 is 25?
    $x = 5$

20. $8 + g = 8$ What number
    $8 + 0 = 8$ plus 8 is 8?
    $g = 0$

21. $\frac{s}{14} = 3$ What number divided
    $\frac{42}{14} = 3$ by 14 is 3?
    $s = 42$

22. $22 - k = 17$ 22 minus what
    $22 - 5 = 17$ number is 17?
    $k = 5$

23. $(7, 5)$ 24. $(4, 0)$ 25. $(5, 6)$
26. $(3, 2)$ 27. $(8, 3)$ 28. $(0, 7)$

29. $x + 48 = 55$ 30. $v - 57 = 72$
    $x = 55 - 48$ $v = 72 + 57$
    $x = 7$ $v = 129$

31. $\frac{b}{2} = 18$ 32. $672 = 21t$
    $b = 18 \cdot 2$ $672 \div 21 = t$
    $b = 36$ $32 = t$

33. false   34. true
35. false   36. true
37. Labrador retriever
38. $d = 22 - 18$
    $d = 4$
    4 thousand
39. $61 + 43 + 17 + 39 + 121 + 18 + 3 + 90 + 22 + 5$
    or 419 thousand
    419,000

40.

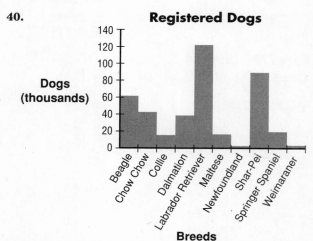

Registered Dogs

Dogs (thousands)

Breeds

Page 775   Chapter 2 Practice Test

1. $+15$ 2. $+10$
3. -25 4. -6
5. $|-8| = 8$

6. $|-3| + |2| = 3 + 2$
$ = 5$

7. $|15| - |-3| = 15 - 3$
$ = 12$

8. $|-20| + |-19| = 20 + 19$
$ = 39$

9. $(1, -6)$ **10.** $(-7, 5)$

11. $(6, 0)$ **12.** $(5, 6)$

13. $(-3, -2)$ **14.** $(2, -3)$

15. $(-2, 3)$ **16.** $(0, -7)$

17. Quadrant IV

18. Quadrant III

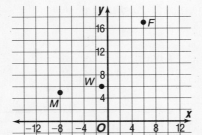

19. Quadrant II

20. Quadrant I

21. Quadrant II

22. Quadrant III

23. $-6 > -12$ **24.** $18 = 18$

25. $-5 < -4$ **26.** $|-7| = 7$

27. $3x + 5x = (3 + 5)x$
$ = 8x$

28. $6p - (-4p) = 6p + 4p$
$ = (6 + 4)p$
$ = 10p$

29. $-9m - (-7m) = -9m + 7m$
$ = (-9 + 7)m$
$ = -(|-9| - |7|)m$
$ = -(9 - 7)m$
$ = -2m$

30. $-8k + (-12k) = (-8 + (-12))k$
$ = -(|-8| + |-12|)k$
$ = -(8 + 12)k$
$ = -20k$

31. $-15a - 6a = -15a + (-6a)$
$ = (-15 + (-6))a$
$ = -(|-15| + |-6|)a$
$ = -(15 + 6)a$
$ = -21a$

32. $10d + (-3d) = (10 + (-3))d$
$ = +(|10| - |-3|)d$
$ = +(10 - 3)d$
$ = +7d$

33. Extend the pattern to include
$123,456 \times 9 + 7$.

$$
\begin{array}{l}
1 \times 9 + 2 = 11 \\
12 \times 9 + 3 = 111 \\
123 \times 9 + 4 = 1111 \\
1234 \times 9 + 5 = 11,111 \\
12,345 \times 9 + 6 = 111,111 \\
123,456 \times 9 + 7 = 1,111,111
\end{array}
$$

$123,456 \times 9 + 7 = 1,111,111$

34. Use the process of elimination.

$$
\begin{array}{r}
\text{T R I E D} \\
+ \text{ D R I V E} \\
\hline
\text{R I V E T}
\end{array}
$$

Looking at the tens digits, if 1 was carried over, then V = 9. If 0 was carried over from the ones digits, V = 0. Assume that V = 0. Then, I = 5 and R = 2. However if R = 2, then T + D = 2. This would mean that both T and D are 1. Since this is impossible, the assumption is incorrect and V = 9.

$$
\begin{array}{r}
\text{T R I E D} \\
+ \text{ D R I 9 E} \\
\hline
\text{R I 9 E T}
\end{array}
$$

Studying the hundreds digits, no possible value for I has I + I = 9. It must be that I = 4 and 1 was carried over from adding the tens digits.

$$
\begin{array}{r}
\text{T R 4 E D} \\
+ \text{ D R 4 9 E} \\
\hline
\text{7 4 9 E T}
\end{array}
$$

The hundreds digits will not carry over anything to the thousands place. Thus, R = 2 or 7. However, we have already concluded that R cannot be 2 if T and D are not equal. So, R must be 7 and 1 is carried over from the thousands to the ten-thousands place.

$$
\begin{array}{r}
\text{T 7 4 E D} \\
+ \text{ D 7 4 9 E} \\
\hline
\text{7 4 9 E T}
\end{array}
$$

T + D + 1 = 7, so T + D = 6. The possible values for T and D are 0 and 6 and 1 and 5. (4 is already assigned and T and D are not equal, so 2 and 4 and 3 and 3 are not possible combinations.) It does not make sense for the first digit of a number to be 0, so T and D are 1 and 5.

Suppose T = 5 and D = 1. Look at the ones digits. We know that 1 is carried over from the ones to the tens place. The D + E would have to be 15. If D = 1, then E would have to be 14. But E must be a single digit. Thus, T = 1 and D = 5.

$$
\begin{array}{r}
\text{1 7 4 E 5} \\
+ \text{ 5 7 4 9 E} \\
\hline
\text{7 4 9 E 1}
\end{array}
$$

5 + E = 11. Therefore, E = 6.

$$
\begin{array}{r}
\text{1 7 4 6 5} \\
+ \text{ 5 7 4 9 6} \\
\hline
\text{7 4 9 6 1}
\end{array}
$$

The result checks.

Therefore, T = 1, R = 7, I = 4, E = 6, D = 5, and V = 9.

35. $q = -13(10)$
$q = -130$

36. $-40 \cdot (-6) = h$
$240 = h$

37. $-5(-8)(3) = r$
$-5[(-8)(3)] = r$
$-5(-24) = r$
$120 = r$

38. $b = \frac{-15}{3}$
$b = -15 \div 3$
$b = -5$

39. $\frac{-12}{-6} = a$
$(-12) \div (-6) = a$
$2 = a$

40. $115 \div (-5) = k$
$-23 = k$

Page 776   Chapter 3 Practice Test

1.

	Older than:					
	Dave	Angie	Bob	Dwight	Andy	Donna
Dave		O	X	X	O	O
Angie	X		X	X	O	O
Bob	O	O		O	O	O
Dwight	O	O	O		O	O
Andy	X	X	X	X		X
Donna	X	X	X	X	O	

Andy is the oldest.

2.

	Adult	Baby	Teenager
left	X	O	O
middle	O	X	O
right	O	O	X

The adult is on the left, the baby is in the middle, and the teenager is on the right.

	Adult	Baby	Teenager
Blonde	X	O	O
Brunette	O	O	X
Redhead	O	X	O

The adult is a blonde, the baby is a redhead, and the teenager is a brunette.

adult, baby, teenager; blonde, redhead, brunette

3. $19 = f + 5$
$19 - 5 = f + 5 - 5$
$14 = f$
Check: $19 = f + 5$
$19 \stackrel{?}{=} 14 + 5$
$19 = 19$ ✔

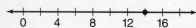

4. $-15 + z = 3$
$-15 + z + 15 = 3 + 15$
$z = 18$
Check: $-15 + z = 3$
$-15 + 18 \stackrel{?}{=} 3$
$3 = 3$ ✔

5. $x - (-27) = -40$
$x + 27 = -40$
$x + 27 - 27 = -40 - 27$
$x = -67$
Check: $x - (-27) = -40$
$-67 - (-27) \stackrel{?}{=} -40$
$-67 + 27 \stackrel{?}{=} -40$
$-40 = -40$ ✔

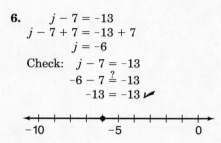

6. $j - 7 = -13$
$j - 7 + 7 = -13 + 7$
$j = -6$
Check: $j - 7 = -13$
$-6 - 7 \stackrel{?}{=} -13$
$-13 = -13$ ✔

7. $-8y = 72$
$\frac{-8y}{-8} = \frac{72}{-8}$
$y = -9$
Check: $-8y = 72$
$-8(-9) \stackrel{?}{=} 72$
$72 = 72$ ✔

8. $-9k = -162$
$\frac{-9k}{-9} = \frac{-162}{-9}$
$k = 18$
Check: $-9k = -162$
$-9(18) \stackrel{?}{=} -162$
$-162 = -162$ ✔

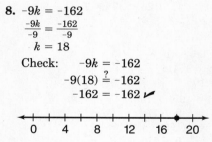

9. $-42 = \frac{p}{3}$
$-42(3) = \frac{p}{3}(3)$
$-126 = p$
Check: $-42 = \frac{p}{3}$
$-42 \stackrel{?}{=} \frac{-126}{3}$
$-42 = -42$ ✔

10. $\frac{n}{-30} = -6$
$\frac{n}{-30}(-30) = -6(-30)$
$n = 180$
Check: $\frac{n}{-30} = -6$
$\frac{180}{-30} \stackrel{?}{=} -6$
$-6 = -6$ ✔

11. $P = 2(s + b)$
$P = 2(4 + 16)$
$P = 2(20)$
$P = 40$

12. $S = 2\ell w + 2wh + 2\ell h$
$S = 2 \cdot 3 \cdot 5 + 2 \cdot 5 \cdot 8 + 2 \cdot 3 \cdot 8$
$S = 30 + 80 + 48$
$S = 158$

13. $E = mc^2$
$325 = m \cdot 25$
$\frac{325}{25} = \frac{25m}{25}$
$13 = m$

14. $C = \frac{5}{9}(F - 32)$
$C = \frac{5}{9}(212 - 32)$
$C = \frac{5}{9}(180)$
$C = 100$

15. $P = 2(\ell + w)$ $A = \ell \cdot w$
$P = 2(48 + 20)$ $A = 48 \cdot 20$
$P = 2(68)$ $A = 960 \text{ m}^2$
$P = 136 \text{ m}$

16. $P = 2(\ell + w)$ $A = \ell \cdot w$
$P = 2(100 + 75)$ $A = 100 \cdot 75$
$P = 2(175)$ $A = 7500 \text{ yd}^2$
$P = 350 \text{ yd}$

17. $P = 2(\ell + w)$ $A = \ell \cdot w$
$P = 2(20 + 20)$ $A = 20 \cdot 20$
$P = 2(40)$ $A = 400 \text{ cm}^2$
$P = 80 \text{ cm}$

18. $g - 8 > -5$
$g - 8 + 8 > -5 + 8$
$g > 3$

Check: Try 5, a number greater than 3.
$g - 8 > -5$
$5 - 8 \overset{?}{>} -5$
$-3 > -5$ ✔

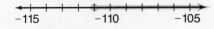

19. $-61 \leq w + 50$
$-61 - 50 \leq w + 50 - 50$
$-111 \leq w$

Check: Try -100, a number greater than or equal to -111.
$-61 \leq w + 50$
$-61 \overset{?}{\leq} -100 + 50$
$-61 \leq -50$ ✔

20. $17 \geq a - (-19)$
$17 \geq a + 19$
$17 - 19 \geq a + 19 - 19$
$-2 \geq a$

Check: Try -5, a number less than or equal to -2.
$17 \geq a - (-19)$
$17 \overset{?}{\geq} -5 - (-19)$
$17 \overset{?}{\geq} -5 + 19$
$17 \geq 14$ ✔

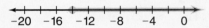

21. $3t \geq -42$
$\frac{3t}{3} \geq \frac{-42}{3}$
$t \geq -14$

Check: Try 0, a number greater than or equal to -14.
$3t \geq -42$
$3(0) \overset{?}{\geq} -42$
$0 \geq -42$ ✔

22. $\frac{p}{-12} > 6$
$\frac{p}{-12}(-12) < 6(-12)$
$p < -72$

Check: Try -84, a number less than -72.
$\frac{p}{-12} > 6$
$\frac{-84}{-12} \overset{?}{>} 6$
$7 > 6$ ✔

23. $-5c > 30$
$\frac{-5c}{-5} < \frac{30}{-5}$
$c < -6$

Check: Try -10, a number less than -6.
$-5c > 30$
$-5(-10) \overset{?}{>} 30$
$50 > 30$ ✔

24. Let a = maximum number of vertebrates
$a + 2574 < 6000$
$a + 2574 - 2574 < 6000 - 2574$
$a < 3426$

There are no more than 3426 vertebrates.

25. Let k = how many times more Cherokee Indians
$44{,}000k = 308{,}000$
$\frac{44{,}000k}{44{,}000} = \frac{308{,}000}{44{,}000}$
$k = 7$

There are 7 times more Cherokee Indians than Creek Indians.

Page 777   Chapter 4 Practice Test

1. 3, 5   **2.** 2, 5, 10   **3.** 2, 3, 5
4. $(-7)^5$ **5.** 40^1 **6.** x^8

7.

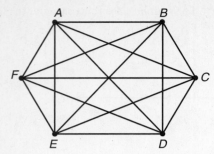

$5 + 4 + 3 + 2 + 1 = 15$
15 games

8. $280 = 2 \cdot 140$
$= 2 \cdot 2 \cdot 70$
$= 2 \cdot 2 \cdot 2 \cdot 35$
$= 2 \cdot 2 \cdot 2 \cdot 5 \cdot 7$

9. $882x^3 = 2 \cdot 441 \quad \cdot \quad x^3$
$= 2 \cdot 3 \cdot 147 \cdot x \cdot x \cdot x$
$= 2 \cdot 3 \cdot 3 \cdot 49 \cdot x \cdot x \cdot x$
$= 2 \cdot 3 \cdot 3 \cdot 7 \cdot 7 \cdot x \cdot x \cdot x$

10. $-696f^2g = -1 \cdot 696 \quad \cdot \quad f^2 \cdot g$
$= -1 \cdot 2 \cdot 348 \quad \cdot \quad f \cdot f \cdot g$
$= -1 \cdot 2 \cdot 2 \cdot 174 \quad \cdot \quad f \cdot f \cdot g$
$= -1 \cdot 2 \cdot 2 \cdot 2 \cdot 87 \quad \cdot \quad f \cdot f \cdot g$
$= -1 \cdot 2 \cdot 2 \cdot 2 \cdot 3 \cdot 29 \cdot f \cdot f \cdot g$

11. $63 = 3 \cdot 3 \cdot 7$
$231 = 3 \cdot 7 \cdot 11$
The GCF is $3 \cdot 7$ or 21.

12. $9xy = 3 \cdot 3 \cdot x \cdot y$
$27x^3y^4 = 3 \cdot 3 \cdot 3 \cdot x \cdot x \cdot x \cdot y \cdot y \cdot y \cdot y$
The GCF is $3 \cdot 3 \cdot x \cdot y$ or $9xy$.

13. $12z^4 = 2 \cdot 2 \cdot 3 \cdot z \cdot z \cdot z \cdot z$
$72z^3 = 2 \cdot 2 \cdot 2 \cdot 3 \cdot 3 \cdot z \cdot z \cdot z$
$120z^2 = 2 \cdot 2 \cdot 2 \cdot 3 \cdot 5 \cdot z \cdot z$
The GCF is $2 \cdot 2 \cdot 3 \cdot z \cdot z$ or $12z^2$.

14. $\frac{95}{155} = \frac{\cancel{5} \cdot 19}{\cancel{5} \cdot 31}$
$= \frac{19}{31}$

15. $\frac{120}{210} = \frac{\cancel{2} \cdot 2 \cdot 2 \cdot \cancel{3} \cdot \cancel{5}}{\cancel{2} \cdot \cancel{3} \cdot \cancel{5} \cdot 7}$
$= \frac{4}{7}$

16. $\frac{65}{104} = \frac{5 \cdot 1\cancel{3}}{2 \cdot 2 \cdot 2 \cdot 1\cancel{3}}$
$= \frac{5}{8}$

17. $\frac{3}{7} < \frac{6}{10}$

18. $\frac{5}{11} < \frac{3}{5}$

19. $\frac{7}{15} > \frac{1}{3}$

20. $(2x^4)(-15x^5) = (2 \cdot -15)(x^4 \cdot x^5)$
$= (-30)(x^{4+5})$
$= -30x^9$

21. $\frac{q^6}{q} = q^{6-1}$
$= q^5$

22. $18 \cdot 18^7 = 18^{1+7}$
$= 18^8$

23. $3^{-2}xy^{-3} = \frac{x}{3^2y^3}$

24. $(st)^{-1} = \frac{1}{st}$

25. $\frac{3^{-4}}{2^{-2}} = \frac{2^2}{3^4}$

Page 778   Chapter 5 Practice Test

1. $-9.8 = -9\frac{8}{10}$
$= -9\frac{4}{5}$

2. $0.125 = \frac{125}{1000}$
$= \frac{1}{8}$

3. Let $N = 1.666\ldots$ Then $10N = 16.666\ldots$
$10N = 16.666\ldots$
$\underline{-\ 1N =\ \ 1.666\ldots}$
$9N = 15$
$\frac{9N}{9} = \frac{15}{9}$
$N = 1\frac{6}{9}$ or $1\frac{2}{3}$
Therefore, $1.\overline{6} = 1\frac{2}{3}$.

4. Rational

5. Integer, Rational

6. Whole, Integer, Rational

7. Sample answer:
$\$10.03 + \$5.84 \to 10 + 6 = 16$
$\$10.03 + \$5.84$ is about $\$16$.

8. Sample answer:
$44.03 - 32.9 \to 40 - 30 = 10$
$44.03 - 32.9$ is about 10.

9. Sample answer:
$20.3 + 59.7 + 62.8 \to 20 + 60 + 60 = 140$
$20.3 + 49.7 + 62.8$ is about 140.

10. $4.75m - 6.2m + 9 = (4.75 - 6.2)m + 9$
$= 1.45m + 9$

11. $6.16q - 19 - (-7.32q) = 6.16q - 19 + 7.32q$
$= 6.16q + 7.32q - 19$
$= (6.16 + 7.32)q - 19$
$= 13.48q - 19$

12. $a = \frac{7}{9} + \frac{5}{9}$
$a = \frac{12}{9}$
$a = 1\frac{3}{9}$
$a = 1\frac{1}{3}$

13. $\frac{27}{18} - \frac{9}{18} = h$
$\frac{18}{18} = h$
$1 = h$

14. $2\frac{3}{8} - 1\frac{5}{8} = p$
$1\frac{11}{8} - 1\frac{5}{8} = p$
$(1 - 1) + \left(\frac{11}{8} - \frac{5}{8}\right) = p$
$0 + \frac{6}{8} = p$
$\frac{6}{8} = p$
$\frac{3}{4} = p$

15. $\frac{1}{6} + \frac{5}{24} = p$
$\frac{4}{24} + \frac{5}{24} = p$
$\frac{9}{24} = p$
$\frac{3}{8} = p$

16. $5\frac{1}{2} - 2\frac{2}{3} = r$
$5\frac{3}{6} - 2\frac{4}{6} = r$
$4\frac{9}{6} - 2\frac{4}{6} = r$
$2\frac{5}{6} = r$

17. $-\frac{6}{7} - \left(-2\frac{10}{21}\right) = y$
$-\frac{6}{7} + 2\frac{10}{21} = y$
$-\frac{18}{21} + 2\frac{10}{21} = y$
$2\frac{10}{21} - \frac{18}{21} = y$
$1\frac{31}{21} - \frac{18}{21} = y$
$1 + \left(\frac{31}{21} - \frac{18}{21}\right) = y$
$1 + \frac{13}{21} = y$
$1\frac{13}{21} = y$

18.
$$u - 7.28 = 14.9$$
$$u - 7.28 + 7.28 = 14.9 + 7.28$$
$$u = 22.18$$
Check: $u - 7.28 = 14.9$
$$22.18 - 7.28 \overset{?}{=} 14.9$$
$$14.9 = 14.9 ✔$$

19.
$$a + \frac{2}{3} = 2$$
$$a + \frac{2}{3} - \frac{2}{3} = 2 - \frac{2}{3}$$
$$a = \frac{2}{1} - \frac{2}{3}$$
$$a = \frac{6}{3} - \frac{2}{3}$$
$$a = \frac{4}{3}$$
$$a = 1\frac{1}{3}$$

Check: $a + \frac{2}{3} = 2$
$$1\frac{1}{3} + \frac{2}{3} \overset{?}{=} 2$$
$$1\frac{3}{3} \overset{?}{=} 2$$
$$2 = 2 ✔$$

20.
$$-9.3 > y - (-4.8)$$
$$-9.3 > y + 4.8$$
$$-9.3 - 4.8 > y + 4.8 - 4.8$$
$$-14.1 > y$$
Check: Try -15, a number less than -14.1.
$$-9.3 > y - (-4.8)$$
$$-9.3 \overset{?}{>} -15 - (-4.8)$$
$$-9.3 \overset{?}{>} -15 + 4.8$$
$$-9.3 > -10.2 ✔$$

21.
$$j + \frac{7}{12} \le 7\frac{1}{2}$$
$$j + \frac{7}{12} - \frac{7}{12} \le 7\frac{1}{2} - \frac{7}{12}$$
$$j \le 7\frac{6}{12} - \frac{7}{12}$$
$$j \le 6\frac{18}{12} - \frac{7}{12}$$
$$j \le 6\frac{11}{12}$$

Check: Try 0, a number less than or equal to $6\frac{11}{12}$.
$$j + \frac{7}{12} \le 7\frac{1}{2}$$
$$0 + \frac{7}{12} \overset{?}{\le} 7\frac{1}{2}$$
$$\frac{7}{12} \le 7\frac{1}{2} ✔$$

22. Sample answer: inductive
See students' explanations.

23. Sample answer: deductive
See students' explanations.

24. $\frac{1}{2} \quad \frac{3}{4} \quad 1$
$\underbrace{\quad}_{+\frac{1}{4}} \underbrace{\quad}_{+\frac{1}{4}}$
yes; $1\frac{1}{4}$, $1\frac{1}{2}$, $1\frac{3}{4}$

25. $5040 \underbrace{\quad}_{÷7} 720 \underbrace{\quad}_{÷6} 120 \underbrace{\quad}_{÷5} 24$
no; 6, 2, 1

1. $\frac{3}{8} \to 8\overline{)3.000}$
$$\begin{array}{r} 0.375 \\ \underline{-2\ 4} \\ 60 \\ \underline{-56} \\ 40 \\ \underline{-40} \\ 0 \end{array}$$
$\frac{3}{8} = 0.375$

2. $-\frac{6}{11} \to 11\overline{)6.0000}$
$$\begin{array}{r} 0.5454 \\ \underline{-5\ 5} \\ 50 \\ \underline{-44} \\ 60 \\ \underline{-55} \\ 50 \\ \underline{-44} \\ 6 \end{array}$$
$-\frac{6}{11} = -0.\overline{54}$

3. $4\frac{8}{9} = 4 + \frac{8}{9}$
$\frac{8}{9} \to 9\overline{)8.000}$
$$\begin{array}{r} 0.888 \\ \underline{-7\ 2} \\ 80 \\ \underline{-72} \\ 80 \\ \underline{-72} \\ 8 \end{array}$$
$4 + 0.\overline{8} = 4.\overline{8}$
$4\frac{8}{9} = 4.\overline{8}$

4. Sample answer:
$14.34 \cdot 5.8 \to 14 \cdot 6 = 84$
$14.34 \cdot 5.8$ is about 84.

5. Sample answer:
$81.2 \div 15.57 \to 80 \div 16 = 5$
$81.2 \div 15.57$ is about 5.

6. Sample answer:
$\frac{3}{7} \cdot 98 \to \frac{1}{2} \cdot 98 = 49$
$\frac{3}{7} \cdot 98$ is about 49.

7. $k = -5\left(\frac{-4}{3}\right)$
$k = -\frac{5}{1}\left(\frac{-4}{3}\right)$
$k = \frac{-5 \cdot -4}{1 \cdot 3}$
$k = \frac{20}{3}$
$k = 6\frac{2}{3}$

8. $1\frac{4}{5} \cdot -1\frac{5}{6} = n$
$\frac{9}{5} \cdot \frac{-11}{6} = n$
$\frac{\overset{3}{\cancel{9}} \cdot -11}{5 \cdot \cancel{6}_{2}} = n$
$\frac{3 \cdot -11}{5 \cdot 2} = n$
$\frac{-33}{10} = n$
$-3\frac{3}{10} = n$

9. $t = \left(\frac{2}{5}\right)^3$
$t = \left(\frac{2}{5}\right)\left(\frac{2}{5}\right)\left(\frac{2}{5}\right)$
$t = \frac{8}{125}$

10. $a \div b = \frac{-8}{9} \div \frac{-4}{3}$
$= \frac{-8}{9} \times -\frac{3}{4}$
$= \frac{24}{36}$
$= \frac{2}{3}$

11. $r \div s = -1\frac{1}{2} \div \frac{21}{30}$

$\quad = -\frac{3}{2} \div \frac{21}{30}$

$\quad = -\frac{3}{2} \times \frac{30}{21}$

$\quad = \frac{-90}{42}$

$\quad = -2\frac{6}{42}$

$\quad = -2\frac{1}{7}$

12. $(2.01)(0.04) = d$

$\quad \begin{array}{r} 0.04 \\ \times 2.01 \\ \hline 0\,04 \\ +008\,00 \\ \hline 0.08\,04 \end{array}$

$d = 0.0804$

13. $2.13 \div (-0.3) = a$

$0.3\overline{)2.13}$

$\quad \begin{array}{r} 7.1 \\ 3\overline{)21.3} \\ -21 \\ \hline 3 \\ -3 \\ \hline 0 \end{array}$

$a = -7.1$

14. $a = (81)(0.02)(1.5)$

$\quad \begin{array}{r} 0.02 \\ \times\ 81 \\ \hline 0\,02 \\ +01\,60 \\ \hline 01.60 \end{array}$

$\quad \begin{array}{r} 1.6\,2 \\ \times\ 1.5 \\ \hline 8\,1\,0 \\ +1\,6\,2\,0 \\ \hline 2.4\,3\,0 \end{array}$

$a = 2.43$

15. $x = 27.9 \div 0.31$

$0.31\overline{)27.9}$

$\quad \begin{array}{r} 90 \\ 31\overline{)2790} \\ -279 \\ \hline 0 \\ -0 \\ \hline 0 \end{array}$

$x = 90$

16. $y = 2.3(-0.004)$

$\quad \begin{array}{r} -0.004 \\ \times\ 2.3 \\ \hline 0012 \\ +00080 \\ \hline 0.0092 \end{array}$

$y = -0.0092$

17. $-51.408 \div (-5.4) = g$

$5.4\overline{)51.408}$

$\quad \begin{array}{r} 9.52 \\ 54\overline{)514.08} \\ -486 \\ \hline 28\ 0 \\ -27\ 0 \\ \hline 1\ 08 \\ -1\ 08 \\ \hline 0 \end{array}$

$g = 9.52$

18. 36, 37, 41, 43, 43

mean: $\frac{36 + 37 + 41 + 43 + 43}{5} = 40$

median : 41

mode: 43

19. 0.1, 0.2, 0.4, 0.6, 1.1, 1.2

mean: $\frac{0.1 + 0.2 + 0.4 + 0.6 + 1.1 + 1.2}{6} = 0.6$

median: $\frac{0.4 + 0.6}{2} = 0.5$

mode: none

20. 2, 3, 6, 7, 8, 8, 9, 16, 21

mean: $\frac{2 + 3 + 6 + 7 + 8 + 8 + 9 + 16 + 21}{9} = 8.9$

median: 8

mode: 8

21. 44, 48, 55, 55, 56, 68, 70

mean: $\frac{44 + 48 + 55 + 55 + 56 + 68 + 70}{7} = 56.6$

median: 55

mode: 55

22. $\frac{7}{8}p \geq -4\frac{1}{8}$

$\quad \frac{7}{8}p \geq -\frac{33}{8}$

$\frac{8}{7} \cdot \frac{7}{8}p \geq \frac{8}{7} \cdot \frac{-33}{8}$

$\quad p \geq \frac{-33}{7}$

Check: Try 1, a number greater than or equal to $\frac{-33}{7}$.

$\quad \frac{7}{8}p \geq -4\frac{1}{8}$

$\quad \frac{7}{8} \cdot 1 \overset{?}{\geq} -4\frac{1}{8}$

$\quad \frac{7}{8} \geq -4\frac{1}{8}$ ✔

23. $0.25w = 6\frac{4}{5}$

$\quad \frac{0.25w}{0.25} = \frac{6\frac{4}{5}}{0.25}$

$\quad w = 27.2$

Check: $\quad 0.25w = 6\frac{4}{5}$

$\quad 0.25(27.2) \overset{?}{=} 6\frac{4}{5}$

$\quad 6.8 \overset{?}{=} 6\frac{4}{5}$

$\quad 6\frac{8}{10} \overset{?}{=} 6\frac{4}{5}$

$\quad 6\frac{4}{5} = 6\frac{4}{5}$ ✔

24. $-0.5h < 12.5$

$\quad \frac{-0.5h}{-0.5} > \frac{12.5}{-0.5}$

$\quad h > -25$

Check: Try -5, a number greater than -25.

$\quad -0.5h < 12.5$

$\quad -0.5(-5) \overset{?}{<} 12.5$

$\quad 2.5 < 12.5$ ✔

25. 384　96　24

$\qquad \times 0.25 \times 0.25$

yes; 0.25; 6, 1.5, 3.75

26. -7　0　7　14

$\quad +7\ +7\ +7$

no

27. 20　16　12.8

$\qquad \times 0.8\ \times 0.8$

yes; 0.8; 10.24, 8.192, 6.5536

28. $0.0021 = 2.1 \times 10^{-3}$

29. $87,500,000 = 8.75 \times 10^{7}$

30. $0.00000743 = 7.43 \times 10^{-6}$

31. $3.9 \times 10^{3} = 3.9 \times 1000$

$\quad = 3900$

32. $5.32 \times 10^{-4} = 5.32 \times \left(\frac{1}{10}\right)^{4}$

$\quad = 5.32 \times \frac{1}{10,000}$

$\quad = 0.000532$

33. $7.02 \times 10^0 = 7.02 \times 1$
$= 7.02$

Page 780   Chapter 7 Practice Test

1. Diana earned a total of \$450 ⟶ 450
Undo her salary ⟶ -250

200

Undo her bonus of \$50 for ⟶ $\div\ 50$
every 25 boxes

4

Diana sold 4×25 or 100 boxes.

2.

Blocks	10	20	30	40	50
Time	15	30	45	60	75

It would take Frank at least 75 minutes to walk 50 blocks.

3. $25 = 2d - 9$
$25 + 9 = 2d - 9 + 9$
$34 = 2d$
$\frac{34}{2} = \frac{2d}{2}$
$17 = d$

Check: $25 = 2d - 9$
$25 \stackrel{?}{=} 2(17) - 9$
$25 \stackrel{?}{=} 34 - 9$
$25 = 25$ ✔

4. $4w + (-18) = -34$
$4w - 18 = -34$
$4w - 18 + 18 = -34 + 18$
$4w = -16$
$\frac{4w}{4} = \frac{-16}{4}$
$w = -4$

Check: $4w + (-18) = -34$
$4(-4) + (-18) \stackrel{?}{=} -34$
$-16 + (-18) \stackrel{?}{=} -34$
$-34 = -34$ ✔

5. $\frac{p}{6} - (-21) = 8$
$\frac{p}{6} + 21 = 8$
$\frac{p}{6} + 21 - 21 = 8 - 21$
$\frac{p}{6} = -13$
$6 \cdot \frac{p}{6} = 6 \cdot -13$
$p = -78$

Check: $\frac{p}{6} - (-21) = 8$
$\frac{-78}{6} - (-21) \stackrel{?}{=} 8$
$-13 - (-21) \stackrel{?}{=} 8$
$-13 + 21 \stackrel{?}{=} 8$
$8 = 8$ ✔

6. $-7 = \frac{d}{-5} + 1$
$-7 - 1 = \frac{d}{-5} + 1 - 1$
$-8 = \frac{d}{-5}$
$-5 \cdot -8 = -5 \cdot \frac{d}{-5}$
$40 = d$

Check: $-7 = \frac{d}{-5} + 1$
$-7 \stackrel{?}{=} \frac{40}{-5} + 1$
$-7 \stackrel{?}{=} -8 + 1$
$-7 = -7$ ✔

7. Let x = number
$\left(\frac{x}{8}\right) - 17 = -15$
$\left(\frac{x}{8}\right) - 17 + 17 = -15 + 17$
$\left(\frac{x}{8}\right) = 2$
$8\left(\frac{x}{8}\right) = 8(2)$
$x = 16$

8. If n is an odd integer, the next consecutive odd integer is $n + 2$. Their sum is $n + (n + 2)$.
$n + (n + 2) = 76$
$n + n + 2 = 76$
$2n + 2 = 76$
$2n + 2 - 2 = 76 - 2$
$2n = 74$
$\frac{2n}{2} = \frac{74}{2}$
$n = 37$
The consecutive odd integers are 37 and 39.

9. $C = 2\pi r$
$C = 2 \cdot \pi \cdot 4.3$
$C \approx 27.02$ cm

10. $C = \pi d$
$C = \pi \cdot 21\frac{1}{2}$
$C \approx 67.54$ in.

11. $7y + 6 = 3y - 14$
$7y + 6 - 6 = 3y - 14 - 6$
$7y = 3y - 20$
$7y - 3y = 3y - 3y - 20$
$4y = -20$
$\frac{4y}{4} = \frac{-20}{4}$
$y = -5$

Check: $7y + 6 = 3y - 14$
$7(-5) + 6 \stackrel{?}{=} 3(-5) - 14$
$-35 + 6 \stackrel{?}{=} -15 - 14$
$-29 = -29$ ✔

12. $3(x + 2) - 6 = 3x$
$3x + 6 - 6 = 3x$
$3x = 3x$
This sentence is always true.
The solution set is all numbers.

13. $\frac{7}{9}d - 7 = \frac{5}{9}d - 3$
$\frac{7}{9}d - 7 + 7 = \frac{5}{9}d - 3 + 7$
$\frac{7}{9}d = \frac{5}{9}d + 4$
$\frac{7}{9}d - \frac{5}{9}d = \frac{5}{9}d + 4 - \frac{5}{9}d$
$\frac{2}{9}d = 4$
$\frac{9}{2} \cdot \frac{2}{9}d = \frac{9}{2} \cdot 4$
$d = \frac{36}{2}$
$d = 18$

Check: $\frac{7}{9}d - 7 = \frac{5}{9}d - 3$
$\frac{7}{9}(18) - 7 \stackrel{?}{=} \frac{5}{9}(18) - 3$
$14 - 7 \stackrel{?}{=} 10 - 3$
$7 = 7$ ✔

14.
$$-3j - 4 < -22$$
$$-3j - 4 + 4 < -22 + 4$$
$$-3j < -18$$
$$\frac{-3j}{-3} > \frac{-18}{-3}$$
$$j > 6$$

Check: Try 8, a number greater than 6.
$$-3j - 4 < -22$$
$$-3(8) - 4 \overset{?}{<} -22$$
$$-24 - 4 \overset{?}{<} -22$$
$$-28 < -22 \ \checkmark$$

15.
$$-3.2 + 14s > 15s$$
$$-3.2 + 14s - 14s > 15s - 14s$$
$$-3.2 > s$$

Check: Try -5, a number less than -3.2.
$$-3.2 + 14s > 15s$$
$$-3.2 + 14(-5) \overset{?}{>} 15(-5)$$
$$-3.2 + (-70) \overset{?}{>} -75$$
$$-73.2 > -75 \ \checkmark$$

16.
$$3(y - 2) \geq 5(y - 7)$$
$$3y - 6 \geq 5y - 35$$
$$3y - 6 + 6 \geq 5y - 35 + 6$$
$$3y \geq 5y - 29$$
$$3y - 5y \geq 5y - 5y - 29$$
$$-2y \geq -29$$
$$\frac{-2y}{-2} \leq \frac{-29}{-2}$$
$$y \leq 14.5$$

Check: Try 0, a number less than or equal to 14.5.
$$3(y - 2) \geq 5(y - 7)$$
$$3(0 - 2) \overset{?}{\geq} 5(0 - 7)$$
$$3(-2) \overset{?}{\geq} 5(-7)$$
$$-6 \geq -35 \ \checkmark$$

17. Let j = cost of jeans
$$2(15.30) + j \leq 85$$
$$30.60 + j \leq 85$$
$$30.60 + j - 30.60 \leq 85 - 30.60$$
$$j \leq 54.40$$

Linda can spend at most $54.40 on jeans.

18. $6 \times 100 = 600$
6 m = 600 cm

19. $8.3 \times 1000 = 8300$
8.3 L = 8300 ml

20. $0.7 \times 1000 = 700$
0.7 kg = 700 g

Page 781   Chapter 8 Practice Test

1. D = {7, 8, 10}; R = {6, 6.5, 9}; yes
2. D = {3, 5, 8}; R = {3, 4, 6, 7}; no
3. D = {1.6, 4, 6, 18}; R = {4, 6, 40}; yes
4. D = {4, 10, 17}; R = {3, 7, 8.5, 9}; no
5. D = {2, 5, 8, 10}; R = {1, 3}; yes
6. D = {-4, 6}; R = {-5, 10, 30}; no
7. Sample answer; positive; see students' explanations.
8. Sample answer; none; see students' explanations.
9. Sample answer; none; see students' explanations.
10. Sample answer; negative; see students' explanations.

11. Rewrite $x + y = 8$ as $y = 8 - x$.

x	$8 - y$	y
0	$8 - 0$	8
2	$8 - 2$	6
4	$8 - 4$	4
8	$8 - 8$	0

Answers will vary.
Sample answer:
(0, 8), (2, 6),
(4, 4), (8, 0)

12.

x	y
-2	6
-2	2
-2	0
-2	-2

Answers will vary.
Sample answer:
(-2, 6), (-2, 2),
(-2, 0), (-2, -2)

13.

x	$\frac{1}{3}x - 2$	y
3	$\frac{1}{3}(3) - 2$	-1
0	$\frac{1}{3}(0) - 2$	-2
1	$\frac{1}{3}(1) - 2$	$-1\frac{2}{3}$
-3	$\frac{1}{3}(-3) - 2$	-3

Answers will vary.
Sample answer:
$(3, -1), (0, -2), \left(1, -1\frac{2}{3}\right), (-3, -3)$

14.

x	y
-4	-11
-2	-3
0	5
2	13
4	21

yes

15. No; since x has the same value for every range value. $x = -2$ is not a function.

16.

x	y
-4	-10
-2	-2
0	-6
2	-2
4	10

yes

17. Let the horizontal axis represent the football rating. Let the vertical axis represent the graduation rate. Graph (1, 95) for a number 1 rating and a 95% graduation rate and (8, 77) for an 8th rating and a 77% graduation rate. Draw the line that contains these points. Thus, 59 corresponds to 15. The Ohio State University had a 59% graduation rate.

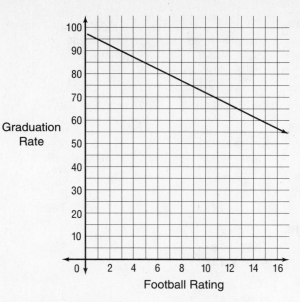

Graduation
Rate

Football Rating

18. slope $= \frac{5-4}{3-7}$

$= \frac{1}{-4}$

19. slope $= \frac{-3-6}{9-(-1)}$

$= \frac{-9}{10}$

20. slope $= \frac{-4-2}{-3-(-5)}$

$= \frac{-6}{2}$

$= -3$

21. slope $= \frac{7-4}{-6-25}$

$= \frac{3}{-31}$

22. Let $y = 0$:

$y = x - 6$

$0 = x - 6$

$0 + 6 = x - 6 + 6$

$6 = x$

The x-intercept is 6.

Let $x = 0$:

$y = x - 6$

$y = 0 - 6$

$y = -6$

The y-intercept is -6.

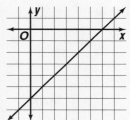

23. Let $y = 0$:

$y = -3 + x$

$0 = -3 + x$

$0 + 3 = -3 + x + 3$

$3 = x$

The x-intercept is 3.

Let $x = 0$:

$y = -3 + x$

$y = -3 + 0$

$y = -3$

The y-intercept is -3.

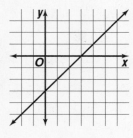

24. Let $y = 0$:

$y = -2x - 9$

$0 = -2x - 9$

$0 + 9 = -2x - 9 + 9$

$9 = -2x$

$\frac{-9}{2} = x$

$-4\frac{1}{2} = x$

The x-intercept is $-4\frac{1}{2}$.

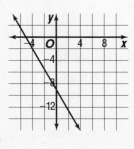

Let $x = 0$:

$y = -2x - 9$

$y = -2(0) - 9$

$y = 0 - 9$

$y = -9$

The y-intercept is -9.

25. slope $= m = \frac{1}{4}$

Let $x = 0$:

$y = \frac{1}{4}x - 3$

$y = \frac{1}{4}(0) - 3$

$y = 0 - 3$

$y = -3$

The y-intercept is (0, -3).

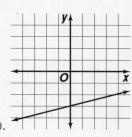

26. Rewrite $2x - y = -1$

as $y = 2x + 1$.

slope $= m = 2$

Let $x = 0$:

$y = 2x + 1$

$y = 2(0) + 1$

$y = 0 + 1$

$y = 1$

The y-intercept is (0, 1).

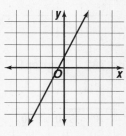

27. Rewrite $x + 3y = 6$

as $y = -\frac{1}{3}x + 2$.

slope $= m = -\frac{1}{3}$

Let $x = 0$:

$y = -\frac{1}{3}x + 2$

$y = -\frac{1}{3}(0) + 2$

$y = 0 + 2$

$y = 2$

The y-intercept is (0, 2).

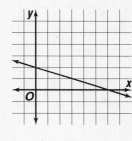

28.

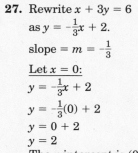

no solution

29.

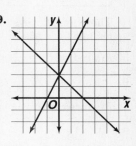

The solution is (0, 2).

30.

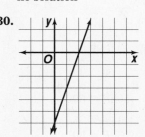

infinitely many solutions

31.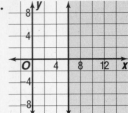

32.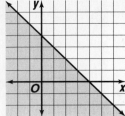

33.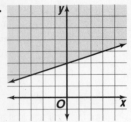

Page 782 Chapter 9 Practice Test

1. $\frac{16}{72} = \frac{2}{9}$ **2.** $\frac{2}{1}$ **3.** $\frac{88}{564} = \frac{22}{141}$

4.

$5	$10	$20
10	0	0
8	1	0
6	2	0
6	0	1
4	3	0
4	1	2
2	4	0
2	2	1
2	0	2
0	5	0
0	1	2
0	3	1

There are 12 ways to make change for a $50-bill.

5. $P(\text{a red card}) = \frac{26}{52}$ or $\frac{1}{2}$

6. $P(\text{a six}) = \frac{4}{52}$ or $\frac{1}{13}$

7. $P(\text{a face card}) = \frac{12}{52}$ or $\frac{3}{13}$

8. $\frac{13}{2.99} = \frac{x}{4.83}$

$13 \cdot 4.83 = 2.99 \cdot x$

$62.79 = 2.99x$

$\frac{62.79}{2.99} = \frac{2.99x}{2.99}$

$21 = x$

9. $\frac{3}{24} = \frac{7}{y}$

$3 \cdot y = 24 \cdot 7$

$3y = 168$

$\frac{3y}{3} = \frac{168}{3}$

$y = 56$

10. $\frac{P}{60} = \frac{40}{100}$

$P \cdot 100 = 60 \cdot 40$

$100P = 240$

$\frac{100P}{100} = \frac{240}{100}$

$P = 24$

40% of 60 is 24.

11. $\frac{P}{80} = \frac{37.5}{100}$

$P \cdot 100 = 80 \cdot 37.5$

$100P = 3000$

$\frac{100P}{100} = \frac{3000}{100}$

$P = 30$

37.5% of 80 is 30.

12. $\frac{21}{B} = \frac{35}{100}$

$21 \cdot 100 = B \cdot 35$

$2100 = 35B$

$\frac{2100}{35} = \frac{35B}{35}$

$60 = B$

21 is 35% of 60.

13. $\frac{75}{250} = \frac{r}{100}$

$75 \cdot 100 = 250 \cdot r$

$7500 = 250r$

$\frac{7500}{250} = \frac{250r}{250}$

$30 = r$

75 is 30% of 250.

14. $\frac{52}{80} = \frac{r}{100}$

$52 \cdot 100 = 80 \cdot r$

$5200 = 80r$

$\frac{5200}{80} = \frac{80r}{80}$

$65 = r$

52 is 65% of 80.

15. $\frac{36}{B} = \frac{45}{100}$

$36 \cdot 100 = B \cdot 45$

$3600 = 45B$

$\frac{3600}{45} = \frac{45B}{45}$

$80 = B$

36 is 45% of 80.

16. $\frac{8}{72} = \frac{x}{567}$

$8 \cdot 567 = 72 \cdot x$

$4536 = 72x$

$\frac{4536}{72} = \frac{72x}{72}$

$63 = x$

63 students would be interested in a music appreciation class. Yes; this is enough for the class.

17. $\frac{85}{120} \approx 0.71 \to \frac{0.71}{100} = 71\%$

18. $0.42 \to \frac{0.42}{100} = 42\%$

19. $\frac{9}{5} = 1.8 \to \frac{1.8}{1} = \frac{180}{100} = 180\%$

20. $0.086 \to \frac{0.086}{1} = \frac{8.6}{100} = 8.6\%$

21. $67.5\% = \frac{67.5}{100}$

$= 0.675$

$67.5\% = \frac{67\frac{1}{2}}{100}$

$= 67\frac{1}{2} \div 100$

$= \frac{135}{2} \times \frac{1}{100}$

$= \frac{27}{40}$

22. $33\frac{1}{3}\% = \frac{33\frac{1}{3}}{100}$

$= 0.3\overline{3}$

$33\frac{1}{3}\% = \frac{33\frac{1}{3}}{100}$

$= 33\frac{1}{3} \div 100$

$= \frac{100}{3} \times \frac{1}{100}$

$= \frac{1}{3}$

23. $10.17\% = \frac{10.17}{100}$

$= 0.1017$

$10.17\% = \frac{10.17}{100}$

$= \frac{1017}{10,000}$

24. $26\% = \frac{26}{100} = \frac{13}{50}$

49 is about 50.

$\frac{13}{50}$ of 50 is 13.

So, the correct choice is a.

25. 47% is about 50% or $\frac{1}{2}$.

550 is about 520.

$\frac{1}{2}$ of 520 is 260.

So, the correct choice is c.

26. $I = prt$
$I = (1550)(0.04)(2)$
$I = \$124$

27. 15% of \$138 = d
$(0.15)(138) = 20.7$
The discount is \$20.70.

28. 10% of \$143 = d
$(0.10)(143) = 14.3$
The discount is \$14.30.

29. $I = prt$; 3 months = $\frac{1}{4}$ year
$I = (1250)(0.105)(0.25)$
$I = \$32.81$

30. decrease;
$19 - 32 = -13$
$-13 = R \cdot 32$
$\frac{-13}{32} = \frac{32R}{32}$
$-0.406 = R$
The percent of decrease is about 41%.

31. increase;
$315 - 245 = 70$
$70 = R \cdot 245$
$\frac{70}{245} = \frac{245R}{245}$
$0.285 = R$
The percent of increase is about 29%.

32. increase;
$201 - 178 = 23$
$23 = R \cdot 178$
$\frac{23}{178} = \frac{178R}{178}$
$0.129 = R$
The percent of increase is about 13%.

33. increase;
$1075 - 1010 = 65$
$65 = R \cdot 1010$
$\frac{65}{1010} = \frac{1010R}{1010}$
$0.064 = R$
The percent of increase is about 6%.

Page 783   Chapter 10 Practice Test

1. 12 | 2   5   5   6   8   8   9
13 | 1   2   3   3
                12 | 2 = 12.2

2. 12.2 years old

3. The range is $53 - 25$ or 28.

4. The median is 39.

5. The upper quartile is 47.

6. The lower quartile is 32.

7. The interquartile range is $47 - 32$ or 15.

8. none

9.

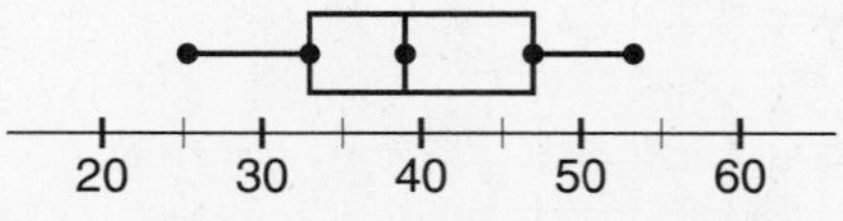

10. The vertical axis is condensed in the graph on the right. Also, the vertical axis in the graph on the left starts at 5, so the graph is deceiving.

11. Doug would probably use the graph on the left because the bars are shorter. This makes it appear that he has bought fewer cards.

12. $6 \times 2 = 12$
12 outcomes

13. $6 \times 6 \times 6 \times 6 = 1296$
1296 outcomes

14. permutation   **15.** combination

16. combination

17. odds of rolling a number less than 5
$= 4:4$
$= 1:1$
The odds of rolling a number less than 5 are 1:1.

18. odds of rolling a composite number
$= 3:5$
The odds of rolling a composite number are 3:5.

19. According to the simulation, Heather makes a putt $\frac{3}{5}$ or 60% of the time. Thus, she misses a putt $\frac{2}{5}$ or 40% of the time. Since blue represents a putt missed, she will need $\frac{2}{5}(40)$ or 16 blue marbles.

20. Red represents a putt made. So, in 120 drawings, Heather can expect $\frac{3}{5}(120)$ or 72 red marbles.

21. P(green and 6) $= \frac{1}{4} \cdot \frac{1}{8}$
$= \frac{1}{32}$

22. P(orange and an odd number) $= \frac{1}{4} \cdot \frac{4}{8}$
$= \frac{4}{32}$
$= \frac{1}{8}$

23. inclusive;
P(vowel or a letter following R) $= \frac{5}{26} + \frac{8}{26} - \frac{1}{26}$
$= \frac{12}{26}$
$= \frac{6}{13}$

24. exclusive;
P(a consonant or the letter E) $= \frac{21}{26} + \frac{1}{26}$
$= \frac{22}{26}$
$= \frac{11}{13}$

25. exclusive;
P(a vowel or a consonant) $= \frac{5}{26} + \frac{21}{26}$
$= \frac{26}{26}$
$= 1$

Page 784   Chapter 11 Practice Test

1.

2.

3.

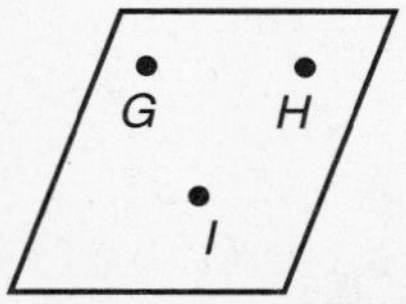

4.

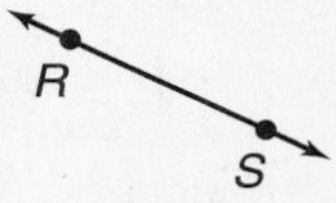

5.

Agriculture:	36%	= 0.36
Public water:	8%	= 0.08
Utilities:	33%	= 0.33
Industry:	23%	= 0.23

Agriculture: $0.36 \times 360 = 129.6 \rightarrow 130°$
Public water: $0.08 \times 360 = 28.8 \rightarrow 29°$
Utilities: $0.33 \times 360 = 118.8 \rightarrow 119°$
Industry: $0.23 \times 360 = 82.8 \rightarrow 83°$

U.S. Water Usage

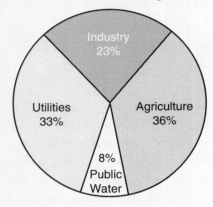

6. $\angle HFG$ and $\angle FCE$ are corresponding so they are congruent. Therefore, $m\angle FCE = 45°$.

7. Since $\angle HCJ$ and $\angle BCD$ are vertical angles, they are congruent. So, $m\angle BCD = 90°$.

8. $\angle JIF$ is supplementary to $\angle CIF$.
So, $m\angle JIF = 180 - m\angle CIF$.
Find the measure of $\angle CIF$.
Notice that $\angle CIF$, $\angle IFC$, and $\angle ICF$ form a right triangle. Since $\angle IFC$ and $\angle HFG$ are vertical angles, they are congruent. Thus, $m\angle IFC = 45°$.
So,
$m\angle CIF + m\angle IFC + m\angle ICF = 180$
$m\angle CIF + 45 + 90 = 180$
$m\angle CIF + 135 = 180$
$m\angle CIF + 135 - 135 = 180 - 135$
$m\angle CIF = 45°$
The measure of $\angle JIF$ is $180 - 45$ or $135°$.

9. Since $\angle KIC$ and $\angle JIF$ are vertical angles, they are congruent. So, $m\angle KIC = 135°$.

10. $x + 35 + 110 = 180$
$x + 145 = 180$
$x + 145 - 145 = 180 - 145$
$x = 35$
The triangle is obtuse.

11. $x + x + x = 180$
$3x = 180$
$\frac{3x}{3} = \frac{180}{3}$
$x = 60$
The triangle is acute.

12. $45 + x + 45 = 180$
$x + 90 = 180$
$x + 90 - 90 = 180 - 90$
$x = 90$
The triangle is a right triangle.

13. $\angle X \cong \angle A$ **14.** $\angle B \cong \angle Y$
15. $\overline{YZ} \cong \overline{BC}$ **16.** $\overline{AC} \cong \overline{XZ}$

17. $\frac{12}{15} = \frac{x}{10}$ **18.** $\frac{7}{6} = \frac{21}{x}$
$12 \cdot 10 = 15 \cdot x$ $7 \cdot x = 6 \cdot 21$
$120 = 15x$ $7x = 126$
$\frac{120}{15} = \frac{15x}{15}$ $\frac{7x}{7} = \frac{126}{7}$
$8\text{ m} = x$ $x = 18\text{ ft}$

19. $x + 125 + 55 + 125 = 360$
$x + 305 = 360$
$x + 305 - 305 = 360 - 305$
$x = 55$

20. $x + 75 + 90 + 90 = 360$
$x + 255 = 360$
$x + 255 - 255 = 360 - 255$
$x = 105$

21. $x + x + 60 + 90 = 360$
$2x + 150 = 360$
$2x + 150 - 150 = 360 - 150$
$2x = 210$
$\frac{2x}{2} = \frac{210}{2}$
$x = 105$

22. A hexagon has 6 sides. Therefore, $n = 6$.
$(n - 2)180 = (6 - 2)180$
$= 4(180)$
$= 720$
The sum of the measures of the interior angles of a hexagon is 720°.

23. A 20-gon has 20 sides. Therefore, $n = 20$.
$(n - 2)180 = (20 - 2)180$
$= 18(180)$
$= 3240$
The sum of the measures of the interior angles of a 20-gon is 3240°.

24.

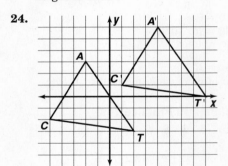

$C'(1, 1)$, $A'(4, 6)$, $T'(8, 0)$

25.

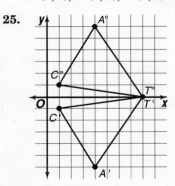

1. $A = bh$
$A = 37 \cdot 15$
$A = 555 \text{ m}^2$

2. $A = \frac{1}{2}bh$
$A = \frac{1}{2}(9)(12)$
$A = \frac{1}{2}(108)$
$A = 54 \text{ ft}^2$

3. $A = bh$
$A = 32 \cdot 17$
$A = 544 \text{ m}^2$

4. $A = \pi r^2$
$A = \pi \cdot 16^2$
$A = \pi \cdot 256$
$A \approx 804.2 \text{ cm}^2$

5. $A = \pi r^2$
$A = \pi \cdot 21^2$
$A = \pi \cdot 441$
$A \approx 1385.4 \text{ in}^2$

6. $A = \pi r^2$
$A = \pi \cdot \left(3\frac{1}{2}\right)^2$
$A = \pi \cdot 12.25$
$A \approx 38.5 \text{ in}^2$

7. $P(\text{shaded}) = \frac{\text{shaded area}}{\text{area of target}}$
$\qquad = \frac{2}{5}$

8.

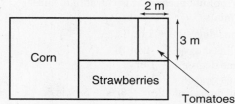

Area of Tomatoes $= \frac{1}{3} \cdot$ area of strawberries

$\qquad 6 \text{ m}^2 = \frac{1}{3} \cdot$ area of strawberries

$\qquad 18 \text{ m}^2 =$ area of strawberries

Area of Strawberries $= \frac{1}{2} \cdot$ area of corn

$\qquad 18 \text{ m}^2 = \frac{1}{2} \cdot$ area of corn

$\qquad 36 \text{ m}^2 =$ area of corn

The area planted in corn is 36 m^2.

9. Front and Back: $2(14 \cdot 8) = 224$
Top and Bottom: $2(14 \cdot 10) = 280$
Two sides: $2(10 \cdot 8) = 160$
The surface area of the rectangular prism is
$224 + 280 + 160$ or 664 in^2.

10. Two bases: $2\left(\frac{1}{2} \cdot 4 \cdot 3\right) = 12$
Front: $8 \cdot 5 = 40$
Bottom: $8 \cdot 4 = 32$
Back: $8 \cdot 3 = 24$
The surface area of the triangular prism is
$12 + 40 + 32 + 24$ or 108 ft^2.

11. $2(\pi r^2) + 2\pi rh = 2(\pi \cdot 3^2) + 2 \cdot \pi \cdot 3 \cdot 20$
$\qquad\qquad\quad = 2(\pi \cdot 9) + 2 \cdot \pi \cdot 3 \cdot 20$
$\qquad\qquad\quad \approx 57 + 377$
$\qquad\qquad\quad \approx 434$
The surface area of the cylinder is about 434 ft^2.

12. Front and Back: $2(4 \cdot 4) = 32$
Top and Bottom: $2(4 \cdot 4) = 32$
Two sides: $2(4 \cdot 4) = 32$
The surface area of the rectangular prism is
$32 + 32 + 32$ or 96 ft^2.

13. Base: $A = s^2$
$\qquad A = 73^2$
$\qquad A = 5329 \text{ cm}^2$
Side: $A = \frac{1}{2}bh$
$\qquad A = \frac{1}{2}(73)(45)$
$\qquad A = \frac{1}{2}(3285)$
$\qquad A = 1642.5$
The surface area is about $5329 + 4(1642.5)$ or
$11,899 \text{ cm}^2$.

14. Base: $A = \pi r^2$
$\qquad A = \pi \cdot 9^2$
$\qquad A = \pi \cdot 81$
$\qquad A \approx 254.5 \text{ m}^2$
Surface: $A = \pi rs$
$\qquad A = \pi \cdot 9 \cdot 12$
$\qquad A \approx 339.3 \text{ m}^2$
The surface area is about $254.5 + 339.3$ or 593.8 m^2.

15. $V = Bh$
$V = 4 \cdot 7 \cdot 9$
$V = 252 \text{ m}^3$

16. $V = Bh$
$V = \left(\frac{1}{2} \cdot 2\frac{1}{2} \cdot 1\right) \cdot 2$
$V = 1.25 \cdot 2$
$V = 2.5 \text{ ft}^3$

17. $V = \pi r^2 h$
$V = \pi \cdot 6^2 \cdot 9$
$V = \pi \cdot 36 \cdot 9$
$V \approx 1017.9 \text{ m}^3$

18. $V = \frac{1}{3}Bh$
$V = \frac{1}{3} \cdot 18 \cdot 15 \cdot 20$
$V = 1800 \text{ cm}^3$

19. $V = \frac{1}{3}Bh$
$V = \frac{1}{3} \cdot 8 \cdot 8 \cdot 9$
$V = 192 \text{ in}^3$

20. $V = \frac{1}{3}\pi r^2 h$
$V = \frac{1}{3} \cdot \pi \cdot 9^2 \cdot 16$
$V = \frac{1}{3} \cdot \pi \cdot 81 \cdot 16$
$V \approx 1357.2 \text{ cm}^3$

1. $\sqrt{81} < \sqrt{90} < \sqrt{100}$
$\sqrt{9^2} < \sqrt{90} < \sqrt{10^2}$
$\quad 9 < \sqrt{90} < 10$
$\qquad\quad 9$
Check: $\sqrt{90} \approx 9.4$

2. $\sqrt{16} < \sqrt{20.25} < \sqrt{25}$
$\sqrt{4^2} < \sqrt{20.25} < \sqrt{5^2}$
$\quad 4 < \sqrt{20.25} < 5$
$\qquad\quad 4$
Check: $\sqrt{20.25} \approx 4.5$

3. $-\sqrt{64} < -\sqrt{62} < -\sqrt{81}$
$-\sqrt{8^2} < -\sqrt{62} < -\sqrt{9^2}$
$\quad -8 < -\sqrt{62} < -9$
$\qquad\quad -8$
Check: $-\sqrt{62} \approx -7.9$

4. $-\sqrt{64} < -\sqrt{71} < -\sqrt{81}$
$-\sqrt{8^2} < -\sqrt{71} < -\sqrt{9^2}$
$\quad -8 < -\sqrt{71} < -9$
$\qquad\quad -8$
Check: $-\sqrt{71} \approx -8.4$

5.

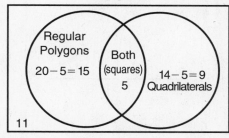

Polygons

$40 - (15 + 5 + 9) = 40 - 29$
$\qquad\qquad\qquad\qquad = 11$

11 tiles

6. $s^2 = 121$
$s = \sqrt{121}$ or $s = -\sqrt{121}$
$s = 11$ or $s = -11$

7. $g^2 = 40$
$g = \sqrt{40}$ or $g = -\sqrt{40}$
$g \approx 6.3$ or $g \approx -6.3$

8. $f^2 = 11$
$f = \sqrt{11}$ or $f = -\sqrt{11}$
$f \approx 3.3$ or $f \approx -3.3$

9. $y^2 = 60$
$y = \sqrt{60}$ or $y = -\sqrt{60}$
$y \approx 7.7$ or $y \approx -7.7$

10.
$c^2 = a^2 + b^2$
$85^2 = a^2 + 77^2$
$7225 = a^2 + 5929$
$7225 - 5929 = a^2 + 5929 - 5929$
$1296 = a^2$
$\sqrt{1296} = a$
$36 \text{ m} = a$

11.
$c^2 = a^2 + b^2$
$17^2 = 15^2 + b^2$
$289 = 225 + b^2$
$289 - 225 = 225 + b^2 - 225$
$64 = b^2$
$\sqrt{64} = b$
$8 \text{ ft} = b$

12.
$c^2 = a^2 + b^2$
$109^2 = a^2 + 91^2$
$11{,}881 = a^2 + 8281$
$11{,}881 - 8281 = a^2 + 8281 - 8281$
$3600 = a^2$
$\sqrt{3600} = a$
$60 \text{ yd} = a$

13. $x = \frac{1}{2}c$
$x = \frac{1}{2}(8)$
$x = 4 \text{ in.}$

14. $x = a\sqrt{2}$
$x = 5\sqrt{2}$
$x \approx 7.1 \text{ ft}$

15.
$a = \frac{1}{2}x$
$4.5 = \frac{1}{2}x$
$2(4.5) = 2\left(\frac{1}{2}x\right)$
$9 \text{ m} = x$

16. $\cos x = \frac{20}{47}$
$\cos x \approx 0.426$
$x \approx 65°$

17. $\tan x = \frac{11}{4}$
$\tan x = 2.75$
$x \approx 70°$

18. $\sin x = \frac{40}{135}$
$\sin x \approx 0.296$
$x \approx 17°$

19. Let x represent the angle of elevation of the sun.

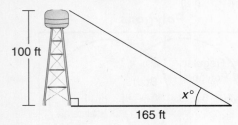
100 ft
$x°$
165 ft

$\tan x = \frac{100}{165}$
$\tan x \approx 0.606$
$x \approx 31.2°$
The angle of elevation of the sun is about 31.2°.

20. Let h represent the vertical rise.

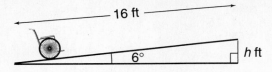
16 ft
6°
h ft

$\sin 6° = \frac{h}{16}$
$(16)(\sin 6°) = h$
$1.67 \approx h$
The vertical rise is about 1.67 feet.

Page 787   Chapter 14 Practice Test

1. yes; monomial

2. yes; binomial because it is the sum of two monomials

3. yes; monomial

4. yes; binomial because it is the difference of two monomials

5. no; because there is a variable in the denominator

6. yes; trinomial because it is the sum of three monomials.

7. $5a^2b$ has degree $2 + 1$ or 3.

8. $12rs^2$ has degree $1 + 2$ or 3.
$3r^2s$ has degree $2 + 1$ or 3.
$5r^4s$ has degree $4 + 1$ or 5.
So, the degree of $12rs^2 + 3r^2s + 5r^4s$ is 5.

9. x^2 has degree 2.
$6xy$ has degree $1 + 1$ or 2.
xy^2 has degree $1 + 2$ or 3.
So, the degree of $x^2 + 6xy + xy^2$ is 3.

10. $(2x^2 + 5x) + (3x^2 + x) = (2x^2 + 3x^2) + (5x + x)$
$= (2 + 3)x^2 + (5 + 1)x$
$= 5x^2 + 6x$

11. $(7a - 11b) - (3a + 4b) = (7a - 11b) + (-1)(3a + 4b)$
$= 7a - 11b + (-3a - 4b)$
$= 7a - 11b - 3a - 4b$
$= 7a - 3a - 11b - 4b$
$= 4a - 15b$

12. $(x^2 - 5x + 3) + (4x - 3)$
$= x^2 + [(-5x) + 4x] + [3 + (-3)]$
$= x^2 + [(-5) + 4]x + [3 + (-3)]$
$= x^2 + (-1)x + 0$
$= x^2 - x$

13. $(3a^2 - b^2 + c^2) - (a^2 + 2b^2)$
$= (3a^2 - b^2 + c^2) + (-1)(a^2 + 2b^2)$
$= 3a^2 - b^2 + c^2 + (-a^2 - 2b^2)$
$= 3a^2 - b^2 + c^2 - a^2 - 2b^2$
$= 3a^2 - a^2 - b^2 - 2b^2 + c^2$
$= 2a^2 - 3b^2 + c^2$

14. $^-3y^2 + 2$
$\underline{(+)\ 4y^2 - 5y - 2}$
$y^2 - 5y$

15. $14a^2 - 3a$ $\longrightarrow$ $14a^2 - 3a$
$\underline{(-)\ 6a^2 + 5a + 17}$ $\underline{(+)\ -6a^2 - 5a - 17}$
$8a^2 - 8a - 17$

16. $(5c)^3 = 5^3c^3$
$= 125c^3$

17. $(4x^2y^3)^2 = 4^2(x^2)^2(y^3)^2$
$\quad\quad\quad\quad = 16x^{2\cdot 2}y^{3\cdot 2}$
$\quad\quad\quad\quad = 16x^4y^6$

18. $-3x(4xy)^2 = -3x(4^2x^2y^2)$
$\quad\quad\quad\quad\quad = -3x(16x^2y^2)$
$\quad\quad\quad\quad\quad = -3 \cdot 16 \cdot x \cdot x^2 \cdot y^2$
$\quad\quad\quad\quad\quad = -48x^3y^2$

19. $x(-5x + 3) = x(-5x) + x(3)$
$\quad\quad\quad\quad\quad = -5x^2 + 3x$

20. $a^2(2a^3 + a - 5) = a^2(2a^3) + a^2(a) - a^2(5)$
$\quad\quad\quad\quad\quad\quad\quad = 2a^5 + a^3 - 5a^2$

21. $-2g(g^3 + 6g + 3) = -2g(g^3) + (2g)(6g) + (-2g)(3)$
$\quad\quad\quad\quad\quad\quad\quad = -2g^4 + (-12g^2) + (-6g)$
$\quad\quad\quad\quad\quad\quad\quad = -2g^4 - 12g^2 - 6g$

22. $(2x + 1)(3x + 2) = (2x + 1)3x + (2x + 1)2$
$\quad\quad\quad\quad\quad\quad\quad = (2x)3x + (1)3x + (2x)2 + (1)2$
$\quad\quad\quad\quad\quad\quad\quad = 6x^2 + 3x + 4x + 2$
$\quad\quad\quad\quad\quad\quad\quad = 6x^2 + 7x + 2$

23. $(3x + 3)(x - 1) = (3x + 3)x + (3x + 3)(-1)$
$\quad\quad\quad\quad\quad\quad\quad = (3x)x + (3)x + (3x)(-1) + (3)(-1)$
$\quad\quad\quad\quad\quad\quad\quad = 3x^2 + 3x + (-3x) + (-3)$
$\quad\quad\quad\quad\quad\quad\quad = 3x^2 + 3x - 3x - 3$
$\quad\quad\quad\quad\quad\quad\quad = 3x^2 - 3$

24. $(-x + 3)(3x - 2) = (-x + 3)3x + (-x + 3)(-2)$
$\quad\quad\quad\quad\quad\quad\quad = (-x)3x + (3)3x + (-x)(-2) + (3)(-2)$
$\quad\quad\quad\quad\quad\quad\quad = -3x^2 + 9x + 2x + (-6)$
$\quad\quad\quad\quad\quad\quad\quad = -3x^2 + 9x + 2x - 6$
$\quad\quad\quad\quad\quad\quad\quad = -3x^2 + 11x - 6$

25. area of top: $A = \ell \cdot w$
$\quad\quad\quad\quad\quad A = 5n(2n)$
$\quad\quad\quad\quad\quad A = 10n^2$

area of bottom: $A = \ell \cdot w$
$\quad\quad\quad\quad\quad\quad A = 5n(2n)$
$\quad\quad\quad\quad\quad\quad A = 10n^2$

area of front: $A = \ell \cdot w$
$\quad\quad\quad\quad\quad A = 5n(n + 3)$
$\quad\quad\quad\quad\quad A = 5n(n) + 5n(3)$
$\quad\quad\quad\quad\quad A = 5n^2 + 15n$

area of back: $A = \ell \cdot w$
$\quad\quad\quad\quad\quad A = 5n(n + 3)$
$\quad\quad\quad\quad\quad A = 5n(n) + 5n(3)$
$\quad\quad\quad\quad\quad A = 5n^2 + 15n$

area of left side: $A = \ell \cdot w$
$\quad\quad\quad\quad\quad\quad A = 2n(n + 3)$
$\quad\quad\quad\quad\quad\quad A = 2n(n) + 2n(3)$
$\quad\quad\quad\quad\quad\quad A = 2n^2 + 6n$

area of right side: $A = \ell \cdot w$
$\quad\quad\quad\quad\quad\quad A = 2n(n + 3)$
$\quad\quad\quad\quad\quad\quad A = 2n(n) + 2n(3)$
$\quad\quad\quad\quad\quad\quad A = 2n^2 + 6n$

The total surface area is $(10n^2) + (10n^2) + (5n^2 + 15n) + (5n^2 + 15n) + (2n^2 + 6n) + (2n^2 + 6n)$ or $34n^2 + 42n$.